# Cambridgeshire's
# MOSSES &
# LIVERWORTS
## — a dynamic flora —

C. D. Preston and M. O. Hill

**2019**

**pisces**publications

Published 2019 by Pisces Publications

First published 2019.

British-Library-in-Publication Data
A catalogue record for this book is available from the British Library.

ISBN 978-1-874357-89-6

Designed and published by Pisces Publications

Visit our bookshop
www.naturebureau.co.uk/bookshop/

Pisces Publications is the imprint of NatureBureau,
36 Kingfisher Court, Hambridge Road, Newbury, Berkshire RG14 5SJ
www.naturebureau.co.uk

Printed and bound by Gomer Press, UK

MIX
Paper from
responsible sources
FSC® C114687

Front cover   Main: Ornamental stonework at Madingley Hall, January 2016 © Peter Leonard. Below left to right: *Orthotrichum obtusifolium*, *Ricciocarpos natans* © Robin Stevenson; *Pseudotaxiphyllum elegans* © Jeff Scott.
Back cover   Top left: Ouse Washes, Sutton, September 2018 © Chris Preston. Top right: East Pit, Cherry Hinton, with *Homalothecium lutescens* in foreground, April 2017 © Peter Leonard. Below: Bryological party at lunch, Wicken Fen, April 2008 © Robin Stevenson.

# Contents

# Foreword

Over 50 years ago, during his Malham Tarn field course in 1964, I asked Michael Proctor some wide ranging questions about bryophyte ecology, biology and evolution. His replies were always along the same lines: bryophytes work very differently from vascular plants and it is extremely difficult to predict what the results of recording, observations and experiments might reveal. This most aptly named *Cambridgeshire's mosses and liverworts – a dynamic flora* exemplifies Proctor's wisdom. Though meticulously documenting data from previous bryophyte floras of what must be by far the best known county in Britain and Ireland, this new flora contains a remarkable amount of new and often surprising information.

As one who has, for more than half a century, made extensive use of numerous UK county bryophyte floras, some dating back to the nineteenth century, I have to say that this is the best I have ever had the pleasure to read. It is going to become one of those volumes that all bryologists will want to have on their bookshelves and should set the benchmark for future regional floras: everything in this flora is exemplary. There seems to be little doubt that this flora is going to top the bryophyte bestseller list not only in the UK but worldwide. In addition to the now standard detailed distribution maps, particular strengths of the new flora include the best information to date on the ecology of individual species and bryophyte communities, including several singularly bryophytic habitats, not to mention details of their phenology. Everyone who reads this flora will learn a great deal. Chris and Mark are to be warmly congratulated for putting pen to paper on their collective observations, knowledge and endeavours now stretching back to the 1960s.

As might be expected, since the previous floras (Proctor 1956, Whitehouse 1964) the bryophyte flora of Cambridgeshire has undergone dramatic changes. Although this new flora documents a significant and depressing loss of bryodiversity in Cambridgeshire I still found it remarkably uplifting, optimistic and positive for the future despite the best endeavours of humans to ruin our planet. Many of the changes and additions to the flora could not have been predicted and, when a future generation of bryologists prepares the next version some 50 years hence, there are certain to be similar revelations. Quite simply this flora is a must read now and will remain so for many years to come.

Jeffrey G. Duckett
Natural History Museum, London
*July 2018*

# Introduction

*'v.c. 29 is beginning to show us a county flora as the dynamic entity we know it must be'*
(Proctor 1984)

Some bryophyte floras have a cover photograph showing a habitat with luxuriant bryophytes, or a portrait of a charismatic rarity, and begin by outlining the bryological richness of their chosen area. We will not do this, and would not expect to be taken seriously if we did. Cambridgeshire (vice-county 29) is not a bryophyte-rich county. The rainfall is low, the geology soft, the soils predominantly calcareous and most of the land is devoted to cereal cultivation. Our species-rich sites are small islands in a sea of arable land. An Irish friend, when told how many bryophyte species we might expect to find in a Fenland tetrad, responded 'We can get more than that on a single rock in County Kerry'.

So why have we written, and why might you want to read, a bryophyte flora of Cambridgeshire? Much of the interest of the county lies in the differing abilities of species to persist in its inhospitable terrain. Some species which are almost ubiquitous in northern and western Britain become scarce plants, restricted to specialised habitats, whereas others prove to be well adapted to the county's landscapes. These differences are highlighted by the strong contrast between the south of the county and the north. The 'upland' south has some gentle variation in topography and has frequent settlements, often by rivers or streams. It is characterised by small parishes and numerous medieval churches, tidy villages, irregular roads and paths which follow ancient routes and some surviving semi-natural habitat. Its geology is moderately varied, with small areas of acidic soils and more extensive deposits of chalk and Boulder Clay. At its centre lies the university town of Cambridge. In the north the older settlements are on 'fen islands' and include the sites of the great Benedictine abbeys of Ely and Thorney; in the far north the county reaches the former port of Wisbech. Between the fen islands lies the truly flat Fenland, land less than 5 m above sea-level, an intensively cultivated but sparsely populated plain of silt and peat soils where the parishes are large and the landscape features include nonconformist chapels, abandoned farm houses, new palazzi interspersed with scruffy old habitations, aggressive dogs, wind turbines and linear washlands. Fields are divided by straight roads, tracks, drains and ditches. In tetrads in such terrain we have sometimes run out of places to bryologise after an hour or two, and have struggled to record 20 species. But, paradoxically, the fact that the northern half of the county is so bryophyte-poor enhances the interest of the flora as a whole. Cambridgeshire provides a contrast with the richer areas of Britain, and within the county the Fenland contrasts with the relative riches of the south.

The landscape of southern Cambridgeshire is not atypical of that of eastern England as a whole, but the county has a longer history of bryophyte recording than most. Our first record dates from 1660. To our considerable surprise, we discovered at a late stage of our work on this flora that the early bryophyte records had not been investigated very thoroughly. We have included details of many hitherto unpublished records, especially those of William Vernon, John Martyn and Leonard Jenyns, and thus present an account of the history of bryology in the county which differs considerably from that of earlier authors. Even so, records made before the 20th century are not numerous, and they often refer to only the most distinctive species. Nevertheless, they throw light on the bryophyte flora before the landscape was transformed after the enclosure acts of the early 19th century. More significantly, bryophyte records have been collected continuously since 1927, initially by Paul Richards and then by Harold Whitehouse between 1950 and his death in 2000. The records accumulated over 90 years provide a database for assessing recent change in the bryophyte flora which is unique in Britain and Ireland.

Although we are lucky to have such a long sequence of bryophyte records from the county, using them to assess change is not a straightforward matter. There have not only been fluctuations in the intensity of recording but also changes in the habitats which have been visited over the years. Until the late 20th century, bryologists concentrated on sites close to Cambridge; when they travelled further afield, they went to nature reserves or other places of known interest. We have tried to achieve an even coverage of the county by making a deliberate effort to record in Fenland as well as in the south, and in ordinary countryside as well as in promising semi-natural habitats. In using the resulting dataset to analyse change, our approach has been to try to understand these historical trends in recording and then to devise measures of change which take them into account. Analysed thus, the records show long-term changes brought about by landscape modification as well as the recent effects of improving air quality and, perhaps, a warming climate. They also show that a surprising number of species recorded from the county have been transient colonists rather than established residents; other species have both established and casual populations. These changes, at different scales and over different periods, have led us to take Michael Proctor's concept of a dynamic flora as our theme.

We have been assisted by many people in carrying out our own survey of the county, which started in 2000, but in particular by Jonathan Graham, Robin Stevenson and Jonathan Shanklin. In reporting the results, we have summarised the records for the commoner species as two maps. One map is of 5 × 5 km square occurrences, a convenient scale for comparing earlier records with those from our survey. The other map is a more conventional tetrad (2 × 2 km) map which gives preference to records from 2000 onwards. In writing the text, we have been inspired by detailed bryophyte floras of western counties such as North Lancashire (Wigginton 1995), Carmarthenshire (Bosanquet *et al.* 2005), Pembrokeshire (Bosanquet 2010) and Mid-west Wales (Bates 2015). We hope that an account of the bryophytes of an eastern county will prove equally interesting.

# The county

## Shape and size

Cambridgeshire as a concept dates from the late Saxon period, when Wessex and Mercia were unified under Edward the Elder (d. 924), the son of Alfred the Great. It was probably created in the early 10th century (Haslam 1984). Our flora covers the Watsonian vice-county (vc 29), which has the boundary of the county as it was when H.C. Watson first divided Britain into vice-county units in 1852 (Figure 2.1). This might seem to be a rather abstruse concept, but vice-counties provide stable units for recording which are used by bryologists (and many other naturalists) throughout Britain and Ireland. References to the county in our text refer to the vice-county unless otherwise stated. The boundaries of all the British vice-counties were explained by Dandy (1969) and can be seen on various websites such as those of the Biological Records Centre, National Biodiversity Network and Beetle News.

Cambridgeshire, vice-county 29, has an area of 2213.5 km². It is slightly larger than the average British vice-county (2080 km²) but slightly smaller than the average English vice-county (2312 km²) as the English vice-counties tend to be larger than those in Scotland and Wales. It includes land in 42 10 × 10 km squares or 'hectads' (eight complete squares and 34 which also have land in other vice-counties), 134 5 × 5 km squares or 'quadrants' (56 complete squares) and 665 2 × 2 km squares or 'tetrads' (447 complete squares). The highest point of the county, 128 m, is in the extreme south-eastern corner, at Castle Camps. The

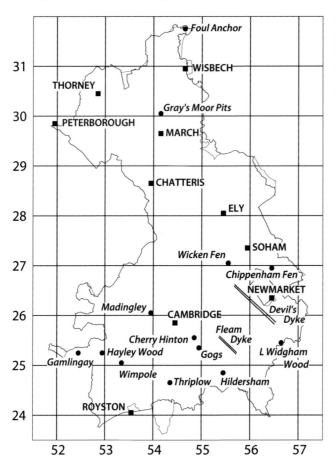

**Figure 2.1** Cambridgeshire (vice-county 29). The squares are the 10-km squares of the Ordnance Survey national grid, prefixed by 52 (TL) or 53 (TF). Where it differs from the vice-county, the boundary of the administrative county covered by earlier floras (Proctor 1956, Whitehouse 1964) is shown as a dotted line. Some of the main towns and villages (capitals) and sites of bryological interest (*italics*) are shown.

maximum altitude falls from south to north (Figure 2.2). More than half the land in the county (56%) lies below 10 m and almost half (49%) lies below 5 m altitude. In the low-lying Fenland permanent settlements were formerly restricted to the 'fen islands', raised land which was free from the risk of flooding. The ridge along which the villages of Aldreth, Haddenham, Wilburton and Stretham are strung is one such 'island', and the raised area dominated by Ely is another.

The earlier bryophyte floras by Proctor (1956) and Whitehouse (1964) followed the borders of the administrative county at the time they were published. This was so close to the vice-county boundary that both Proctor and Whitehouse (following Perring *et al.* 1964) treated them as identical. In fact there are small differences between the two, resulting from boundary changes after 1852. These differences were clearly set out by Crompton & Whitehouse (1983) and are shown on our base-map. In adopting the vice-county boundary we have excluded one significant set of records available to Whitehouse, from the parishes of Heydon and Great and Little Chishill (TL43, 44; vc 19), and a few records from the vicinity of the Ship Inn at Brandon Creek near Littleport (TL68, 69; vc 28). The exclusion of the area in vc 19 means that, unlike the earlier floras, we do not cover any ground in TL43. The Local Government Act 1972 (implemented in 1974) retained the name Cambridgeshire for the administrative county but completely changed its meaning by amalgamating the historic county with Huntingdonshire and the Soke of Peterborough. Since then the administrative county has differed very substantially from the vice-county.

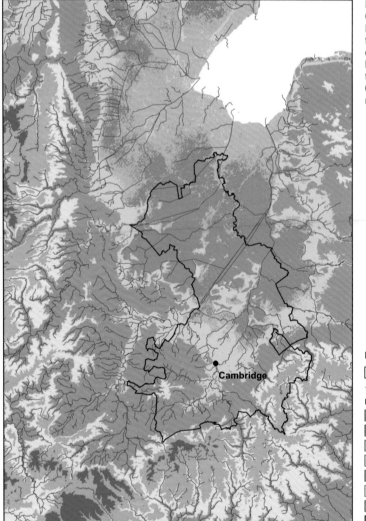

**Figure 2.2** The relief and drainage of Cambridgeshire and the surrounding area. Plotted by Stephanie Rorke using relief data from the EU Copernicus dataset, watercourse data from the Ordnance Survey (OS Open Rivers) and the vice-county boundary from the National Biodiversity Network. Contains OS data © Crown copyright and database right (2018).

**Legend**

☐ Cambridgeshire

— Watercourse

**Height above sea level (m)**

-25 - 1
>1 - 2
>2 - 5
>5 - 20
>20 - 75
>75 - 100
>100 - 140
>140

# Climate

Inspection of climate maps (Figure 2.3) shows that Cambridgeshire lies in the driest region of Britain, an area of eastern England which has the lowest rainfall and the least number of wet days per year. The mean July temperatures are high (although exceeded by those in the London area) but the mean January temperatures are only middling, less than those in the south and west (and in the London 'heat island') but higher than those in the upland areas of Wales and Scotland.

Mean monthly values for the mapped parameters, and other measures of temperature and rainfall, are provided in Table 2.1. Rainfall is fairly evenly distributed during the year, with February, March and April the driest months. Authors writing about the climate of Cambridgeshire have usually followed Watt's (1938) lead in emphasising that it is an oceanic climate with continental features. It differs from more oceanic areas in Britain in having warmer summers and colder winters, more variation in temperature within each month, low annual rainfall and a tendency for the summer months to be wetter than the winter months. However, Watt drew attention to the high relative humidity of the Cambridge summer, a feature which he (as an Aberdonian) thought was responsible for the 'depressing, enervating effect of the Cambridge climate'.

The mean annual rainfall of Cambridgeshire is actually lower than that of Jerusalem (590 mm). This is a remarkable but uninformative statistic. In contrast to the rather evenly distributed rainfall in Cambridgeshire, very little rain falls between May and September in Jerusalem (and of course the mean temperatures for the summer months are over 10° higher).

The subdued relief of Cambridgeshire means that variation in climate within the county is low. Hodge & Seale (1966) listed mean annual rainfall (1881–1915) from eight scattered sites and found that it ranged from 521 to 589 mm. Carroll et al. (2008) compared observations from the Cambridge Botanic Garden, in the city, with those made in rural Swaffham Prior, some 13 km to the north-east. They found small but statistically significant differences between the two sites for the period 1959–2006, with the Botanic Garden having higher mean annual temperatures and slightly higher monthly means from October to May, although the monthly means were higher at Swaffham Prior in the summer months (June–September). The Botanic Garden had a higher mean annual rainfall and more wet days, but the differences were very slight (only 15 mm in the annual mean). It is difficult to imagine that differences of this magnitude would lead to an observable difference in the bryophyte flora in otherwise identical habitats. They must certainly be outweighed by differences in microclimate such as those between the north- and south-facing sides of a tree trunk or a house roof, which often have obvious differences in their bryophyte cover, or between the south-west- and north-east-facing sides of the Devil's Dyke.

A single 30-year mean, the measure traditionally used to measure climate, tells us nothing about change over the years. When the geography of the Cambridge area was reviewed in 1965, J.A. Steers considered that there was no need to repeat Watt's (1938) work on climate. He explained that 'despite opinions often strongly held there has been no appreciable change since 1938!' (Steers 1965). Today we might say the opposite; that despite the opinions of some contrarians, the climate has changed since 1965. Carroll et al. (2008) showed that annual mean temperatures at the Botanic Garden had remained fairly constant up to the end of the 1980s and then risen rapidly in recent times (Figures 2.4–2.5). The number of days with frost and the number with snow have also decreased over time (Figure 2.6). Skating on the county's waters is no longer 'enjoyed every other year', as it was when Watt was writing in 1938, nor has the Cam been 'converted into a highway' within the last decade. The coldest extremes in the Botanic Garden weather records (which date from 1899) were all experienced in 1963 or earlier, whereas the hottest have all occurred since 1990. There is no evidence for changes in annual rainfall (Figure 2.7).

**Table 2.1** Mean values for the 30-year period 1981–2010 for various parameters of climate at Cambridge University Botanic Garden, Cambridge.

|  | Jan | Feb | Mar | Apr | May | Jun | Jul | Aug | Sep | Oct | Nov | Dec | Annual |
|---|---|---|---|---|---|---|---|---|---|---|---|---|---|
| Daily maximum temperature (°C) | 7.5 | 8.1 | 11.2 | 14.0 | 17.5 | 20.4 | 23.1 | 22.8 | 19.5 | 15.2 | 10.8 | 7.7 | 14.8 |
| Daily minimum temperature (°C) | 1.6 | 1.2 | 3.0 | 4.4 | 7.2 | 10.2 | 12.4 | 12.1 | 10.0 | 7.2 | 3.9 | 1.8 | 6.2 |
| Daily mean temperature (°C) | 4.5 | 4.7 | 7.1 | 9.2 | 12.4 | 15.3 | 17.7 | 17.5 | 14.7 | 11.2 | 7.3 | 4.7 | 10.5 |
| Days with air minimum below 0°C | 10 | 10 | 6 | 3 | 0.5 | 0 | 0 | 0 | 2 | 5 | 10.5 | 47 |
| Days with grass minimum below 0°C | 18 | 17 | 15 | 10 | 4 | 0.5 | 0 | 0 | 1 | 6 | 12 | 17.5 | 101 |
| Total rainfall (mm) | 46 | 35 | 39 | 40 | 47 | 52 | 51 | 54 | 53 | 58 | 55 | 47 | 576 |
| Wet days (days with over 1 mm rain) | 11 | 8.5 | 10 | 9 | 8.5 | 9 | 8.5 | 8 | 8.5 | 9.5 | 10 | 9.5 | 110 |

**(a)**

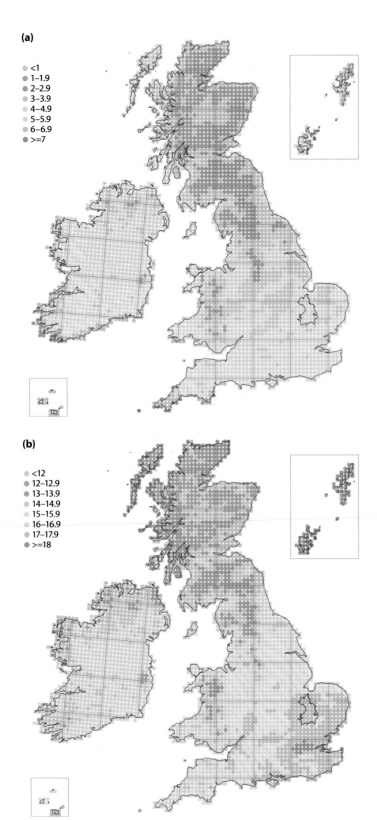

- <1
- 1–1.9
- 2–2.9
- 3–3.9
- 4–4.9
- 5–5.9
- 6–6.9
- >=7

**(b)**

- <12
- 12–12.9
- 13–13.9
- 14–14.9
- 15–15.9
- 16–16.9
- 17–17.9
- >=18

**Figure 2.3** The Cambridgeshire climate in a national context. (a) Mean January temperature (°C), (b) Mean July temperature (°C), (c) Rainfall (mm), (d) Number of days with over 1 mm of rain. Maps taken from Pescott & Preston (2014) with the Cambridgeshire outline added.

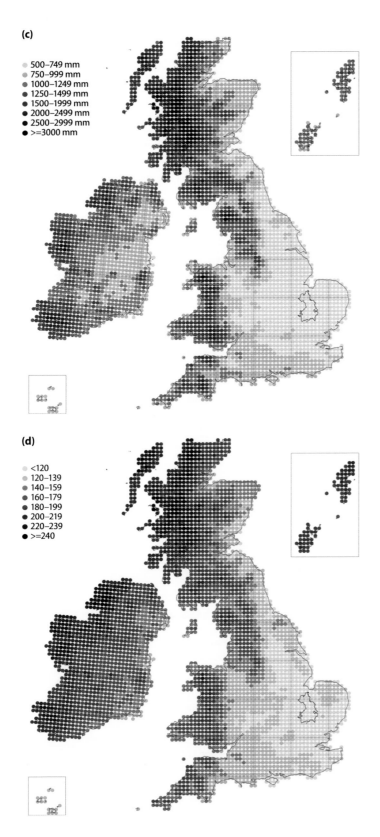

**(c)**

- 500–749 mm
- 750–999 mm
- 1000–1249 mm
- 1250–1499 mm
- 1500–1999 mm
- 2000–2499 mm
- 2500–2999 mm
- >=3000 mm

**(d)**

- <120
- 120–139
- 140–159
- 160–179
- 180–199
- 200–219
- 220–239
- >=240

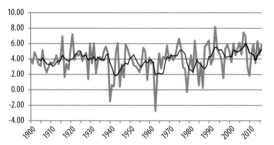

**Figure 2.4** Mean January temperature (°C), measured at Cambridge University Botanic Garden, 1900–2016. The black line is the five-year moving average.

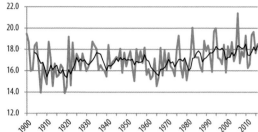

**Figure 2.5** Mean July temperature (°C), measured at Cambridge University Botanic Garden, 1900–2016. The black line is the five-year moving average.

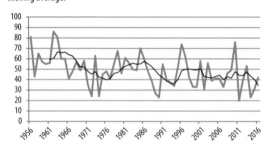

**Figure 2.6** Number of days with air frost, measured at Cambridge University Botanic Garden, 1956–2016. The black line is the five-year moving average.

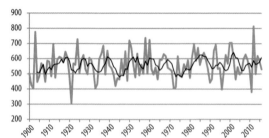

**Figure 2.7** Annual rainfall (mm), measured at Cambridge University Botanic Garden, 1900–2016. The black line is the five-year moving average.

To the modern bryologist, the most noticeable climatic extremes are droughts. The wettest and driest extremes in the Botanic Garden meteorological records are fairly evenly spread (Carroll *et al.* 2008), and so droughts continue to be an occasional feature of the county's climate. In the 20th century there were major droughts in southern and eastern England in 1921–22, 1933–34, 1959, 1976, 1990–92 and 1995–97 (Marsh *et al.* 2007). Rackham (1999) argued that an exceptional number of hot, dry summers between 1970 and 1999 and a reduction of spring rainfall in the 1990s had reduced the numbers of primroses in the county's boulder-clay woods, and it is possible that they might also have affected some of the woodland bryophytes. The most noticeable drought in our recording period, from January 2000 to March 2018, was in 2003 (Marsh 2004).

## Geology, soils and building stones

### Solid geology
The geology of Cambridgeshire is relatively straightforward. Introductory accounts are given by Hey & Perrin (1960), Forbes (1965) and Sparks & West (1965), with more detailed accounts in the memoirs published with the British Geological Survey maps. Figures 2.8–2.9 show the surface geology of the county, mapped in tetrads.

The Palaeozoic rocks underlying Cambridgeshire are deeply buried, and only Mesozoic strata of Jurassic and Cretaceous age are exposed, or lie immediately under a covering of Quaternary drift deposits. These strata dip gently from north-west to south-east, so the oldest strata are exposed in the north-west and successively younger layers are exposed south-eastwards. They outcrop in bands running across the county at right-angles to the dip, from south-west to north-east. The oldest are the Upper Jurassic clays originally laid down as marine sediments (Figure 2.8a). Oxford Clay is restricted to two areas on the western fringes of the county, in the south-west between Gamlingay and Papworth St Agnes (where its exposures are very localised as much is covered by Boulder Clay) and in the Peterborough area. Some interesting arable bryophytes were found on acidic Oxford Clay near Papworth St Agnes in 1960, but the main bryological importance of the Oxford Clay is as the parent material for the brick-making industry. There are massive brickpits in the county near Peterborough, and the brick-making plants here and those (now closed) over

**Figure 2.8** Surface geology of Cambridgeshire, mapped in tetrads. (a) Jurassic strata, (b) Woburn Sands, (c) Gault Clay, (d) Chalk. On the Jurassic map, black symbols show Oxford Clay; frogspawn, Upware Limestone; open symbols, other strata (mainly Ampthill and Kimmeridge Clays). On all maps, large symbols indicate an area of over 1 km². Derived from British Geological Survey 1: 50,000 Series maps.

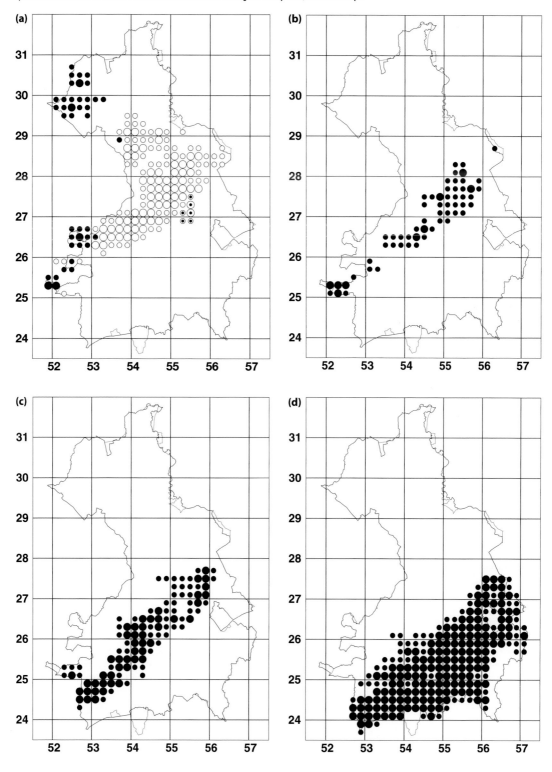

the county boundary in Bedfordshire were point-sources of $SO_2$ pollution. The younger Upper Jurassic strata, mainly the Ampthill and Kimmeridge Clays, are exposed in a broad band across the centre of the county. The Jurassic clays also underlie the northern part of the county where they are overlain by peat and alluvial sediments or other drift deposits, except sometimes on the fen islands. There is a small area of Jurassic limestone near Upware, a Corallian Limestone, which must have been deposited in clearer seas than the rest of the Jurassic deposits. It is similar to the much more widespread Corallian Limestones of Oxfordshire.

The oldest of the Cretaceous strata is that which has long been known to Cambridgeshire botanists as the Lower Greensand, though the term now used by geologists, the Woburn Sands (a formation of the Lower Greensand), is more precise. It is found in a narrow band south of the Jurassic clays (Figure 2.8b). In the Gamlingay area it provides an acidic, sandy substrate on which the former bogs and heaths of Gamlingay developed, and here it still supports remnants of a calcifuge flora. Although it extends eastwards across the county, it does not support such distinctive vegetation elsewhere although it is sometimes the explanation for the presence of an occasional calcifuge species on a ditch bank or in a hedgerow. The geology then reverts to another belt of marine clay, the Gault, which is more calcareous than the Jurassic clays (Figure 2.8c). It passes along the north side of Cambridge and is the source of the Cambridge 'yellow brick', very different in colour from the red bricks of the Oxford Clay. Like the subdued topography of the county, its yellow bricks are perhaps an acquired taste.

The youngest of the Cretaceous rocks is the chalk, which occupies the south-east of the county and forms the low hills which constitute its highest ground (Figure 2.8d). At the junction of the Gault and the chalk lies a very thin band known (rather confusingly) as the Cambridge Greensand, insignificant bryologically but the source of the phosphatic nodules which were widely quarried as 'coprolites' in the second half of the 19th century in a brief mining boom. The chalk varies in its properties with age. The Lower Chalk includes a narrow band of Totternhoe Stone or Burwell Rock, the most valued of the chalk building stones in the county. Springs arise when water permeating through the chalk reaches hard bands of chalk rock such as the Burwell Rock, or the very narrow band of Melbourn Rock at the base of the Middle Chalk. The Middle and Upper Chalks are even purer limestones than the Lower Chalk; the Upper Chalk is richer in flints than the strata below it. The well-drained, highly calcareous chalk supports a large suite of characteristic bryophytes (see Chapter 11).

### Drift geology

The clay-with-flints deposits which form an acidic capping to the chalk in many areas of southern England do not extend as far north as Cambridgeshire. The most important of the drift deposits in the south of the county is Boulder Clay, a thick glacial till (Figure 2.9a). This occurs as two very extensive deposits which cover the chalk plateau above the very gentle scarp slope in both the south-west and south-east of the county. There are also much more scattered deposits in the southern Fenland, and some of the fen islands are capped by Boulder Clay. The Boulder Clay predates the last glaciation (when the ice sheets did not extend as far south as Cambridgeshire). It is typically calcareous but varies in composition; the eastern Boulder Clay along the Breckland margin has an appreciable proportion of sand.

The gravel deposits in the county have a variety of origins (Figure 2.9b) but a broad distinction is made between the 'high-level gravels' or 'head gravels' and the 'Terrace Gravels'. The high-level gravels include the sand and gravels of Hildersham Furze Hills and those on the top of the Gog Magog Hills. They appear to have been deposited under glacial conditions but the precise origin of each of these deposits can only be established by careful investigation. The gravels at the Travellers' Rest Pit north-west of Cambridge, for example, which extend north to Girton, have recently been shown to date from the last glacial but one (the Wolstonian); the nearby but lower Observatory Gravels must have been deposited later in the Wolstonian (West & Gibbard 2017). The Terrace Deposits are more extensive than the high-level gravels, and are either associated with the modern river (Third to First Terraces) or (Fourth Terrace) are spreads of gravel associated with the margin of the Wolstonian glaciation (e.g. Bottisham Heath). The names reflect the fact that they were laid down as terraces at different heights above the modern rivers. The river terraces, from the highest and oldest, the Third Terrace, to the lowest and youngest, the First Terrace Gravels, were deposited after the last (Ipswichian) interglacial and date from the last glacial period, called the Devensian in Britain and the Weichselian in Europe (Worssam & Taylor 1969). The sands on the Breckland fringe of the county are mainly Terrace Gravels (although this is not the case further east in Breckland proper).

In the north of the county the really flat Fenland is covered by deposits which have been laid down since the last glacial period, and overlay all the earlier geology. In the northernmost Fenland these are marine silts; further south these give way to peats deposited by waterlogged plant communities (Figures 2.9c, d).

**Figure 2.9** Surface geology of Cambridgeshire, mapped in tetrads. (a) Boulder Clay, (b) Sands and gravels, (c) Marine and freshwater alluvium, (d) Peat. On the Alluvium map, black symbols show marine or marine and freshwater alluvium; open symbols, freshwater alluvium. On all maps, large symbols indicate an area of over 1 km². Derived from British Geological Survey 1: 50,000 Series maps.

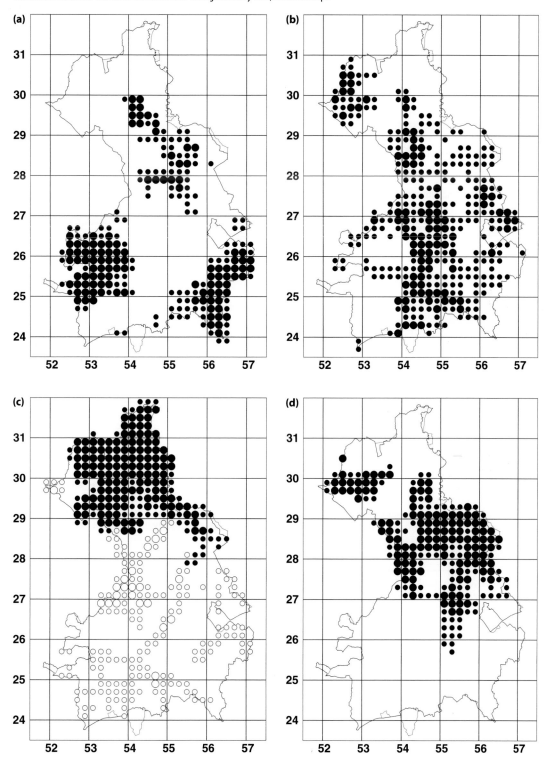

This simple surface pattern conceals a history of successive marine incursions and regressions, leaving an interleaved series of silt and peat deposits with the beds of silt thickening towards the coast. The drained peat has become oxidised and has eroded away; what remains is often scarcely recognisable as the sort of peat that survives in the undrained Wicken Fen. As the peat shrinks and erodes 'bog oaks' are sometimes exposed, especially in a band where the Fenland approaches upland areas. These subfossil trees include pine and yew as well as oak. Some particularly massive trees, rooted in the Jurassic, Gault or Boulder Clays underlying the peat sediments, grew in the high forest which succumbed to the original rise in water levels in the Neolithic (Godwin 1978).

## Soils

The study of soils in Cambridgeshire, as in Britain as a whole, changed radically after the Second World War. The proponents of the new approach regarded the work of their predecessors as 'rather sketchy and haphazard' (Hey & Perrin 1960). They embarked on a detailed new survey of the region, placing more emphasis on the genesis of soils as well as their current properties, classifying the soils into local series and relating these series to broader units recognised nationally and internationally. A feature of the new approach was the production of detailed soil maps, whereas previously 'it was generally assumed that the geological drift map afforded a reasonable substitute' (Perrin & Hodge 1965). Introductory accounts of the soils of Cambridgeshire, based on the new approach, were provided by Hey & Perrin (1960) and Perrin & Hodge (1965); the latter paper includes a soil map covering the entire county. More detailed studies were later published by the Soil Survey as maps and accompanying memoirs (e.g. Hodge & Seale 1966, Seale & Hodge 1976).

In view of the close relationship between terrestrial bryophytes and the soil on which they grow, it is perhaps surprising that these detailed soil studies have so far proved to be of rather limited use to the bryologist. A knowledge of the 'drift' geology of a site is normally all that is needed to interpret the bryophytes found there. This is perhaps due in large part to the youth of the county's soils. In some flat areas (e.g. on the Boulder Clay) soil may have been developing since the last interglacial, but on sloping surfaces the existing soils would have been lost by solifluction in the prevailing periglacial climate of the last glacial period. Most of our soils date from the current interglacial, and in many cases are only centuries old (many soils on the fen peat, for example, began to develop after drainage 150–400 years ago). They are therefore still closely related to their parent materials. As Perrin & Hodge (1965) concede, the recent age of the soils, the lack of climatic variation in the county and the relative uniformity of the vegetation until clearance for agriculture 'means that variations in soil formation, and thus in the soil pattern, are mainly defined by the interplay of topography and parent material'. As the county's topography is so subdued, the influence of parent material dominates. The deep ploughing of agricultural soils also reinforces their relationship to the parent material. Other bryophytes grow directly on the parent materials in quarries, on disturbed sites and of course on other substrates such as building stones and trees which are unrelated, or only indirectly related, to the soils below.

A feature of the chalk soils of the county which was emphasised by Coombe (1987) is the scarcity of really shallow rendzina soils over solid chalk, such as those which support the large population of *Pulsatilla vulgaris* on Therfield Heath just over the county boundary in Hertfordshire. Such soils are classified as the Icknield Series by the Soil Survey and are often found on steep slopes, so that their absence in Cambridge reflects the topography of the county. In the area mapped by Hodge & Seale (1966), which included the region between Cambridge and Newmarket, these occupied just 0.3% of the area, compared to 10.3% of the area for soils of the Moulton complex, deeper brown earth soils on more gentle chalk slopes which incorporate some overlying till, probably derived from periglacial solifluction or glacial meltwaters. West (2017) has recently reassessed these soils at a site near Swaffham Bulbeck, where they reach a depth of nearly 3 m in places. He recommended that they should be treated as a drift deposit in their own right, which he called Moulton Head; this appears to be derived from the wastage of material originally deposited in the Anglian glacial period (our most extensive glaciation).

Coombe (1987, 1988) also described the effect of periglacial soil patterns on the vegetation of Newmarket Heath, where stripes or polygons of acidic soil are set in a predominantly calcareous matrix. Unfortunately only a few robust pleurocarpous mosses can usually be found in the dense grass turf on Newmarket Heath, so these patterns are not reflected in the bryophyte cover. However, hollows in arable fields in Cambridgeshire, generally but perhaps controversially known as pingos (cf. Worsley *et al.* 1995), are also of periglacial origin and are of greater bryological interest. Taylor (1981) established the periglacial origin of the best known of these sites, the *Lythrum hyssopifolia* hollows south of Cambridge, but there are also similar depressions supporting *Lythrum* and *Riccia* species in the Chippenham area.

### Building stones and roofing materials

The building stones of Cambridgeshire have been reviewed by Purcell (1967) and Clifton-Taylor (2014), and we have drawn freely on their accounts. The only building stone found naturally in the county is provided by hard layers in the Lower Chalk, known as 'clunch', especially one layer known in the county as 'Burwell Rock' and elsewhere as 'Totternhoe Stone'. Clunch was quarried in three areas, one in Eversden, Barrington and Haslingfield, the second in Cherry Hinton and the third at Reach and Burwell. Chalk was widely used as a building stone and can be seen in domestic, church and college buildings and in some old walls. According to Purcell (1967) nearly all the surviving stone buildings in Cambridge dating from before *c.* 1500 are of clunch. However, they have usually been faced with brick or more durable stone as even the hardest chalk is relatively soft, easily weathered and thus far from ideal for external work. Its soft texture does make it suitable for carving inside buildings, as surviving work in (for example) Burwell parish church and Ely Cathedral shows. Flint, found with the chalk, is used in many churches and walls, and some secular buildings, often mixed with stones ('fieldstone rubble').

In the absence of good stone in the county, builders often turned to the limestones of Jurassic age found in the counties to the north-west. The grandest of all our buildings, Ely Cathedral, is largely built of Barnack Stone, a coarse shelly limestone from Northamptonshire. The oldest surviving college court is Old Court, Corpus Christi, built in the 1350s. Much humbler than Ely Cathedral, it is nonetheless a substantial building and has a core of clunch from Cherry Hinton, faced by a golden-yellow Northamptonshire limestone, with window and door surrounds of Burwell Rock and a few details of Barnack Stone (Rackham 1987). The highly prized Barnack Stone appears to have been worked out by the 15th century (the medieval quarries of Barnack Hills and Holes now support species-rich grassland). King's College Chapel, Cambridge, is partly built of Weldon Stone, also from Northamptonshire, and partly of a Permian magnesian limestone from Yorkshire. Great St Mary's church, Cambridge, also used Weldon Stone when it was rebuilt between 1478 and 1536. In addition to their direct use, the prized building stones were recycled from demolished monasteries such as Ramsey Abbey, Thorney Abbey and Barnwell Priory and thus found their way into Cambridge college buildings. By the 17th century the favoured Jurassic limestone was Ketton Stone, from Rutland, a fine-grained and durable oolitic limestone most famously seen in the Wren Library at Trinity College but also in many 18th and early 19th century college buildings. It continued to be used into the late 20th century at Downing College. Ancaster Stone from Lincolnshire was used in the 19th century, as in St John's College chapel. Some major 18th and 19th century buildings in Cambridge are built of a Jurassic limestone from much further afield, Portland Stone from Dorset, including the Senate House, the Fitzwilliam Museum and Gibbs' Building at King's College.

Thus from medieval times to the present day the main building stones in the county have been calcareous, and they therefore reinforce the calcareous nature of its geology rather than provide a contrasting substrate. The soft Jurassic limestones are readily colonised by bryophytes, especially when moist, and although the major buildings are too well kept (and too well guarded) to be happy hunting grounds for the bryologist, ancillary structures and lesser buildings are always worth examining. The 18th century gravestones made of oolite in many churchyards are especially rewarding (Figure 2.10), although it is difficult not to be

**Figure 2.10** The 18th-century limestone gravestone of Elizabeth Swan (died 1747) in Madingley churchyard, May 2018. Her descendant John Swan arranged for the lettering to be recut in 1857; he died in the same year and his dull Victorian gravestone is the one on the left. Photo: Chris Preston.

distracted by their delightful carving. As far as we know the geology and history of these gravestones has not been studied.

Building stones other than chalk and the Jurassic limestones are less frequent. Carstone, a deeply coloured iron-rich Cretaceous sandstone, is quarried and widely used in Norfolk but rarely in Cambridgeshire (St Mary's church, Welney, the only Carstone church we have examined in the county, is only yards from Norfolk). The rarity of Carstone here is no bad thing, as Robin Stevenson (2003) has found that it supports a poor bryophyte flora. Sandstone gravestones, frequent in many areas of Britain, are infrequent in the county. From the 19th century onwards churchyard monuments were made of a wider range of materials than formerly, including granite. Recent gravestones are usually made of highly polished stone, the 'granite' of monumental masons, an intensely bryophobic substrate.

In a county which lacks good building stone but has so much clay, it is not surprising that brick has long been a popular alternative. Brick was used for major buildings such as the former Bishop's Palace at Ely, all but one of the larger country houses in the county (including Madingley Hall and Wimpole Hall), many Cambridge college buildings (including the gatehouses of Jesus, St John's and Trinity), the Cambridge Corn Exchange and innumerable commercial and domestic buildings, great and small.

Roofing materials are often colonised by bryophytes, but they are, for obvious reasons, the least studied of the county's habitats. In the Cotswolds stone tiles have proved to support scarce *Grimmia* and *Schistidium* species (Martin 2007). Similar tiles, 'Collyweston slates', were occasionally used in Cambridge until the 17th century, from quarries near Collyweston in Northamptonshire. They survive on some college buildings, but we have not been able to sample any bryophytes on them. Collyweston slates were formerly used to roof the Round Church in Cambridge but they have been replaced by similar Stonesfield slates from Oxfordshire. Unfortunately an annoying barrier designed to prevent slates from this high-pitched roof from falling to the ground also catches falling clumps of moss. Tile roofs are frequent, as are a variety of natural and artificial slates. Slate provides a rare example of a widespread imported acidic substrate which may be colonised by calcifuge bryophytes. Thatch roofs are found in small numbers in many Cambridgeshire villages. Proctor (1956) noted that they 'often support a luxuriant moss growth which would bear closer study than it has hitherto received'. Now they are almost all protected by galvanised chicken-wire and thus are colonised only by those calcifuge bryophytes which can also tolerate high metal concentrations.

## Current land use

The land cover of the vice-county, based on satellite images from the period 2006–08, can be calculated from the UK Land Cover Map 2007 (Morton *et al.* 2011). The proportions of land in the main land-use categories are set out in Table 2.2 and the largest land-use category in each 1-km square mapped in Figure 2.11. These show the overwhelmingly arable nature of the county, with 76% of the land occupied by arable crops and a further 14% classified as improved grassland. The low (predominantly northern) flatlands having an even higher proportion of arable (82%), less grassland and built-up land and even less woodland, but more freshwater. Woodlands occupy only 2% of the county and only two 1-km squares have broad-leaved woodland as the predominant land cover, TL5670 (fen carr at Wicken Fen) and TL6469 (planted woodland at Chippenham Fen). One distinctive area of the county which is visible in Figure 2.11 as an area of improved grassland is the 'studland' around Newmarket, an area devoted to the equine industry. The stud farms in this area are characterised by manicured hedges and neat fences, intensively managed grassland, linear shelter belts and small plantations, often of beech; they are largely inaccessible to bryologists. The only concentrations of semi-natural grassland are along the diagonal line of the Ouse Washes which cuts across Fenland and at Wicken Fen, including the recent areas reclaimed there from arable land.

The main crops grown in the county at the start and end of our survey are listed in Table 2.3. This table is based on figures published by DEFRA which cover the administrative county, but they provide a good indication of the crops of vc 29. There are few differences between 2000 and 2016. Statutory set-aside had been abolished by 2016, but the difference is in part compensated for by an increase in the area of fallow land.

## Land use history

### Fen drainage
In considering the history of land use, the 'upland' areas of the county need to be separated from the Fenland areas which are (or were) liable to flooding. In the Fenland, drainage has been attempted since

**Figure 2.11** The predominant land cover in the 1-km squares of Cambridgeshire, derived from the Land Cover Map 2007 © NERC (CEH) 2011. Key to colours: Pale brown, arable; black, built-up areas and gardens; green, improved grassland; red, semi-natural grassland; blue, freshwater; violet, brickpits (misclassified as heath); yellow, broad-leaved woodland.

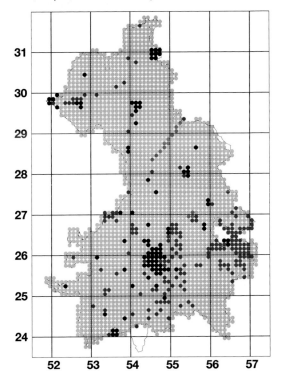

**Table 2.2** Land cover of Cambridgeshire (vc 29), 2007, showing the difference between land below 5 m and that at or over 5 m.

| Altitude | <5 m | ≥5 m | Total |
|---|---|---|---|
| Arable (%) | 82.4 | 69.5 | 75.8 |
| Improved grassland (%) | 9.5 | 17.5 | 13.6 |
| Built and gardens (%) | 3.4 | 7.4 | 5.5 |
| Woodland (%) | 0.9 | 3.4 | 2.2 |
| Rough grass and heath (%) | 2.8 | 2.1 | 2.4 |
| Freshwater (%) | 1.0 | 0.2 | 0.6 |

**Table 2.3** Crops grown in the administrative county of Cambridgeshire, with the percentage of the total area of arable, horticultural and set-aside land devoted to them in 2000 and 2016.

| Crops | Percentage area | |
|---|---|---|
| | 2000 | 2016 |
| **Cereals** | | |
| Wheat | 51.2 | 49.2 |
| Winter barley | 5.7 | 5.0 |
| Spring barley | 1.8 | 6.7 |
| Oats | 0.4 | 0.9 |
| Others | 0.1 | 0.3 |
| **Other arable crops** | | |
| Oilseed rape | 6.8 | 12.2 |
| Sugar beet | 8.3 | 4.7 |
| Field beans | 3.3 | 4.5 |
| Potatoes | 4.6 | 3.7 |
| Maize | 0.1 | 1.6 |
| Others | 4.2 | 2.9 |
| Uncropped/bare fallow | 0.4 | 4.4 |
| **Horticultural crops** | | |
| Vegetables and salad crops | 2.7 | 3.4 |
| Orchard fruit ('Top fruit') | 0.5 | 0.3 |
| Others | 0.4 | 0.2 |
| **Set-aside** | 9.5 | 0.0 |

Roman times. The major drain known as Morton's Leam was constructed in 1478–80 to carry waters from the River Nene near Peterborough to Wisbech without flooding the intervening Fenland (Taylor 1973). The project was masterminded by John Morton, Bishop of Ely from 1478 to 1486, later Archbishop of Canterbury and Lord Chancellor. This approach to drainage was developed in the major schemes undertaken in the 17th century by Sir Cornelius Vermuyden for the Earl of Bedford and his fellow 'Adventurers'. The parallel Old Bedford River (1637) and New Bedford River (1651) which cut across the county's Fenland and are separated by the Ouse Washes are his handiwork, as are several other major drains. The first Bedford River was designed to drain land in the summer, whereas the New Bedford River sought to drain the land throughout the year (Darby 1940). Although these schemes initially achieved a degree of success, the unforeseen effects of the shrinkage of the drained peat soon caused problems. However, the development of wind-powered pumps from the late 17th century allowed these difficulties to be surmounted, and stimulated further drainage schemes. The use of steam engines for drainage began in the county at Upware in 1821 and 40 years later Babington (1860: xvii) noted that 'The employment of steam has made the removal of the water so certain that the whole level may be cited as a pattern in farming. With the water many of the most interesting and characteristic plants have disappeared, or have become so exceedingly rare that the discovery of single individuals of them is a subject for wonder and congratulation'.

### Effects of parliamentary enclosure
South of the Fenland, John Ray, the Martyns and the young Relhan botanised in a largely unenclosed landscape. Although there had been piecemeal enclosure of some common land from medieval times (Taylor 1973), the open 'common fields' remained in most areas. There were small groups of hedged fields ('closes') around many of the county's villages, but these gave way to the large expanses of open arable fields (Figure 2.12) or, on the chalk, broad areas of open sheepwalk. Some early maps show this landscape in great detail, most notably the wonderful maps of Gamlingay plotted by Thomas Langdon for Merton

College, Oxford in 1602 (Bendall 1992). Open fields surrounded Cambridge on all sides. Ancient woods in the county had long been reduced to the scattered and named woods we know today, usually on the furthest fringes of the parish. The special habitats within this landscape, including the 'moors' around Cambridge and the complex of acidic habitats at Gamlingay, are dealt with in later chapters. We have few pre-enclosure bryophyte records for more ordinary habitats; even then the bryological interest was concentrated in scattered habitats surrounded by agricultural land.

Parliamentary enclosure came late to Cambridgeshire, so that the open fields survived until the Revolutionary and Napoleonic Wars (1793–1815). Then the need to feed an increasing population combined with bad harvests and the insecurity of the wartime situation led to great pressure for agricultural improvement, of which enclosure was seen as the first stage. The proportion of land enclosed at this period, and in a second wave of enclosure in the 1820s and 1830s, was higher (53%) than in any other county except Oxfordshire (54%). The Cambridge total is reduced by the large area of Fenland which was virtually unaffected by enclosure. Some 70% of the land in the south of the county was enclosed, a development described by Turner (1980) as 'the most concentrated agricultural organisational change that there had ever been, certainly in that county and probably in any county'. This was followed by agricultural improvement, including the drainage of wetlands (including the 'moors' around Cambridge) and the ploughing up of ancient grassland (Crompton 1997, Preston 2000, Wittering 2013).

Looking back towards the end of a long life, Leonard Jenyns reflected that no young naturalist could 'have been placed in a richer or more attractive neighbourhood' for natural history than his friend C.E. Broome in Swaffham Bulbeck (or Jenyns himself in nearby Bottisham) in the early 1830s (Blomefield 1887). 'The whole district not merely abounded in birds, insects, shells, and plants, but in certain localities were to be found many rare species, of plants especially, seldom met with in other parts of England'. Broome and Jenyns belonged to the last generation of Cambridgeshire naturalists who could have made such claims. The deleterious effects of agricultural improvement on the vascular plants were highlighted in Babington's *Flora of Cambridgeshire* (1860). Jenyns himself presented his natural history notes to the Cambridge University Museum of Zoology in 1869, commenting that they might be of interest as Cambridgeshire is 'a County which, through drainage and enclosure, has lost of late years so many of its rarer species of birds and other animals' (Preece & Sparks 2012).

**Figure 2.12** The arable landscape of south Cambridgeshire before enclosure. This scene, painted *c.* 1800 by Richard Relhan, son of the botanist of the same name, shows Haslingfield from the Barton side of the Bourn Brook. Reproduced by kind permission of the Syndics of Cambridge University Library.

### The changing agricultural landscape

Babington and Jenyns were writing in the 1860s at the height of mid-Victorian agricultural prosperity, a prosperity which began to fall after 1870 when increasing globalisation led to enhanced competition on world markets. The county has retained an overwhelmingly arable landscape to the present day, but within this landscape, land-use changes have reflected fluctuations in agricultural fortunes, the emergencies of war and the increasing effects of the application of science and technology to agricultural processes. During the agricultural depressions between 1860 and 1939 some of the most marginal arable land in the county, on the western clays, was abandoned. A.G. Tansley's masterpiece *The British islands and their vegetation* includes photographs of 20-year and 50-year old 'hawthorn thicket scrub' on abandoned arable land on the Boulder Clay of south-west Cambridgeshire. 'This scrub has established itself widely on derelict arable or pasture land in this district, of which a considerable extent has been abandoned from time to time because it is too expensive to cultivate when prices are low' (Tansley 1939).

As Tansley was writing, the agriculture of the county was described for the British Association by McMillan (1938). 'Though in some districts large farms stretch as far as the eye can see, Cambridgeshire as a whole may be regarded as a county of small farms, small-holdings, and market or cottage gardens'. There are few areas now in which the farms do not stretch as far as the eye can see. Whereas in 1932–33 about 90% of the agricultural area in Cambridgeshire (excluding the Isle of Ely) belonged to farms which were larger than eight hectares (Pettit 1941), by 2016, according to DEFRA statistics, 93% of the administrative county belonged to farms larger than 50 hectares and 84% to farms of over 100 hectares. Since the War the county has experienced other changes in agricultural practices which have been well documented for Britain as a whole by Stoate (1996) and Robinson & Sutherland (2002), for the current administrative county of Cambridgeshire by Preece & Sparks (2012) and for the adjacent county of Suffolk by Sanford & Fisk (2010). The effects of these changes on one Cambridgeshire parish, Bassingbourn, were described by Sell (1989).

Preece & Sparks (2012) show that the changes in Cambridgeshire include the rapid decline in the number of horses used in agriculture and the concomitant decrease in the acreage of oats from 1914 onwards. There has been a marked move away from mixed farming, with a decline in the area of permanent grassland from the inter-war years, a fall in the number of sheep and the area of land sown to fodder roots from the late 19th century and in the number of cattle since 1950. In the post-war years winter wheat has been grown increasingly at the expense of barley. New crops have introduced, peaked in popularity and then sometimes declined. Orchard fruits increased greatly in area in the first half of the century then fell back to the earlier levels in the second half; potatoes increased over the same period and have similarly declined; sugar beet became a significant crop in the inter-war years but declined towards the end of the century and since the 1970s oilseed rape has been a popular crop. Agricultural intensification has led to the enlargement of fields, the loss of hedges and ditches and the increasing use of fertilisers, herbicides and pesticides. In the north of the county, the peat soils have continued to shrink and erode after drainage, so that the future of arable farming on some land in these areas is doubtful.

In addition to the grubbing up of hedgerows in the post-war years, a virulent outbreak of Dutch Elm Disease also resulted in the loss of thousands of the county's elm trees in both rural and urban areas. The current outbreak appears to have started in Gloucestershire *c.* 1965 (Rackham 1986). Oliver Rackham first noticed it at Hayley Wood on 24 July 1970, when it had begun to affect a single, free-standing tree (*Rackham notebook* 177: 3414). In 1971 a Forestry Commission survey found that trees with the early stages of the disease were widespread in the southern part of the county, and by 1972 trees with more advanced symptoms had increased in frequency (Gibbs & Howell 1972, 1974). After its devastating initial impact the disease has persisted at a lower level and it continues to affect trees as they grow from suckers, although both individual trees and a few elm groves and some stands of woodland elms have survived.

### Extractive industries

Many of the county's geological deposits have been quarried in historic and recent times, including Oxford and Gault Clays (for brick-making), Coralline Limestone (initially for agricultural use, later for use in the manufacture of asphalt), chalk (for building stone and cement) and Terrace Gravels (for aggregates). In addition the Cambridge Greensand was formerly exploited for coprolites. As described above, the quarrying of chalk for building stone has a long history in the county and some of the old, abandoned clunch pits (such as those at Haslingfield and Orwell) are still of bryological interest.

At the time of parliamentary enclosure in the early 19th century, land was often set aside for a 'parish pit'. Anderson (1958) inspected 95 enclosure awards for parishes in Cambridgeshire (excluding the Isle of Ely) and found that 77 made provision for parish chalk, clay or gravel pits. Where the soils in the parish varied, provision was sometimes made for more than one pit; 17 parishes were provided with two pits and

21 with three, four or five. The proportion of enclosure awards which set aside land for a pit decreased after 1815, suggesting that by then their importance in parish life might have been declining.

One trend which applied to the quarrying of chalk, clay and gravel was that frequent small pits in the 19th century were replaced by a few large pits in the 20th century. Quarrying of chalk at Cherry Hinton stopped in 1984 (Taylor 1999), and the largest quarry is now a nature reserve. Since 2000 there have been active chalk pits at Barrington (until 2008) and in the extreme south of the county at Steeple Morden as well as a limestone quarry at Dimmock's Cote near Upware. There are still active brickpits near Whittlesey, as well as a large private nature reserve (Kings Dyke) in an area where extraction stopped in the 1970s. The Terrace gravels have been extracted at many sites north of Cambridge in the valleys of the Cam and Great Ouse, and near Chippenham, and disused pits are sometimes preserved for public amenity (Milton Country Park) or wildlife (Fen Drayton Lakes RSPB reserve).

### Conservation: SSSIs, nature reserves and the wider countryside

The post-war conservation movement proceeded alongside the agricultural revolution and attempted to mitigate its effects. The Nature Conservancy was established by Royal Charter in 1949 and empowered to notify Sites of Special Scientific Interest (SSSIs) under the National Parks and Access to the Countryside Act of 1949 (Sheail 1976), although for many years it had few powers to protect them. The first Cambridgeshire SSSIs, scheduled in 1951, included sites which were already well known for their bryophytes, such as Great Heath Wood at Gamlingay, Hayley Wood, Little Widgham and Out Wood, the Roman Road, Devil's Dyke, Fleam Dyke, Cherry Hinton Chalk Pits and Hildersham Furze Hills. Two reports by the County Council, describing and mapping common lands in the county (Cambridgeshire County Planning Department 1956) and the early SSSIs (Cambridgeshire and Isle of Ely County Council Planning Department 1965), remain useful reference works. The SSSIs of particular bryological interest are listed in Table 2.4.

**Table 2.4** Sites of Special Scientific Interest and nature reserves of bryological interest in Cambridgeshire. For the explanation of the tetrad grid references, see Chapter 19.

| SSSI name | Grid reference | Habitat | Designation* | Comments |
|---|---|---|---|---|
| Alder Carr [Hildersham] | TL54P | Alder wood | SSSI | |
| Balsham Wood | TL54Z, 55V | Ancient wood | SSSI | |
| Barrington Chalk Pit | TL35V | Chalk pit, actively quarried until 2008, now partly used for land-fill | SSSI | A geological SSSI for the Cambridge Greensand exposure |
| Bassenhally Pit | TL29Z | Long-disused gravel workings with marsh, scrub and woodland | SSSI | |
| Beechwoods | TL45X | Beechwood on chalk | WT | See Chapter 11 |
| Brackland Rough | TL66J, 67F | Damp woodland | SSSI, WT | Known to bryologists as Fordham Hall Yard Woods |
| Buff Wood | TL25Q, V | Wood with ancient core | SSSI, WT | See Rackham (1990, 2003) |
| Cambourne | TL35E, J | Woods, lakes | WT | |
| Carlton Wood | TL65L | Ancient wood | SSSI | Inadequately recorded |
| Cherry Hinton Pit | TL45X, Y | Disused chalk pits | SSSI, WT | See Chapter 11 |
| Chippenham Fen and Snailwell Poor's Fen | TL66J, P | Fen, planted woodland | NNR, SSSI | See Chapter 10 |
| Dernford Fen | TL45Q | Fen, fen carr | SSSI | Inadequately recorded |
| Devil's Dyke | TL56, 65, 66 | Chalk grassland on ancient earthwork | SSSI | See Chapter 11 |
| Elsworth Wood | TL36A, B | Ancient wood | SSSI | |
| Eversden and Wimpole Woods | TL35F, G, K, L | Ancient and recent woodland, parkland | NT, SSSI | See Chapter 13 |
| Fen Drayton Lakes | TL36J, P, 37F, K | Disused gravel pits | RSPB | |
| Fleam Dyke | TL55H, L, M, R | Chalk grassland on ancient earthwork | SSSI | See Chapter 11 |
| Fowlmere Watercress Beds | TL44C | Aquatic habitats, scrub and secondary woodland | RSPB, SSSI | |
| Fulbourn Fen | TL55H, I | Neutral grassland, secondary woodland | SSSI, WT | |
| Furze Hill [Hildersham] | TL54P | Grassland and disturbed sand and gravel | SSSI | See Trist (1988) |
| Gamlingay Wood | TL25G, L | Ancient wood with sand lens | SSSI, WT | See Chapter 8 |
| Gog Magog Golf Course | TL54W, X | Chalk grassland | SSSI | Inadequately recorded |
| Great Wilbraham Common | TL55I | Calcareous grassland | SSSI | |
| Hardwick Wood | TL35N, P | Ancient wood | SSSI, WT | |
| Hayley Wood | TL25W | Ancient wood | SSSI, WT | See Chapter 8 |
| Hildersham Wood | TL54H | Ancient wood | SSSI | See Faulkner (1963) |

The history of nature reserves in the county goes back to 1899, when the National Trust bought two acres of Wicken Sedge Fen for £10 to establish its first nature reserve (Friday & Chatfield 1997). The National Trust expanded its holdings at Wicken as and when opportunities arose; the entomologist G.H. Verrall, who had bought up many small parcels of land, bequeathed 239 acres at Wicken to the Trust in 1911. The Cambridgeshire and Isle of Ely Naturalists' Trust (Cambient) was founded in 1956; this is now the Wildlife Trust for Cambridgeshire, Bedfordshire and Northamptonshire.[1] However, the Trust initially took the view that 'agreement safeguarding the interest of naturalists may generally be preferable to acquisition [of property], not least in view of the very slender financial resources of the Trust' (Cambient 1959). It was Cambridge City Council who acquired Lime Kiln Close, Cherry Hinton, in 1957 and declared it 'a nature reserve for public use' (Cambient 1958). The purchase by Cambient of their first reserve, Hayley Wood, bought for £5,000 in 1962 after a successful public appeal and thus saved from the depredations of a Bedfordshire timber-merchant, was therefore a significant moment. The major reserves of bryological interest are also listed in Table 2.4.

The 'grain mountains' built up in the European Union countries in the late 20th century gave rise to the 'set-aside' scheme. From 1992 until 2007 farmers in receipt of grants were obliged to leave a proportion of their fields uncropped, although they were not allowed to let them tumble down to scrub so the abandoned arable landscapes of the 1930s were not re-created. The documentation of the effects of modern agriculture on farmland bird populations and plant pollinators has stimulated conservation measures such as the provision of marginal strips along arable fields sown with plants intended to support pollinators, to provide food for seed-eating birds or to create invertebrate habitats to sustain insectivores.

1 One of the earliest and most significant acts of Cambient was to found *Nature in Cambridgeshire* as the county's first journal of natural history; volume 1 was published in 1958. The journal was abandoned by its sole parent in 1985 and left to die, but fortunately it was adopted by independent well-wishers and continues to be the primary means of documenting the county's non-avian natural history.

**Table 2.4** cont'd. Sites of Special Scientific Interest and nature reserves of bryological interest in Cambridgeshire. For the explanation of the tetrad grid references, see Chapter 19.

| SSSI name | Grid reference | Habitat | Designation* | Comments |
|---|---|---|---|---|
| Holland Hall (Melbourn) Railway Cutting | TL34R | Chalk cutting | SSSI | Potentially interesting but bryologically unknown |
| Kingfishers Bridge | TL57L | Newly created fen | PNR | |
| Kings Dyke | TL29N, P | Disused brick pits | PNR | |
| Kingston Wood and outliers | TL35G, H | Ancient wood | SSSI | See Reynolds (2003) |
| Langley Wood | TL64B | Ancient wood | SSSI | |
| Lattersey | TL29Y | Disused clay pit | WT | |
| Lower Wood | TL65G | Ancient wood | WT | |
| Madingley Wood | TL35Z, 45E | Ancient wood | SSSI | See Chapter 8 |
| Nene Washes | TL29, 39, TF30 | Washland | RSPB, SSSI | |
| Orwell Clunch Pit | TL35Q | Chalk grassland | SSSI | |
| Ouse Washes | TL37, 47, 48, 58, 59 | Washland | RSPB, SSSI, WT | |
| Out and Plunder Wood | TL65M, S | Ancient wood | SSSI | |
| Overhall Grove | TL36G, L | Ancient secondary wood | SSSI, WT | See Rackham (1990, 2003) |
| Papworth Wood | TL26W | Ancient wood | SSSI | |
| Park Wood [Brinkley] | TL65H, M | Ancient wood | SSSI | Inadequately recorded |
| Roman Road | TL45X, 54, 55 | Chalk grassland | SSSI | See Chapter 11 |
| Sawston Hall Meadows | TL44Z | Spring-fed meadows | SSSI | Nearby woods also of interest |
| Soham Wet Horse Fen | TL67B | Moist neutral grassland | SSSI | |
| Stanground Wash | TL29D | Acidic railway ballast, washland | WT | |
| Stow-cum-Quy Fen | TL56B | Pools, chalk grassland, scrub | SSSI | |
| Ten Wood | TL65S, T | Ancient wood | SSSI | |
| Thriplow Meadows | TL44I | Grassland | SSSI | See Crompton (1972) |
| Upware North Pit | TL57L | Wetland | PNR, SSSI | |
| Waresley Wood | TL25S | Ancient wood | SSSI, WT | Only a sliver is in vc 29 |
| Whittlesford-Thriplow Hummocky Fields | TL44I, P | Winter-flooded hollows in arable fields | SSSI | See Chapter 12 |
| Wicken Fen | TL56P, U, TL57K, Q | Fen, fen carr | NNR, NT, SSSI | See Chapter 10 |

* Abbreviations: NNR, National Nature Reserve; NT, National Trust; PNR, Private nature reserve; RSPB, Royal Society for the Protection of Birds; WT Wildlife Trust; SSSI, Site of Special Scientific Interest. Where more than one of these designations has been applied to a site, their boundaries are not necessarily identical.

There has been an increase in woodland planting in recent years (see Chapter 8). More surprising developments, perhaps, have been the recent large-scale extension of Wicken Fen and the creation nearby of a new wetland, Kingfisher's Bridge, both on former arable land.

### Population growth

Population density in Cambridgeshire is typical of that of rural southern England (see map in Pescott & Preston 2014). The population of the county, from 1801 onwards, can be derived from census results which have been summarised for four of the county's administrative regions (Cambridge, South and East Cambridgeshire and Fenland) which approximate to the vice-county (Figure 2.13). The population increased rapidly in the first half of the 19th century. Between 1851 and 1901 rural stagnation or depopulation was balanced by the growth of Cambridge, resulting in little overall change. The rapid growth after the Second World War occurred in all four regions, with South Cambridgeshire growing the most rapidly. The reasons behind the very visible expansion of Cambridge in recent years include the 'Cambridge phenomenon', the growth in the number of science- and technology-based companies based in and around the town (Koepp 2002). The population of most of the other towns in the county increased by over 50% between 1961 and 2011, including Chatteris (90%), Ely (107%), March (70%), Soham (114%) and Whittlesey (72%) although the tide of expansion and prosperity has not yet reached Wisbech (30%).

## Air pollution

### Sulphur

Perhaps the main driver of change in the British bryophyte flora in the last few decades has been the reduction in sulphur dioxide ($SO_2$) pollution. Most $SO_2$ is derived from the burning of fossil fuels, and levels of pollution in Britain increased in the 19th and early 20th centuries with the increasing use of coal and later oil for domestic heating, power generation and other industrial purposes. The national map (Figure 2.14) shows that in 1970 Cambridgeshire had moderately high levels of $SO_2$ pollution, with concentrations which were much lower than those in London and the industrial areas of northern England but much higher than those found in most of the rural areas to the west. The London Brick Company (LBC) works near Peterborough and just over the county boundary in Bedfordshire were important sources of $SO_2$ pollution in the county. The distinctive smell of the Peterborough brickpits was a familiar one to us at Monks Wood, 18 km away, when the wind was blowing from the Peterborough direction. LBC was later taken over by Hanson who stopped brick-making in Bedfordshire in 2008. One of the reasons that Oxford Clay was favoured for brick-making was its high organic content, which greatly increased its calorific value but contributed to the sulphur emissions. The brickpits were also a source of other pollutants, including levels of fluorine which were so high that they caused fluorosis in farm animals (Fuge & Andrews 1988) and might well have been toxic to bryophytes.

The Great Smog of London in 1952 made it clear that action was required to stop pollution by particulate matter, another consequence of coal burning, and led to the Clean Air Acts of 1956 and 1968. Concentrations of $SO_2$ began to fall c. 1960 as smokeless fuels, which have a lower sulphur content, began to be used in place of coal. By the 1980s there were international agreements to limit levels of sulphur emissions. Concentrations in Britain continued to fall steadily after 1970 with the decline in heavy industry, the replacement of coal by gas (a fuel with a very low sulphur content), efforts to disperse industrial emissions more widely (by the use of taller chimneys) and then by the use of desulphurisation technology to reduce them (RoTAP 2012). According to the National Atmospheric Emissions Inventory, $SO_2$ emissions fell by 96% between 1970 and 2015.

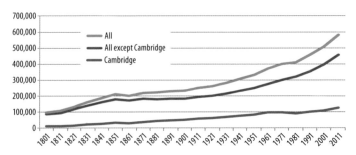

**Figure 2.13** Growth in the population of Cambridge and the rest of Cambridgeshire, from the decadal census figures. There was no census in 1941.

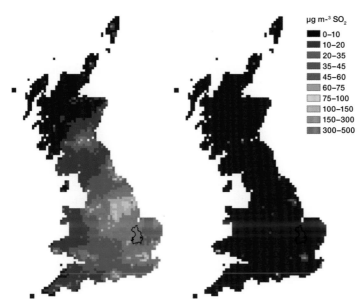

**Figure 2.14** Modelled levels of SO₂ pollution in Britain in 1970 (left) and 2005 (right), plotted by Dr Oli Pescott from data generated by the FRAME model (v 7.00.0) of Dore *et al.* (2007) and Matejko *et al.* (2009). The map illustrates in 10-km squares the maximum value for its component 5-km squares. The outline of Cambridgeshire is shown in black.

μg m⁻³ SO₂
- 0–10
- 10–20
- 20–35
- 35–45
- 45–60
- 60–75
- 75–100
- 100–150
- 150–300
- 300–500

Bryologists (and lichenologists) became familiar with the adverse effects of 'smoke' in the 19th century, although it was not until 1958 that they began to realise that SO₂ was the most important factor in emissions. The absence of many bryophyte species, particularly epiphytes, from the more polluted areas of eastern England was apparent from the distribution data collected for the first national bryophyte atlas (Hill *et al.* 1991–94) and was studied in detail by Gilbert (1968, 1970) in Newcastle upon Tyne. In a study of species-poor urban bryophyte communities Gilbert (1971) predicted that 'North Sea gas conversion, higher chimneys and the eventual economic extraction of sulphur from flue gases will allow additional species to invade British towns' and in the 1980s the first signs of a recovery in pollution-sensitive species were detected. For reviews of the effects on bryophytes of declining SO₂ at the national scale, see Adams & Preston (1992), Hill & Preston (2014) and Pescott *et al.* (2015).

### Nitrogen

Two main groups of these pollutants are recognised, ammonia (NH₃) and the nitrogen oxides (NOₓ). The concentrations of both have fallen nationally in recent decades, although the decline in ammonia emissions (10% since 1980; figures are not available for earlier years) has been less marked than the decline in NOₓ (63% since 1970) or SO₂. The main sources of ammonia are from livestock, especially cattle but also pigs and poultry. 'Emissions of NH₃ from livestock derive primarily from the degradation of urea (or uric acid for poultry) in excreta. NH₃ is emitted from the entire manure management process, during production, handling, storage and use or application to land' (RoTAP 2012). The effects of NH₃ pollution can be very marked, and in severely polluted areas bryophytes and lichens on rocks or trees can be replaced by black algal slime. However, such effects are restricted to the immediate vicinity of livestock units, and so they are not encountered in the overwhelmingly arable landscape of Cambridgeshire. The other group of pollutants are the nitrogen oxides (NOₓ), including nitric oxide (NO) and nitrous oxide (NO₂). The major source of these pollutants is road traffic, and although concentrations of NOₓ in Britain are falling nationally, levels remain stubbornly high in urban areas. There have been relatively few observations of the effect of NOₓ on bryophytes, either experimentally or in the field (Pescott *et al.* 2015).

# 3

# Bryophyte recording in Cambridgeshire, 1660–1999

## Early records: John Ray and William Vernon, 1660–1724

The story of Cambridgeshire bryology begins with the great naturalist **John Ray** (1627–1705), but it must be admitted that it is not an impressive beginning. Ray included bryophytes, as well as lichens, algae and fungi, in his first book, *Catalogus plantarum circa Cantabrigiam nascentium* (1660), a catalogue of Cambridgeshire plants, but at this time the taxonomic study of these groups had hardly started. Some of Ray's few entries for these cryptogams covered the most distinctive species, others were so vague that they cannot be related to modern species concepts. The only one of Ray's five bryophyte entries which we have been prepared to equate to a current species is *Adiantum aureum majus*, a name then applied to *Polytrichum commune* and plausibly recorded by Ray from the watery places on Hinton Moor. The other four are unidentifiable (see Oswald & Preston 2011). Thus *Lichen*, growing 'in moist shady places', was presumably based on thallose liverworts such as *Marchantia polymorpha* and *Pellia endiviifolia*.

Ray left Cambridge in 1662 and he summarised the observations he and his colleagues had made between 1660 and 1662 in a brief *Appendix* to the *Catalogus* which appeared soon after his departure (Ray 1663). It includes four bryophyte entries. *Hepatica stellata*, 'On the north side of Peterhouse chappel abundantly, observed by Mr Dent' is female *Marchantia polymorpha* and the next species listed in the *Appendix*, *Hepatica umbellata*, 'On the moors', is perhaps the male plant. *Muscus triangularis aquaticus* 'In the river beyond Stretham ferry' is clearly *Fontinalis antipyretica* and we can identify *Muscus filicinus* with a fair degree of confidence as *Thuidium tamariscinum*, not least because it is still found in 'Kingston and Eversden woods, and the woods about Balsham'. Both sexes of *Marchantia polymorpha* can now be found in the court around Peterhouse Chapel but we have failed to refind *Fontinalis* at Stretham. Despite his early *Marchantia* record, the apothecary **Peter Dent** (1628/29–1689) added no new bryophyte entries when he prepared a second edition of the *Appendix* in 1685.

In later years Ray worked with several friends and correspondents to describe more mosses and liverworts in his British flora, *Synopsis methodica stirpium Britannicarum* (1690, 1696). **William Vernon**, a Fellow of Peterhouse, was a member of his circle and can be regarded as Cambridge's first bryologist. Like several of the leading naturalists in the late 17th century, he attended the Friday evening meetings of the informal Temple Coffee House (Botanic) Club when he was in London in the 1690s (Riley 2006). He was a correspondent of Samuel Doody, Martin Lister, James Petiver, Richard Richardson and Hans Sloane (Stearns 1952) and a friend of Adam Buddle, who he famously described in 1703 as 'the top of all the moss-croppers' (Turner 1835). He had entered Peterhouse in 1685 at the age of 18 and became a Fellow in 1692. Vernon is also remembered as a pioneer entomologist who was possibly responsible for the discovery of three British butterflies, Bath White, Queen of Spain Fritillary and Duke of Burgundy (Salmon 2000); the first was known to Petiver as 'Vernon's half-Mourner' and the last as 'Mr Vernon's Small Fritillary' (Petiver 1699, 1702). His other claim to fame is his collecting trip to Maryland with the German physician David Kreig in 1697–98; the plants he brought back were studied by Ray and many survive in the Sloane herbarium. Vernon visited Ray in 1704, a year before Ray's death, finding him 'very old and infirm in body, tho' his parts are very vivid'. Vernon himself may have died by 1706 (Riley 2006), though the date and circumstances of his death are unknown. He is commemorated by the North American genus *Vernonia* (Asteraceae).

Vernon obviously developed an interest in bryophytes rapidly, as Ray told Edward Lhuyd in August 1694 that he 'hath been more industrious in searching out, and more successful in finding the species of that Tribe [mosses] then any man I know' (Gunther 1928). He must have visited Ray shortly afterwards, as Ray (1696: 30) tells us that he found *Aulacomnium androgynum* on the trunks of trees near Ray's house; Ray collected it and the published record was the first from Britain. Some 30 plants and fungi are included in this edition of the *Synopsis* on the basis of Vernon's descriptions or specimens. The published records include the first British records of *Bryum pseudotriquetrum* from Hinton and Teversham Moors, *Calliergonella cuspidata* from Hinton Moor 'and other the like places' and *Climacium dendroides* from Gamlingay. One of the other mosses sent by Vernon to Ray was *Splachnum ampullaceum*, but Ray just has four dots in the 1696 *Synopsis* in place of the locality, obviously adding them in the vain hope that he would be able to insert the details later.

A vivid insight into Vernon's botanical interests comes from his annotated copy of Ray's *Synopsis* (1696), which was acquired by Hans Sloane and survives in the British Library; it is unsigned and has not received much attention from historians. There are numerous annotations in Vernon's handwriting and the notes against the bryophyte entries are particularly frequent (Figure 3.1). Some of these annotations are clearly legible, others are now very faint. They provide Cambridgeshire localities for an additional 25 species, of which 19 can be matched to modern species. These include Vernon's sites for *Splachnum ampullaceum* – he wrote 'Cherry-hinton Teversham Gamlingay &c' over Ray's four dots, as well as 'aestate', indicating that it fruits in summer. This is one of the crucial entries which confirm that the annotations are indeed by Vernon, along with the note against a vascular plant, a species of *Potentilla* (p. 141), 'In Marilandia vidi' [I saw it in Maryland]. Vernon has added fruiting times for several bryophytes, as well as critical assessments of some of Ray's entries. Many of his mosses were found at Gamlingay, where he recorded both wetland species (e.g. *Aulacomnium palustre*, *Philonotis fontana*, *Sphagnum*) and plants of drier ground (e.g. *Bartramia pomiformis*, *Pogonatum nanum*, *Tortula subulata*).

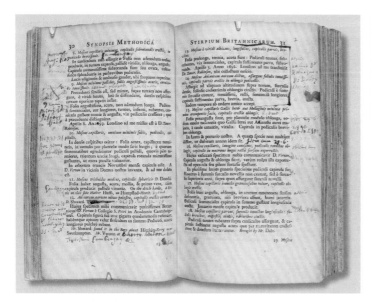

**Figure 3.1** William Vernon's copy of Ray's *Synopsis* (1696), pp. 30–31. Vernon added Gamlingay as a locality for *Bartramia pomiformis* (species 11) and three sites for *Splachnum ampullaceum* (species 12, foot of page 30) but wrote 'oblitus sum' [I have forgotten] against another plant he had sent to Ray, *Racomitrium canescens sens. lat.* (species 16, p. 31). © The British Library Board (969.f.20).

**Figure 3.2** *Plagiochila asplenioides* in the Sloane herbarium (BM), much the oldest Cambridgeshire liverwort specimen, 'found in Madingley Wood near Camb:' and almost certainly collected by Vernon. Photo: Fred Rumsey (Natural History Museum).

Two specimens in the Sloane Herbarium (BM) were almost certainly collected by Vernon and are much the earliest bryophyte specimens from the county. *Plagiochila asplenioides* from Madingley Wood appears to be labelled in Vernon's handwriting and is our first record of a leafy liverwort (Figure 3.2). The other specimen is an immature *Weissia*, perhaps *W. controversa*, from Chesterton. There are a few other specimens collected by Vernon in Buddle's and Petiver's herbaria in the Sloane collection, but we have found no more with localities. The British moss in Sherard's herbarium (OXF) mentioned by Clokie (1964) as a Vernon collection is merely a specimen of *Thuidium tamariscinum* with a Vernon name cited as a synonym.

Two species, one of which is *Funaria hygrometrica*, were described by Vernon in Ray's *Synopsis* from material from Hinton Moor 'found by Mr. Davies of Peterhouse', presumably **John Davies**, who was a Fellow of Peterhouse from 1690 to 1704, rather than his younger brother Richard who was also at Peterhouse but was an undergraduate in the mid 1690s. (Their father was Mutton Davies of Gwysaney, Flintshire.)

J.J. Dillenius revised the accounts of the bryophytes thoroughly for his third edition of Ray's *Synopsis* (1724) but he included no additional records from Cambridgeshire, a reflection of the absence of any bryological activity in the county at that time.

## The first county lists: John and Thomas Martyn, 1725–1784

### John Martyn

Cambridge University established a Professorship of Botany in 1724. The first professor, Richard Bradley, was a horticulturist rather than a field botanist. His successor, **John Martyn** (1699–1768), elected in 1733, had an unusual background but his interests in field botany and taxonomy were much more conventional (Walters 1981).

John Martyn was the son of a London merchant (Allen 2004a). He was privately educated and at the age of 16 he was put to work in his father's counting house. However, two years later he made friends with one of the London apothecaries and he soon found that he was much more attracted to botany than to business. By 1720 he was throwing himself into his new hobby with great enthusiasm, starting a herbarium and botanising in the spring mornings before reporting for work. He translated Tournefort's *Histoire des plantes qui naissent aux environs de Paris* (1698) in 1720–21 and planned a similar work covering London. In 1721 this self-confident young man founded a Botanical Society, now regarded as the first such formally constituted society in the world, acting as its secretary and obtaining Dillenius's agreement to serve as President (Allen 1967). He began to give lecture courses on botany in London in 1725, and in 1727 he was invited privately 'by above twenty scholars' to lecture to them in Cambridge. This appears to have led him to covet Bradley's chair of Botany. His credentials were bolstered by the publication of *Methodus plantarum circa Cantabrigiam nascentium* in 1727 (discussed in more detail below) and of the first lecture of his botany course (Martyn 1729a). More obviously designed to impress was his *Historia plantarum rariorum*, a lavishly illustrated and (as it turned out) over-ambitious work designed to appear in parts. The first part, published in 1728, was advertised (in Martyn 1729a) as a 'Folio on Imperial Paper', bore Hans Sloane's imprimatur as President of the Royal Society and was conspicuously dedicated to the Society's President, Council and Fellows. Martyn's translation and adaptation of Tournefort appeared in 1732 and included many British localities. In less orthodox fashion, Martyn sought to advance his prospects by undermining Bradley's reputation in a series of pseudonymous articles in *The Grub-street Journal*, which he founded with a co-editor, Richard Russell, in 1730 (Williamson 1961). This satirical publication, perhaps closest to *Private Eye* amongst modern publications, achieved a brief popularity and its editors did not hesitate to use it as a vehicle for pursuing their own quarrels. According to John Martyn's son Thomas (1770), there was an agitation in 1731 to turn Bradley out of the Professorship. In the event Bradley died in 1732 and John Martyn was elected to the Chair in February 1733.

For his initial course in Cambridge Martyn offered 30–40 lectures in April, June and August 1727 for which he charged three guineas. 'The whole Day before each Lecture will be spent in gathering Plants in the Country; where those, who desire it, may have opportunities of seeing them in the places where they grow. And to comply with those, who either thro' want of *Leisure*, or the Inclemency of the *Weather*, are confin'd at home; the *Plants* will be brought home, and there demonstrated, without any farther trouble to the Audience' (Martyn 1727b). This is the first record of botanical excursions in the University. Martyn was following the established practice of the London apothecaries, although his London course, which took place in May, July and September in 1727, assumed that 'there are but few, whose *Leisure* will allow them to attend in the *Gardens* and *Fields*' (Martyn 1726, 1728). After he was elected to the Professorship, Martyn's interest in Cambridge botany was short-lived. He had married in 1732 and prolonged absences from London were no doubt a less attractive prospect, and less practical, than they had been in his bachelor days. Thomas Martyn's memoir (1770) explains that 'In the year 1735 he read his last Course of Lectures in Botany at Cambridge; labouring under great disadvantages for want of a Botanic Garden, and not finding sufficient encouragement to warrant so long a neglect of his practice as the Course must necessarily occasion'. John Martyn had begun to practice physic in 1727 and was clearly no longer willing to sacrifice his medical income for the sake of his professorial duties. In his later years he concentrated on the classics, publishing translations of Virgil's *Georgics* (1741) and *Bucolics* [*Eclogues*] (1749); further comments on Virgil were published posthumously (1770). He resigned as Professor in 1762 but presented the University with his botanical books and his *Hortus Siccus* in 1765. The herbarium was stored in unsuitable conditions and much of it had to be discarded in the 19th century, but the books (now in the University Library) survive as a lasting legacy. He is commemorated by the monospecific genus *Martynia* (Martyniaceae), a Mexican species collected and initially named for him by his friend William Houston.

Martyn's bryophyte records come from the brief period of active work in the county between 1727 and 1735. *Methodus plantarum circa Cantabrigiam nascentium* (1727a) was hastily printed for his first lecture course in Cambridge. It simply listed the species reported by Ray in the *Catalogus* and its appendices, rearranged from alphabetical into systematic order. Martyn then planned a revised edition which would update the work, based on records in his interleaved and annotated copies of Ray (1660) and Martyn (1727a). His copies of these two books survive, bound into a single volume (Figure 3.3). They appear to have been annotated concurrently rather than consecutively and are in effect a draft of the revised edition. Martyn began to produce the new edition in *c.* 1729 (T. Martyn 1770) but only the first 24 pages were printed and made available to his students (Martyn 1729b). Fortunately for us, these cover all the cryptogams. Martyn listed 32 mosses and liverworts, of which 26 can be equated to modern species and

**Figure 3.3** John Martyn's interleaved and annotated copy of his own *Methodus* (Martyn 1727a: 5). The bryophytes noted here were included in the incomplete second edition (1729b). Reproduced by kind permission of the Syndics of Cambridge University Library (classmark CCD.47.414).

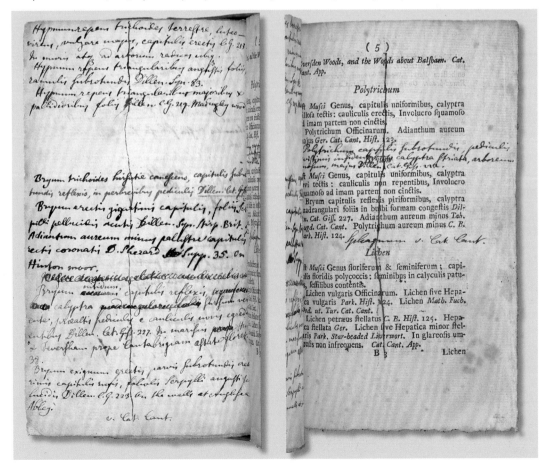

13 were recorded for the first time in the county. Most of these are, not unexpectedly, common plants such as *Grimmia pulvinata* (on walls everywhere), *Phascum cuspidatum* and *Tortula muralis*. More interesting records include *Rhytidiadelphus triquetrus* in Madingley Wood and the epiphytes *Cryphaea heteromalla*, *Frullania dilatata* (frequent on trees) and *Radula complanata*. He found some species known to Ray or Vernon in new localities, including *Calliergonella cuspidata* and *Polytrichum commune* at Gamlingay. Two sites within easy walking distance of Cambridge appear for the first time in a Cambridgeshire flora, Moor Barns, a spring-fed bath and adjacent copse at Madingley (Swale & Belcher 1993), and a well at Coton where *Fontinalis antipyretica* grew. Martin credits 'Mr Davies' with three of the records in the *Methodus*, *Bryum argenteum*, *Platyhypnidium riparioides* and *Tetraphis pellucida*. Davies is listed by Martyn (1763) as Richard Davies MD which allows him to be identified as **Richard Davies** of Shropshire who was admitted to Queens' College in 1726 and was a Fellow there from 1730 to 1740. His record of *Tetraphis* was almost certainly a misidentification but it was accepted in all Cambridgeshire lists until Proctor (1956) queried it.

An interleaved copy of Martyn's *Methodus*, incorporating the 24 pages of the second edition, is copiously annotated by **Richard Jackson** (1704/05–1782). Jackson entered Trinity in 1723 and was elected to a fellowship in 1730. His inscription on the title page reads 'Ri: Jackson, Coll: Trin: Cant: Soc. 1730.' He almost certainly attended Martyn's lectures. He added the names of three bryophytes to his *Methodus*. *Polytrichum montanum et minus, capsulâ quadrangulari* is the only one which we can identify with any certainty, as *Polytrichum juniperinum*. It was presumably seen at Gamlingay (where Jackson recorded some flowering plants). Jackson later left Trinity but he bequeathed his library to the College and an estate in Staffordshire to endow the Jacksonian professorship, now awarded to physicists (Carter 2004).

Some bryophyte specimens from Martyn's herbarium survive in CGE. We have not found any labelled from Cambridgeshire localities (most are unlocalised), but they deserve more detailed study.

## Thomas Martyn

When John Martyn resigned as Professor of Botany in 1762, his son **Thomas Martyn** (1735–1825) was elected as his successor. Unlike his father, Thomas had a conventional academic education as an undergraduate at Emmanuel College from 1752 and then as a Fellow of Sidney Sussex from 1758 until he married the Master's sister in 1773. On marrying he had to vacate his fellowship but he had been ordained in 1759 and was therefore able to take up posts as a clergyman in various parishes, eventually retiring to Pertenhall, Bedfordshire, in 1804 (Boulger 2004a). He continued to lecture on Botany at Cambridge until 1796, when 'his state of health now unfitted him, in a great measure, for this labour; and, in truth, there was so little zeal for the study in the University, that it was scarcely possible to form a Class!' (Gorham 1830). Martyn retained the professorship until his death, holding it in all for an extraordinary 63 years.

As a child living in Chelsea, Thomas Martyn had sometimes visited the aged Sir Hans Sloane and he was already interested in botany by the time he arrived in Cambridge in 1752 (Gorham 1830). In October 1760, writing from Cambridge, he told Richard Pulteney 'I have been pretty diligent this season in collecting the vegetable inhabitants of this county; that, having nearly exhausted them, I might give myself up to the foreign plants in our Botanic Garden ...'. (The 'old' Botanic Garden had just been founded and was then in the process of construction.) On 2 April 1761 he told Pulteney that 'my winter excursions ... have not been attended with any great success' but he listed 42 'Cambridgesh[ire] Mosses' he had collected; the list includes one plant now classified as a clubmoss, 28 mosses, two liverworts and 11 lichens (Figure 3.4). Martyn commented that 'they are most of them I suppose common ones, you will see however that the Catalogue of Cambridge Plants is somewhat encreased' and he offered to send Pulteney specimens of any he lacked in his collection (*Martyn letters*). Martyn sent him some specimens later that month and Pulteney later (25 July) confirmed that Martyn's identifications were correct, 'as far as I can judge'. All the bryophytes listed in the letter were later reported by Martyn (1763) except for *Hypnum abietinus* (sic; now *Abietinella abietina*). On 10 September Martyn reported that 'Having nearly exhausted the plants of this county, my walks have been but few this summer; especially as the vicinity of the Botanic Garden is a decoy to an idle man'. Gorham (1830) claimed that a 'long list of Cambridgeshire Lichens, Mosses, and other Cryptogamous plants, discovered by Mr. Martyn in his rambles, forms the postscript of this letter' so we were disappointed to find, on examining the original letter, that the list is actually quite the reverse, 'a List of the Mosses w[hi]ch are wanting to compleat my collection'.

In February 1762 Martyn was elected Professor, but that year 'a multiplicity of business' prevented him making any botanical excursions. He read his first course of lectures in 1763 and in them he promoted the Linnaean system of classification, of which he was one of the earliest British advocates. *Plantae Cantabrigienses*, also published in 1763, provided a checklist of the flowering plants, bryophytes, lichens,

**Figure 3.4** Thomas Martyn's list of 'Cambridgesh[ire] Mosses' sent to Richard Pulteney in a letter dated 2 April 1761. Linnean Society.

fungi and algae known from the county, arranged according to this system. The checklist was followed by 'Herbationes Cantabrigienses', lists of plants in 13 groups of sites in the county, many 'within the Compass of a moderate Walk' from Cambridge, some requiring longer journeys and one which could 'easily be executed by a Voyage down the River'. However, despite the title, well over half the book was devoted to its third section, an Appendix listing rarer species in other counties of England and Wales. The short title was also misleading in another way – although it is in Latin, the rest of the book differs from Cambridgeshire's earlier floras in being written in English.

Martyn listed 52 bryophyte taxa (47 species and five additional varieties) in his checklist. This was a major advance on any previously published list, although 31 of the taxa appear in his father's unpublished manuscripts or in the privately circulated *Methodus*. Of the remaining 21, five had already been recorded by Vernon, although these records were not known to the Martyns. Excluding these, and taxa of doubtful identity, leaves 10 first records. These include several common pleurocarpous mosses (*Amblystegium serpens, Cratoneuron filicinum, Hypnum cupressiforme, Leptodictyum riparium* and *Pseudoscleropodium purum*), as well as the less frequent pleurocarps *Ctenidium molluscum, Leucodon sciuroides* and *Neckera complanata*. The other additional moss is *Pohlia melanodon* from Hinton Moor; *Lophocolea bidentata* is the only additional liverwort. The limited range of sites mentioned for bryophytes by Thomas Martyn is striking. Gamlingay, Hinton Moor, Madingley and Moor Barns are the only places mentioned more than once and he clearly visited these, but the others, cited for a single species, were all derived from Ray's publications or known to John Martyn. The absence of any mention of bryophytes at the Devil's Dyke or the Gog Magog Hills is notable, as these areas of chalk grassland had been known since Ray's time for their rich assemblages of flowering plants. *Ctenidium molluscum* is the only characteristically chalk species on Martyn's list, and even that might have been collected on one of the calcareous 'moors'. In part the explanation for this must lie in the fact that many, although not all, the chalkland specialists are small acrocarpous mosses and these were clearly not well known at this time.

Martyn published nothing else of direct relevance to the Cambridgeshire flora during his long professorship (for accounts of his other botanical work see Boulger 2004a, Henrey 1975 and Walters 1981). His biographer Gorham (1830), who had acted as Martyn's curate, married into the Martyn family and treated his subject with sustained and abject flattery, reported that Martyn 'continued his researches for Cambridgeshire plants, with great diligence, during 13 years after the publication of his *Plantae Cantabrigienses*' but even if this was true for the flowering plants, it certainly did not apply to the cryptogams. In 1777, shortly after he left Thriplow in Cambridgeshire for a living in Buckinghamshire, Martyn told Pulteney that he was 'now very busy on a *Flora Cantabrigiensis*' but the project was postponed and in 1783 he handed over his manuscripts to Richard Relhan.

## Richard Relhan's *Flora Cantabrigiensis*, 1785–1820

**Richard Relhan** (1754–1823) was born in Dublin, the son of a prominent physician, and educated at Westminster College. He then took advantage of that school's special link with Trinity College to enter Cambridge as an undergraduate in 1773. In 1781 he was appointed as chaplain of King's College, and it was while he was in that post that he prepared the first edition of *Flora Cantabrigiensis* (1785). He reverted to Latin for the text of the flora, except for the habitat and locality entries. Three appendices, published in 1786, 1788 and 1793, provided entries for additional species and completely revised editions of the *Flora* appeared in 1802 and 1820. Relhan accepted the college living of Hemingby, Lincolnshire, in 1791 and like John Martyn he devoted time in later life to translations of a classical author, in this case Tacitus. He is commemorated by the small South African genus *Relhania* (Asteraceae).

It is easy to imagine that Relhan was a prosperous Georgian clergyman but this was far from the case. In March 1799 the Literary Fund, founded in 1790 to provide financial relief for authors in distress, agreed that 'a Donation of Twenty Pounds be presented to the Rev. Richard Relhan of Cambridge, Author of the Flora Cantabrigiensis; He being in almost extreme distress with a wife and several children' (*Royal Literary Fund archive*). Relhan's application for this initial grant has not survived, but by October of that year he approached the Fund again on the grounds that since that donation 'I have suffered an almost incredible variety of wretchednesses … some of my children have not stirred out of doors for three months for want of common necessaries, – as to Linen there is hardly a change of it for any one of the family, I am reduced to the hard necessity of wearing but one shirt a week'. He followed this up with a further letter in March 1800 explaining that he would have printed a fourth supplement to the flora 'containing about 130 Plants discovered in Cambridgeshire since the third supplement was published, had not my misfortunes forced me (in order to provide necessaries for my family) to sell my Books'. Relhan explained that his living as a clergyman 'is sequestered for the consequences of my former distresses' and that he was 'now in infinite difficulties, and terribly ashamed by the threats of my Landlord to seize on my effects for rent'. This produced a further grant of £20. In another application in November 1801 Relhan explained that he was suffering 'a continuation of my misfortunes' but 'obliged to forbear from taking pupils, as I am busily employed in a new edition of my Flora'. These letters to the Fund were written from Cambridge, as were further letters sent in 1806 and 1812, the prefaces of all three editions of his *Flora* and a letter from his widow Maria in 1823. This suggests that the *Oxford Dictionary of National Biography* (Boulger 2004b) is in error in suggesting that he lived in retirement in Hemingby, and it explains how he was able to continue his work on the Cambridgeshire flora until 1820.

Previous authors of Cambridgeshire floras had included bryophytes, lichens, fungi and algae in addition to vascular plants, but Relhan's treatment of these groups was more detailed. He realised that these groups needed the greatest amount of work, telling Martyn on 26 November 1783 that 'I have seriously begun my difficult task; and though I shall get very well through that part of the Flora which will be chiefly yours, yet I shall look forward to *Cryptogamia* with terror'. He clearly received some help from James Dickson, as shortly afterwards (9 December) he told Martyn that 'Dickson, of Covent Garden, is a most wonderful fellow; he was quite uneducated; but, by his own industry, has acquired an accurate knowledge of the Cryptogamian plants. His zeal for science must have been amazing; and he communicates the result of his labours with a generosity which I have experienced from only Mr. Martyn, and a very, very few' (Gorham 1830). Dickson was then the leading British bryologist and the first to revive the subject after a barren period in the middle of the 18th century (Preston 1991).

It is fortunate that most of Relhan's work on his *Flora* was undertaken before the widespread enclosures in the county and subsequent agricultural improvement of many sites in the early 19th century. In the first edition of the flora he listed 66 taxa which he considered to be species and six additional varieties. He added 11 species in the first appendix, four in the second and eight (plus one variety) in the third. There were 104 species (plus two varieties) in edition 2 and 128 species in edition 3. The localised records in the third edition show that the sites which were well known to previous generations are still prominent in this *Flora*, including Gamlingay (25 records, including 17 from the Bogs or Heath), Madingley Wood (13) and Moor Barns or Madingley Bath (nine). New sites for bryophytes include the Gog Magog Hills (16), mentioned for just four species in the first edition but with many more mentions by the third, and Sawston Moor (10), which appears first in the 1793 Appendix. The 17 records from Hinton Moor in the second edition of the flora were omitted from the third, perhaps because the site had been enclosed and drained between the publication of these editions. In many cases (e.g. *Aulacomnium palustre*, *Bryum pseudotriquetrum*, *Scorpidium scorpioides*) the Hinton Moor locality was replaced by Shelford Moor, a site which had not previously been mentioned. There are a few records from several sites in and around Cambridge, including Barnwell, the

Botanic Garden (the 'old' garden on the north side of Downing Street), Coe Fen, the Hill of Health, Newnham, Paradise and Pembroke College. In the east of the county there were records from the Newmarket area (10, including five from Newmarket Heath) and Wood Ditton (five), and in the south there was a single record from Juniper Hill, Hildersham.

Very few specimens collected by Relhan have survived. He was one of the early Fellows of the Linnean Society and his herbarium was acquired by the Society. According to a note by C.C. Babington in his annotated copy of Babington (1860), it was regarded as of little value, as most of the specimens were unlocalised, and at the sale of the Linnean Museum in 1863 (cf. Gage & Stearn 1988) it was sold for the value of the case in which it was contained. There are 16 specimens given by Relhan to William Skrimshire and now at Wisbech Museum (WBCH; see below) and these include three with localities, *Polytrichum piliferum*, *Sphagnum squarrosum* and *S. tenellum* from Gamlingay (Figure 3.5). There is

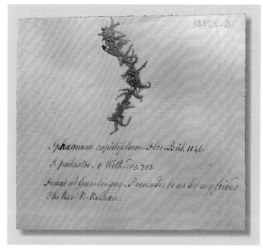

**Figure 3.5** *Sphagnum tenellum*, collected by Richard Relhan at Gamlingay and preserved in the herbarium of his friend William Skrimshire (WBCH).

also a Relhan specimen of *Bryum pseudotriquetrum* from Hinton Moor at BM (*Sowerby drawings*). The records published in *Flora Cantabrigiensis* which are unsupported by specimens have to be assessed more subjectively. The descriptions of species in the *Flora* are no help, as they were extracted from the works of other authors. A few of the species reported by Relhan are now known to be well outside their British range, including *Anomobryum julaceum* and *Saccogyna viticulosa*. The occurrence of the northern and western *Dicranum majus* in a Cambridgeshire woodland is just possible but we have not accepted the record in the absence of a specimen. It is particularly frustrating not to know the correct identity of *Reboulia hemisphaerica*, recorded by Relhan from three of the 'moors' at a time when the species was not separated from *Preissia quadrata*. We have rejected some specimens because the reported habitat seems unlikely – *Solenostoma gracillimum* from dry, chalky places at Cherry Hinton is presumably *Leiocolea turbinata* (which was not then recognised in Britain) and *Rhizomnium punctatum* is unlikely to have grown in sandy places on the Gog Magog Hills. After assessing the records and rejecting those that we consider doubtful, we have accepted 85 species on the basis of Relhan's records; a further three are referable to the species aggregates *Campylium stellatum sens. lat.*, *Racomitrium canescens sens. lat.* and *Ulota crispa sens. lat.* Of the 85 species, 40 are first Cambridgeshire records. These include several common acrocarpous mosses, including *Barbula convoluta*, *B. unguiculata*, *Bryum capillare* and *Ceratodon purpureus*, as well as the rarer *Pterygoneurum ovatum*, found 'on the mud Walls at the first cottage in Trumpington, next to Cambridge, &c.' (Relhan 1793). The moors near Cambridge produced a last few wetland species, most notably *Scorpidium scorpioides*, and there were many new calcifuges from Gamlingay, including the moss *Polytrichum piliferum* and the liverworts *Cephalozia bicuspidata*, *Lophozia ventricosa* and *Odontoschisma sphagni*. Relhan's *Flora* was the first to record several characteristic chalk species, mostly from the Gog Magog Hills, including *Abietinella abietina*, *Encalypta vulgaris*, *Homalothecium lutescens*, *Microbryum curvicollum* and *Tortella tortuosa*.

## William Skrimshire, John Hemsted and other bryologists of the Relhan era

Relhan identifies five botanists who contributed bryophyte records to the later editions of his flora. Of these, **William Skrimshire** (1766–1829) is the most significant. Skrimshire was a surgeon who lived at Bushy Place, Wisbech, where he had a garden and a peppermint plantation. He is described by Relhan (1802) as 'happily devoted to natural science' (*Scientiae Naturali feliciter dedito*) and Crompton (1994) and Crompton & Nelson (2000) have provided detailed biographical accounts which describe his interest in many branches of natural history. Although he might seem to have been isolated in Wisbech, he clearly benefited from a network of friends and correspondents. On 14 September 1795, for example, Skrimshire wrote to tell James Sowerby that he had collected *Riccia glauca* both on dry ground and floating on the surface of the water (Boulger & Britten 1918). He must have given some of the aquatic plant to John Pitchford, a Norwich surgeon who visited Wisbech later that year; Pitchford showed it to Thomas Woodward who immediately identified it as 'a much better thing', *Riccia* (now *Ricciocarpos*) *natans*, and mentioned it in a letter to J.E. Smith (17 November 1795) as one of the 'very good things' found by Skrimshire around Wisbech (*Smith letters*; Crompton & Nelson 2000).

Although there are only two records from Skrimshire in Relhan's (1820) bryophyte account, his collection of bryophyte specimens survives in Wisbech Museum (WBCH) and provides quite a few more. The specimens are mounted on paper, labelled in Skrimshire's very clear handwriting and stored between the sheets of a bound volume (Figure 3.6). There are 30 specimens collected in the Wisbech area, plus many others which are unlocalised or contributed by other collectors from elsewhere. Unfortunately for us, Wisbech is on the county boundary and several of the more precisely localised specimens were collected just over the boundary into West Norfolk. Thus his *Riccia natans*, 'Found in a ditch at Outwell, between the town [Wisbech] and the Toll-Gate 1795' grew in Norfolk, and the same is almost certainly true of a specimen labelled '*Riccia glauca*', which is actually *R. cavernosa*, 'Gathered by the side of some silt-pits, in a field opposite the Black-Boy-Low, Walsoken 1796'. We have assumed that specimens simply labelled 'Wisbech' were collected in Cambridgeshire. Unsurprisingly, most of these are common species. *Brachytheciastrum velutinum* from trees, *Leptodictyum riparium* from posts in a pond, *Plagiomnium undulatum* from a ditch side near Bushy Place and *Tortula lanceola* from banks are amongst the more interesting collections.

**Figure 3.6** William Skrimshire's fruiting specimens (WBCH) of *Brachytheciastrum velutinum* 1796 (left) and *Amblystegium serpens* 1795 (right).

The other significant recorder mentioned by Relhan (1802, 1820) is the clergyman **John Hemsted** (1747?–1824). Oswald (1991) provides an account of this little-known figure, highlighting the vascular plant specimens he sent to James Edward Smith and James Sowerby for inclusion in their multi-volume, illustrated work *English Botany*. He also sent them bryophytes, and the species illustrated from his material were *Anomodon viticulosus* (Smith 1795), *Microbryum rectum* (Smith 1796a, 1801), *Pohlia carnea* (Smith 1796b), *Ephemerum serratum sens. lat.* (Smith 1798) and *Scorpidium scorpioides* (Smith 1802). The text for *Anomodon viticulosus* suggests that he sent *Fissidens adianthoides* too, but the plate for that species is based on material from Kensington Gardens. Relhan (1802, 1820) includes Hemsted's records of *Microbryum rectum* and *Ephemerum serratum*, and an *Aloina* from Wisbech. There are several specimens in Skrimshire's herbarium (WBCH) from Hemsted although some are unlocalised, such as *Seligeria calcarea* 'From my friend the Revd. Mr. Hemsted 1797'. Many of the localised records are from Newmarket or Newmarket Heath, places which straggle the county boundary with Suffolk. It is sometimes unclear whether material such as that of *Anomodon*, 'Sent by the Revd. Mr. Hemsted from Newmarket 1796.', came from Newmarket or whether that was Hemsted's address. Some of the specimens, such as *Microbryum rectum* and *Tortella tortuosa*, may have come from the Devil's Dyke, which crosses Newmarket Heath and is in Cambridgeshire, although the Dyke is not a site named by Hemsted. We have cited Hemsted's Newmarket records in this flora when appropriate, but the reader should bear in mind these uncertainties.

The remaining three botanists named by Relhan are credited with a single record. **James Dickson** (1738–1822), already mentioned, was the first to find *Seligeria calcarea* in the county (Dickson 1790). According to the account in *English Botany* (Smith 1794), he found it with the Norfolk botanist **James Crowe** (1750–1807). **John Savery Tozer** (c. 1790–1836) was also a noted bryologist; he was admitted to St John's College in 1808, took his BA in 1812 and was a fellow of the college from then until 1827. Relhan (1820) published his record of *Polytrichastrum formosum* from Gamlingay as the first county record; he must surely have seen other species here and it would be interesting to know whether any specimens survive in herbaria. Tozer is commemorated by the moss *Epipterygium tozeri*, which he discovered by the River Dart near Totnes. The third figure is the most obscure, **John Holme** (*c*. 1760–1829). Holme was elected a fellow of Peterhouse from 1785, and was Vicar of Cherry Hinton from 1808 to 1820 and Rector of Freckenham, on the Suffolk side of the county boundary near Newmarket, from 1816 to 1829. He became a Fellow of the Linnean Society in 1820 and made a number of interesting vascular plant records in the county but his bryophyte record, *Tortula aristata*, found between Snailwell and Newmarket (Relhan 1820), refers to a variant of the common *Barbula unguiculata*.

## J.S. Henslow, his friends and students, 1821–1838

### Henslow's bryophyte collections

Thomas Martyn would have resigned his professorship at some time between 1813 and 1818 if he could have manoeuvred his friend J.E. Smith (Sir James Smith after his knighthood in 1814) into position as his successor. However the prospect of Smith's election provoked strong opposition, despite his botanical eminence, as he was neither a member of the University nor even a committed member of the Church of England (Kennett 2016). Martyn therefore retained the post until his death in 1825. His successor, appointed soon afterwards, was the unimpeachably Cantabrigian and Anglican Professor of Mineralogy, J.S. Henslow.

**John Stevens Henslow** (1796–1861) was clearly a charismatic figure to many of his students, and indeed to his recent biographers (Walters & Stow 2001). After his appointment as Professor he combined lectures in botany with field excursions. In this he was reviving the practice first started by John Martyn a century earlier, but his inspiration came from the Scottish universities, including the field trips led by W.J. Hooker, then Regius Professor of Botany at Glasgow (Allan 1967, Allen 1999). Henslow also founded the current Botanic Garden, for which land was obtained in 1831. It was in these early years, when his lectures were particularly well attended, that Henslow taught the undergraduate Charles Darwin (Walters & Stow 2001). Henslow's interest in plant variation, expressed both in the planting plan of the Garden (Parker 2006) and in his herbarium collections (Kohn *et al.* 2005, Parker 2014), is thought to have been an important influence on Darwin. In 1837 Henslow was appointed Rector of the Suffolk village of Hitcham, a rich living, and in 1839 he moved there with his family. Thereafter his energies were largely devoted to his parishioners and to other enterprises such as the Ipswich Museum, although he returned to Cambridge annually for five weeks to give his botany course in the Easter term.

Henslow's interest in bryophytes has hitherto been under-estimated, largely because his specimens have been stored in different places in the Cambridge herbarium (CGE), with only a minority held in packets with the main bulk of the modern collections. We have tried to assemble all the relevant specimens and use them to reassess his bryological activities. There is a range of material. Some Cambridgeshire specimens are mounted neatly on paper and carefully labelled by Henslow (Figure 3.7). Most of the labels identify Henslow himself as the collector. However, there are also numerous specimens still more or less in the condition in which they were collected, labelled in pencil by Henslow on small labels roughly torn from sheets of scrap paper. These were sometimes named by Henslow, at least to genus, and usually have a locality and date but he did not name himself as the collector (not surprisingly, as these are presumably the original field labels). Most of these specimens were placed in paper packets by Arthur Gray, the herbarium technician in the inter-war years, and stamped in purple ink as 'Mus. Henslow'. Gray presumably found them in the packets in which they were collected but if so none of these survive. Some of the Henslow specimens were identified in the 20th century and were known to Proctor (1956) and Whitehouse (1964); others have only been critically examined after we relocated them.

**Figure 3.7** J.S. Henslow's mounted specimens (CGE) of *Scorpidium revolvens* from Gamlingay, collected in 1827 (lower specimen) and 1829 (upper, fruiting specimen) and labelled *Hypnum aduncum*.

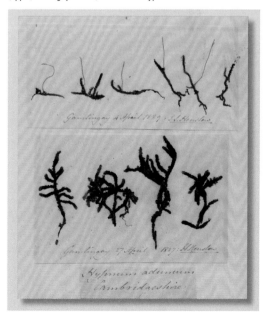

Henslow's annotated copy of Relhan (1820) is a further, if much more limited, source of records. An 'x' against a species apparently indicates plants Henslow knew, or collected, in the county, although there are many more specimens than there are annotated species. There are a few localised records. The only dated records were made in 1838. A few species have purely nomenclatural annotations.

Henslow's earliest bryophyte specimens date from 1821, the year he took his MA and published his first scientific paper, on the geology of the Isle of Man (Walters & Stow 2001). It was in 1821 that he began, with Leonard Jenyns, to collect herbarium specimens systematically with a view to covering the entire British flora (Parker 2014). The bryophyte specimens were all collected between 4 March and 16 April and come from sites around Cambridge, especially Madingley (including, almost certainly, Madingley Wood) but also Baitsbite, Coton, the Gog Magog Hills and Trumpington church. Most are common species, but it is interesting that as a beginner he was able to find *Cryphaea heteromalla* and *Orthotrichum striatum* at Madingley and *Pterygoneurum ovatum* and *Tortula lanceola* on the Gogs. More specimens survive from 1821 than any later year, although he continued to collect bryophytes from sites around Cambridge until 1838, his last full year in Cambridge. Additional collecting localities include Coe Fen, Cherry Hinton, Fen Ditton, Horningsea, Quy Water and Shelford Common. All the neatly mounted specimens were collected between 1821 and 1829. Some of the specimens collected in this decade, and all those collected from 1830 onwards, survive as unmounted material with only the initial pencil labels. There are only two specimens collected by Henslow in the county after he moved to Hitcham in 1839, from Coton (1842) and Gamlingay (1857).

Many of the sites in which Henslow collected mosses are those where he took his class on excursions after he began to teach botany in 1827. The programme for the 'herborizing excursions' in 1830 is set out in a surviving circular (Henslow 1830).

[Friday] April 30. – Cambridge to Whitwell Farm and the Petrifying Spring at Coton.
[Friday] May 7. – Cambridge through Chesterton to King's Hedges.
[Friday] May 14. – Cambridge to Cherryhinton and thence to Shelford Common.
[Tuesday] May 18. – Whitewood and the Heath near Gamlingay.
[Tuesday] May 25. – Banks of the Cam between Chesterton and Backsbite. Fen and fields on each side of Bottisham-lode, between the river and Anglesea-abbey.

The 1830 programme for the botanical excursions includes a table of species recorded at the different sites. The list includes a few bryophytes, showing that these were amongst the plants covered.

The first three excursions in 1830 would have been on foot; for the last the party may have taken 'a barge down the river' as Darwin remembered such excursions when he attended Henslow's lectures and excursions in 1829–31 (Barlow 1958: 60). Gamlingay was the furthest locality, at the western edge of the county, and it is the only locality at any distance from Cambridge where Henslow collected numerous bryophyte specimens. The pattern of recording when Henslow was Professor therefore represented a return to that which is apparent under the Martyns. A few easily accessible sites were visited repeatedly, often after 1827 for teaching purposes.

Henslow first visited Gamlingay in 1824 with the naturalist **Leonard Jenyns,** later **Leonard Blomefield** (1800–1893), who had been his slightly younger contemporary at St John's College. Jenyns was then Curate (and later Vicar) of Swaffham Bulbeck, conveniently close to his father's house at Bottisham Hall, and Henslow had married his sister Harriet Jenyns in December 1823. The exploratory visit to Gamlingay, on 24–25 August, is well documented in Jenyns' natural history diary (Crompton 1997). Gamlingay had been known for its calcifuge flora since the time of Ray, and Jenyns listed many of its 'botanical treasures'. He also noted great quantities of lizards, Grayling butterflies 'abundant in every part of the Heath' and Silver-washed fritillaries, new to Cambridgeshire, in White Wood. The highlight of the visit was the discovery of the Natterjack Toad population on the Heath, and Jenyns returned with several live specimens so that he could 'become acquainted with their habits and manners' (*Jenyns diary*). (Most of them survived until 1 October when he found that two had died in the night, whereupon Jenyns 'took the hint and smothered the remaining five in spirits, lest they should follow the same fate'.) Amongst the feast of natural history at Gamlingay there was clearly time for a little bryology, and specimens of *Sphagnum papillosum* and *S. teres* from Gamlingay Bogs and fruiting *Pseudoscleropodium purum* from White Wood survive from this visit in Jenyns' herbarium (with *S. papillosum* and *P. purum* also present in CGE, less precisely localised by Henslow to Gamlingay).

After Henslow started to teach botany the student excursion to Gamlingay, involving an overnight stay in a Gamlingay inn, became an annual highlight. A few organisational details survive (*Lecture list*). The party numbered 16 in 1851 and 27 in 1857. The total cost of the 1851 excursion was £7 16s 6d, and the undergraduates paid half a guinea (10s 6d) each towards this. Much the most expensive item was the hire of the coach (five guineas). Dinner was 2s 3d each, and the party drank 7s worth of ale and paid 1s for the hire of a band; breakfast cost 1s 6d a head. The remaining expenses were 5s for servants, 7s 6d for 'Ostler and P. Boys' and 2s paid at White Wood. There is a particularly rich assortment of specimens collected by Henslow on 27 April 1827, presumably the date of the first student excursion there, with further material gathered in 1829, 1833, 1838 and 1857. Together these specimens provide further tantalising glimpses of the rich Gamlingay flora (see Chapter 10).

### Henslow's contemporaries and students

**Leonard Jenyns**' bryophyte collection survives at the Bath Royal Literary and Philosophical Institution (BTH). Almost all his Cambridgeshire specimens were collected between 1822 and 1825 at Bottisham, with a few from nearby sites (Swaffham Bulbeck, Swaffham Prior, Anglesey Abbey) and from the Gog Magog Hills. Although Jenyns remained at Swaffham Bulbeck until 1849 (Wallace 2005), there is only one later specimen, *Ricciocarpos natans*, collected near Ely in 1838, so his interest in bryophytes seems to have been short-lived. Jenyns' annotated copy of Relhan (1802) has marks against three common bryophytes but in the next edition (1820) he noted 10 species as occurring in the Bottisham area, and most of these are represented by surviving specimens in BTH or CGE. Henslow and Jenyns exchanged specimens, hence the presence of some of the vouchers in CGE. The material gathered on their joint excursion to Gamlingay is mentioned above. Jenyns was primarily a zoologist, with very wide-ranging interests (Preece & Sparks 2012).

**Christopher Edmund Broome** (1812–1886) was a lifelong friend of Jenyns. The two met when Broome was the pupil of a clergyman in a parish adjacent to Swaffham Bulbeck (Blomefield 1887). He was already interested in natural history at this young age. He initially entered Worcester College, Oxford, in 1831 but transferred to Trinity Hall, Cambridge, in March 1832. Unusually, he attended Henslow's lectures for three successive years, 1833–35 (*Lecture list*). He had originally intended to become a clergyman, but he abandoned his plans for ordination because of 'conscientious scruples' (Anon. 1887). He was a noted mycologist, doing much work with M.J. Berkeley, and his obituaries emphasise his 'power of sheer hard work' (Murray 1887). In later life both Jenyns and Broome lived near Bath and they were co-founders of the Bath Field Club. Broome's moss collection should be at Bath (BTH), but only a list survives there, as the specimens themselves were sent out on loan in 1978 and never returned. Most were collected near Cambridge in 1835, with *Dicranella varia* from Upware the only one from elsewhere in the county. There is at least one Broome specimen in CGE, from Henslow's herbarium, also collected in 1835 (*Microbryum davallianum*, Histon). A single Cambridgeshire liverwort survives in his herbarium at Bath, collected at Burwell Fen in 1832 and labelled simply *Marchantia*; it is the only specimen of *Preissia quadrata* from the county.

**Miles Joseph Berkeley** (1803–1889), born at Biggin Hall near Oundle, was not only a great mycologist but also a specialist bryologist, unlike any of the Cambridgeshire figures of the Henslow era. His *Handbook of British Mosses* was published in 1848. He met Henslow and Jenyns during his time as an undergraduate at Christ's College, Cambridge, between 1821 and 1825 and on a summer field trip to Scotland he also got to know the Scottish cryptogamist R.K. Greville (Price 2004). Like so many of his Cambridge contemporaries he became a clergyman, spending much of his career in his native Northamptonshire at Thornhaugh (1826–1829), Apethorpe with Woodnewton (1833–1868) and finally at Sibbertoft (1868–1889). According to Price, 'Berkeley and his wife produced a family of fifteen, and intense labours were needed to support them all, since stipends were small'. Unfortunately Berkeley was based just too far from Cambridgeshire to do much fieldwork in the county and although he sent interesting specimens to both Henslow and Jenyns from Huntingdonshire and Northamptonshire, there are few from Cambridgeshire in their collections. He collected *Rhynchostegium confertum* in Cambridge in 1824 (BTH) and gathered three specimens at Parson Drove in 1828 (CGE), including *Didymodon tophaceus* and *Drepanocladus aduncus*.

The herbarium of **William Lewes Pugh Garnons** (1791–1863) at Saffron Walden (SWN) includes a small collection of bryophytes (eight species) gathered in Cambridge in 1825, 1827 and (one specimen) 1837. Garnons had been an undergraduate at Sidney Sussex College (1811–1814) and he became a Fellow of the college in 1817, the year that he obtained his MA. He took the degree of Bachelor of Divinity in 1824 and in 1848 he returned to his native county as vicar of Utling, Essex. He was a naturalist with an interest in entomology as well as botany and he had been an unsuccessful candidate for the Professorship of Botany when Henslow was appointed in 1825 (Walters & Stow 2001).

In his later years **Charles James Fox Bunbury** (1809–1886) could not remember when he first became interested in botany but he was certainly identifying flowering plants for himself by the age of nine, and he took up bryophytes in the winter of 1824–25, several years before he entered Trinity College in 1829 (Bunbury 1894). Despite his botanical interests, which he pursued both in Britain and abroad for the rest of his life, he is not listed as attending Henslow's lectures, and his herbarium (CGE) includes only a few Cambridgeshire bryophytes, collected between 1829 and 1831. Bunbury's herbarium includes that of Francis King Eagle (1785–1856) who had acquired specimens from many 19th-century bryologists. These include some from Cambridgeshire but most of them are labelled with nothing except the name of the county.

Small numbers of specimens collected by Henslow's students survive. Those collected by **Henry Edward Lowe** (1814–1895) are instructive. Lowe did not enter Trinity College until 1832 but there are specimens in his herbarium (WARMS) collected in Cambridgeshire in March 1826 (*Ctenidium molluscum* from Cherry Hinton), March 1827 (*Dicranella varia*, also Cherry Hinton) and October 1829 (a scrap of *Bryum argenteum* from Madingley turnpike), all fruiting. They match specimens collected by Henslow and it is clear that Lowe must have had access to these specimens in his undergraduate years and removed pieces for his own collection. He attended Henslow's lectures in 1835 (*Lecture list*). He himself collected bryophytes in the county from 1834 until 1837, the year he obtained his BA. In addition to the specimens in his herbarium at WARMS, there are one or two in CGE dated 1834 which were presumably collected by him (the labels, though anonymous, are in his handwriting) and given to Henslow. Lowe later lived in Staffordshire and Warwickshire, working as a clergyman and schoolmaster. An Anglo-Catholic, he published two contributions to the religious controversies which were such a feature of Victorian England.

**William Higgins Coleman** (*c.* 1816–1863) was admitted to St John's College in 1832. As an undergraduate he kept botanical notebooks and a phenological diary, although he did not attend Henslow's lectures. His notes include references to only two bryophytes, *Encalypta vulgaris* on the Gog Magog Hills on 25 January 1835 (*Coleman Calendar*) and an undated record of *Fontinalis antipyretica* 'In the spring-head of the Coton copse water' (*Coleman Localities*). There are undated specimens collected by Coleman of the *Fontinalis* from Coton and of *Orthotrichum anomalum* from Madingley church (OXF). Although he was ordained in 1840, Coleman went on to become a schoolmaster and to collaborate with R.H. Webb on an excellent vascular plant flora, *Flora Hertfordiensis* (Webb & Coleman 1849; see James 2009). He also made significant bryophyte collections near Hertford in the 1840s (Swinscow 1959).

A specimen of *Polytrichum commune* from Gamlingay (CGE) dated 1836 is labelled 'Leefe' and so was presumably collected by **John Ewbank Leefe** (1812 or 1813–1889), who attended Henslow's lectures that year and later became a clergyman in Co. Durham but continued his interest in botany, studying willows. **Harry Baber** (1817–1892), another future clergyman, collected fruiting *Fontinalis* at Coton in 1837 (E). C.C. Babington's collections are dealt with in the following section. There must almost certainly be other specimens collected by Henslow's students in British herbaria but attempting to trace them would be a time-consuming task. A good way of checking for their presence in a herbarium is to look first at the *Fontinalis antipyretica* specimens, as most of those known to have collected bryophytes on Henslow's excursions gathered this species from the luxuriant fruiting population at Coton.

## Henslow's checklists (1829, 1835)

Soon after his appointment as Professor, in 1829, Henslow produced a checklist of British plants for the use of his class, in which he marked those which occurred in Cambridgeshire (Henslow 1829); a second edition followed six years later (Henslow 1835). It was intended 'as a pocket companion, if interleaved for registering the habitats and periods of flowering of the rarer plants, &c. or for marking off the specimens as they are prepared for the herbarium' (Henslow 1835). The 1829 edition listed 118 bryophyte species and four additional varieties, with 119 species and five additional varieties in 1835. These totals are smaller than the 128 species included in the final edition of Relhan's flora, partly because Henslow tidied up the treatment of some species which had been included under two or even three names by Relhan. He also omitted a few species reported by Relhan. In leaving out *Lunularia cruciata* and *Oxyrrhynchium hians* he was probably following the national authorities, as Hooker (1833), Henslow's source for the 1835 *Catalogue*, treated *O. hians* as a synonym of *Kindbergia praelonga* and omitted *Lunularia* entirely because of confusion with *Reboulia*. Other species were almost certainly omitted by mistake, such as *Seligeria calcarea* and *Weissia controversa* which were listed as Cambridgeshire species in the 1829 but not the 1835 edition. The Catalogues provide the first published record for six species, *Microbryum davallianum*, *Orthotrichum diaphanum*, *Rhynchostegiella tenella* and *Syntrichia latifolia* in 1829 and *Anthoceros punctatus* and *Riccia fluitans* in 1835. All of these except *S. latifolia* are represented by specimens in Henslow's herbarium (CGE).

The importance of the bryological activity of the Henslow era to our understanding of the former bryophyte flora of the county lies in the surviving specimens rather than the rather few additional published records. Over 80 species are represented by specimens collected by Henslow and his contemporaries. Almost all are localised and the vast majority dated, reflecting a change in collecting practice which (for Cambridgeshire bryophytes) apparently took place in the early years of the 19th century. After modern re-examination, the specimens collected in the Henslow era provide first records for 25 Cambridgeshire species, including some species which were only recognised in Britain long after the specimens were collected (e.g. *Bryum algovicum, B. rubens, Fissidens incurvus, Sphagnum teres*). Only 18 species are marked in Henslow's annotated Relhan (1820), and there are specimens of 12 of these in Henslow's herbarium and of a further four in the herbaria of Jenyns (BTH) or Garnons (SWN). The two species not represented in contemporary collections are *Eurhynchium striatum* and *Mnium hornum*.

## The Victorian depression, 1839–1900

Henslow's departure for Hitcham in 1839 was the start of a long period, extending for the rest of the century, in which there were no botanists with a long-term interest in the county's bryophytes. The paucity of information for this period is all the more frustrating as this was a time when bryologists were very active elsewhere in Britain. There was a succession of national moss floras and an increasing number of county floras were published in the latter part of the century (Preston 1991).

**Isaac Brown** (1803–1895) collected *Splachnum ampullaceum* from 'Gamlingay Bogs' in June 1841 (E), the last record from the county and the only one supported by a specimen. Brown, who ran a Quaker school in Hitchin until it was destroyed by fire in 1845, was a member of the Botanical Society of London with some interest in bryophytes (Allen 1986, Swinscow 1959). He had obviously taken a liking to Gamlingay, as he had already collected the orchid *Hammarbya paludosa* there in 1839 and 1840 (Crompton 2001).

The history of Cambridgeshire bryology would have been very different if **Charles Cardale Babington** (1808–1895), Henslow's successor as Professor of Botany from 1861 until his death, had surveyed bryophytes for his meticulously documented *Flora of Cambridgeshire* (1860). Babington clearly had the opportunity to take up the group. He may have collected *Funaria hygrometrica* at Bottisham Fen in 1830, as the specimen (CGE) is labelled in his handwriting, and he certainly collected *Ricciocarpos natans* at Barton in 1831 (BM). He also noted in his journal on 28 February 1835 that he 'Walked with Henslow, etc., to Madingley, and found a good many mosses' and on 7 March 'Broome and I went to Girton and Histon, found a few mosses' (Babington 1897). However, he was clearly not inspired by bryophytes and there are only a few later signs of any awareness of the group. He copied the few localised manuscript records from Henslow's annotated Relhan (1820) into his own copy, and added a few records of his own including the distinctive aquatics *Fontinalis antipyretica* in a pond at West Wratting (undated) and *Ricciocarpos natans* from Ely West Fen (1853).

F.O. Bower arrived at Cambridge as a young student in October 1874 from Repton School, where he had already decided that botany would be his life's study (Bower 1938). He found that Babington 'offered in the calendar an elementary course of lectures chiefly on descriptive botany, but in the Easter term only. I sampled those lectures and found them wanting both in spirit and substance. The calendar also announced 'herborizing excursions, should the circumstances permit': as far as I was aware, the circumstances never did permit'. He concluded that 'the official teaching of botany in Cambridge University was moribund in the summer, and actually dead during the winter'. Babington ceased to lecture in 1891, when he noted on 28 April 'Proposed to commence but no men came' (*Lecture list*).

The bryological darkness of the 19th century is briefly illuminated by a burst of activity between 1874 and 1883. There are records for this period from three different sources, only coincidentally clustered so closely together in time. The first of these is a set of three volumes of 'Saffron Walden Mosses. Collected by F.Y. Brocas 1874.' in Saffron Walden Museum (SWN). Letters held with the collection show that **Frederick Yorke Brocas** (1826–1891) proved to be an elusive figure when the historian David Allen tried to investigate his life, though there is now a more complete biography on the herbaria@home website. By 1874 Brocas had some experience as a bryologist, having published a single volume of specimens, *British mosses No. 1*, from Basingstoke in 1852 as well as a collection of ferns, *A companion to the fernery*, in 1854. In the 1850s he was making his living by the sale of botanical specimens, but between 1853 and 1858 he also worked part-time for the Linnean Society as Assistant Librarian (Gage & Stearn 1988). It is not clear why Brocas was collecting bryophytes in the Saffron Walden area in 1874. The three volumes of bryophyte specimens may have been prepared for the Museum, or perhaps for the rich Quaker banker and philanthropist G.S. Gibson of Saffron Walden who had written *The flora of Essex* (1862) but who was later prevented from pursuing his botanical interests because of business commitments and civic duties (Allen 2004b). In addition to his botanical work, Brocas (1887) published a poem to commemorate Queen Victoria's Golden Jubilee, selling copies at a halfpenny each or three for a penny.

The Saffron Walden volumes are made up of paper folders, with the specimens affixed to the inside of the folded sheet and its localities on the facing page (if there is more than one locality, the origin of the mounted material is not always indicated). Most specimens are from the Essex side of the county boundary and they provide an invaluable insight into its 19th-century flora, which included pollution-sensitive epiphytes such as *Antitrichia curtipendula*, *Cryphaea heteromalla*, *Leucodon sciuroides*, *Neckera pumila* and *Orthotrichum lyellii* (Jermyn 1974). Brocas visited only two areas in Cambridgeshire, 'Corporal Hill', Great Chesterford (presumably Coploe Hill, Ickleton), where he collected the chalk grassland pleurocarps *Abietinella abietina*, *Brachythecium glareosum*, *Entodon concinnus* and *Homalothecium lutescens*, and the area between Hildersham and Linton, where he found *Brachythecium albicans*, *Dicranum scoparium*, *Fissidens dubius*, *Polytrichum juniperinum* and *Syntrichia ruralis* on Hildersham Furze Hills and some waterside species (including *Anomodon viticulosus*) by the river.

The second, more extensive set of Cambridgeshire specimens was collected by two undergraduates and (subsequently) recent graduates of St John's College, G.D. Haviland and J.J. Lister. **Joseph Jackson Lister** (1857–1927), who was admitted to St John's in December 1875 and matriculated in 1876, was from a Quaker family which was distinguished even by Cambridge standards. His grandfather Joseph Jackson Lister (1786–1869) was a microscopist, his father Arthur (1830–1908) a mycologist known for his work on Mycetozoa (slime moulds) and his paternal uncle Joseph (1827–1912) became Lord Lister, a famous pioneer of antiseptic surgery. All three were Fellows of the Royal Society. 'Our' Lister was a keen naturalist even as a child. After graduation he was appointed Demonstrator in Comparative Anatomy. In 1887–88 he travelled as volunteer naturalist on HMS Egeria, collecting plants and animals in the South Pacific. Several of his collections were named for him, including Lister's Palm, *Arenga listeri*, endemic to Christmas Island. He returned to Cambridge in 1891 and he was based there until his death (Hickson 1928). Following family tradition, Lister was elected FRS in 1900. His sister Gulielma Lister (1860–1949) began by helping their father with his studies of slime moulds and ended up becoming a leading expert in the group herself. Gulielma had to be satisfied with being one of the first group of women to be elected Fellows of the Linnean Society (1905), as the Royal Society did not vote to accept women as Fellows until 1945. **George Darby Haviland** (1857–1901) entered St John's a few months after Lister, in August 1876. He trained as a doctor in Cambridge and after working for a while in London at St Bartholomew's Hospital he went out to Borneo for four years, where 'he employed, for collecting, Dyaks whom he had trained, and he always made it a point to mention their names on the labels' (Stapf 1907). He returned to Kew to work up his plant collections and then left for South Africa to study termites, but he disappeared under mysterious circumstances. He went out cycling in Natal one day in 1901 and was never seen again, although his cycle was found a year later (Stapf 1907). According to his obituary, his retiring disposition and almost morbid modesty limited his achievement as a naturalist.

Haviland and Lister's Cambridgeshire mosses still retain their own distinctive packets in CGE, most of them labelled by Lister (Figure 3.8a). There are quite a few duplicates (from Henry Boswell's herbarium) in OXF labelled by Haviland in Botanical Record Club packets. A few were collected in 1878 but most were gathered in the winters of 1879/80 and 1880/81. The last specimen, and the only one collected by Haviland alone, is dated August 1881 (Figure 3.8b). They visited such familiar locations to Cambridge bryologists as Cherry Hinton, Coton (where they added *Bryoerythrophyllum recurvirostrum* to the county flora), Gamlingay (where they were the last to collect *Aulacomnium palustre*), the Gog Magog Hills and Madingley Wood, but they also made the first bryophyte records from the 'new' Botanic garden (*Cratoneuron filicinum*), Hardwick Wood and Wilbraham Fen. Their most surprising find was *Pleurozium schreberi*, found at Hardwick Wood in 1880 and only seen there once again, in 1965.

The third contributor to the burst of records between 1874 and 1883 was **Hugh Neville Dixon** (1861–1944), who was an undergraduate at Christ's College, Cambridge between 1879 and 1883. In finding *Tortula vahliana* at Cherry Hinton in 1882 (Figure 3.8c) he achieved the (possibly unique?) feat of adding a moss to the British flora during his undergraduate years,[2] although this was not apparent at the time as there were two earlier records which turned out to be erroneous (and in any event the species was already known from Ireland). His collecting was largely restricted to well-known sites in the immediate vicinity of Cambridge, but he managed to find all four of our *Microbryum* species on the chalk (thus adding *M. floerkeanum* to the county list) and he collected *Palustriella falcata* at Empty Common, where it must have survived coprolite digging in the previous decade. The only specimens collected elsewhere in the county were two from Wicken Fen, *Bryum pseudotriquetrum* and *Campylium stellatum*, collected in June 1883, the first known bryophyte records from the site (though by June Dixon might have been concentrating on flowering plants, which he noted assiduously in his copy of Babington's *Flora*). On leaving Cambridge Dixon

2 Though at the age of 21 he was not the youngest person to find a moss new to Britain, as W.J. Hooker famously found *Buxbaumia aphylla* in Norfolk in 1805 when he was 20.

**Figure 3.8** Herbarium packets labelled by late 19th- and early 20th-century collectors (CGE). (a) J.J. Lister, with the collectors' names added by the herbarium technician Arthur Gray, (b) G.D. Haviland, (c) H.N. Dixon, (d) P.G.M. Rhodes.

took a post as principal of a private school for deaf children at Northampton. He also became the leading British bryologist of his generation, author of *The student's handbook of British mosses*, which in its three successive editions remained the standard identification guide from its publication in 1896 until it was finally superseded in 1978.

Otherwise, the only other records from the second half of the 19th century come from a handful of collections in CGE of species which are always likely to catch the eye of non-bryologists. *Ricciocarpos natans* was collected by **William Hillhouse** (1850–1910) at Fulbourn in 1879 during the brief period when he was Babington's Assistant Curator of the Herbarium (1878–1882); he went on to become Professor of Botany at Birmingham (Boon & Outen 2011). **Arthur Sidney Shrubbs** (1858–1922), who worked as an assistant in the Botany School for over 50 years and possessed 'an exceptionally intimate knowledge of the local flora' (Seward 1922), gathered *Sphagnum denticulatum* at Chippenham in 1898. The lichenologist **Charles du Bois Larbalestier** (1838–1911) collected *Leucodon sciuroides* unwittingly when assembling lichen specimens for the exsiccatae distributed as *Lichen-herbarium* (1879). It is a striking indication of the under-recording in 19th-century Cambridgeshire that no bryologist recorded this very distinctive species in the county between 1763 and 1930, even though many visited Gamlingay.

Babington eventually died in 1895. By retaining his professorship until the end, even though he was prevented by failing health from taking an active share in the work of the Department in his final years (Babington 1897: I), Babington did no more than follow the precedent of all but one of his predecessors. However, times were changing, and by his continued occupation of the Chair, coupled with his steadfast opposition to the laboratory-based science associated with his energetic successor Harry Marshall Ward (Allen 1999), Babington arguably did as much to retard the cause of taxonomy in his later years as he had done in his youth to advance it.

## Revival terminated by war, 1901–1914

The first records of the 20th century were made by visitors to Chippenham Fen. **Ethel Mary Hough** (1879–1960) of Newnham College collected *Campylium protensum* here in 1902 (NMW). Miss Hough passed her Part II exams in 1904 (as a woman, she was sent a Certificate in the post rather than awarded a Degree at a graduation ceremony) and she joined the Beginners Section (Section II) of the Moss Exchange Club in 1905. She was still a member of the British Bryological Society in 1952 but we know nothing more about her bryological interests. The well-known bryologist **Coslett Herbert Waddell** (1858–1919), botanising with the algologist **William West** (1848–1914) in 1904, collected *Riccia fluitans* and *Ricciocarpos natans* at Chippenham for distribution to members of the Moss Exchange Club. West also collected *Seligeria calcarea* at Cherry Hinton in 1906.

The next significant contribution was made by two men who, like Haviland & Lister, were undergraduates at the same college, although in this case the college was Pembroke and both studied Classics rather than Natural Sciences. **Leonard John Sedgwick** (1883–1925) was interested in botany before entering Pembroke in 1902. Although he was reading Classics, he apparently also joined the excursions arranged for botany students. After leaving Cambridge in 1905 he entered the Indian Civil Service where he continued for some years to combine his administrative work with botanical collecting. He wrote papers on both Indian bryophytes and flowering plants; his collections include the type material of *Bryocrumia vivicolor*, a monotypic moss genus (O'Shea & Buck 2001). His enthusiasm was also the motivating force behind the foundation of the *Journal of Indian Botany* in 1919. Eventually his linguistic and administrative abilities led to his appointment as officer in charge of the Census of India, a post which left him no time for botany. He died suddenly in India, of 'enteric' (typhoid fever), aged only 42 (Saxton 1926).

**Philip Grafton Mole Rhodes** (1885–1934) entered Pembroke College two years later than Sedgwick, in 1904, as a student of Classics and Theology. 'He was a great lover of Nature and Natural History from his youth and was an enthusiast to the end' (Jones 1935). His earliest surviving bryophyte specimen from the county (*Fontinalis antipyretica* from Coe Fen, Cambridge) was collected shortly after he arrived, in December 1904. Like Sedgwick, he 'started working those parts of the county more easily accessible from Cambridge' (Rhodes 1911). His dated records suggest that he continued to record in the county until 1909 (Figure 3.8d). He studied the bryophytes and lichens of the Channel Islands at the same time, and published records based on springtime visits in 1907–09 (Rhodes 1910). He was ordained as a Church of England priest in 1911, after he left Cambridge, but he defected to the Roman Catholic church c. 1915. After training in Switzerland, he became a Doctor of Divinity and a Professor of Dogmatic Theology at Oscott College, Birmingham before becoming a parish priest in Evesham. His natural history interests turned in his later years to pyrenomycete fungi, often described as 'little black dots'. He died at the early age of 49 and was described as 'saintly' in his obituary (Jones 1935). He had given his large moss herbarium before his death to the BBS, who passed it on to BM; his liverworts went to the Birmingham Natural History Museum (now BIRM).

A major source for Sedgwick's Cambridgeshire bryophyte records is the file kept by P.W. Richards from 1927 onwards (see Figure 3.9 for one example). Richards did not specify the source of these records, but it seems likely that it was the card index of the Cambridge Botanical Survey Club (CBSC). According to the Cambridge Natural History Society card index for vascular plants, the CBSC card index was kept in a tin box in the herbarium and it certainly included vascular plant records made by Sedgwick as well as many by Rhodes, who was apparently the main compiler. If the bryophyte records were not extracted from this card index (which has not been seen for decades), they must presumably have come from a similar source. We know nothing else of the Botanical Survey Club, but would like to know more. Might it have been part of the equally obscure 'scheme for collecting further material for a new Flora of Cambridgeshire' which, according to Evans (1911), was promoted by H. Marshall Ward when he was Professor of Botany (1895–1906)? Other Sedgwick records come from a few specimens in CGE and over 30 in LSR, but the latter (which were originally held by Uppingham School) only became known to Cambridge bryologists in 2017. Rhodes' records come from similar sources, including the Richards file supplemented by a few specimens in BIRM, BM, CGE and in Sedgwick's collection in LSR.

Sedgwick's specimens show that he visited a range of sites around Cambridge in 1904 and 1905, extending south to Hildersham Furze Hills (where he was the first to find *Rhodobryum roseum*) and east to Chippenham. He discovered a good calcicole flora in Haslingfield Pit and also made the first bryophyte records from Dernford Fen. His first records of *Campyliadelphus elodes* and *Didymodon rigidulus* and an early record of *D. fallax* suggest that he had a good eye for the smaller and more challenging taxa. We probably have too few of Rhodes' localised records to assess the extent of his fieldwork, but he appears to have concentrated on the bryophytes of the chalk. He realised that *Campyliadelphus chrysophyllus*, not previously recorded from the county, was frequent in old chalk turf, and he collected *Aloina rigida* at Cherry Hinton. He was apparently the first bryologist to visit the Devil's Dyke since Henslow's time, discovering *Tortella inclinata* there but misidentifying it as *T. flavovirens*. The 19th-century bryologists had neglected liverworts, and Rhodes made the first records of *Leiocolea turbinata* and *Lophocolea heterophylla*, and the first since Relhan of *Conocephalum conicum* and *Metzgeria furcata*. Rhodes also made the first bryophyte records since Dixon from Wicken Fen, where he recorded *Fissidens adianthoides* and *Plagiomnium elatum*. There is no evidence that either Rhodes or Sedgwick visited the western or the eastern boulder-clay woods although Sedgwick, like his predecessors, knew Madingley Wood. Consequently neither found such characteristic and easily identified boulder-clay woodland species as *Cirriphyllum piliferum*, *Eurhynchium striatum*, *Homalia trichomanoides* and *Plagiochila asplenioides*.

A few of the specimens in Sedgwick's collection were collected by, or with, 'A.C.S.', now known from the Leicester packets to be **Arthur Carlile Sturdy** (1883–1919) and not A.C. Seward, Marshall Ward's successor as Professor, as has sometimes been assumed. Sturdy was another Pembroke undergraduate, who matriculated with Sedgwick in 1902. He graduated in 1906 and transferred to St Bartholomew's Hospital to pursue a medical career. He volunteered for service in the Royal Army Medical Corps in 1915, survived service on the Western Front (where he won a Military Cross in 1917 for conspicuous gallantry) but died of dysentery in Bombay in 1919.

Rhodes (1911) summarised the records he and Sedgwick had accumulated in a brief checklist of bryophytes in A.H. Evans' 'A short flora of Cambridgeshire, chiefly from an ecological standpoint'. Rhodes based his paper on Relhan's records updated with his own and Sedgwick's. He clearly did not know of Henslow's specimens, although as a lichenologist he did discover Larbalestier's by-catch of *Leucodon* at Gamlingay. Evans had devised six divisions of the county based on geology, and many of Rhodes' records are simply localised to these regions. *Syntrichia laevipila*, for example, is listed as '1, 2, 3 Rs.', indicating that Rhodes had found it in the Alluvial and Peat (1), Clay, other than Boulder Clay (2) and Chalk (3) districts but not on the Greensand at Gamlingay (4), Boulder Clay (5) and Blown sand on the eastern fringe (6). In his introduction Rhodes briefly described the bryophytes of the fens ('the patches of fen now remaining, as at Quy and Chippenham, produce little ...') and the chalk ('much more interesting'). He under-estimated the boulder-clay woods, which he admitted 'have not been well worked, but do not appear to be rich'. He had little interest in liverworts and added only 'a few species noticed incidentally by the writer round Cambridge' to the existing records. In all, Rhodes accepted records of 122 moss taxa and 21 liverworts (of which 81 mosses and 10 liverworts had been seen in the 20th century).

An interest in field botany revived in the Botany School after the appointment of **Charles Edward Moss** (1870–1930) as Curator of the Herbarium (Preston 2012). Moss, a pioneer ecologist and very much a northerner, was invited by Professor A.C. Seward to become Curator, 'to his great surprise and gratification'. He took up the post in 1908 and was clearly a very popular teacher, although some of his older contemporaries were offended by his outspokenness (Ramsbottom 1931, Tansley 1931). He collected *Sphagnum denticulatum* and *S. palustre* at Gamlingay in 1910, the only evidence we have of his interest in Cambridgeshire's bryophytes. Moss obtained a divorce from his wife in 1917 and almost immediately afterwards emigrated to South Africa to take up a professorship in Johannesburg, divorce being regarded then as *ipso facto* scandalous (Bunting *et al.* 1995).

The neglect of the woodland bryophytes apparent in Rhodes' account was in part remedied when **Robert Stephen Adamson** (1885–1965) contributed moss records to Evans' (1913) additions to the 'Short flora'. Like Moss and so many other members of the pioneer generation of ecologists Adamson was a northerner, born in Manchester and educated at Edinburgh University. After obtaining a doctorate at Edinburgh he was based in the Botany School between 1908 and 1912, where his best-known work was his detailed survey of Gamlingay Wood (Adamson 1912). Adamson reported 16 taxa in his supplement to the 'Short flora' that were additional to those listed by Rhodes, and extra records of a further 30 mosses (seven of which were said to be the first records since Relhan). Unfortunately almost all the records are localised only to the geological districts, and we have not been able to trace his bryophyte specimens. Adamson returned to Manchester as a Lecturer in Botany from 1912 until 1923, when he was appointed Professor of Botany at the University of Cape Town. His sizeable vascular plant herbarium was donated to BM but his bryophytes are not there. Adamson appears to have been an able bryologist and we still hope that his specimens might turn up somewhere, so that we could check the identity and discover the localities for such species as *Bryum archangelicum, B. intermedium, Palustriella commutata* and *Plagiomnium cuspidatum*.

**Ronald Harold Compton** (1886–1979) updated the records of liverworts in Evans' supplement, drawing on 'the results of his year's work on the *Hepaticae*' (Evans 1913). He had found nine species during the year and provided localised records for them all. None of them were then thought to be new to the county, but we regard his *Lunularia cruciata* as the first certain record and two more were recorded for the first time in the 20th century. Compton, who had graduated in 1909, was employed as a Demonstrator in the Botany School between 1911 and 1913. In 1914 he went on a botanical expedition to New Caledonia and after service in the First World War he too emigrated to South Africa, serving as Director of the National Botanic Gardens in Kirstenbosch from 1919 until his retirement in 1953 (Codd 1980).

The last records before the Great War were made by the undergraduate **Arthur William Graveson** (1893–1979) in 1914. Like so many who made bryophyte records in their undergraduate years, Graveson was already a committed naturalist when he arrived at Cambridge in 1911. His father was a botanist and Graveson had attended the Quaker school at Bootham, York, where his interest in natural history was encouraged. His herbarium, at North Hertfordshire Museum Service (HTN), shows that he collected flowering plants throughout his time as an undergraduate but all we know of his interest in bryophytes is drawn from his one surviving natural history diary for this period, covering 1914 (*Graveson diary*). In this Graveson carefully recorded his botanical observations, complete with drawings of some species. He does not seem to have passed his bryophyte records on to anyone else, and until now they have rested in the obscurity of the diary. He made frequent trips from Cambridge, on foot or bicycle, alone or with one of several friends. He started on 16 January, the day after he returned to Cambridge, at Cherry Hinton, and continued recording bryophytes until 6 March (Kingston Wood); after this he concentrated on flowering plants. He recorded two moss species which were not in Evans' 'Short flora', *Fissidens incurvus*, which he thought was 'not recorded from Cambridgeshire so may be a mistake' (although with hindsight there is every reason to think that it was correct) and *Isothecium alopecuroides*, which he identified with rather more confidence ('there does not seem much doubt of its identity'). After serving with the Friends' Ambulance Unit during the War he became a schoolmaster. His early notes suggest that he would have made an excellent bryologist but he does not seem to have continued his interest in the group after the War, though he retained a lifelong passion for flowering plants (Preston 2012, 2013).

The First World War put an end to the revival in Cambridge field botany. There were few direct casualties, the most serious loss being the death in January 1916 of the very popular A.S. Marsh, who had been heavily involved in fighting at the Battle of Loos the previous autumn but found time to write to a friend, 'If you are fond of *Antirrhinum orontium*, this is the country for it' (Tansley 1916). Other young members of the Botany School were dispersed by the War and when the Armistice was eventually signed in 1918 most of the leading field botanists of the pre-War era had left the Department. No doubt many would have left for new posts anyway, but the turnover would perhaps have been more gradual and allowed for the replacement of at least some of those who left. As it was, a revival of interest in field botany in general, and bryology in particular, had to await the arrival of a new generation of undergraduates in the late 1920s.

## Start of systematic recording, 1927–1949

### Paul Richards and Eustace Jones
**Paul Westmacott (Meredith) Richards** (1908–1995), who only used the name Meredith in his early years, was a remarkably precocious child. He was already sufficiently interested in botany to be given Bentham & Hooker's *Handbook of the British Flora* and its accompanying volume of illustrations when he was 7½ years old (Stanley *et al*. 1998). He was spared boarding school because of his delicate health, but his delicacy was perhaps more apparent than real. It certainly did not prevent him, while still a schoolboy, from becoming an active member of the Moss Exchange Club (1920), publishing his first bryological paper (1923), 'A preliminary moss-flora of Glamorgan', and making one record (of *Fissidens fontanus*) which was sufficiently interesting to be cited under his name in the third edition of H.N. Dixon's *The student's handbook of British mosses* (1924). He entered Trinity College, Cambridge as an undergraduate in 1927, graduating in 1931 and staying on to study the rain forest of Sarawak, work for which he was awarded a PhD in 1935. He was

elected as a fellow of Trinity in 1933, obtained a teaching post in the Botany School in 1938 and remained in Cambridge until he became Professor of Botany at the University College of North Wales in 1949. He retired in 1977 and returned to live in Cambridge the following year. He then resumed his attendance on the excursions which he had founded 40 years previously, and he was bryologising with Harold Whitehouse on the day before the accident which led to his death (Whitehouse 1996).

As might be expected, Richards began recording bryophytes when he arrived in Cambridge. It is tempting to suggest that his first record was *Syntrichia montana* on Trinity Bridge. This is one of six records dated 1927, and therefore made during his first few months at University. He made numerous records in the following years. By 1937, when he sent a typescript list of new vice-county records of mosses to the British Bryological Society's recorder, he had found 17 taxa which were additions to those published for Cambridgeshire in the Census Catalogue. They include *Campylopus flexuosus*, *C. pyriformis*, *Didymodon sinuosus*, *Ditrichum gracile*, *Fissidens crassipes* and the county's only record of *Rhytidium rugosum*, plus several which no longer stand as first records because earlier specimens have since come to light.

In his early years in Cambridge Richards also started a loose-leaf file for Cambridge bryophyte records, one page per species with the pages arranged alphabetically (*Richards file*; Figures 3.9, 3.10). This was to be more significant in the longer term than Richards' personal recording, as it provided a permanent record to which others could contribute. The file was clearly adapted from an earlier one as the faded title 'Coniferae, Pteridophyta, Bryophyta, Lichen and Algae Records', written by someone else, is still just legible on the spine. The sequence of entries suggests that the file must have been started by 1929. Richards added to his file references to published records and the details of specimens, including many of Henslow's collections, in CGE. He also transcribed the records from Sedgwick discussed above. The modern records are attributed in the list of sources to members of the Cambridge Natural History Society, of which Richards, Tom Tutin

**Figure 3.9** P.W. Richards' record sheet for *Microbryum davallianum* (*Richards file*). The title and the first entries are in Richards' handwriting; some of the later entries were added by E.W. Jones, E.F. Warburg and M.C.F. Proctor.

**Figure 3.10** P.W. Richards' record sheet for *Anomodon viticulosus* (*Richards file*). Records of this conspicuous species have been added to the sheet by P.C. Hodgson, E.W. Jones, E.F. Warburg, H.L.K. Whitehouse, P.J. Chamberlain and F.H. Perring in addition to Richards himself.

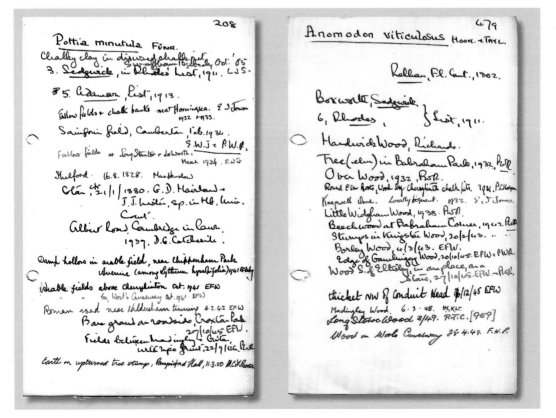

and 'Heff' Warburg were active members (Clapham 1978). A card index for vascular plants, maintained on similar lines, was set up by David Valentine for the CNHS in 1937 (*CNHS minutes*).

An early contributor of records to Richards' file was **Eustace Wilkinson Jones** (1909–1992). Jones' interest in bryophytes had been sparked when, as a very small boy, he saw *Schistostega* glowing in a cave but, unlike Richards, he was unable to make much further progress with them until he arrived in Cambridge in 1928 to read Natural Sciences (Jones 1983, 1991). There his interests in bryophytes developed under Richards' influence. He remained in Cambridge after his graduation in 1931 to study for a PhD on algal physiology, before leaving for Oxford in 1934. The earliest of the records Jones added to Richards' file was for *Rhytidiadelphus squarrosus*, dated 1929. By 1932 he was recording small acrocarps such as *Bryoerythrophyllum recurvirostrum*, *Didymodon sinuosus*, *Eucladium verticillatum* and *Pseudocrossidium revolutum*, the last two new to the county; in 1934 he added *Ephemerum recurvifolium*, *Pseudocrossidium hornschuchianum* and *Seligeria calycina* to the county list. He was an even sharper-eyed bryologist than Richards and the first person in the county to get to grips with the species then included in the genus *Barbula*. In Oxford Jones combined a career in forestry with impressive studies of the bryophytes of Oxfordshire and Berkshire and of African hepatics. 'Jonah' remained an active field bryologist into old age, familiar at BBS meetings as a rather unworldly figure, a notoriously bad driver but 'a fine scholar, a serious, shy and humble man of the highest principles, untainted by ambition and academic politics' (J.G. Duckett, cited by Richards 1993).

The only other people to make more than a handful of records in the county in the inter-war years were T.G. Tutin and P.C. Hodgson. **Thomas Gaskell Tutin** (1908–1987), the future flora writer, was an exact contemporary of Richards who read Natural Sciences at Cambridge between 1927 and 1930 then stayed on until 1933 in a series of short-term posts which he alternated with foreign expeditions (Clapham 1978). His early bryophyte records, made between 1929 and 1932, were of rather conspicuous species, no doubt collected to assist his friend Richards with his recording work. **Peter Charles Hodgson** (b. 1910) entered Corpus Christi College in 1929; the College Admissions register notes that he was born in Wokingham, the son of a 'country gentleman'. He made his bryophyte records in 1931–32, during his undergraduate years. Some of his vouchers are in CGE and they include that for *Plagiochila asplenioides* at Wicken Fen, the only Fenland record. He graduated in 1933 but we can discover nothing of his later life. Some scientists who were to become notable in other fields also contributed one or two records of conspicuous bryophytes to Richards' file in this period include the following (with the date(s) of their bryophyte records and their main claims to fame in brackets): **Valentine Jackson Chapman** (1939; algologist and saltmarsh ecologist), **George Ivor Crawford** (1931; marine zoologist), **Humphrey Gilbert Carter** (*c.* 1935; Director of the University Botanic Garden and inspirational teacher), **Hugh Cary Gilson** (1931–32; Director of the Freshwater Biological Association), **Harry Godwin** (1929; ecologist and pollen analyst), **Thomas Maxwell Harris** (1928; palaeobotanist), **Charles Plowright Petch** (1929; co-author of *Flora of Norfolk*) and **William Thomas Stearn** (1932; taxonomist, Linnaean scholar and author of *Botanical Latin*).

A further innovation of Richards was to start regular field excursions for students, held on Saturday afternoons and designed to complement a course of five lectures on bryophytes he began to give to Part II (final year) students in 1938. Three excursions were held in 1938, by coach to Little Widgham Wood on 5 February, by cycle to Fleam Dyke on 19 February and by coach to Icklingham in the Suffolk Breckland on 5 March. Members of the Botany School staff attended some of the first excursions, including the Professor, F.T. Brooks, the ecologist Alex Watt and Humphrey Gilbert Carter. Amongst the others on the first excursion were Tom Tutin and the undergraduate **Harold Leslie Keer Whitehouse** (1917–2000), who had entered Queens' College in 1936. Whitehouse had become interested in bryophytes as a schoolboy but had failed to make much progress with them, even growing *Pseudoscleropodium purum* in a pot in a vain attempt to encourage it to fruit so that he could identify it using Dixon's *Student's Handbook* (Preston 2001). The 26 species found on the first excursion were listed by Richards on a scrap of paper; this is reproduced by Richards & Whitehouse (1988) who provide many details of the early excursions.

### Wartime bryology

As we have seen, bryology in the county stopped at the outset of the First World War and did not resume until almost a decade after the Armistice; the disruptive effects of the War were immediate and long-lasting. By contrast, bryophyte recording not only continued during the Second World War but actually intensified; there are more records available from Cambridgeshire for the wartime years than for the whole of the inter-war period.

Some of the records come from the Botany School excursions, which were now well established. Harold Whitehouse made his first significant records on these excursions, *Weissia sterilis* on Fleam Dyke in

1940 (although it was initially identified as *Trichostomum brachydontium*) and a single tuft of the instantly recognisable *Leucobryum glaucum* growing in an old coppice stump in Little Widgham Wood in 1941. That excursion to Widgham Wood on 1 March 1941 was something of an epic. The coach failed to reappear for the return journey and it was impossible to ring to discover its whereabouts as the telephone lines had been cut by an air raid on Newmarket. The 26 participants had walked three miles towards Dullingham before they met up with it; the youngest participant, Paul Richards' three-year old daughter Catherine, had to be carried on the shoulders of an undergraduate. The coach then broke down and the party eventually returned on the 8.22 train from Dullingham, reaching home after 9 pm (Richards & Whitehouse 1988). To Catherine Richards it was 'an unforgettable adventure'; to 21st-century bryologists, who sometimes find that their woodland excursions are cancelled because of gusty winds, it is perhaps a more thought-provoking story. In 1943 and 1944 the western boulder-clay woods Home Wood, Longstowe or Kingston Wood were visited rather than Widgham Wood as these could be reached by taking the train to the Old North Road station on the Oxford-Cambridge line.

**John Rishbeth** (1918–1991) included bryophytes in his pioneer study of the flora of Cambridge walls, crediting Paul Richards and Harold Whitehouse with the identification of his material (ms list in *Richards file*). Rishbeth was yet another schoolboy naturalist, with sufficient expertise to collect plant specimens for the British Museum (Natural History) on a Public Schools' Exploring Society expedition to Newfoundland in 1937. The bulk of his study of walls was carried out in his undergraduate years (1937–1940), but the results were not published until after the War (Rishbeth 1948). We have not traced the original records from this survey, we simply know the number of walls on which Rishbeth recorded each species. The bryophyte records were dated 1940–41 by Harold Whitehouse (*Whitehouse file*) although, according to his obituary, Rishbeth was away from Cambridge between 1940 and 1945 (Woods 1995). Rishbeth returned to Cambridge in 1946 to undertake research for a PhD and after a brief period in Jamaica he returned to the Botany School in 1953, becoming a distinguished plant pathologist.

**Edmund Fredric ('Heff') Warburg** (1908–1966) made as many records during the wartime years as Paul Richards. Like Richards and Tutin, he had arrived in Cambridge as an undergraduate in 1927 and he stayed on to study for a PhD, and then as a Research Fellow at his College, Trinity, until he was appointed Assistant Lecturer at Bedford College, London, in 1938. He was an active member of the Natural History Society during his Cambridge years, and contributed many flowering plant records to its card index. He appears to have begun to take an interest in bryophytes only after his appointment to the London post, attending the excursion to Little Widgham Wood in February 1939 and recording species in Long Plantation, Longstowe, in 1940. Once he joined the RAF photographic unit at Medmenham, Buckinghamshire, in 1941, and found that he had little else to occupy his leisure moments, he began to study mosses seriously. He usually spent his leave in Cambridge and would join Richards for bryological trips (Richards 1967). Harold Whitehouse, who had interrupted his PhD to join the Medmenham unit, would recall with a wry smile that for a few months he knew more mosses than 'Heff'. But Warburg soon surpassed him and went on to become the leading British bryologist of his generation. 'His ability to detect small and obscure plants such as Seligerias and sterile Tortulaceae was extraordinary' (Richards 1967) and to Jones (1983) he 'seemed to have a sixth sense that told him when he had an unusual bryophyte in his hand'. His additions to the Cambridgeshire flora did indeed include several 'Tortulaceae', including *Didymodon luridus, D. nicholsonii* (with Richards) and *Trichostomum brachydontium* in the 1940s and *Pottiopsis caespitosa* and *Tortella inflexa* on brief return visits in the 1960s. One of his additions to the county list, *Plagiothecium nemorale*, was collected at Hayley Wood with the Cambridge ecologist **Alexander Stuart Watt** (1892–1985).

The geneticist **David Guthrie Catcheside** (1907–1994) also contributed to the wartime bryophyte records, largely on the Botany School excursions. Catcheside was a Londoner and a boyhood naturalist whose interest in mosses was sparked by the Curator of the South London Botanical Institute, W.R. Sherrin. Through Sherrin he became friends with Paul Richards and other botanists such as Ted Wallace and Ted Lousley; the group became known as 'Sherrin's Boys' (Catcheside 1983, Richards 1995). Catcheside joined the Moss Exchange Club in 1923 and attended its meeting at Llanberis in 1924. He took his first degree at King's College, London and had established himself as a geneticist by the time that he was appointed a Lecturer in the Botany School in 1937; he was Harold Whitehouse's PhD supervisor. The appointment of the 'outsider' Catcheside to a Cambridge lectureship was somewhat unusual; Paul Richards is quoted as saying that 'he brought us into the modern world' (Fincham & John 1995). He nearly succeeded F.T. Brooks as Professor at Cambridge but the electors were unable to decide between him and Harry Godwin, and could only resolve their deadlock by persuading one of their number, G.H. Briggs, a senior member of staff who had not wanted the post, to accept it (Robertson 1986). Other institutions courted Catcheside and he eventually left Cambridge in 1952 to take up the newly established Chair of Genetics at Adelaide.

**Norman Willison Simmonds** (1922–2002) also recorded bryophytes in 1941–1943, especially in sites round Cambridge. Simmonds was then an undergraduate who matriculated in January 1941 and read Part II Botany, graduating in 1943. He obtained a scholarship to work in the Imperial College of Tropical Agriculture in Trinidad in 1945 and became an expert in tropical crops; he later wrote a monograph *Bananas* and edited *The evolution of crop plants* as well as writing a book on *Early Scottish angling literature* (Lockwood 2003). We have the records he added to Richards' file but we have not been through his voucher specimens (E). Another geneticist, the Londoner **Ralph Arnold Lewin** (1921–2008), recorded a few bryophytes in 1941 including the first list of species from Chippenham Fen which he made with his undergraduate contemporary **Phyllis Mary Priestley** (1920–1999). Ralph Lewin wrote an early Biological Flora account, for *Sonchus asper* and *S. oleraceus* (1948). He spent most of his career at the Scripps Institute of Oceanography in California, whose website describes him as the 'father of green algae genetics'. It was he who worked out why the fur of polar bears turns green in captivity, and in addition to studies of algae he wrote books on faeces and a translation of Winnie-the-Pooh into Esperanto. Mary Priestley (later Mrs Cullen) was the daughter of J.H. Priestley (1883–1944), an inspirational Professor of Botany at the University of Leeds. After a brief period of genetical research she became a science teacher, retiring in 1985 as Head of Science at St John's College Choir School, Cambridge. Two more wartime undergraduates reading Natural Sciences made some bryophyte records in 1941, **John Carpenter** (1921–2008), who added *Aphanorrhegma patens* to the county flora, and **Peter Saki Bassett Digby** (1921–2017), who made the first acceptable record of *Hylocomium splendens*. Digby went on to an academic career as a marine zoologist, studying the life cycles of zooplankton and the physiology of calcification (Anon. 2018).

### Post-war years

The post-war period was a time of renewal for British bryology. Some of the senior members who had led the British Bryological Society through the inter-war years had died during the War, including its leading experts on mosses, H.N. Dixon, and liverworts, W.E. Nicholson. Both Catcheside and Richards were amongst those involved in planning the future activities of the Society (Richards 1983); another member of the younger generation, Fred Sowter of Leicester, pressed the Society to publish a journal and became the first editor of the *Transactions of the British Bryological Society* (Jones 1973). Harold Whitehouse also attended the first full-scale meeting of the Society after the War, at Appleby in 1946, but was far too junior to be involved in these discussions.

In Cambridgeshire Richards continued to record bryophytes in the county and the first issue of the *Transactions* included notes on two of his more notable finds in 1946, *Herzogiella seligeri* and *Ptilidium pulcherrimum* (Richards 1947a, b). In 1947 he found the invasive alien *Orthodontium lineare* at Croxton. However, the total number of records fell off after 1945 without Warburg's input. Other than Richards, the only substantial contributor in the late 1940s was **Peter James Chamberlain** (1927–2005) in 1948–49. Chamberlain did his first degree in London, coming to Cambridge in 1948 to register for a PhD on the experimental taxonomy of bryophytes under Paul Richards. He returned to University College, London in 1950 as an Assistant Lecturer in Botany before writing his thesis, but in 1952 'suddenly changed careers and abandoned his mosses for the violin', eventually becoming a well-respected music teacher (Anon. 2008). **Ann Pamela Conolly** (1917–2010) visited Doddington Wood, Fenland's only ancient woodland, in 1946, shortly before it was grubbed out; with the exception of three species recorded by Tutin in 1932, her list of bryophytes from the wood is the only one we have (see Chapter 8). Conolly had been an undergraduate at Newnham College before the War but was then teaching at Bedford College for Women in London; she joined Tutin at Leicester in 1947 but retained her links with Cambridge into old age.

## The Whitehouse era, 1950–1999

### One flora, Proctor (1956)...

Paul Richards left Cambridge in 1949 to become Professor of Botany at Bangor. Fortunately, from 1950 onwards bryological recording was continued by **Harold Whitehouse** and **Michael Proctor** (Figure 3.11). Whitehouse's PhD studies had been interrupted by the War, but he submitted his thesis in 1947 and joined the Botany School staff as a Demonstrator. His bryological activity certainly increased markedly following Richards' departure. In 1950 he started a notebook *Bryophyte Lists East Anglia*, beginning with a list from Sparrows' Grove on 10 May. The notebooks were continued as *East Anglian Bryophytes* until there were six in total, with frequent entries until 1963 and a few more until October 1968 (*Whitehouse diary*). He also arranged to replace Richards' loose-leaf file with a set of foolscap sheets, one per species, with duplicated headings and columns (*Whitehouse species file*; Figure 3.12). By February 1951 he had finished copying all

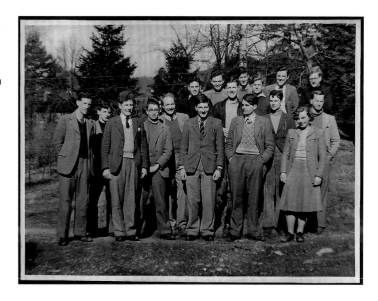

**Figure 3.11** Harold Whitehouse (far left) and Michael Proctor (front centre, with striped tie) on a Cambridge Botany School excursion to the Lake District, March–April 1950. Others in the party include P.J. Chamberlain (obscured, fifth from left), Susan Balkwill (front right), Franklyn Perring (fourth from right, far back row) and Richard West (far right, far back row). Photo: Pat Whitehouse.

the entries from Richards' file to these new sheets; the last entries in Richards' file were made on 1 February and from 10 February onwards Proctor, Whitehouse and others were entering new records onto these sheets. Finally, Whitehouse took over the running of the bryological excursions, which were now a well established feature of the Botany School year. However he remained a professional geneticist and he never gave any formal tuition on bryophytes, saying firmly that he regarded them as plants to be studied in the field rather than subjects for the lecture theatre.

**Michael Charles Faraday Proctor** (1929–2017) entered Queens' College, Cambridge in 1948, and after graduating in 1951 he went on to do a PhD on the taxonomy and ecology of *Helianthemum* in Britain. He had become interested in natural history in his childhood, investigating the commons around Harrow and then the richer habitats of the New Forest and Purbeck around his childhood homes (Birks & Birks 2018). His first few bryophyte records in Cambridgeshire were made in 1949, some with his exact contemporary at Queens', **Franklyn Hugh Perring** (1927–2003). Proctor made many more records between 1950 and 1953 including *Plagiomnium cuspidatum* from the lawn of Old Court, Queens' College, in 1950, the first of his new vice-county records. Proctor also became a superb photographer during his Cambridge years and his photos illustrated the early New Naturalist volumes *Wild flowers* (Gilmour & Walters 1954) and *Mountain flowers* (Raven & Walters 1956). In 1954 he took a post with the Nature Conservancy in Bangor but that job proved to be too bureaucratic for him and he moved to the University of Exeter in 1956, where he remained until he retired in 1994 (Birks

**Figure 3.12** H.L.K. Whitehouse's record sheet for *Microbryum davallianum*, which was continued onto a second page (*Whitehouse species file*). Whitehouse has transcribed the records from Richards' file (Figure 3.9) then added later records. Most are in his handwriting but a group of three, just above the red line marking the cut-off point for Proctor's flora (1956), have been added by M.C.F. Proctor.

? New – years only

Name of Species :- Pottia davalliana (Sm.) C. Jens.
(P. minutula (Schleich.) Fürnr.)
Early records :- Martyn 1763 }
(1785 } See P. truncata
Relhan (1802
(1820
Henslow Mus. Shelford 16·8·1828; Cat. Brit. Plts. 1835 Gymnostomum conicum. Recorded for Cambs.
G.D. Haviland & J.J. Lister in Herb. Univ. Cant. Coton, c. f. 21·1·1880.
L.J. Sedgwick. Chalky clay in disused chalk pit, Swaffham Bulbeck, Oct. 1905.
Rhodes 1911 3 Sedgwick. 52/56
Adamson 1913 5.

| Habitat. | Locality. | Grid Ref. | Date. | Collector. |
|---|---|---|---|---|
| Fallow fields & chalk banks | Near Horningsea. | 4 6 | 1932 1933 | E.W. Jones |
| Sainfoin field | Comberton. | 3 5 | Feb. 1934 | E.W.J. & P.W.R. |
| Fallow fields | Long Stanton & Lolworth | 3/4 6, 3 6 | March 1934 | E.W.J. |
| In lawn | Gilbert Road, Cambridge. | 4 6 | 1939 | D.G. Catcheside |
| Damp hollow in arable field | Near Cherry Hinton Park Avenue (among Lythrum hyssopifolia) | 6 6 | 1941 | E.F. Warburg |
| Arable fields | Above Cherryhinton | 4 5 | Oct. 1941 | E.F.W. |
| " " | By Worts Causeway | 4 5 | Oct. 1941 6·10·54. | E.F.W. G. Halliday. |
| | Roman road near Hildersham turning. | 5 4(5) | 4·3·43 | E.F.W. |
| Bare ground. | Roadside, Croxton Park | 2 5(6) | 27·10·45 | E.F.W. |
| Fields | Between Madingley & Girton, with ripe fruit | 4 6 | 22·9·46 | P.W.R. |
| Earth on uptured tree-stump. | Pampisford Hall | 5 4 | 11·3·50 | M.C.F. Proctor. |
| Edge of field | Old railway cutting nr. Babraham | 52 50 | 10.2.51 | M.C.F.P. |
| Earth on uptured stump | Cambridge–Babraham road | 49 52 | 12.2.51 | M.C.F.P. |
| | Roadside nr. Weston Colville | 59 54 | 11.3.51 | M.C.F.P. |
| Dyke of New Bedford Level [illegible] | N.E. of Mepal | 4½ 8⅔ | 15.1.56 | G.H. |
| Earth on uptured stump | Bird Sanctuary, Adams Rd. | 43 58 | 24.11.51 | H.L.K.W. |
| | Chalk-pit behind Hill's Trees | 484 538 | 2.55 | G.H. |
| Stubble field | Gogs c.f. | 501 533 | 14.10.56 | H.L.K.W. |
| Sainfoin field | near Blackthorn Spinney, Dry Drayton | 3 6 | 11.11.56 | " |
| Arable field | near Nine Wells, [illegible] c.f. | 4 5 | 9.12.56 | " |
| Sainfoin field | near "Aconite Wood", Pampisford | 5 4 | 27.1.57 | " |
| Stubble field | near Nine Wells, Thriplow | 45 47 | 27.9.58 | " |
| " " | between Barrington & Shepreth | 387 483 | 11.10.58 | M.C. Anderson |
| With Riccia spp. & Lythrum hyssopifolia in damp hollow in arable field | near Whittlesford | 4 4 | 1.11.58 | D.E.C. & H.L.K.W. |
| | Chalkpit Plantation, Babraham | 517 508 | 8.11.58 | H.L.K.W. |
| Fallow field on | Lower Chalk nr. Guilden Morden c. [illegible] | 276 428 | 15.11.59 | P.J. Bourne |
| Grass field | Fulbourn | 528 560 | 6.12.59 | H.L.K.W. |
| Path | By wood, Barrington c.f. | 378 508 | 10.1.60 | P.J.B. |
| Stubble field | Coploe Hill c.f. | 493 426 | 31.1.60 | P.J.B. & H.L.K.W. |
| Fields | Near Madingley brick-pits c.f. | 404 614 | 6.2.60 | S.J.P. Waters |
| Stubble field | Near Brinkley Wood c.f. | 602 556 | 14.2.60 | P.J.B. |

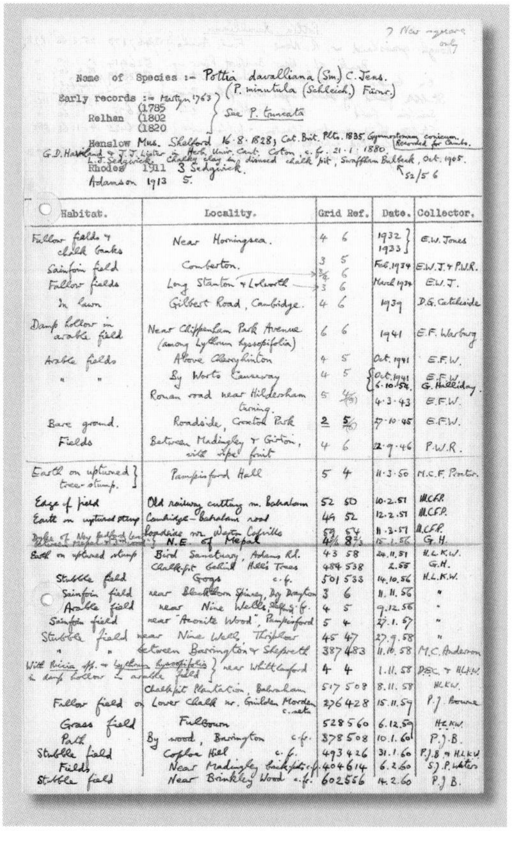

& Birks 2018). Here physiological studies of bryophytes became a major feature of his research. A younger student, **Geoffrey Halliday**, who graduated in 1955 and went on to work on a PhD on the taxonomy and ecology of *Arenaria* and *Minuartia*, also recorded bryophytes between 1954 and 1958. He concentrated on flowering plants for the rest of his career, taking a particular interest in the floras of Cumbria and Greenland. **Arthur Oliver Chater** had learned flowering plants as a child from his parents, who were both botanists. He spent a week recording flowering plants in north Cambridgeshire when he was an undergraduate, in July 1955. He also gathered some bryophytes for Michael Proctor to identify and these included *Orthotrichum cupulatum*, which was not seen again in the county for 30 years. He too later concentrated on flowering plants, at least until the publication of his *Flora of Cardiganshire* (2010), the county flora nonpareil. However, he interleaved his botanical work with studies of various invertebrate groups (discovering the bristletail *Dilta chateri*) and is currently mapping the plant parasitic microfungi of Cardiganshire.

**Reginald Ernest Parker** (1921–2012) made a valuable set of records in 1952–53. He had joined the BBS in 1949 when he was a research student at the University College of North Wales, Bangor. When Derek Ratcliffe arrived at Bangor in 1950 they became close friends. 'Reg and Derek travelled around North Wales in search of plants on Reg's motorbike, with Reg shouting details of their destination, what plants to look out for, what their distinguishing characters were, and so on over his shoulder to Derek who was clinging on in the pillion seat' (Birks & Birks 2015). After leaving North Wales Parker lived briefly at Linton Hall, Linton, and registered as a research student in plant ecology in Cambridge, supervised by Dr Watt. By then he was clearly an astute bryologist who was equally adept at identifying pleurocarps and acrocarps (see *Rhynchostegium megapolitanum*). Many of his best records were made around Linton including first vice-county records of *Riccia cavernosa* and *Scleropodium cespitans* at Hildersham Hall, *Metzgeria violacea* in the Alder Carr at Hildersham and *Grimmia dissimulata* (then thought to be *G. trichophylla*) in Linton itself. Parker left Cambridgeshire to take up a post at Queen's University, Belfast. Some readers, like C.D.P., might have used his book *Introductory statistics for biology* (Parker 1973) without realising that it was written by a one-time bryologist.

When Richards realised that he would be unable to find time to write the bryophyte flora of Cambridgeshire that he had planned, he asked Michael Proctor to do so. The resulting flora was published in the *Transactions of the British Bryological Society* (Proctor 1956). The flora was based on the records accumulated by Richards and those which had been made after his departure; Proctor expressed his particular thanks to Whitehouse for his help. He was able to borrow the Skrimshire herbarium from Wisbech and include details of these specimens, hitherto unknown to Cambridge bryologists. In the flora he cited records in six areas of the county, defined geologically: Fens, Chalk, western Clay Plateau, eastern Boulder Clay, Breckland and Gamlingay Greensand. These were similar to the regions recognised by Evans (1911), although the clay was divided geographically rather than geologically. 'The south of the county is reasonable well covered', Proctor commented, 'but records are sparse from the bryologically rather uninviting areas of flat arable land north of Ely. However, even in the neighbourhood of Cambridge this type of country is poor in bryophytes ...'.

Proctor (1956) accepted records of 34 liverwort species (including five he considered extinct, i.e. not seen in the 20th century), one hornwort (extinct) and 200 mosses (13 extinct). As he attributed most of the records he cited to individual recorders, the proportion of the more notable records contributed by different individuals can be quantified. Richards himself was responsible for more 20th-century records than anyone else (25%), followed by Proctor (18%), Jones (11%), Whitehouse (8%), Parker (7%), Warburg (6%) and Halliday (5%). The remaining 20% were attributed to over 40 others. It is notable that the only large group of bryophytes for which Richards' contribution was clearly outnumbered by the records of another bryologist was Pottiaceae, for which Proctor cited more than twice as many of his own records.

### ... followed rapidly by another, Whitehouse (1964)

The second flora of the county was the result of the plan by three of the county's vascular plant specialists, Frank Perring, **Peter Derek Sell** (1929–2013) and **Stuart Max Walters** (1920–2005), to produce a new flora to mark the tercentenary (in 1960) of the publication of John Ray's *Catalogus*. Both Sell and Walters were on the Botany School staff, and Perring was employed as the 'Senior Worker' on the *Atlas of the British Flora* project, based in an office by the Botanic Garden but also fully involved in the life of the department. All three, though they were not bryologists, were 'bryo-friendly' and would occasionally take specimens to Harold Whitehouse for identification; Peter Sell also collected more systematically in his home village of Bassingbourn. They invited Whitehouse to contribute a bryological section to the flora.

Whitehouse's brief was to provide a relatively short text for each species followed by a summary of the distribution in 10-km squares. Existing records on Whitehouse's species sheets were easily gridded and summarised as grid squares, but achieving an adequate coverage of the county at this scale was a major task. Records of flowering plants had been collected from 1-km grid squares in the county since 1952, so the bryologists had some catching up to do. Whitehouse was continuing to pursue his academic research (the first edition of his influential book *Towards an understanding of the mechanism of heredity* was published in 1963) and this work, combined with his teaching duties, his research on tuberous bryophytes (which began with the discovery of *Hennediella stanfordensis* at the Lizard in 1958), his leadership of the Botany School bryophyte excursions and his commitment to his young family, can have left him little time for additional fieldwork. In July 1959, therefore, he issued an appeal to other naturalists in the county to help fill the gaps by sending him collections of bryophytes for identification. This pointed out that, for bryophytes, 'even the most abundant species have been recorded from only about half the squares'. He listed the number of the 50 commonest species recorded from each 10-km square on the circular, and this list showed that no common species at all were recorded from several squares including those around Whittlesey (TL29), Chatteris (TL38), Thorney (TF20), and North Wisbech (TF40), and fewer than five from Tadlow (TL24), Over (TL37), Benwick (TL39) and even Ely (TL58).

Whitehouse's appeal was successful in providing records from the north of the county. The Headmistress of Ely High School for Girls, Miss B. Tilly, sent specimens collected at Stretham (TL57) by D. Clarke, D. Blackmore and F. Stevens and at Littleport (TL58) by Iris Firby. Whitehouse identified specimens sent in 1959–60 from around Whittlesey, March, Manea, Wimblington and Murrow (TL29, 38, 39, 48, 49, 59, TF30, 40) collected by P.F. Lumley; by W. Jackson (who also sent material gathered by A. Acton, J.B. Kukula, C.R. Ladds, B. Reeve, R.J. Savage and M. Scott); and by Mrs V.T. Gotobed (who also sent plants collected by Ivy Coulson, Jacqueline Cox, Valerie Elderkin, Mary Frost, Ann and Jill Graves, M. Mayhew, Jean Muffett, Mrs Nicholas, C. Readshaw, Carol Sisson, Angela Ward and Carolyn Wallis). In the east O.E. Wallis collected material he and 'S.V.C.' had collected from Barway, Chippenham, Fordham, Isleham and Soham (TL57, 66). Many of these helpers collected common species growing in ordinary habitats, such as *Bryum argenteum*, *B. capillare*, *Ceratodon purpureus* and *Tortula muralis* found by Jackson from the backyard of Irving's Fish Shop in the High Street, March. However, Reeve discovered a rich pioneer flora at Gray's Moor Pits, where he collected *Bryum creberrimum*, *Hygroamblystegium humile* and *Riccardia multifida* new to the county and also discovered *Riccia rhenana* two days after it was first found further south in Cambridgeshire. He and Jackson gathered more *H. humile* at Guyhirn, and Reeve collected *Bryum intermedium* at Wimblington and *Dicranella schreberiana* at March, two further additions to the county list. This was a remarkable haul for a non-bryologist. Whitehouse kept meticulous records of all the material he identified, including precise grid references for all records of even the commonest species. However, for the commonest species he only transferred a single record from each 10-km square to his species sheets.

The help of the Botanical Society of the British Isles was also enlisted. 'As a side-line' at a weekend meeting held in Wisbech in September 1959 to record vascular plants in the county's northernmost 10-km squares, 'members collected bags of bryophytes from each square' (Perring 1961). This produced a few records, though some were localised only to the hectad.

The most important result of the appeal for help in 1959 was that Whitehouse recruited the services of **Philip John Bourne** (1914–1965). Bourne was secretary to the Board of Governors of the United Cambridge Hospitals but he suffered from ill-health which eventually led to his early retirement in 1963. He and his wife Joan Elsie Bourne (Figure 3.13) started by visiting Chishill (TL43), an area from which only five common species were known, on a sunny afternoon in September 1959 (Bourne 1960; this area is in vc 19 and excluded from our flora). Somewhat to his surprise, Whitehouse told him that they had collected 14 species, including 10 new

**Figure 3.13** Philip and Joan Bourne, photographed in the 1950s.

to the square. He soon became an assiduous collector, targeting the under-recorded areas (Figures 3.14, 3.15). As a result of his fieldwork, and that of the others described above, the number of species/square records for the county increased from 1397 to 1808 in the last four months of 1959. By the time Bourne finished collecting, in 1963, he had visited 39 10-km squares and 164 tetrads in vc 29, making over 2000 records, all precisely localised. More than 600 of them were additions to their 10-km squares (Whitehouse 1965). Whitehouse encouraged him to collect from stubble fields, as he was becoming increasingly interested in their tuberous species, and Bourne discovered the non-calcareous fields on Oxford Clay at Papworth St Agnes where he collected *Riccia sorocarpa* and *Acaulon muticum*, both new to the county. Whitehouse, who quickly went to see these species for himself, also found *Bryum gemmilucens* there. Bourne was the first to collect the commoner arable species *Bryum violaceum* and *Dicranella staphylina*, although Whitehouse collected them soon afterwards. He also added *Rhynchostegiella litorea* to the county list, from West Wickham.

**Figure 3.14** Tetrads in vc 29 in which P.J. Bourne collected bryophytes, 1958–1963.

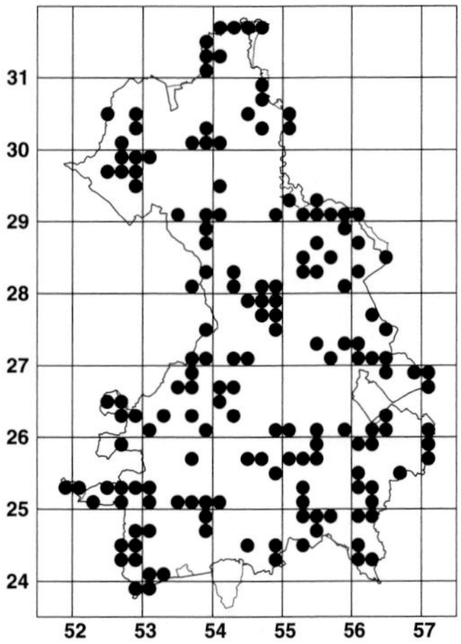

Some specialist botanists also contributed records to Whitehouse's species sheets. **Clifford Charles Townsend** (1926–2018) was working for the Eastern Gas Board and living in Cambridge when he recorded bryophytes in the county between 1955 and 1959. He later joined the staff at the Royal Botanic Gardens, Kew where he was chiefly responsible for writing several volumes of the excellent *Flora of Iraq*. He retained his interest in bryology, publishing numerous bryological papers from his home address in Twickenham as Kew staff are not allowed to study bryophytes in work time. **David Franklin Chamberlain** also recorded bryophytes in Cambridgeshire as a young man (1960–64), living with or revisiting his family who had moved to Cambridge in 1955. He had been interested in flowering plants since the age of four but by 1959 his primary allegiance had changed to bryophytes, partly under the influence of Harold Whitehouse. He went to Oxford in 1960 for his initial degree and followed it with a DPhil with Heff Warburg and Roy Perry, his choice of subject (the bryophyte genus *Pottia*) suggested in part by his field experience in Cambridgeshire. He spent his later career at the Royal Botanic Garden, Edinburgh, working on flowering plants professionally but retaining his interest in bryophytes, to which he has returned in retirement. Unlike these two, **Gigi Crompton** is not a bryologist but she collected specimens for Whitehouse to identify, particularly from Thriplow Meadows and Thriplow Peat Holes, sites she was studying in detail (Crompton 1959, 1972).

**Figure 3.15** An example of Harold Whitehouse's meticulous notes on Philip Bourne's collections (*Whitehouse site files*). All were written on the back of students' examination answers (which are traditionally written on one side of the paper only). A circled 65 indicates species hitherto unrecorded from TL65 and records marked with a circled F were transferred to the relevant species sheet (see Figure 3.12 for the record of *Pottia davalliana*).

P. J. Bourne 14. 2. 60

Roadside near Dullingham 612 588 | (Middle chalk) Stubble field near Brinkley Wood 602556 | Wooded parish pit near Dullingham 611590

Bryum argenteum (65) (F) ✓
(" bicolor ?)
Funaria hygrometrica c.fr. (F) ✓
Phascum cuspidatum c.f. (65) ✓(F)
Pottia davalliana c.f. (65) ✓(F)
Bryum erythrocarpum c.ge. (65) ✓(F) ✓
Barbula unguiculata ✓(F) ✓
Mnium hornum (F) ✓
Aulacomnium androgynum (65) ✓(F)
Dicranella heteromalla (F) ✓
Eurhynchium confertum c.f. (65) ✓(F)
Mnium affine (F) (65) ✓
Brachythecium velutinum c.f. (F) ✓
Plagiothecium denticulatum c.f. (F) ✓
Eurhynchium praelongum ✓
(Bryum capillare ?) ✓
Lophocolea heterophylla ✓
Hypnum cupressiforme ✓
Dicranoweisia cirrata c.ge. (F) ✓
Bryum capillare (F) ✓
Ceratodon purpureus ✓
Pseudoscleropodium purum (F) ✓

20 spp., 27 new

Several of Whitehouse's colleagues in the Botany School contributed relatively small numbers of records. **Eric Alan George** (1920–2005) came from a Cambridgeshire family and at school he was encouraged in his early interest in natural history by the noted local naturalist William Palmer. His undergraduate course was interrupted by war service (in the Royal Artillery) so that although he entered Downing College in 1938 and passed his Part I exams in 1940 he did not graduate until 1947. He then became the assistant to Professor E.G. Pringsheim and on his retirement in 1950 took over as Curator of the Culture Collection of Algae and Protozoa. This was initially based in the Botany School but transferred to its own premises in

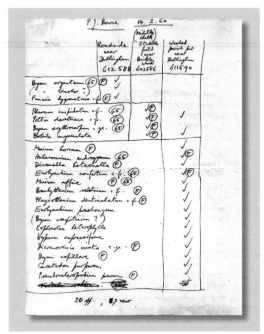

Storey's Way, as the Culture Centre of Algae and Protozoa, in 1970 (Belcher & Swale 2005/06). George made one or two bryophyte records in 1940 and 1948 but rather more between 1959 and 1962. He had a long-standing interest in the freshwater algae of Cambridgeshire and he visited several clay pits in the county in 1959–60, recording *Riccia rhenana* at Madingley and collecting what later proved to be *Tortula schimperi* at Gray's Moor. His last bryophyte records were made in Hayley Wood in 1962, presumably when sampling the diatoms there (George 1963). Other members of the University who contributed some bryophyte records between 1956 and 1964 included three students who completed PhD theses on ecological topics in the 1960s. **Margaret Cordue Anderson** (1937–2000) worked on the measurement of light in woodland, **Michael Henry Martin** on nutrient availability in woodland soils and **Stephen John Preston Waters** on the calcicole/calcifuge problem. Martin discovered *Nowellia curvifolia* at Hayley Wood (Martin 1963) and Waters made the equally remarkable find of three *Racomitrium* species on clinker at Madingley (Whitehouse 1962).

We now know that the professional horticulturist and keen amateur bryologist **Tom Laflin** (1914–1972) listed the bryophytes he saw in several sites in the county between 1950 and 1965. His large bryophyte herbarium was donated to CGE after his death and his extensive species lists from the sites he visited were later deposited there by his family. It is while we were looking through these recently that we discovered his Cambridgeshire records. The most interesting list is that for Swansley Wood which he visited in 1965, not long before the wood was grubbed out in 1967–68.

The published flora (Whitehouse 1964) included details of the bryophytes recorded up to the end of 1962. A few extra records, including the first of what were to be a remarkable set of calcifuge species found at Wicken Fen, were included as a note added in proof (Whitehouse 1964: xvi). In total Whitehouse included 37 liverwort species (including three he considered extinct), one extinct hornwort and 224 mosses (19 extinct). In the preface (p. xi), Perring *et al.* (1964) noted that 'interest in the mosses and liverworts of the county has been steadily increasing in recent years, largely through Dr Whitehouse's own interest and enthusiasm'. In a review of the flora, Eustace Jones noted that about 29 bryophyte taxa had been added to the county flora since Proctor's flora. 'Perhaps the chief factors responsible for the remarkable number of additional records in recent years have been the abundance and zeal of keen-eyed young collectors, the facility with which they can obtain a working knowledge of the British bryophyte flora as compared with 30 years ago, and the motor car, which has permitted much more thorough working of parts of the county that are beyond the half-day cycle ride from Cambridge that used to limit our activities' (Jones 1965).[3] Twelve bryophytes were recorded in 'all squares', the 31 10-km squares with a substantial area of land in the county. This was evidence of the effectiveness with which the commoner bryophytes had been recorded by Philip Bourne and others since 1959.

Harold Whitehouse ceased to keep records on his species sheets at the end of 1961 (when he completed the first draft of the flora). He continued to identify samples collected by Philip Bourne until 1963; after this Bourne suffered increasingly from ill health and was unable to continue collecting. Henceforth Whitehouse's bryophyte recording in the county was largely confined to the excursions which he had led since 1950.

### Bryophyte excursions, 1950–1999

The winter excursions, usually run weekly from the Botany School on Saturday afternoons, followed an established pattern from the 1950s until the mid 1980s. At the start of the Michaelmas term, in October, there was often a flowering plant excursion to Cherry Hinton and a couple of fungus forays, so the bryophyte excursions took place in the short November days and were held at sites close to Cambridge. However, there was no competition from others in the Lent term and the excursions were held at increasing distances from Cambridge as the days lengthened (Figure 3.16). They began in the early afternoon, allowing time for lunch after Saturday morning lectures. In the 1950s and 1960s students cycled to the closer sites and a coach was hired for transport to more distant venues. The programme for 1957/58 is typical, with visits to Madingley Wood (23 November) and Wort's Causeway Beechwood and the Roman Road (30 November) in the autumn and then excursions at weekly intervals from 18 January to Trumpington churchyard and Byron's Pool; Cherry Hinton chalk pit; Coe Fen; Wandlebury; Whitepits Plantation; Gamlingay Wood; Hildersham Hall; and finally, on 8 March, Devil's Dyke. From *c.* 1969 a departmental minibus was available and a research student would often volunteer to drive. This allowed rather more distant places to be visited, as in 1974/75 when the excursions were to Hardwick Wood and Woodwalton

---

3   Cambridge botanists, wedded to their cycles, were perhaps more reluctant than most to take to the motor car. Allen (1986) notes that '[G.C.] Druce had acquired a car by as early as 1909 and even a poorish country vicar like [E.S.] Marshall had followed his example by 1914'. Koepp (2002) argues that 'modern forms of transportation have never been a Cambridge strongpoint'.

**Figure 3.16** Jim Dickson, Harold Whitehouse and Alan Hamilton at Cavenham Heath, Suffolk, in front of the Whitehouse family's car (a Standard Companion), March 1965. Photo: John Birks.

Fen in November, and to Devil's Dyke, Wicken Fen, Hayley Wood, Chippenham Fen and Icklingham in the Suffolk Breckland in February and early March. Nevertheless, the overall pattern of the excursions shows a strong concentration round Cambridge.

The excursions were intended to teach bryophytes and here Harold Whitehouse came into his own. A slight and physically unprepossessing figure who retained the 'make do and mend' philosophy of the wartime years long after others had moved to more conspicuous consumption, he would begin by distributing a species list for the site and sometimes a list of common Cambridge species. Newcomers, in an era when there was a strong division in the University between academic and assistant staff, would often assume that he was a technician sent out to distribute the handouts. In the field his expertise soon became apparent as he would quietly and with infinite patience explain the features of the common species. 'He had a charming way of feigning interest when common plants were brought to him for identification. He would tilt his head to one side and say 'I think this is *Ceratodon purpureus*', as if there was really some room for doubt, his manner even implying that the specimen was, in its way, quite notable. He and his listener were well aware that he knew it was common old *Ceratodon*, but never for a moment did he wish to imply that a beginner was silly or ignorant. On the contrary, his pupils were made to feel that they had found something valuable' (Hill 2000). Inevitably Whitehouse tended to pass his own interests on to his disciples. Duckett (2018) has pointed out that he tended to produce acrocarpophiles and pleurocarpophobes, although the lack of specialist expertise in pleurocarpous mosses was perhaps a wider feature of British bryology in the second half of the 20th century. Whitehouse recorded the species found on each visit on a copy of the site list, and any additions were carefully credited to the students who had found them (Figure 3.17). Thus the undergraduate **Julian Lyddon Harding** was credited with the discovery of *Sciurohypnum populeum*, new to the county, when he found it on a bryophyte excursion to the Devil's Dyke in 1960. Whitehouse's site files, which include the various lists and associated correspondence, cover over 60 separate localities in Cambridgeshire (*Whitehouse site files*). At the end of the year he circulated a summary of the season's highlights and he published the most significant records periodically in *Nature in Cambridgeshire* (see our Bibliography).

**Harry John Betteley Birks** (Figure 3.18) was co-leader of the excursions from 1968 to 1982, while he was on the Botany School staff. His bryological interests complemented those of Whitehouse as he was primarily interested in the species of the north and west. He had come to Cambridge as an undergraduate in 1963 and his detailed account of the *Past and present vegetation of the Isle of Skye*, based on his PhD thesis, was published in 1973. His best find on the Cambridgeshire excursions was *Lophozia perssonii*, found at Cherry Hinton in only its third British locality. **Christopher David Preston** was invited by Whitehouse to be a co-leader of the excursions in 1978, and joined him in publishing an annual summary of bryophyte records from 1987 onwards (Preston & Whitehouse 1987–99). He had arrived in Cambridge in 1973 to read Natural Sciences, and was a regular attender on Whitehouse's excursions from November 1974. His first major bryological project, in 1978–79, was a survey with Whitehouse of the '*Lythrum* hollows' near Whittlesford (see below). In 1980 he was appointed as Frank Perring's successor as the botanist at the Biological Records Centre, a post he held until his retirement in 2015. In this capacity most of his activities were directed towards vascular plants, but bryophytes were included in his duties and he was able to ensure that Whitehouse's detailed records of Cambridgeshire bryophytes were incorporated into the database. The British Bryological Society's mapping scheme was then in full swing, culminating in the first BBS *Atlas* (Hill *et al.* 1991–94). **Charles Robin Stevenson** of King's Lynn joined the team leading the excursions in 1995. He suggested the venue for the last excursion of 1999, to the disused orchard at Rummers Lane, Wisbech St Mary, and his later fieldwork revealed the rich bryophyte flora of the orchards of Cambridgeshire and Norfolk.

Some of the students who attended the excursions in the post-war years were doubtless simply attracted by the opportunity for an afternoon in the open air, and the knowledge that they would not have to recount anything they were told in an examination. Richards & Whitehouse (1988) also suggest that 'the excursions were something of a matchmaking establishment!'. However, many of those who attended as undergraduates or as research students were committed botanists who went on to distinguished research careers in Cambridge or elsewhere. Many such are listed by Richards & Whitehouse (1988) including, in chronological order and in addition to others mentioned elsewhere in this account, **Christopher Donald Pigott** (Lancaster), **Peter John Grubb** (Cambridge), **Oliver Rackham** (1939–2015, Cambridge), **James Holms Dickson**

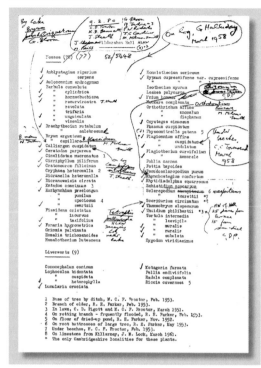

**Figure 3.17** Harold Whitehouse's species list for Hildersham Hall, circulated on the excursion held on 9 February 1980 and annotated with his field notes made on that occasion (*Whitehouse site files*). After the excursion he transcribed the notes neatly onto another copy of the list which also survives in the files.

(Glasgow), **Jeffrey Graham Duckett** (Queen Mary, London), **Hilary Helen Birks (née Lees)** (Bergen), **John Dransfield** (Kew), **Honor Clare Prentice (née Gautby)** (Lund), **Brian Huntley** (Durham), **Caroline Mary Pannell** (Oxford), **Quentin Charles Bargrave Cronk** (British Columbia) and **Ian Mark Turner** (Singapore). The medical student **Jonathan Duncan Sleath** also attended while he was an undergraduate (1979–82), and after he left Cambridge he continued to combine his medical career with his interest in bryology. Several of those who came on excursions collected specimens which have now been deposited in public herbaria, including John Birks (E), David Chamberlain (E), Jeff Duckett (BM), **Ian Michael Evans** (LSR), Geoffrey Halliday

**Figure 3.18** Peter Grubb, Mike Lock and John Birks at Winterton, Norfolk, September 1965. Photo: Hilary Birks.

(E), Mike Lock (CGE), **Malcolm George McFarlane** (1935–2017, BM), Oliver Rackham (CGE) and **Peter Frederick Yeo** (1929–2010, CGE). These provide a valuable record of the species which were regularly encountered in these years. Paul Richards was a regular attender after he returned to live in Cambridge in 1978, and he cut the cake at the fiftieth anniversary excursion to Little Widgham Wood in 1988.

Until the late 1970s the excursions had been well attended by students, but the numbers then declined for no obvious reason and there were no students attending by the mid 1980s. However, Whitehouse had always invited other interested bryologists to join the excursions and these continued to value the opportunity to bryologise together after the students stopped coming. In 1986 it was clear that there was no need to fit into the constraints of the student timetable, and the arrangements were adjusted. Excursions were retimed to start on Saturday mornings, with participants travelling by private car to meet at the chosen venue at 11 a.m. This allowed a wider range of sites to be visited, and the primary emphasis changed from teaching to recording. In 1987–89, for example, a special effort was made to visit a range of churchyards, whereas previously Trumpington was repeatedly visited to demonstrate the churchyard flora to students. After his retirement one of Harold Whitehouse's main projects was the stereo photography of bryophytes, and some excursions were arranged to venues where he might find species that he had not yet photographed. BBS members and others who attended the excursions at various times between the 1970s and the 1990s were **Marie Agneta Silvester Burton**, **George Bloom** (1916–2007), **Robert Alan Finch** (1939–2006), **Nicholas Graham Hodgetts**, **Nicholas Jardine**, **Richard Pearse Libbey** (1911–1987), **Angela Elizabeth Newton**, **Ronald Derek Porley** and **Philip Edward Stanley**. Others who travelled from further afield and were therefore less regular attenders included **Kenneth John Adams** (Essex), **John Campbell Gardiner** (1905–1989, London), **Philip Edgar Jackson** (1920–2000, Rutland), **Monica Dorothy Milnes-Smith** (1912–2003, London), **Alan Outen** (Bedfordshire), **Alex C. Smith** (1920–2007, Suffolk) and **Martin James Wigginton** (Northamptonshire).

### Other recording projects 1964–1999

As mentioned briefly above, a note on the surprising discovery by **John Michael Lock** of the calcifuge species *Hookeria lucens*, *Polytrichum commune*, *Sphagnum fimbriatum* and *Tetraphis pellucida* at Wicken Fen in 1963 was added to the 1964 flora at proof stage. Mike Lock graduated from Cambridge with a botany degree in 1963 but he then did a more adventurous PhD than many of his contemporaries, on 'Vegetation in relation to grazing and soils in the Queen Elizabeth National Park, Uganda'. In the course of this research, he established plots designed to exclude elephants, hippopotamuses and other large grazing animals. He also continued to study the development of the calcifuge flora at Wicken (Lock 1964, 1968, 1990), and many further records were made there by others on bryological excursions. There was particular interest in the flora of the 'Godwin Plots', experimental plots set up by Sir Harry Godwin in 1927 to study the effect of different cutting regimes on the fen vegetation (Friday *et al.* 1999). Whereas the calcifuge species could conceivably have been overlooked in some areas of the fen, it was clear that colonies of *Sphagnum* could not possibly have been present when Godwin and his successors were recording the vegetation of these areas in detail. **Alan Christopher Leslie** carried out a detailed survey of the bryophytes of Godwin plots 1–5 in June 1974, along with a more general survey of the calcifuge species on the Fen, while he was an undergraduate (Leslie 1974).

**Mark Oliver Hill** wrote to Harold Whitehouse in November 1964, at the start of his third undergraduate year in Cambridge, to say that he was interested in bryophytes and to ask whether he could help with any under-recorded areas of the county. He had already started to make a systematic record of the species he had seen in the county and when he left the University he put together the records he had made between 1963 and 1966 in a loose-leaf file (Hill 1967) which he sent to Whitehouse in April 1967. The covering letter explained that 'I have written them up as a private 'flora'; indeed I have almost written them in the form of a letter to you'. The manuscript (Figure 3.19) provides an independent view of the distribution and habitat of Cambridgeshire's species, for Hill explained that 'I disagree with a great deal that you say in your 1964 flora. In some cases I think that what you say is straightforwardly wrong ... Most of the emendations I propose are, however, additions rather than alterations'. Two of the taxa he collected were not sorted out until later, *Syntrichia virescens* (initially confused with *S. laevipila*) and *Didymodon umbrosus* (not recognised and published as a British plant until 1978). Hill did little recording in Cambridgeshire from 1967 until he returned to live in Cambridge in 1986, but then resumed his regular attendance on the bryological excursions.

The winter-flooded hollows in arable fields south of Cambridge were also the subject of special study. The initial interest in these followed the discovery of *Lythrum hyssopifolia* by Gigi Crompton in one such hollow in 1958; **David Edwin Coombe** (1927–1999), visiting the site shortly afterwards, found *Lythrum* in a second hollow growing with the liverworts *Riccia cavernosa*, *R. glauca* and (as it later transpired) *R. subbifurca*.

**Figure 3.19** Mark Hill's account of *Rhytidiadelphus triquetrus* in the manuscript summarising his early bryophyte records (Hill 1967). Department of Plant Sciences, Cambridge University.

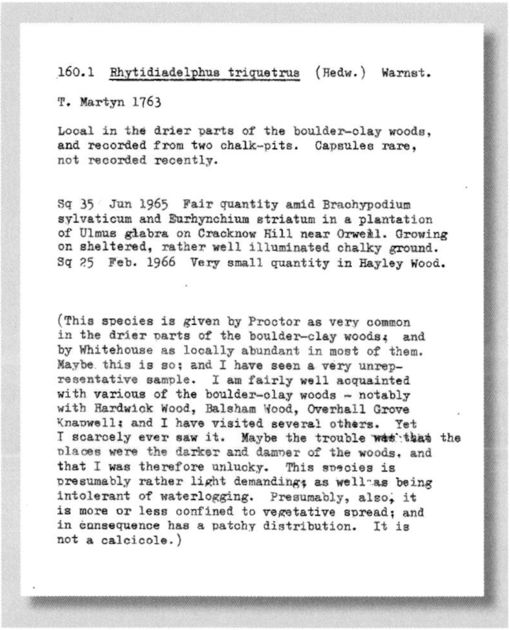

```
160.1  Rhytidiadelphus triquetrus  (Hedw.)  Warnst.

T. Martyn 1763

Local in the drier parts of the boulder-clay woods,
and recorded from two chalk-pits.  Capsules rare,
not recorded recently.


Sq 35  Jun 1965  Fair quantity amid Brachypodium
sylvaticum and Eurhynchium striatum in a plantation
of Ulmus glabra on Cracknow Hill near Orwell.  Growing
on sheltered, rather well illuminated chalky ground.
Sq 25  Feb. 1966  Very small quantity in Hayley Wood.


(This species is given by Proctor as very common
in the drier parts of the boulder-clay woods; and
by Whitehouse as locally abundant in most of them.
Maybe this is so; and I have seen a very unrep-
resentative sample.  I am fairly well acquainted
with various of the boulder-clay woods - notably
with Hardwick Wood, Balsham Wood, Overhall Grove
Knapwell; and I have visited several others.  Yet
I scarcely ever saw it.  Maybe the trouble was that the
places were the darker and damper of the woods, and
that I was therefore unlucky.  This species is
presumably rather light demanding; as well as being
intolerant of waterlogging.  Presumably, also, it
is more or less confined to vegetative spread; and
in consequence has a patchy distribution.  It is
not a calcicole.)
```

Interest in the hollows was renewed in 1978 when Alan Leslie discovered that *Lythrum hyssopifolia* was more widespread than had hitherto been realised, and Harold Whitehouse and Chris Preston continued this survey, finding many more *Lythrum* hollows and surveying their bryophytes during the few autumnal days or weeks between the harvesting and the ploughing of the fields (Preston & Whitehouse 1986b, Preston 1989). **Paul Adam**, who made a wide-ranging study of British saltmarshes for his PhD thesis, surveyed the vascular plants and bryophytes of the tiny 'Cambridgeshire saltmarsh' with **John Robert Akeroyd** and added two salt-tolerant bryophytes, *Hennediella heimii* and *Phascum cuspidatum* var. *piliferum*, to the county flora (Adam & Akeroyd 1978).

A checklist of the vascular plants and bryophytes of the county was published by Crompton & Whitehouse (1983), with an updated list of the 10-km squares from which all the species had been recorded. This included 47 liverworts (including four not seen after 1949), one extinct hornwort and 247 mosses (14 not seen after 1949). These totals included 10 liverworts and 27 mosses found in the county since the 1964 flora.

**Nicholas Graham Hodgetts** began recording bryophytes in the county in 1984, initially around his parents' home in Great Shelford. He had done his degree at Goldsmiths' College, London in 1978–81 but, although his initial interest was stimulated there, he did not start looking at bryophytes seriously until he worked as a botanical surveyor for Lincolnshire Wildlife Trust in 1982–83. By the time that he enrolled for the taxonomy MSc at Reading University, in 1984, he was a committed bryologist.

### Databasing the records

In 1984 the British Bryological Society (BBS) and the Biological Records Centre (BRC), based at Monks Wood near Huntingdon, were seeking financial support for the computerisation of the data collected since 1960 by the BBS Mapping Scheme in order to produce a national atlas of bryophytes. The Nature Conservancy Council was sympathetic, but also wary of supporting the computerisation of many records which were localised simply to a 10-km square. They did not feel that such records would provide the detailed localities which they needed for conservation purposes. They therefore agreed to join BRC in supporting the processing of localised records from particular counties. These records could be used to identify important sites for bryophytes in the county and would also contribute to the eventual atlas. Angela Newton was employed to work at BRC from January 1985 to work on this project. As she wrote, 'it seemed logical to start with Cambridgeshire, a vice-county with a long history of bryological recording and an enormous fund of advice and information in the person of Dr H.L.K. Whitehouse' (Newton 1986). She computerised records from the manuscripts described in our Bibliography as *Whitehouse diaries*, *Whitehouse site files*, *Whitehouse species file* and Hill (1967). These comprised all the main sources of data available to Whitehouse except for those records of common species collected by Bourne and others which had not been transferred to the species sheets. (We have digitised these records in preparing the current flora.) The records were input directly from the species sheets or, for less structured manuscripts, transferred to standard recording cards and input from these. The computerised records included details of locality, recorder and date but not details of habitat or presence of sporophytes, which were not then available as fields in the BRC database. Newton (1985, 1986) summarised the sites of bryological importance in a 'Bryophyte site register', based on the resulting database and also incorporating much information from Whitehouse's site files. These data were the basis for the Cambridgeshire records mapped in the first national bryophyte atlas (Hill *et al.* 1991–94).

Subsequent records from the county, including those from the bryophyte excursions, were compiled onto record cards as they were made and subsequently added in batches to the BRC database.

# Reflections on the history of recording

The history of bryophyte recording in the county is not only of intrinsic interest but also provides the essential background information which is needed for an informed comparison between the records from our survey and those we have inherited from our predecessors. It is perhaps too easy for a Cambridgeshire bryologist to emphasise the long history of bryophyte recording in the county and to gloss over the rather intermittent timing of the records made before the 20th century and the limited areas of the county which were surveyed by bryologists.

The sporadic nature of the early records is shown by the details of the published floras and checklists (Table 3.1), by the list of recorders who have discovered three or more species new to the county (Table 3.2) and by a histogram showing the number of species recorded as new to the county per decade (Figure 3.20). None of the major figures before the 20th century were specialist bryologists. Admittedly Vernon and Relhan, as well as studying flowering plants, had a specialist interest in cryptogams, including both bryophytes and lichens, as well as butterflies (Vernon) and fungi (Relhan). The Martyns quickly lost interest in fieldwork in the county and Henslow's interest in bryophytes was very much secondary to his interest in flowering plants.

The limited geographical range of the early records can be seen from Figure 3.21. As far as we can tell from the meagre evidence available, Vernon concentrated on Gamlingay. The fieldwork of the three professors, John Martyn, Thomas Martyn and Henslow, was tied in to their teaching and thus concentrated on sites around Cambridge, with Gamlingay again visited on occasion for its rich calcifuge flora. Only Relhan seems to have attempted to cover a wide range of sites in the county. Collections made by William Skrimshire (Wisbech), John Hemsted (Newmarket), Leonard Jenyns (Bottisham) and Frederick Brocas (Saffron Walden) provide useful if very limited sources of information for localities outside Cambridge. Hemsted is one of the more obscure characters in our story; we have few records made by him, and most of them are imprecisely localised.

**Table 3.1** The number of bryophyte species recorded from the county in published floras and checklists, and the number we regard as known from the county at the time of their publication, based on the records accepted for this flora. Infraspecific taxa have been disregarded.

| Publication | Number of species reported | | Accepted number of species recorded by this date | |
|---|---|---|---|---|
| | Mosses | Liverworts | Mosses | Liverworts |
| Ray (1660) | 4 | 1 | 1 | 0 |
| J. Martyn (1729b) | 27 | 5 | 33 | 4 |
| T. Martyn (1763) | 43 | 4 | 42 | 5 |
| Relhan (1785) | 58 | 8 | 51 | 8 |
| Relhan (1802) | 84 | 20 | 71 | 13 |
| Relhan (1820) | 105 | 23 | 80 | 15 |
| Henslow (1829) | 98 | 20 | 99 | 15 |
| Henslow (1835) | 97 | 22 | 102 | 18 |
| Rhodes (1911) | 115 | 21 | 128 | 21 |
| Proctor (1956) | 200 | 35 | 208 | 33 |
| Whitehouse (1964) | 224 | 38 | 234 | 40 |
| Crompton & Whitehouse (1983) | 247 | 48 | 255 | 45 |
| This flora | 287 | 54 | 287 | 54 |

**Table 3.2** Recorders who have added three or more species to the county flora, arranged in chronological order, with the years and number of their records. A record made jointly by two recorders has been included in both totals.

| Recorder | Dates of first records | Number of first records | Recorder | Dates of first records | Number of first records |
|---|---|---|---|---|---|
| J. Ray | 1660–1663 | 3 | T.G. Tutin | 1932, 1942–43 | 3 |
| W. Vernon | c. 1696 | 19 | H.L.K. Whitehouse | 1940–93 | 22 |
| J. Martyn | c. 1729 | 11 | E.F. Warburg | 1941–45, 1961–62 | 10 |
| T. Martyn | 1760–63 | 10 | M.C.F. Proctor | 1950–53, 1982 | 16 |
| R. Relhan | 1785–1820 | 38 | R.E. Parker | 1952–53 | 7 |
| W. Skrimshire | 1796–97 | 6 | C.C. Townsend | 1955–56 | 4 |
| J.S. Henslow | 1821–57 | 19 | B. Reeve | 1959 | 5 |
| L. Jenyns | 1824 | 4 | P.J. Bourne | 1960 | 5 |
| F.Y. Brocas | 1874 | 4 | S.J.P. Waters | 1961–65 | 4 |
| G.D. Haviland | 1878–81 | 5 | J.M. Lock | 1961–65, 1990 | 7 |
| J.J. Lister | 1878–81 | 4 | M.O. Hill | 1965–2018 | 18 |
| H.N. Dixon | 1882–83 | 5 | J.G. Duckett | 1966–68 | 3 |
| L.J. Sedgwick | 1904–05 | 4 | H.J.B. Birks | 1966–77 | 5 |
| P.G.M. Rhodes | 1905–09 | 8 | P. Adam | 1977 | 3 |
| R.S. Adamson | 1913 | 6 | C.R. Stevenson | 1988-2010 | 7 |
| P.W. Richards | 1927–49, 1986–88 | 30 | C.D. Preston | 1988–2017 | 13 |
| E.W. Jones | 1932–34 | 11 | | | |

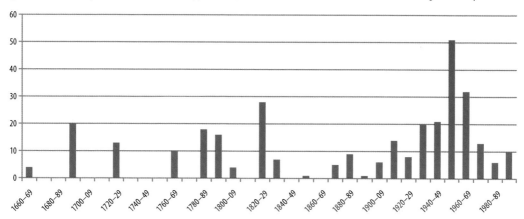

**Figure 3.20** Number of species found new to the county per decade, 1660–1999. The dates of the individual first records are given in the species' accounts.

It was only with the arrival of Paul Richards in Cambridge in 1927 that records began to be collected systematically by a specialist bryologist; after his departure in 1949 Michael Proctor and Harold Whitehouse were able to take over, with Whitehouse continuing as an active resident bryologist until the end of the century. We therefore have a good sequence of records made in the second half of the 20th century from many of the bryologically interesting sites in the county (Figure 3.22). However, the only concerted attempt to cover those areas which lacked such hotspots, and in particular the uninviting arable expanses of Fenland, was made between 1959 and 1962 in order to provide data for the 1964 flora, with Philip Bourne's fieldwork carrying on until 1963.

One distinctive feature of the bryological exploration of the county is the contribution made in the 19th and 20th centuries by numerous able botanists who lived in Cambridge for a few years while attending the University. We have attempted to provide some brief details of the later lives of those who contributed records before 1950 and then moved on. We are conscious that we have done scant justice to the many who attended Whitehouse's excursions after 1950 and subsequently became distinguished botanists, but to have dealt with them even briefly would have meant extending this chapter to an even more inordinate length. It is nevertheless apparent from our research that in most cases those who have contributed botanical records were people who had a well-developed interest in natural history when they arrived in Cambridge as freshmen. Paul Richards, exceptionally, managed to make very good progress with bryophytes during his schooldays. Those who had tried rather less successfully to tackle bryophytes, like Eustace Jones and Harold Whitehouse, were perhaps more typical, and there were others who were already interested in natural history when they arrived at university but were introduced to bryophytes there. However, there is surprisingly little evidence of people being inspired to take up natural history from scratch during their period at Cambridge. In most cases the University provided an environment in which they were able to develop an existing interest, often, one suspects, by contacts with academic staff or fellow students made outside the formal lectures and practical classes.

Another feature of the Cambridgeshire bryophyte records is that virtually all are localised and dated to at least a year. Even when the aim of the recording was to provide records for the lists of 10-km squares in the 1964 flora, Harold Whitehouse always asked his recorders for the precise localities in which their collections were made, and ensured that these details were preserved in his records. He never engaged in or promoted 'square-bashing', the collection of records localised only to a 10-km grid square. Significantly, the only such records in our database are a few made in 1959 on the Wisbech meeting organised by the Botanical Society of the British Isles. Furthermore, Whitehouse normally noted all the species seen during the excursions he led, rather than simply recording additions to the existing site list. This has given us a database of localised and precisely dated records in which common species are as well recorded as rare ones, and thus one which is particularly amenable to statistical analysis.

**Figure 3.21** The distribution of sites in which bryophytes were recorded by (a) Ray and Vernon, (b) John and Thomas Martyn, (c) Richard Relhan and his contemporaries, (d) J.S. Henslow and his contemporaries. Records are mapped in 5-km squares; sites simply repeated from earlier authors are omitted.

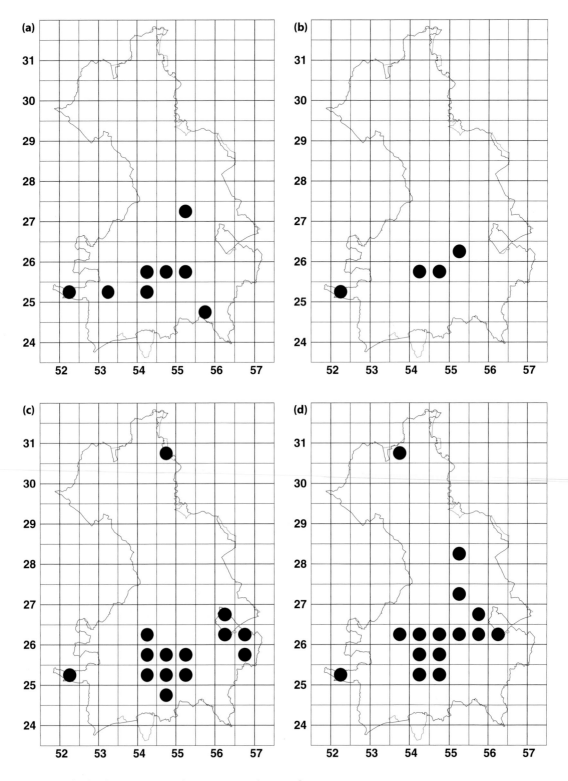

**Figure 3.22** The 5-km squares in Cambridgeshire visited by Cambridge bryophyte excursions, (a) 1938–1959, (b) 1960–1979, (c) 1980–1999, (d) 2000–18. Symbols of increasing size indicate 1, 2–5, 6–9 and 10 or more visits during the period in question. Details of excursions between 1938 and 1979 are taken from a summary drawn up by Harold Whitehouse (*Whitehouse site files*); for later excursions, details are taken from the BBS database.

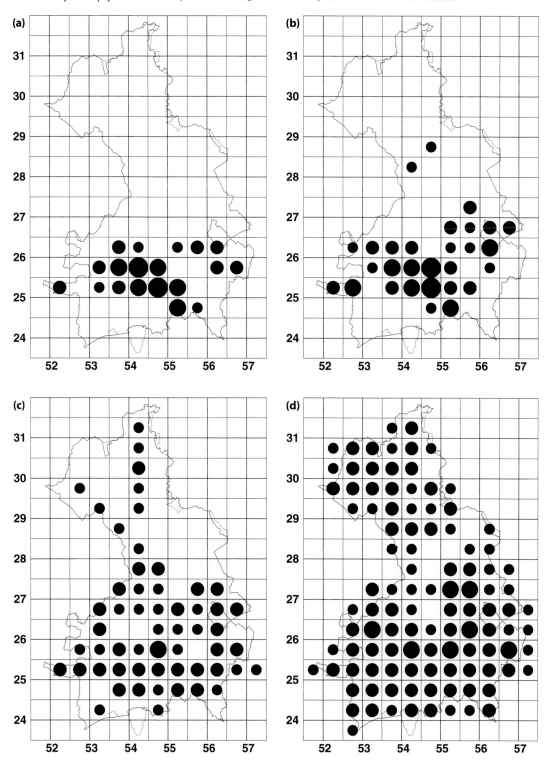

# 4

# The recent survey, 2000–2018

In January 2000, following the death of Harold Whitehouse, we had to consider plans for recording bryophytes in the county. M.O.H. had thought for some years that the Cambridgeshire bryologists needed to focus on a project, and suggested a new survey of the county. We published plans for this in *Nature in Cambridgeshire* (Preston & Hill 2000b). At this stage the project was envisaged as a 10-year survey of the 5 × 5 km squares of the county. We included maps illustrating the progress of the survey with the annual bryophyte records (Preston & Hill 2001–09). The final 5-km squares were surveyed, as planned, in December 2009 (Preston & Hill 2010). However, by then we had begun to think that we had sufficient records that maps of species summarised by 2 × 2 km squares (tetrads) might be more informative.

Although the fieldwork had been completed on time, we did not succeed in writing up the flora immediately afterwards. The closure of Monks Wood Experimental Station in 2008 was disruptive, and by the time that we had settled down to a life of weekly commuting to our new workplace, at Wallingford in Oxfordshire, our botanical lives were dominated by our contributions to the national bryophyte atlas (Blockeel *et al.* 2014) and to various other projects. It is only now that we are both retired that we have been able to complete the flora.

The field survey was the main focus of the Cambridgeshire Bryophyte Group, an informal local group of the British Bryological Society (Figures 4.1, 4.2). The bryophyte excursions are now run by this group; they were organised by C.D.P. from 2000 to 2009 and have been led by M.O.H. from 2010 onwards. Since

**Figure 4.1** The 70th anniversary Cambridge Bryological excursion, Little Widgham Wood, 10 February 2008. Left to right, Tom Charman, Steve Hartley, Pete Michna, Alison Jukes, Jo Denyer, Mark Hill, Oliver Rackham, Robin Stevenson, Jonathan Graham, Simon Damant, Chris Preston, Nick Jardine. Photo: Richard Fisk.

**Figure 4.2** Bryologists at Scolding Drove, Thorney, 2 April 2016. Left to right, Jonathan Shanklin, Nick Jardine, Mark Hill (kneeling), Chris Preston, Steve Hartley, Jonathan Graham, Mick Burton, Lewis Saunders. Photo: Robin Stevenson.

2000 we have met fortnightly between September/October and March/April. We have usually met at a church, a convenient rendezvous and one where latecomers have no difficulty in finding the party, before going on to other sites. We concentrated almost exclusively on Cambridgeshire until 2009, but thereafter we held more meetings outside the county. At the outset of our survey we aimed for 'a fairly even balance of recording' between the different areas of the county and the areas we visited are mapped in Figure 3.22. Numerous people have helped us record on the excursions. We have listed those people who have attended frequently while they have lived in or near Cambridgeshire in the List of Recorders (Appendix 4).

Although many people have joined us on bryophyte excursions, few have recorded bryophytes independently in the county. We have ourselves undertaken additional fieldwork for the flora, together and separately. Jonathan Graham and Robin Stevenson have recorded tetrads in the north of the county and have helped to ensure that we have adequate knowledge of arable Fenland. In recent years Jonathan Shanklin has recorded liverworts systematically. As he has been visiting most of the county's tetrads in recent years to record flowering plants, this means that our maps for the commoner liverworts are more complete than those for the commoner mosses.

We have included in the records on which this flora is based the result of a few special surveys. The most remarkable of these is the study of both derelict and working orchards by Robin Stevenson (Lush *et al.* 2009, Stevenson 2006, Stevenson & Rowntree 2009, Stevenson *et al.* 2017). He has recorded the bryophytes on a sample of individual trees in many orchards. We have records from 951 apple trees and 173 pears surveyed in our county between 2006 and 2013, and we have often cited these in the accounts of epiphytic species. In addition to these 1124 trees in Cambridgeshire, Robin has recorded many more orchard trees in Norfolk.

A Survey of the Bryophytes of Arable Land (SBAL) was organised by the British Bryological Society in 2001–05, a project designed to document the flora of individual fields (Preston *et al.* 2010; Figure 4.3). We recorded 76 fields in Cambridgeshire, complete with some environmental readings including pH, and we have also cited this dataset in the species accounts.

We are aware of very few commissioned vegetation surveys which have included bryophytes, a notable exception being a survey of the wetland vegetation of Chippenham Fen NNR (Smith & Harding 2001). Jonathan Graham was commissioned to survey the bryophytes of Cherry Hinton chalk pit before and after the major management works in 2008–9 and 2012 (Graham 2009a, 2009b, 2012), the Cambridge Botanic Garden in 2010–11 (Graham 2011) and Gray's Moor Pit in 2013 (Graham 2013). Both Jonathan Graham and Owen Mountford have kept their eyes open for aquatic bryophytes, especially *Riccia fluitans* and *Ricciocarpos natans*, during the fieldwork for their forthcoming Fenland Flora (which covers vascular plants in the whole Fenland basin, not just vc 29). Their records have certainly improved our knowledge of these species, which cannot be surveyed adequately in the bryophyte season.

Our field records were normally noted on recording cards. From 2000 until 2009 we retained these cards, if necessary making neat copies of them when we returned from the field (Figure 4.4). The records were input at intervals from these cards into the BBS database held by the Biological Records Centre (BRC)

**Figure 4.3** Mark Hill, Jonathan Graham and Chris Preston starting work on the BBS Survey of the Bryophytes of Arable Land in a set-aside field near Boxworth, November 2001. Photo: Gill Stevens.

**Figure 4.4** One of the recording cards compiled on the 70th anniversary excursion to Little Widgham Wood, 10 February 2008. Biological Records Centre, Centre for Ecology and Hydrology.

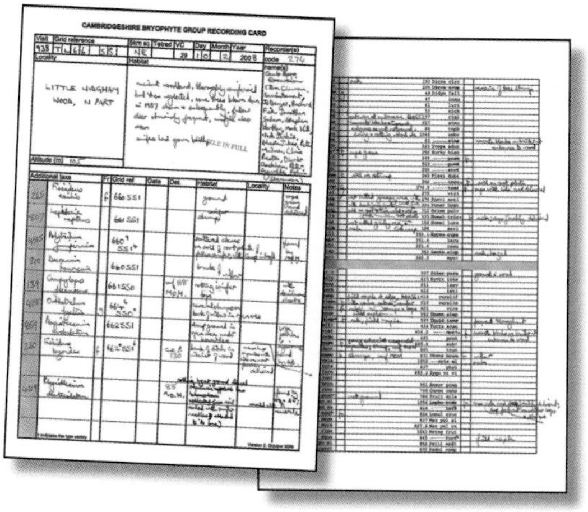

at the Centre for Ecology and Hydrology, Wallingford. The cards are deposited in the BRC archive (C.D.P. holds photocopies). Subsequently we have digitised the records immediately after we have made them and have not retained the original field cards. Only time will tell whether we, or our successors, will regret the absence of a paper copy of these records. We have made notes on the habitat of individual species and the presence of sporophytes and included these details with the digitised records. The database is therefore in effect an electronic notebook which we have used to write the species accounts, and it represents the permanent record of the observations on which they are based. We have been most assiduous in making notes on the habitats of the scarcer and more specialised species, and we cannot (for example) produce an adequate list of the trees on which common and generalist bryophytes such as *Brachythecium rutabulum* grow. This gap in the information available to us might best have been filled by a quadrat-based survey of common habitats.

In comparing our records with those made in the county between 1660 and 1999, we have been able to make use of the records from the database initially digitised by Angela Newton and also held in the database at BRC (see Chapter 3). As these records were input when the database structure was simpler, we have had to consult the original manuscript sources (listed in the Bibliography) or the record cards at BRC for habitat details of these earlier records.

The closing date for the records from the recent survey was 10 March 2018. However, the division of species into habitat clusters (Chapter 6) was based on the records available by January 2016 and most of the habitat statistics (including, for example, the data on the hosts of epiphytic species) were calculated from the records collected by 30 April 2017.

# Basic statistics on bryophytes and bryophyte recording

The bryophyte records from the county, derived from the historic sources outlined in Chapter 3, and the records from the recent survey, described in Chapter 4, are held in the British Bryological Society's database, managed at the Biological Records Centre, Wallingford. This flora is based on 59,422 records from Cambridgeshire (excluding superseded, doubtful and erroneous records). Some aspects of these records are discussed in this chapter.

## Distribution of records over time

Of the 59,422 records, 36,713 (62% of the total) were made during the recent survey and the remaining 22,709 (38%) are earlier observations. Of the historic records, only 2205 were made between 1660 and 1949, compared to 10,103 between 1950 and 1964 and 10,401 between 1965 and 1999.

The 2000s were the most active period of recording (Figure 5.1). C.D.P. was especially active at that time. He made 31% of the records, either solo (20%) or with one or two other recorders (11%). There is rather little variation in the number of species recorded per decade since 1950 (Figure 5.2). In the 1960s 239 species were found, almost equal to the 242 found in the 2010s. Given the large increase in epiphytes since 1980, this high early value suggests that other habitats were then richer.

The number of new species added to the county list since Whitehouse's 1964 flora has averaged 1.2 per annum, excluding those which came to light as a result of the study of historic herbarium specimens. This rate of addition has not decreased in recent years, and the average for the recent survey period (2000–18) is slightly higher, at 1.4 species per annum.

In most habitats bryology is only feasible in Cambridgeshire in the winter months; conditions are too dry and the vegetation is too dominated by flowering plants in the summer. Most of our records (97%) can be dated to a month, and 80% of these have been made between October and March, with 8% in April and only 12% between May and September. February is the peak month, with 16.5% of the records, and bryologists have been least active in July and August, which each have less than 2% of the dateable records.

## Spatial spread of records

We have historic (pre-2000) records from 114 of the county's 134 quadrants and from 370 of the county's 665 tetrads. In the recent survey, from 2000 onwards, we have recorded in all quadrants and in 558 tetrads. The number of records from these squares is shown in Figure 5.3. The number of records reflects both the effort spent recording in the square and the species-richness of the square.

**Figure 5.1** Numbers of records made in each decade during the period 1927–2017.

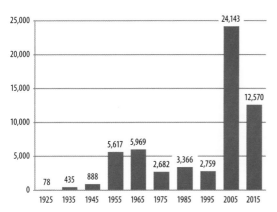

**Figure 5.2** Numbers of species found per decade during the period 1927–2017.

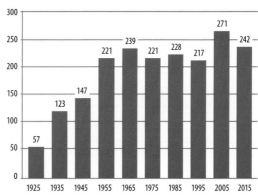

**Figure 5.3** The number of records available from the quadrants and tetrads of Cambridgeshire. (a) Quadrants, 1660–1999, (b) Quadrants, 2000–18, (c) Tetrads, 1660–1999, (d) Tetrads, 2000–18. Symbols of increasing size indicate 1–99, 100–199, 200–299, 300–599, 600–999 and 1000 or more records on the quadrant maps and 1–9, 10–49, 50–99, 100–499 and 500 or more on the tetrad maps.

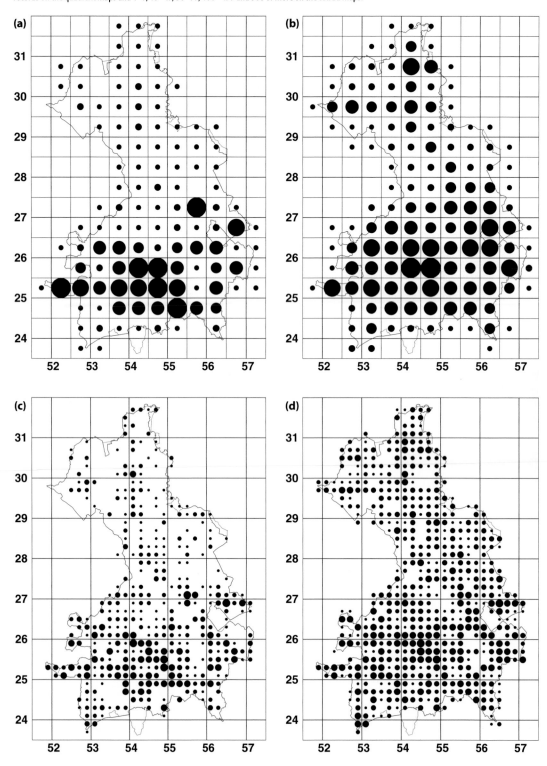

In the past, there was a strong bias against Fenland recording, which we attempted to redress during the period 2000–17. Of the 665 tetrads in the county, 324 have an average altitude less than 5 m. These tetrads are the real Fenland (Figure 5.4). Of the remaining tetrads, 'Cambridge' tetrads are defined as those in an 8-km square centred on Cambridge (Hill 2016). The 'Upland' tetrads are the rest. A visit was defined as a unique combination (Hectad, Quadrant, Date), or for pre-1950 records (Hectad, Quadrant, Year). In the analysis of tetrads, we have excluded visits on which less than 10 species were recorded in a given tetrad. We were broadly successful in levelling out the proportion of tetrads visited, except for Cambridge, which was much more intensely recorded in both time periods (Table 5.1). The upland tetrads were more frequently revisited than those in Fenland, and in the post-2000 period, the difference was about 30%. The average number of species per visit in the upland tetrads was also higher by 36%.

Bringing the data together to calculate species richness per tetrad we find that in the period 2000–17 there were on average 60% more species recorded per tetrad in the uplands than in Fenland (Table 5.2). Given that an upland visit produced on average 36% more species than a Fenland visit, and that 3% more

**Table 5.1** Visits to Cambridge, Fenland and Upland tetrads before and after 2000; revisits are the average number of visits to those tetrads which received at least one visit.

| Area | Tetrad count | Proportion visited | | Mean count per visit | | Revisits | |
|---|---|---|---|---|---|---|---|
| | | 1927–99 | 2000–17 | 1927–99 | 2000–17 | 1927–99 | 2000–17 |
| Cambridge | 16 | 56% | 100% | 24.4 | 28.8 | 8.4 | 6.5 |
| Fenland | 324 | 14% | 62% | 21.4 | 24.3 | 1.7 | 1.6 |
| Upland | 325 | 40% | 64% | 24.2 | 33.0 | 2.6 | 2.1 |
| Total | 665 | 28% | 64% | 23.2 | 29.2 | 2.7 | 2.0 |

**Table 5.2** Species totals and species density in tetrads; average species counts are calculated relative to all tetrads in the county.

| Area | Tetrad count | Tetrad species counts | | | Average species counts | | |
|---|---|---|---|---|---|---|---|
| | | 1927–99 | 2000–17 | All time | 1927–99 | 2000–17 | All time |
| Cambridge | 16 | 680 | 1180 | 1343 | 42.5 | 73.8 | 83.9 |
| Fenland | 324 | 1773 | 6539 | 7253 | 5.5 | 20.2 | 22.4 |
| Upland | 325 | 5829 | 10,515 | 12,692 | 17.9 | 32.4 | 39.1 |
| Total | 665 | 8282 | 18,234 | 21,288 | 12.5 | 27.4 | 32.0 |

**Figure 5.4** A relatively varied Fenland tetrad on the county boundary at Lady Nunn's Old Eau, TF31W, November 2016. Photo: Robin Stevenson.

tetrads were recorded in the uplands than in Fenland, this means that about 15% of the difference (1.60/1.36 - 0.03) is attributable to the combination of more uniform terrain and less intense revisiting in Fenland.

Total numbers of records are higher in northern Fenland compared with southern Fenland (Figure 5.3), because of the presence of commercial orchards and some remaining disused orchards around Wisbech and of disused brickpits near Whittlesey. Fenland orchards were hardly surveyed before 2000. At that time, recording in Fenland concentrated on Wicken Fen.

## Recorders

Almost half the records in the database (46%) have been made on the bryological excursions run by the Botany School and later as a local group of the BBS. The proportion is lower for pre-2000 records (35%) than for records made in the recent survey (53%). Chris Preston, Harold Whitehouse, Jonathan Shanklin, Philip Bourne, Mark Hill, Jonathan Graham, Robin Stevenson, Nick Hodgetts and Paul Richards (in that order) contributed most records as individuals, and they are the only bryologists to have made more than 500 records in the county. Unlike other bryologists, both Nick Hodgetts and Jonathan Shanklin have included records made on bryological excursions amongst their personal records, leading to some duplication in the database. Cliff Townsend, Alan Leslie, Michael Proctor, 'Heff' Warburg, John Birks, Eustace Jones, Bob Finch and Mike Lock contributed between 200 and 499; except for Bob Finch, almost all of their records were made before 2000.

As we mention in Chapter 4, one of our most active recent recorders, Jonathan Shanklin, has concentrated on liverworts. He has recorded them in 403 tetrads including 78 in which he was the sole recent recorder. Because his lists were usually only of liverworts, they were short, and most of them were not included in the data analysed for Tables 5.1 and 5.2. Specifically, he made 793 tetrad records of species not found there by other recorders. Of these, 745 were liverworts. His liverwort tetrad records are 39% of all post-1999 tetrad liverwort records. We have had to take this bias into account when analysing the Cambridgeshire data.

## Length of lists of species from sites

Within quadrants, each record was ascribed to a site, standardised to allow repeat visits to be identified. Thus 'Hayley Wood' and 'Hayley Wood SSSI' are recognised as a single site, which also includes all more detailed localities such as 'Hayley Wood, North Quarter'. Churchyards were all signified by a name including 'church', such as 'Ashley church E'. For this churchyard, two sites had to be recognised, one in the eastern quadrant TL66SE and 'Ashley church W' in TL76SW. Cemeteries were likewise given a name including 'cemetery'. Some other sites refer to individual features such as chalk pits, but the majority were more generic. Sites in Cambridge other than Addenbrooke's, the Botanic Garden, churches, cemeteries and woods were distinguished by quadrant and tetrad. Thus 'Cambridge W (N)' is in TL45NW tetrad N, including Coe Fen and Newnham, and received 62 visits.

With sites reckoned in this way, there were 707 sites. These received 4202 site visits, of which 1354 had a list length of one, where 'list length' is defined as the number of distinct species on a site visit. Longer list lengths were progressively less frequent (Figure 5.5) and the longest list was 75 species from Wimpole Hall in 2014.

## Precision of records

A grid reference is now regarded as an essential component of a bryological record. Harold Whitehouse began to use grid references soon after he started his East Anglian bryophyte diaries in 1950. On one early occasion, when listing species from the Gog Magog Hills on 11 November 1950, he used the Cassini grid, a military grid which had been widely used during the Second World War. It is not absolutely clear from the notebooks when he moved on to the current National Grid, but he had certainly done so by February 1952. Records made before 1950, and those made during the 1950s by those recorders who had not yet adopted the grid, have been gridded retrospectively to hectad or, if the details of the original record allow it, to a smaller grid square. Since 1960 almost all records have had grid references supplied by the original recorder.

The precision of records has generally increased. Almost all Cambridgeshire records have been localised to the quadrant scale, so that the 10-km square (hectad) precision has hardly been used (Figure 5.6). Records localised only to quadrants have gradually disappeared. There were no such records in the 2010s. In the same period there were only 216 records localised to tetrad. The monad had become the standard recording unit for field records, with 69% of records being made at that scale. In the 1960s and the 1980s more than half the records were at 100 m resolution, and in the 2000s just under half (49.6%). In the 1960s most of P.J. Bourne's collections were precisely localised, and churchyards, which are small and easily localised, were visited in the 1980s. The fall in the precision of recording in the 2010s is unexpected.

## Number of species

There are records of 341 species from Cambridgeshire: one extinct hornwort, 53 liverworts (including 15 which were last seen before 2000) and 287 mosses (including 41 last seen before 2000).

## Species counts per quadrant

Species frequency may be calculated as the count of quadrants in which they are recorded in the database. The median quadrant count is 14, about 10% of the total, which is the frequency of the five mosses *Bryum algovicum*, *Cirriphyllum crassinervium*, *Ephemerum minutissimum*, *Hypnum jutlandicum* and *Seligeria calycina*. These are by definition uncommon in the county. Above 50 out of the 134 quadrants, the distribution of frequencies is irregular but fairly even (Figure 5.7). Species with lower frequency are more numerous, with 48 species having been found in only a single quadrant. At the other end of the scale, there are 20 species that have been found in at least 120 quadrants (Table 5.3). These ubiquitous plants are all mosses, and

**Figure 5.5** Numbers of lists in relation to list length.

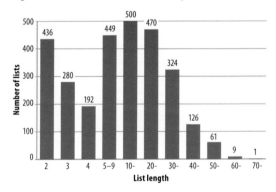

**Figure 5.6** Precision of records in decades from 1920s to 2010s; the 28 records purporting to be with 1 m precision have been included in the 10 m category. A tetrad is a 2-km square and a quadrant is a 5-km square.

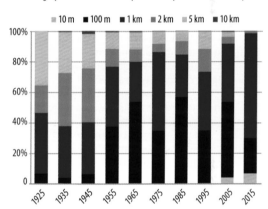

**Figure 5.7** Numbers of species in categories of quadrant frequency; the maximum quadrant frequency is 132 out of 134 quadrants.

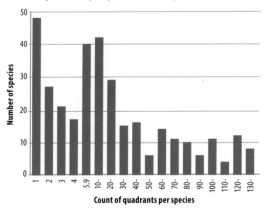

**Table 5.3** Species found in 120 or more of the 134 quadrants.

| Species | Quadrants | Species | Quadrants |
|---|---|---|---|
| Amblystegium serpens | 130 | Grimmia pulvinata | 124 |
| Barbula convoluta | 125 | Hypnum cupressiforme | 128 |
| Barbula unguiculata | 132 | Kindbergia praelonga | 132 |
| Brachythecium rutabulum | 132 | Orthotrichum diaphanum | 130 |
| Bryum argenteum | 130 | Oxyrrhynchium hians | 128 |
| Bryum capillare | 131 | Phascum cuspidatum | 126 |
| Bryum dichotomum | 131 | Pseudocrossidium hornschuchianum | 122 |
| Bryum rubens | 124 | Rhynchostegium confertum | 128 |
| Ceratodon purpureus | 126 | Syntrichia montana | 120 |
| Funaria hygrometrica | 127 | Tortula muralis | 127 |

although they have distinct habitats, suitable substrates are found almost everywhere: in hedgerows, on tracks, on concrete and in arable fields.

## Species-richness maps

The numbers of species recorded in the county's quadrants before 2000 are compared in Figure 5.8 to the totals seen in the recent survey. The more even coverage of the county in recent years is reflected in the species totals. Fewer species have been recorded since 2000 in some quadrants that include sites which were often visited in the 20th century; examples are TL45SE (Gog Magog Hills, Roman Road), 54NW (Hildersham Hall, Pampisford Hall) and 55SW (Fleam Dyke, Worsted Lodge). The fall in records in the quadrants is not simply a reflection of the reduced concentration of effort in these areas in the 21st century, but it also reflects the genuine changes in species-richness of the chalkland sites which are discussed in Chapter 11.

The numbers of mosses and liverworts recorded in the county's tetrads are shown in Figure 5.9. The richest tetrads for liverworts are TL25F (Great Heath Plantation), TL25L (Gamlingay Wood), TL25W (Hayley Wood), TL45E (Madingley Wood), TL45N (S. Cambridge, including the Botanic Garden), TL56G (Anglesey Abbey) and TL66P (Chippenham Fen). The most striking feature of this map, however, is the scarcity of liverworts in Fenland, something that will not surprise those who have recorded in these tetrads.

## Reproduction of species: sporophytes and vegetative propagules

Sporophytes have been seen on approximately half of the liverwort species known from the county, and two-thirds of the mosses (Table 5.4). Specialised vegetative propagules (deciduous leaves, bulbils, gemmae, tubers) are more frequently present in the liverwort species (35%) than the mosses (21%). These figures are certainly under-estimates, as propagules may not have been noted on species which were recorded long ago, or on only a few occasions, or even on common species if propagules (such as tubers) occur only occasionally and have to be searched for carefully. In addition, many species reproduce vegetatively by methods which are not included in the figures in Table 5.4, such as the protonemal gemmae of mosses or the fragmentation of fragile leaves.

There are 13 extant species (one liverwort, 12 mosses) which were known to fruit before 2000 but which have not been seen with capsules in the recent survey. Most of these are rare, and our failure to refind fruiting material may just be a matter of chance, but there are a few pleurocarps where we suspect, from the older fruiting records, that fruiting was more frequent in the 19th and early 20th centuries than it is today. The best examples are *Ctenidium molluscum* and *Homalothecium lutescens* (see species accounts). Early collectors showed a greater preference for fruiting plants than their modern counterparts, so the proportion of fruiting plants in herbarium collections is not a reliable indication of the proportion in the wild. However, the fact that the early bryologists were able to collect fruiting specimens of species which have not been seen with sporophytes in the last 90 years does suggest a decline in the frequency of fruiting plants.

**Table 5.4** Number of species on which sporophytes (fruits) and specialised vegetative propagules (deciduous leaves, bulbils, gemmae, tubers) have been recorded in Cambridgeshire.

| | Hornworts and liverworts | | Mosses | | |
| --- | --- | --- | --- | --- | --- |
| | Fruits recorded | Fruits not recorded | Fruits recorded | Fruits not recorded | Total |
| **Propagules recorded** | 9 | 10 | 32 | 27 | 78 |
| **Propagules not recorded** | 19 | 16 | 157 | 71 | 263 |
| **Total** | 28 | 26 | 189 | 98 | 341 |

**Figure 5.8** The number of species recorded from the quadrants of Cambridgeshire (a) between 1660 and 1999, (b) in the recent survey, 2000–18.

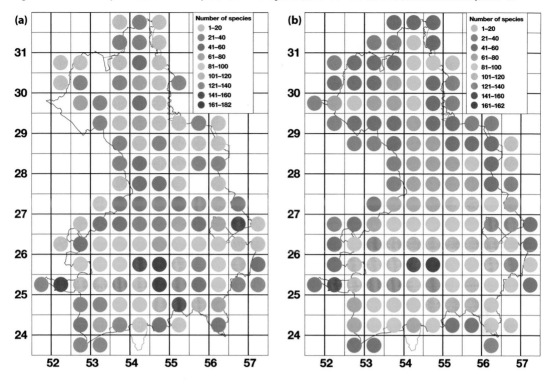

**Figure 5.9** The number of species recorded from the tetrads of Cambridgeshire in the recent survey, 2000–18 (a) liverworts, (b) mosses.

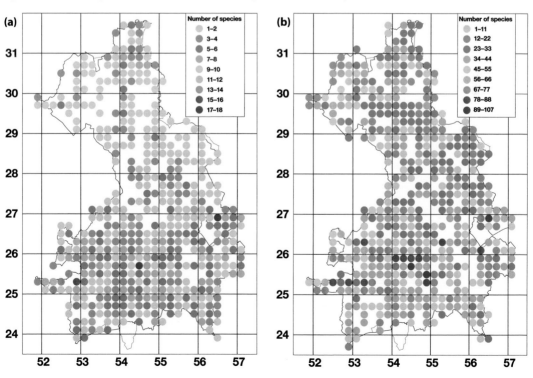

# 6

# Clustering species into habitat groups

For the purpose of analysis, we have clustered the species into groups. For this we used records made from 1920 onwards and we carried out the clustering in 2016, two years before we finished recording. All records were allocated to a habitat, using a list of habitats based on the EUNIS habitat classes employed by Hill *et al.* (2007) with some additional broad categories (Churches and chapels, Cemeteries, Towns, Villages, Open country). Clustering was based on summarised species lists for habitats on site visits, with a visit defined as a unique combination of hectad, quadrant (5 × 5 km square) and date. Lists from a site may be from several habitats. For example, in March 2000 we visited Foul Anchor in the extreme north of the county, recording nine ruderals and *Hennediella heimii* in the 'Saltmarsh', seven common pleurocarps plus *Phascum cuspidatum* and *Tortula muralis* on the sea wall (habitat classified as 'Open country') and 10 common species in the hamlet (habitat classified as 'Village'). *Phascum cuspidatum* was present in all these habitats and was therefore accorded three entries, one for each habitat on the visit. For clustering species, only those visits with at least 10 species were included. The Foul Anchor visit produced 26 species overall and therefore qualified comfortably. Note that the limit of 10 applied to the visit, not the habitat, so that the nine species from the sea wall were counted.

The resulting dataset comprised 36,324 records. The species were clustered into 10 groups by perpendicular spherical k-means using the program Spherikm (Hill *et al.* 2013). For the purposes of the analysis, varieties were omitted, except for *Syntrichia ruralis* var. *ruraliformis* and var. *ruralis*. The number of clusters was selected by trial and error as the minimum that could distinguish fairly obvious major groups. Fifteen species were not classified by the computer program because they were present only in short lists or were discovered after the clustering was made. These were added to the following clusters: Calcicole *Plasteurhynchium striatulum, Rhytidium rugosum, Scleropodium touretii*; Ruderal *Lophozia excisa*; Acid and Fen *Bryum bornholmense, Calliergon giganteum, Cephaloziella rubella, Dicranella cerviculata, Ephemerum cohaerens, Palustriella falcata, Preissia quadrata*; Wood *Plagiothecium laetum*; and Epiphyte *Orthotrichum pumilum, O. obtusifolium, Metzgeria consanguinea*. The long-extinct species from Gamlingay and the Cambridge 'moors' were all assigned to Acid and Fen. *Weissia longifolia* var. *longifolia* was separated from var. *angustifolia* and ascribed to the Arable cluster. In 2016 the database contained many fen records of *Plagiomnium affine*, which we have subsequently deleted. *P. affine* has accordingly been moved to the Common cluster, which was the next best fit (though a very poor one; its fit to the Shade cluster was almost equally good). Finally *Bryum archangelicum* was moved to the Ruderal cluster, as all its occurrences were in short lists except for a single one in Cherry Hinton chalk pit.

With these adjustments, the composition of the groups is summarised in Table 6.1. The full lists for the clusters are given in the following chapters (as indicated in the table). Most of the clusters consist of habitat specialists, found in one habitat or in a closely related group of habitats, such as the Arable,

**Table 6.1** Cambridgeshire species clusters, with numbers of species in each cluster and their mean frequency in quadrants for species recorded in the recent survey; key species are those most typical of the cluster.

| No. | Cluster name | Key species | Count | Not seen since 1999 | Mean frequency (%) 2000 onwards | Chapter with further details |
|-----|--------------|-------------|-------|---------------------|--------------------------------|------------------------------|
| 1 | Arable | *Phascum cuspidatum* | 23 | 2 | 30.9 | 12 |
| 2 | Ruderal | *Barbula unguiculata* | 25 | 2 | 49.2 | 14 |
| 3 | Calcicole | *Homalothecium lutescens* | 51 | 9 | 8.9 | 11 |
| 4 | Built | *Grimmia pulvinata* | 31 | 0 | 40.0 | 14 |
| 5 | Water | *Leptodictyum riparium* | 31 | 3 | 15.6 | 16 |
| 6 | Shade | *Fissidens taxifolius* | 13 | 1 | 39.5 | 8 |
| 7 | Common | *Brachythecium rutabulum* | 16 | 0 | 72.9 | 14 |
| 8 | Epiphyte | *Orthotrichum affine* | 34 | 0 | 25.0 | 15 |
| 9 | Acid & Fen | *Dicranum scoparium* | 75 | 32 | 4.1 | 10 |
| 10 | Woodland | *Mnium hornum* | 41 | 7 | 14.8 | 8 |

Calcicole and Woodland clusters. The Ruderal and Shade clusters are made up of species which are found in a wider range of disturbed and shaded sites, respectively, and the Common cluster includes the species with the widest ecological range in the county. A striking and somewhat unsatisfactory cluster is 'Acid and Fen', which is the largest cluster and has on average the rarest species. This came about because of the temporary acidification of the surface peat at Wicken Fen, which was invaded by calcifuge species, some of which were found otherwise only in acid microhabitats in ancient woods. The clustering based on species lists could not distinguish clearly between genuine fen species and calcifuges. They have been divided on the basis of Ellenberg R values (Hill *et al.* 2007), as described in Chapter 10. All the clusters reflect occurrence in the habitats currently available in Cambridgeshire, and we would not expect to obtain the same clusters in other counties with different climate, topography or soils.

A few very rare species were misclassified by the process described above. *Plagiochila porelloides* and *Plagiomnium cuspidatum*, both calcicoles in the Cambridgeshire context, were ascribed to the Built and Common clusters. *Bryum donianum* and *Hennediella stanfordensis*, waterside species, were ascribed to the Epiphyte and Shade clusters. *Pleuridium acuminatum*, a calcifuge, was ascribed to the Shade cluster. *Thuidium assimile* has been found in three lawns and a disused gravel pit. It was included in the Shade cluster but grew where well illuminated. Elsewhere in Britain it is a calcicole, but its Cambridgeshire records hardly show this. Finally, *Hedwigia ciliata sens. lat.* was assigned to the Water cluster because it was found as a casual in two single tufts on elder and wood near water. These misclassifications have not been reassigned, as they make almost no difference to the statistics.

## Description of clusters

It is useful to compare the clusters by relating their species to the northing (the northern component of the Ordnance Survey grid reference) and the altitude of their sites, not because these factors directly affect the flora but because of their correlation with geology and land-use. Site altitude was estimated by averaging mean altitudes of the monads recorded within them, using the dataset that underlay the altitude profiles in the national bryophyte atlas (Blockeel *et al.* 2014). Clusters can be arranged on these axes by taking the mean altitude and northing for the sites where their members occur (Figure 6.1). The following remarks apply to the 135 species found in at least 30 sites.

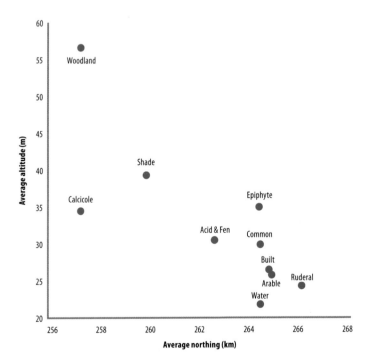

**Figure 6.1** Species clusters in relation to northing and altitude. The x-axis shows the average northing of records according to the Ordnance Survey national grid; the y-axis shows their average altitude.

The **Arable cluster** is an easily recognisable group, though most of the species except for *Bryum violaceum* also occur in other habitats. The two commonest are *Bryum rubens* and *Phascum cuspidatum*, which are found also in gardens, churchyards and bare patches in grassland. Its main affinities are with the Ruderal and Water clusters. *Dicranella staphylina* and *Tortula truncata* are relatively uncommon on the chalk and therefore have a somewhat northern distribution, with average northing about 276 km. Conversely, the most southern arable species (18 km to the south of these species, northing 258 km) are *Ephemerum recurvifolium*, *Microbryum davallianum* and *M. floerkeanum*, which are more common on the chalk than in the fens. *Leptobryum pyriforme* is found as an arable bryophyte mainly on fen peat, and has the lowest mean altitude (13 m).

The **Ruderal cluster** is close to the Arable cluster, and in other analyses, not shown here, it was divided into two groups, one of which occurs commonly in arable fields. The other group, comprising *Marchantia polymorpha*, *Brachythecium albicans*, *Brachythecium mildeanum*, *Pseudocrossidium hornschuchianum*, *Syntrichia ruralis* var. *ruraliformis* and *Tortula protobryoides*, is characteristic of waysides and waste places. The Ruderal cluster also includes *Didymodon tophaceus*, which is found in wetter parts of gravel and clay workings but is also closely aligned to the Water cluster.

The **Calcicoles** occur mainly on the chalk in the south. Those with a wider distribution, such as *Aloina aloides*, *A. ambigua*, *Didymodon fallax* and *Homalothecium lutescens*, colonise disturbed sites such as mineral workings throughout the county. They have clear affinities with the Ruderal group. *Aneura pinguis*, *Aloina aloides* and *Tortula lanceola* have relatively low mean altitudes, 25–30 m. They grow mainly on the chalk and chalky Boulder Clay, but have scattered Fenland localities.

Species of the **Built cluster** were defined especially by the large number of our visits to churchyards. They therefore include *Rhytidiadelphus squarrosus* (lawns) and *Lunularia cruciata* and *Didymodon nicholsonii* (paths), as well as mosses that grow on brickwork and masonry. Members of the cluster differ in how much they are concentrated in the south of the county. The two most northerly are *Orthotrichum cupulatum* and *Schistidium crassipilum*, and the two most southerly are *Didymodon nicholsonii* and *D. sinuosus*. Most differed little in mean altitude, but *Rhynchostegium murale* and *Tortula marginata*, averaging 41 m and 51 m, were well above the rest, and *Didymodon umbrosus* was well below them, averaging 16 m.

Species in the **Water cluster**, with a mean altitude of 22 m, are on average the lowest in the landscape. Some of them such as *Conocephalum conicum* and *Cratoneuron filicinum* are found mainly in the south, while *Riccia fluitans*, *Leskea polycarpa* and *Drepanocladus aduncus* are mainly in the north.

The **Shade cluster** is quite small, with only 10 species found in more than 20 sites. They differ from the Woodland species in often occurring in scrub or churchyards as well as in woods. They occupy a lower position in the landscape, averaging 39 m as opposed to 57 m.

The 14 species in the **Common cluster** are mostly very common. However, three less frequent species, *Bryoerythrophyllum recurvirostrum*, *Dicranoweisia cirrata* and *Syntrichia laevipila*, are included here. Of these, *D. cirrata* was formerly more plentiful, declining with the loss of acid rain. It is almost equally well aligned to the Shade cluster. *B. recurvirostrum* is included here because it does not have a profile aligned to any of the other groups; it has vague affinities with the Ruderal, Built and Shade clusters. The inclusion of *Syntrichia laevipila* may be due to a few earlier misidentifications. It missed being included in the Epiphyte cluster by a whisker. It is and always was an epiphyte.

The **Epiphyte cluster** was strongly influenced by records from orchards, which are mostly in Fenland. The three species with lowest mean altitude are *Syntrichia papillosa*, *S. virescens* and *Zygodon conoideus*, while *Orthotrichum pulchellum* was mostly found on higher ground. Not all members of the cluster are exclusively epiphytic. *Brachytheciastrum velutinum* and *Campylopus introflexus* are often on dead wood. *Zygodon viridissimus* is often on concrete or masonry. *Syntrichia virescens* is often found on paths and roofs, and only just falls in this cluster.

The **Acid and Fen cluster** is, as noted above, a composite resulting from the acidification of fen peat at Wicken and to some extent at Chippenham (where decaying logs also provide an acidic substrate). Most of the species are rare or very rare, and the cluster has the highest percentage of species not seen since 1999 (43%). The cluster is separated into Acid and Fen groups in Chapter 10.

Six of the 10 higher-altitude species in the **Woodland cluster** are ancient woodland species in the sense of Preston & Hill (2016), i.e. they have been found in twice as many ancient woodland sites as other sites. Of the other four, *Plagiothecium nemorale*, *Porella platyphylla* and *Rhytidiadelphus triquetrus* were classified in this paper as woodland species with a strong preference for ancient woods. Only *Neckera complanata* has a somewhat weaker preference. The lower-altitude species in the cluster are more mixed, and the two lowest, *Lophocolea heterophylla* and *Aulacomnium androgynum*, occur frequently in other habitats. *L. heterophylla* is closely aligned to the Shade cluster. *A. androgynum* is closely aligned to the Acid and Fen cluster.

## Changes in habitat recording over time

Over the 91 years of recording summarised in Table 6.2, there has been wide variation in habitats visited. Up to the 1940s, Calcicolous, Wetland and Woodland species (clusters 3, 5, 9, 10) made up more than 44% of the records. This proportion dropped gradually to 27% in the 1990s. In 2000s, a strong effort was made to record other habitats, especially in Fenland. In the 2010s these species accounted for only 13% of the records. The proportions of Built-environment and Ruderal species increased. Arable species had two main peaks, the first corresponding to Harold Whitehouse's intensive work on them in the 1960s and 1970s, and the second corresponding to the BBS Survey of Bryophytes of Arable Land in the 2000s. The proportion of Epiphyte records fell to a low of 3 or 4% during the period 1950–1979 and thereafter rose again as air pollution abated.

**Table 6.2** Percentage of records in species clusters over the period 1927–2017, summarised by decade.

| Cluster | 1920s | 1930s | 1940s | 1950s | 1960s | 1970s | 1980s | 1990s | 2000s | 2010s |
|---|---|---|---|---|---|---|---|---|---|---|
| Arable | | 5 | 3 | 4 | 10 | 9 | 5 | 5 | 8 | 4 |
| Ruderal | 6 | 5 | 6 | 12 | 14 | 12 | 12 | 12 | 17 | 17 |
| Calcicole | 19 | 14 | 10 | 13 | 9 | 9 | 7 | 7 | 4 | 4 |
| Built | 9 | 7 | 9 | 10 | 8 | 6 | 15 | 14 | 18 | 18 |
| Water | 21 | 11 | 6 | 7 | 6 | 5 | 3 | 4 | 5 | 3 |
| Shade | 6 | 5 | 10 | 9 | 9 | 9 | 7 | 7 | 7 | 8 |
| Common | 6 | 10 | 22 | 29 | 28 | 23 | 27 | 25 | 24 | 21 |
| Epiphyte | 7 | 6 | 7 | 3 | 3 | 4 | 5 | 10 | 10 | 17 |
| Acid & Fen | 18 | 10 | 6 | 4 | 4 | 9 | 6 | 3 | 2 | 1 |
| Woodland | 9 | 26 | 22 | 10 | 10 | 14 | 11 | 13 | 6 | 5 |

# 7

# Analysing changes in the bryophyte flora

During our fieldwork in the county we have noticed some large changes in its bryophyte flora, such as the increase in epiphytes and loss of calcifuges, but the finer details of change can be determined only by data analysis. We used the computer program Frescalo (Hill 2012), which reports on change by means of a 'time factor'. The time factor for a species is calculated only for those regions where the species is prevalent. Thus, a species confined to the south of the county can have the same time factor as one that is widespread. Roughly speaking, it is a measure of how frequent the species is in relation to a suite of frequent 'benchmark species' that are used as comparators.

The input data for Frescalo consist of presence records for sites during each of the seven decades 1950–1959, 1960–1969 etc., finishing with the incomplete decade 2010–17. A typical record is '*Plagiochila asplenioides* found in Hayley Wood in decade 1990–1999'. In fact, it was found there twice, on 21 November 1992 (when 41 other species were recorded) and on 15 November 1998 (when 42 other species were recorded). When all species records for Hayley Wood in that decade are lumped together, the total is 58 species. However, *Dicranum montanum*, which was found in 1990, and *Frullania dilatata*, which was found in 1994, were reported as individual records, not as parts of a list. They were excluded from the 1990–1999 records for Hayley Wood because short lists, with nine or fewer records, were not eligible. Thus for the analysis, the species complement of Hayley Wood for the decade was 56 species.

The reason for aggregating multiple visits in the analysis is to prevent much-visited sites such as the Cherry Hinton chalk pits and Wicken Fen being over-represented. The purpose of excluding records from short lists is to prevent an over-representation of unusual records with no supporting information. *Dicranum montanum* was never refound in Hayley Wood and is anyway far too rare in the county to have a reliable time trend. *Frullania dilatata* was increasing rapidly in the 1990s. Its occurrence in Hayley Wood was somewhat notable in 1994 but the picture of its increase made from longer lists is perfectly adequate (see Chapter 15).

A side effect of excluding records from short lists is that Jonathan Shanklin's intensive recording of liverworts is not shown in our time factors. The extreme example is *Cololejeunea minutissima*, found in 28 sites during 2010–17 if his records are included, and from only seven if not. A more typical example is *Lophocolea heterophylla*, with 92 sites if his records are included and 39 sites if not.

Our records have been allocated to habitats, as described in Chapter 6. There have been large changes in recording preferences over the years (Figure 7.1). In the years before 2000 there was little recording in towns and villages; churchyard recording started in the 1980s. Arable fields were visited mainly in the 1960s, 1970s and 2000s. Ancient woods, fens and chalk habitats were much less visited after 2000. The main other habitats were open countryside averaging 13%, recent woodland 8%, halls and associated parkland 7% and riversides and streamsides 5%. There were 27 smaller habitats making up 13% of all records.

The worst-recorded decade was the 1970s, with only 1463 distinct records of species in sites (Table 7.1). In the 1950s and 1960s the totals were boosted

**Figure 7.1** Percentage of species records from selected habitats, in decades 1950–2017. Key to habitat types: Calc – chalk grassland and chalk pits; Fen – fenland; A wood – ancient wood; Arable – arable fields; Church – churchyards and cemeteries; Town – towns and villages; Other – all other habitat types.

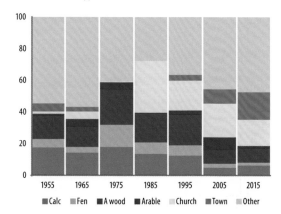

**Table 7.1** Counts of distinct species per decade, summed over sites.

| Decade | Count of species in sites |
|---|---|
| 1950–1959 | 2315 |
| 1960–1969 | 2525 |
| 1970–1979 | 1463 |
| 1980–1989 | 2422 |
| 1990–1999 | 2098 |
| 2000–2009 | 16,109 |
| 2010–2017 | 5824 |

by recording for the two floras (Proctor 1956, Whitehouse 1964) and in 1980s recording became one of their primary objectives of the bryophyte excursions (see Chapter 3). In the 1970s most records were made on the student excursions or in detailed surveys of the calcifuges at Wicken Fen. Not only were relatively few records made in this decade, but towns, villages and churchyards were largely ignored. For example there was only one record of *Didymodon rigidulus* during the decade, found in the Botanic Garden. There were seven records of *D. vinealis* but even it appears to become less frequent during the 1970s (Figure 7.4a). So far as possible, the computer program Frescalo corrects for under- or over-recording of particular habitats. It does this by measuring the similarity of a given site to other sites in the area, and comparing records from the given site with those from sites that are similar. For the Botanic Garden, the most similar four sites are three adjacent tetrads in Cambridge and, less obviously, the Cherry Hinton chalk pits. For Hayley Wood, the most similar sites are Buff Wood, Gamlingay Wood, Longstowe Wood and Kingston Wood. Note that all are ancient woods.

In spite of these precautions, there was a tendency for recording preferences to be reflected in the estimated time factors. A rather extreme example is *Bryum violaceum* (Figure 7.2), which peaks in the two periods of maximum recording of arable fields. *B. rubens*, which has a broader range of habitats than just arable fields, was less affected. Likewise, *Orthotrichum anomalum* and *Schistidium crassipilum* show a sharp increase in the 1980s when churchyards were recorded intensively. This problem is discussed below.

It can be seen in Figure 7.1 that the biggest change in recording practice was the inclusion after 1980 of many records from churches, cemeteries, towns and villages. We accordingly reanalysed the data after removal of these habitats. With this adjustment, *Orthotrichum anomalum* and *Schistidium crassipilum* (Figure 7.3) showed no marked change in the 1980s, but in the period 2000–17 they increased markedly, by a factor of about 2.6. If we exclude churchyard and urban records, *O. anomalum* was recorded from 26 sites in 2010–17. The substrates were as follows: concrete 15, roofs four, and single occurrences on a garden urn, a walnut trunk and on flat stonework in a garden. The substrates at the remaining four sites were not recorded. Concrete in the countryside was formerly not a significant habitat for either *O. anomalum* or *S. crassipilum*. Indeed, on an excursion to Woodbury Low Farm in 2004, we found both species but still thought that such occurrences were unusual.

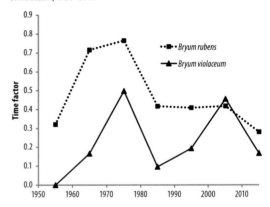

**Figure 7.2** Relative frequency of two arable species, *Bryum rubens* and *B. violaceum*, 1950–2017.

**Figure 7.3** Relative frequency of two species of the built environment, *Orthotrichum anomalum* and *Schistidium crassipilum*, 1950–2017, showing (a) the trend if churches, cemeteries, towns and villages are included and (b) the trend if they are excluded.

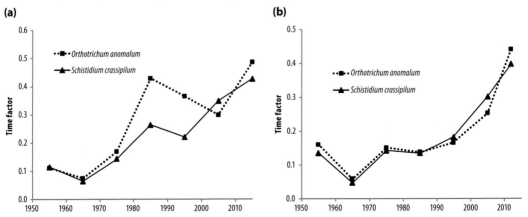

The picture for *Didymodon vinealis* and *D. rigidulus* is more enigmatic (Figure 7.4). *D. rigidulus* was almost certainly under-recorded up to the 1980s. Thereafter it seems to have increased, like *O. anomalum* and *S. crassipilum*. *D. vinealis* has been more stable. Harold Whitehouse knew it well and pointed it out to students. In the 1950s the Cambridge Bryophyte Excursions found it in six places, and Whitehouse found it in nine additional places. Additionally it was found in churchyards in Trumpington and Fowlmere, and in the villages Babraham, Shelford, Guilden Morden, Swaffham Bulbeck and Upend. We think that it has been stable over the recording period. The brief apparent decline in the 1970s (Figure 7.4a) was attributable to recorders avoiding towns and villages in that decade. The longer apparent decline (Figure 7.4b) was the result of relatively assiduous recording, mainly by Whitehouse, in the 1950s and 1960s.

In summary, there were great biases in species recording. These can to some extent be corrected in an analysis of the full dataset. We suggest a method for analysing time trends in species of the built environment. Analysis of trends in more localised habitats, such as ancient woods and fens, is presented in the following chapters and the results are also cited in some of the accounts of individual species.

**Figure 7.4** Relative frequency of *Didymodon vinealis* and *D. rigidulus*, 1950–2017, showing (a) the trend if churches, cemeteries, towns and villages are included and (b) the trend if they are excluded.

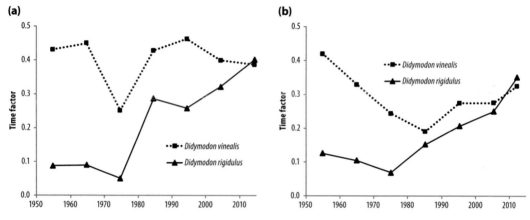

# 8

# Woodland

## Cambridgeshire's woodland

Cambridgeshire lies in the least wooded area of mainland Britain, the eastern arable belt. Only 3.3% of the current administrative county is woodland (Woodland Trust 2017). The two other English counties or unitary authorities with less than 5% woodland cover are Lincolnshire and the East Riding of Yorkshire. The proportion of woodland in vice-county 29 on the land cover map is even lower than that in the administrative county, just 2.2% (Chapter 2). Evidence from place-names, and historical records from the Domesday Book onwards, indicate that the eastern belt has been characterised by a low proportion of woodland for many centuries (Rackham 1990).

Cambridgeshire also has a low proportion of ancient woodland (woodland which was in existence by AD 1600). In England, the areas with less than 1% of ancient woodland are Cambridgeshire (0.69%), Norfolk, North Lincolnshire and the East Riding, along with Bristol, Leicestershire and the West Midlands and a group of counties in the north-west (Cheshire, Merseyside, Greater Manchester, Lancashire). The proportion of ancient woodland in the vice-county is again considerably less than that in the administrative county. The ancient woodlands of Cambridgeshire are now almost restricted to the Boulder Clay and are found in two areas, in the south-west, extending eastwards to Madingley Wood west of Cambridge, and in the south-east (Figure 8.1). Almost all except for the ancient secondary woods (White Wood, Overhall Grove) were formerly managed as coppice with standards. Coppicing fell into disuse in the early 20th century; the last commercial coppicing in Hayley Wood, for example, took place in 1922–23 (Rackham 1975, 2003). The history of the western woods has been well studied, particularly by Oliver Rackham. Several are now

**Figure 8.1** Ancient woodland in Cambridgeshire, mapped in tetrads. The open circle marks Doddington Wood, which was grubbed up in the 1940s.

**Figure 8.2** Coincidence map of species in the Woodland habitat cluster. The northerly concentrations are at Wicken Fen (TL57K), Chippenham Fen (TL66P) and Gray's Moor Pits (TF40A).

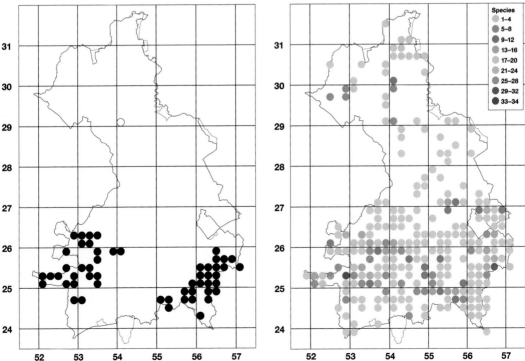

protected as SSSIs and in some cases as nature reserves (Table 2.4) and coppicing has been revived in some of the reserves, notably at Hayley. The only sites listed on the Ancient Woodland inventory (Robinson 1987) which are not on the Boulder Clay are the southernmost woods of the western block, Gilrags Wood and Rouses Wood, which are on Gault Clay in the Cam valley, but we also treat White Wood, on the Woburn Sands, as an ancient wood (see below). We have records from two ancient woods which no longer exist. Doddington Wood, the last surviving ancient woodland in Fenland, was visited by T.G. Tutin in 1932 and Ann Conolly in 1946 but was grubbed up soon afterwards. The presence of *Cirriphyllum piliferum*, *Isothecium alopecuroides* and *Plagiothecium nemorale* suggests that it had some similarity to the boulder-clay woods. Swansley Wood, one of the western boulder-clay woods, was last visited by T. Laflin in 1965, again shortly before its destruction in 1967–68.

The recent woods in the county, which date from after AD 1600, include plantations on estates or in the open countryside, and secondary woodland which has arisen naturally on disused chalk and gravel pits or, rather rarely, on abandoned arable land. The planted woods grow on a wider range of soils than the ancient woods, and are composed of a rather wider range of tree species. There are no conifer plantations of any size in the county, but some existing ancient woods were felled and replanted with conifers in the 1950s and 1960s, notably Borley Wood, Ditton Park Wood and Great and Little Widgham Wood in the east and parts of Gamlingay Wood in the west. (In recent years there has been much 'deconiferisation' at Borley, Ditton Park and Gamlingay). Woodland planting has revived in recent years. Small 'millennium woods' were established on the outskirts of numerous villages in 2000 and subsequent plantings sponsored by the Woodland Trust have brought new woods, open to the public (and the bryologist), to areas of the county which hitherto have lacked woodland completely. Bryologically, the most interesting new woods may turn out to be the extensions of existing woods. These include 800 Wood, an extension planted alongside Madingley Wood to celebrate the 800th anniversary of Cambridge University (but soon threatened by a proposed new busway) and woodland planted alongside the Beechwood Nature Research on the Gog Magog Hills.

## The woodland species

The 41 Woodland bryophytes recognised by the clustering analysis are listed in Table 8.1 and their distribution is mapped in Figure 8.2. The Woodland cluster is the third largest of the habitat groups; only the Calcicole and the Acid and Fen species are more numerous and these are also the only groups with species which are, on average, less frequent (Chapter 6). The group has a strong association with the county's ancient woods (see below). One of the reasons for the richness of the bryophyte flora of woodland is the diversity of its microhabitats, as shown by the wide range of pH preferences of the species in the Woodland cluster from the calcifuges of rotting wood to the calcicoles found on coppice stools of ash and field maple. There are a few epiphytes in the Woodland cluster but most epiphytes are more widespread in the county and are grouped in a habitat cluster of their own (see Chapter 15). Most of the 13 species in the Shade cluster (Table 8.2, Figure 8.3) are also frequent in the county's woodlands, although many also occur in other habitats.

In an earlier analysis we have investigated the extent to which there are 'ancient woodland bryophytes' in the county (Preston & Hill 2016). We identified 30 species with a strong association with ancient woodland. Of these, 25 are members of the Woodland habitat cluster and are asterisked in Table 8.1; the remaining species comprise four in the Acid and Fen cluster (*Calypogeia fissa*, *Chiloscyphus pallescens*, *Dicranum montanum*, *Polytrichastrum longisetum*) and one Epiphyte

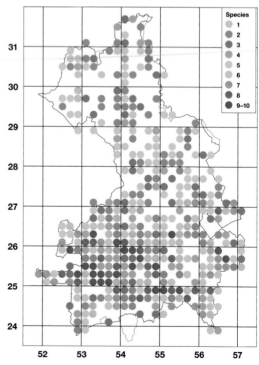

**Figure 8.3** Coincidence map of species in the Shade habitat cluster.

**Table 8.1** Species in the Woodland habitat cluster. Species which have not been recorded in the recent survey are not italicised. An asterisk indicates species with a strong preference for ancient woodland (Preston & Hill 2016). Ellenberg R values are a measure of pH of the substrates on which the species grow, assessed for Britain and Ireland by Hill *et al.* (2007) and ranging from 1 (extremely acidic) through 3 (acidic), 5 (moderately acidic), 6 (basic) to 7 and 8 (strongly basic). Counts of site visits are for those visits on which at least 10 species were recorded, and are therefore zero for species that were found only on visits when fewer records were made. For details of the clustering analysis, and the definition of a site, see Chapter 6.

| Species | R | Typical woodland habitat(s) | Sites | Visits |
|---|---|---|---|---|
| Lophocolea heterophylla | 4 | Rotting wood; tree trunks | 229 | 512 |
| Aulacomnium androgynum | 3 | Rotting wood | 112 | 223 |
| Eurhynchium striatum | 6 | Woodland floor | 104 | 250 |
| Neckera complanata | 7 | Coppice stools; tree bases | 95 | 168 |
| Cirriphyllum piliferum | 6 | Woodland floor | 93 | 183 |
| Mnium hornum | 4 | Rotting wood; soil at tree bases | 82 | 240 |
| Isothecium alopecuroides | 6 | Coppice stools; tree bases | 82 | 155 |
| Thuidium tamariscinum* | 5 | Woodland floor | 77 | 193 |
| Orthodontium lineare | 3 | Rotting wood | 77 | 165 |
| Plagiothecium nemorale | 5 | Tree bases & nearby soil; rotting wood | 72 | 142 |
| Homalia trichomanoides* | 7 | Coppice stools; tree bases | 66 | 140 |
| Dicranella heteromalla | 3 | Soil at tree bases | 65 | 152 |
| Isothecium myosuroides | 4 | Coppice stools; tree bases | 64 | 112 |
| Atrichum undulatum* | 5 | Woodland floor | 61 | 158 |
| Porella platyphylla | 8 | Coppice stools; tree bases | 48 | 128 |
| Anomodon viticulosus* | 8 | Coppice stools; tree bases | 48 | 85 |
| Plagiothecium curvifolium* | 3 | Rotting wood; tree bases | 42 | 69 |
| Rhytidiadelphus triquetrus | 6 | Woodland floor | 40 | 70 |
| Fissidens bryoides* | 5 | Woodland floor | 33 | 53 |
| Fissidens exilis* | 5 | Woodland floor; disturbed soil | 29 | 51 |
| Plagiochila asplenioides* | 6 | Woodland floor | 17 | 67 |
| Ephemerum minutissimum | 5 | Disturbed soil | 16 | 25 |
| Dicranum tauricum* | 3 | Rotting wood | 14 | 20 |
| Platygyrium repens* | 5 | Tree trunks | 11 | 17 |
| Tetraphis pellucida* | 3 | Rotting wood | 10 | 25 |
| Herzogiella seligeri* | 3 | Rotting wood | 10 | 21 |
| Pohlia wahlenbergii* | 6 | Disturbed soil on rides | 8 | 16 |
| Lepidozia reptans* | 2 | Rotting wood | 6 | 16 |
| Nowellia curvifolia | 2 | Rotting wood | 5 | 16 |
| Lejeunea cavifolia* | 6 | Coppice stools | 5 | 14 |
| Hypnum andoi* | 4 | Rotting wood; tree trunks | 5 | 7 |
| Pseudotaxiphyllum elegans* | 3 | Disturbed or heavily shaded soil | 4 | 11 |
| Ptilidium pulcherrimum* | 4 | Tree trunks | 4 | 8 |
| Pleuridium subulatum* | 5 | Disturbed soil | 3 | 7 |
| Fossombronia pusilla* | 5 | Disturbed soil | 3 | 6 |
| Pellia neesiana* | 5 | Moist soil | 3 | 6 |
| Cephalozia connivens* | 1 | Rotting wood | 2 | 2 |
| Campylopus fragilis | 3 | Rotting wood | 2 | 2 |
| Weissia rostellata* | 5 | Disturbed soil on rides | 1 | 4 |
| Cephalozia lunulifolia* | 2 | Rotting wood | 1 | 1 |
| Plagiothecium laetum* | 3 | Tree trunks | - | - |

**Table 8.2** Species in the Shade habitat cluster. For explanation of columns, see Table 8.1.

| Species | R | Typical habitat(s) | Sites | Visits |
|---|---|---|---|---|
| Fissidens taxifolius | 7 | Woodland floor; shaded banks | 420 | 818 |
| Plagiomnium undulatum | 6 | Woodland floor | 274 | 504 |
| Lophocolea bidentata | 4 | Shaded soil; tree trunks; rotting wood | 267 | 538 |
| Fissidens incurvus | 7 | Woodland floor; shaded banks | 227 | 353 |
| Thamnobryum alopecurum | 7 | Woodland floor | 183 | 358 |
| Pellia endiviifolia | 7 | Stream banks | 165 | 378 |
| Oxyrrhynchium pumilum | 7 | Woodland banks | 122 | 166 |
| Fissidens viridulus | 7 | Disturbed soil; stream banks | 108 | 154 |
| Plagiomnium rostratum | 6 | Moist soil | 48 | 82 |
| Cirriphyllum crassinervium | 7 | Tree bases | 25 | 54 |
| Thuidium assimile | 8 | Calcareous turf | 3 | 8 |
| Hennediella stanfordensis | 6 | Trampled soil | 3 | 7 |
| Pleuridium acuminatum | 5 | Disturbed soil | 3 | 3 |

(*Orthotrichum speciosum*). Ancient woodland provides a number of habitats for calcifuges including the bark of some trees such as birch and oak, rotting wood and acidic or leached soils which have not been ploughed or subjected to recent agricultural improvement. Many of our ancient woodland calcifuges have a much wider habitat range in counties with more frequent acidic soils.

## Analysis of ancient woodland data

This analysis covers the ancient woodlands, which have been visited by bryologists since recording began. To minimise the over-recording of liverworts, records made solely by Jonathan Shanklin are excluded. In addition to the woods listed on the Ancient Woodland inventory (Robinson 1987), we have included White Wood, Gamlingay, which was mapped as Broome Wood in 1602 (Oswald & Preston 2011). White Wood is on the Greensand Ridge and is currently managed as a plantation. It is noted for its calcifuge flora, described in Chapter 10.

The eastern and western boulder-clay woods are remarkably similar. Indeed, the only clear differences between them are that *Plagiochila asplenioides* and to a lesser extent *Plagiomnium rostratum* are more frequent in the west. Their commonest species during the period 1950–2017 are shown in Table 8.3. There has, as explained below, been a recent surge in epiphytes, so that the 'top 20' for 2010–17 includes *Orthotrichum affine, O. diaphanum, Rhynchostegium confertum* and *Ulota bruchii* and has lost *Atrichum undulatum, Dicranoweisia cirrata, Lophocolea bidentata* and *Plagiothecium nemorale*.

Ancient woods have been sampled rather unevenly over time. The five most visited woods were Gamlingay, Hardwick, Hayley and Madingley in the west, and Ditton Park Wood in the east. These have been regularly sampled. In our sampling period 2000–17 we have visited many smaller woods as well as the large ones (Table 8.4). This could result in a sampling bias, with the species that occur in large woods being less well represented in the later period. To avoid any such bias, species frequency has been reported only for those sites where the species has been found at least once. For example, *Thuidium tamariscinum* was found in 40 out of the 57 ancient woods sites.

Change in the frequency of *T. tamariscinum* has been reported only for these woods, as 'Relative frequency %', i.e. the frequency of *T. tamariscinum* relative to all species in the woods where it has been found. A value of 2.5% for *T. tamariscinum* in a given decade should therefore be interpreted as meaning that in that decade, one in 40 of the distinct species records from sites with *T. tamariscinum* were in fact that species.

To test for significant change, chi-squared values were calculated comparing the period 2000–17 with 1950–99. As measured by chi-squared, there were no statistically significant declines, but *Fossombronia pusilla*, known from only four sites (chi-square = 3.5), and *Pohlia nutans*, known from eight (chi-square = 3.1), were borderline cases (Figure 8.4). *Aulacomnium androgynum* and *Ceratodon purpureus* showed some evidence of decline (Figure 8.5), but the comparison 2000–17 with 1950–99 was not significant because they increased and then decreased. Both of these species peaked in the 1980s, when acid rain was still affecting the pH of exposed substrates. There has also probably been a slight decline of *Dicranoweisia cirrata* and *Lophocolea heterophylla* (Figure 8.6). We think it likely that the recent increase in records of *L. heterophylla* may be a consequence of Jonathan Shanklin's assiduous search for liverworts on our excursions.

The two most significant increases were shown by *Orthotrichum affine* and *Ulota bruchii* (Figure 8.7),

**Table 8.3** The 20 most frequent species in ancient woods, 1950–2017. To assess frequency, each species was allocated one point for each site/decade combination (i.e. a point for every decade in which it was recorded in each site).

| Species | Habitat cluster | Typical woodland habitat(s) |
|---|---|---|
| *Amblystegium serpens* | Common | Banks; tree bases; eutrophic bark |
| *Atrichum undulatum* | Woodland | Woodland floor |
| *Brachythecium rutabulum* | Common | Woodland floor; rotting wood |
| *Cirriphyllum piliferum* | Woodland | Woodland floor |
| *Dicranoweisia cirrata* | Common | Stumps; rotting wood; acid bark |
| *Eurhynchium striatum* | Woodland | Woodland floor |
| *Fissidens taxifolius* | Shade | Woodland floor; shaded banks |
| *Homalia trichomanoides* | Woodland | Coppice stools; tree bases |
| *Hypnum cupressiforme* | Common | Trees; stumps; rotting wood |
| *Isothecium alopecuroides* | Woodland | Coppice stools; tree bases |
| *Kindbergia praelonga* | Common | Soil; tree bases; rotting wood |
| *Lophocolea bidentata* | Shade | Shaded soil; tree trunks; rotting wood |
| *Lophocolea heterophylla* | Woodland | Rotting wood; tree trunks |
| *Metzgeria furcata* | Epiphyte | Tree trunks |
| *Mnium hornum* | Woodland | Rotting wood; soil at tree bases |
| *Oxyrrhynchium hians* | Common | Ditch sides; eutrophic soil |
| *Plagiomnium undulatum* | Shade | Woodland floor |
| *Plagiothecium nemorale* | Woodland | Tree bases & nearby soil; rotting wood |
| *Thamnobryum alopecurum* | Shade | Woodland floor |
| *Thuidium tamariscinum* | Woodland | Woodland floor |

Table 8.4 Decadal sampling of ancient woods 1950–2017; values are counts of distinct species found in each wood in each decade. If woods cover more than one 5-km square, they are treated as separate sites.

| Site name | 1950s | 1960s | 1970s | 1980s | 1990s | 2000s | 2010s | Total |
|---|---|---|---|---|---|---|---|---|
| Balsham Wood | | 24 | | 27 | | 52 | | 103 |
| Balsham Wood N | | 3 | | | | 15 | | 18 |
| Basefield Wood | | | | | | 47 | 1 | 48 |
| Basefield Wood E | | | | | | 48 | 27 | 75 |
| Borley Wood | 15 | | | | 1 | 50 | | 66 |
| Bourn Wood | 1 | | | | | 18 | | 19 |
| Brinkley Wood | | 15 | | | | | | 15 |
| Buff Wood | 22 | 23 | 41 | | 1 | 46 | 24 | 157 |
| Cadge's Wood | | 5 | | | | | | 5 |
| Carlton Wood | | | | | | 22 | | 22 |
| Charcoals Wood | | 5 | | | | | 42 | 47 |
| Cobb's Wood | | | | | 2 | 26 | | 28 |
| Combers Wood | | | | | | | 38 | 38 |
| Combers Wood W | | | | | | | 4 | 4 |
| Ditton Park Wood | 34 | 22 | | | 51 | 53 | 59 | 219 |
| Elsworth Wood | | | 27 | 39 | | 44 | | 110 |
| Eltisley Wood | 1 | 11 | | | | 54 | | 66 |
| Eversden Wood | 23 | 1 | | 2 | 49 | 62 | | 137 |
| Eversden Wood E | | | | | | 23 | | 23 |
| Gamlingay Wood | 58 | 49 | 27 | 51 | 64 | 55 | 59 | 363 |
| Gilrags Wood E | | | | | | 13 | | 13 |
| Gilrags Wood W | 8 | | | | | 19 | | 27 |
| Great Chitlings Wood | | | | | | | 28 | 28 |
| Great Widgham Wood | | 15 | | 36 | | | | 51 |
| Hardwick Wood | 22 | 50 | 34 | 34 | 36 | 61 | 32 | 269 |
| Hayley Wood | | 63 | 46 | 47 | 58 | 68 | 21 | 303 |
| Hildersham Wood | 19 | 1 | 29 | | | 34 | | 83 |
| Kingston Wood | | | | 38 | 33 | 49 | | 120 |
| Kirtling Wood N | | | | | | 40 | | 40 |
| Kirtling Wood S | | | | | 34 | 45 | | 79 |
| Knapwell Wood | | | | 35 | | 30 | | 65 |
| Langley Wood | 10 | 37 | | | | 54 | 1 | 102 |
| Little Chitlings Wood | | | | | | | 29 | 29 |
| Little Widgham Wood N | | 23 | | 39 | | 52 | | 114 |
| Little Widgham Wood S | | 15 | | 1 | | 46 | | 62 |
| Longstowe Wood | | | 28 | 5 | | 28 | | 61 |
| Lower & Gt Coven's Woods | 15 | 1 | | 29 | 54 | 38 | 36 | 173 |
| Madingley Wood | 52 | 46 | 23 | 41 | | 30 | 1 | 193 |
| Madingley Wood W | | 3 | | | | 37 | 2 | 42 |
| Marmer's Wood | | | | | | 49 | | 49 |
| Monkfield Wood | | | | | | 24 | 23 | 47 |
| Out Wood | 8 | | | | | 53 | | 61 |
| Out Wood N | | 5 | | | | 1 | | 6 |
| Over Wood | | | | | | 38 | | 38 |
| Overhall Grove | 30 | 13 | 37 | | | 30 | | 110 |
| Papworth Wood | 16 | | 30 | | | 36 | 32 | 114 |
| Park Wood, Brinkley | 2 | | | | | | | 2 |
| Pickmore Wood | | | | | 1 | | 24 | 25 |
| Plunder Wood | | | | 2 | | 3 | | 5 |
| Rivey Wood | 12 | | | | | 5 | | 17 |
| Rouses Wood | 1 | 11 | | | | 22 | | 34 |
| Sparrows Grove | 23 | | | | | 34 | | 57 |
| Swansley Wood | | 33 | | | | | | 33 |
| Ten Wood | | 1 | | | 39 | 51 | 34 | 125 |
| Waresley Wood | | | | | | | 18 | 18 |
| White Wood | 32 | 8 | 12 | 30 | 9 | | 29 | 120 |
| Wood S of Parsonage Farm | | | | | 1 | | | 1 |

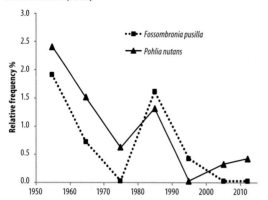

**Figure 8.4** Relative frequency per decade of *Fossombronia pusilla* (4 sites) and *Pohlia nutans* (8 sites).

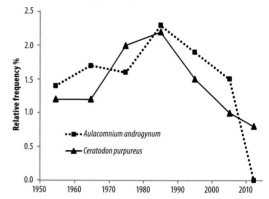

**Figure 8.5** Relative frequency per decade of *Aulacomnium androgynum* (21 sites) and *Ceratodon purpureus* (24 sites).

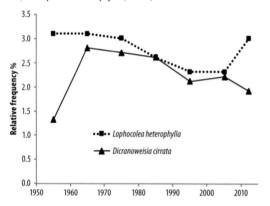

**Figure 8.6** Relative frequency per decade of *Dicranoweisia cirrata* (41 sites) and *Lophocolea heterophylla* (47 sites).

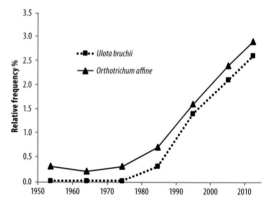

**Figure 8.7** Relative frequency of *Orthotrichum affine* (46 sites) and *Ulota bruchii* (37 sites).

but numerous other epiphytes were increasing: *Cryphaea heteromalla*, *Frullania dilatata* (Figure 8.8), *Orthotrichum diaphanum*, *O. lyellii*, *O. pulchellum*, *O. stramineum*, *Radula complanata*, *Syntrichia montana* (epiphytic in the ancient woodland context), *S. virescens*, *Ulota phyllantha* and *Zygodon viridissimus* (Figure 8.8). The increase of *Campylopus introflexus* (Figure 8.9) is undoubtedly real; until 1975 it was recorded only at Wicken Fen. *Rhynchostegium confertum* is more puzzling. The low number of records in the 1950s and 1960s may perhaps be due to it being regarded as small and boring, but it is weakly calcicolous and may therefore have genuinely increased. Another increaser was *Herzogiella seligeri*, known from only six sites.

Porella platyphylla and Anomodon viticulosus are commonly thought to be declining. In ancient woods this can hardly be true (Figure 8.10). Indeed *A. viticulosus* showed a statistically significant increase though it remains uncommon; the apparent increase may be because we have deliberately searched for these species in recent years.

Two characteristic species of ancient woodland, *Plagiochila asplenioides* and *Rhytidiadelphus triquetrus* (Figure 8.11) have always been very local in Cambridgeshire. *R. triquetrus* disappeared completely during the last three decades of the 20th century, but has made an apparent return in the 21st, with records from Balsham, Eltisley, Eversden, Gamlingay, Langley and Out Woods. Outside ancient woodland it is an occasional colonist, and it may possibly have recolonised some ancient woods. It has not been refound in Buff, Hardwick, Hayley or Madingley Woods since the 1960s, but since 2010 is has spread to two disturbed sites near Madingley. *P. asplenioides* is perhaps more persistent, but it is very much reduced since the days when it was so abundant in Hayley Wood that Oliver Rackham could collect plentiful material for student practicals. However, at the whole-site scale, its decline is not significant.

With these exceptions, the flora of ancient woods has been rather stable, as shown by the trends shown in Figures 8.12–8.15. The trends show a few puzzling features, such as the anomalously low frequency of

**Figure 8.8** Relative frequency of two epiphytes in ancient woodland, *Frullania dilatata* (34 sites) and *Zygodon viridissimus* (18 sites).

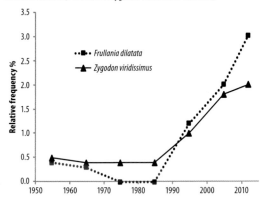

**Figure 8.9** Relative frequency of *Campylopus introflexus* (23 sites) and *Rhynchostegium confertum* (44 sites).

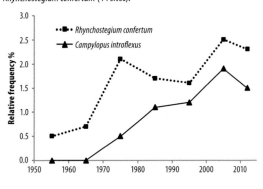

**Figure 8.10** Relative frequency of *Porella platyphylla* (19 sites) and *Anomodon viticulosus* (21 sites).

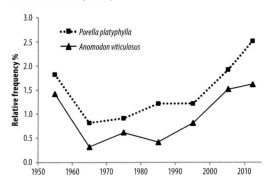

**Figure 8.11** Relative frequency of *Rhytidiadelphus triquetrus* (11 sites) and *Plagiochila asplenioides* (13 sites).

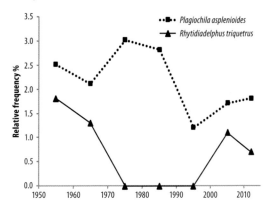

**Figure 8.12** Relative frequency of *Cirriphyllum piliferum* (45 sites) and *Thuidium tamariscinum* (40 sites).

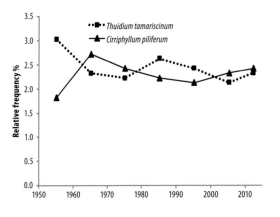

**Figure 8.13** Relative frequency of *Homalia trichomanoides* (39 sites) and *Neckera complanata* (35 sites).

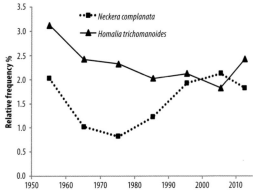

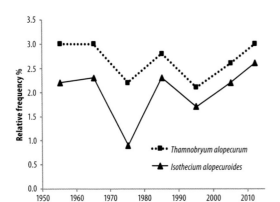

**Figure 8.14** Relative frequency of *Isothecium alopecuroides* (44 sites) and *Thamnobryum alopecurum* (51 sites).

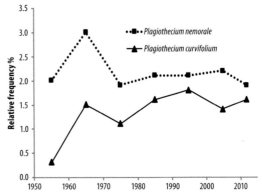

**Figure 8.15** Relative frequency of *Plagiothecium curvifolium* (26 sites) and *P. nemorale* (41 sites). These species were not recorded reliably during the 1950s.

*Isothecium alopecuroides* during the 1970s. This is almost certainly due to a temporary lapse in recording. The low abundance of *Neckera complanata* during the period 1960–1989 may, however, be due to acid rain affecting the relatively exposed habitats of this species more than those of *Homalia trichomanoides*.

## Gamlingay Wood, Hayley Wood and Madingley Wood

These three sites characterise the well-studied oak-maple-hazel woodlands of the western Boulder Clay. It might almost be argued that Hayley Wood is the archetypal ancient wood, as it was the subject of Oliver Rackham's first book, *Hayley Wood* (1975), and much further study (Figures 8.16, 8.17). It has a compact outline, almost square (or squircular) in shape, which it has retained almost unchanged since at least 1251. The only major change was caused by the Bedford and Cambridge Railway which sliced off the northern edge of the wood in 1863. It also isolated a triangle of grassland over ridge-and-furrow between the railway and the wood. This 'tumbled down' to woodland during the agricultural depression which affected the western claylands particularly badly in the inter-war years. The resulting secondary oak woodland now forms an integral part of the wood, The Triangle. Coppicing was revived in 1963–64 and there are now 14 coppice plots, each of one acre.

Gamlingay Wood is more geologically varied than Hayley, as part lies over Boulder Clay and part on a 'sand lens'. It has a very well-documented history and its borders have been stable since medieval times (Rackham 1992). Until 1599 the western and eastern parts were in different ownership; a large ditch and bank still marks the former property boundary. Between 1949 and 1963 two-thirds of the wood was felled and replanted with conifers, ash, oak and hybrid poplar. Many of the planted conifers did not do well, and have now been removed, although some remain and add to the diversity of the site. Like Hayley, Gamlingay is a Wildlife Trust reserve.

Madingley Wood has a very different history to the other two woods (Rackham 2003, Rackham & Coombe 1996). It has a series of large internal earthworks which perhaps suggest that it was occupied during the Iron Age, and only became woodland later. Its medieval history is poorly documented, but it is clear from an early 17th-century lease that by then it was an ordinary coppice-with-standards wood. More than half the wood was grubbed out in the early modern period and 19th-century maps show that there were four fields surrounded by hedges in the eastern half of the wood; these later reverted to woodland. Some areas were planted with conifers in the late 19th century but conifers do not thrive on calcareous Boulder Clay. A chalk pit outside the ancient wood became overgrown and was incorporated into the woodland during the 19th century. As might be expected from its proximity to Cambridge, there is a long history of plant recording which extends back to John Ray (flowering plants) and William Vernon (bryophytes). The Madingley estate was bought by the University in 1948 and since then the wood has been used for ecological observations and experiments.

Hayley Wood (22 species) and Gamlingay Wood (21) have more of the 30 'ancient woodland bryophytes' identified by Preston & Hill (2016) than any other woods in the county; indeed the next highest total is just 14. Madingley came in equal ninth place in this ranking, with nine species. Hayley and Gamlingay are

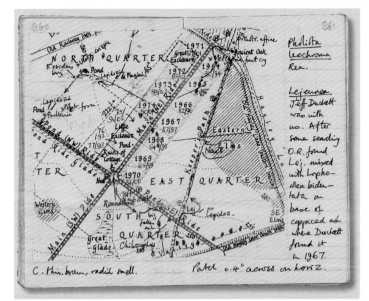

**Figure 8.16** A map of Hayley Wood from Oliver Rackham's notes on the bryophyte excursion on 14 November 2009, when *Lejeunea cavifolia* was seen again on the same coppice stool where it had been discovered in 1966. Reproduced by kind permission of the Master and Fellows of Corpus Christi College Cambridge (*Rackham Hayley Wood notebook* 36: 960–61).

**Figure 8.17** Oliver Rackham on the excursion of 14 November 2009, examining *Lejeunea cavifolia* on the coppice stool on which it was discovered in 1966. Photo: Jeff Duckett.

considerably larger than Madingley, and the situation is also complicated by the tendency of calcifuges to be ancient woodland species in Cambridgeshire. (Wicken Fen, with no pretensions to ancient woodland, also has, or had, nine of these species). However, there is little doubt that in part the difference reflects the differences in woodland history. There is a striking parallel with the situation described by Rackham & Coombe (1996) for flowering plants, as they reported that 28 ancient woodland vascular plant species had recently been seen in Hayley, 24 in Gamlingay and 14 in Madingley Wood. However, if extinct species are included in the vascular plant figures the Madingley total increases by nine to 23, a comparable figure to those of the larger woods. The historical bryophyte records are less detailed, but the fact that the only record of our most characteristic ancient woodland bryophyte, *Plagiochila asplenioides*, from Madingley is a 17th or early 18th-century specimen in the Sloane Herbarium (Figure 3.2) suggests that the same might have been true for the bryophytes. Like the oxlip, *Primula elatior*, it was presumably a casualty of the later clearances.

Only three of the 22 ancient woodland bryophytes in Hayley Wood have been recorded in the adjoining patch of secondary woodland known as The Triangle, namely the ground-dwelling species *Atrichum* undulatum, Plagiochila asplenioides and Thuidium tamariscinum. Most of the other species occur in the ancient part of the wood on acidic ground (seven species) or on rotting wood (eight); the remainder grow epiphytically on oak trunks (one) or old coppice stools (three). Several are very rare, or have not been seen anywhere in the wood in recent years. The Triangle lacks rotting wood, coppice stools and disturbed soil in coppice plots, and this is the probable reason for the absence of most species, rather than limited powers of dispersal.

The number of species in the habitat clusters defined in Chapter 6 is enumerated for each wood in Table 8.5. As described above, there is a broad overlap between the Woodland cluster and the ancient woodland bryophytes identified by Preston & Hill (2016) so the low total of Woodland species at Madingley is not surprising. Gamlingay and Hayley clearly have a much richer calcifuge flora. They also have more Aquatic species than Madingley, which lacks ponds, but Madingley has more Epiphytes.

The occurrence of epiphytes in the three woods is summarised in Table 8.6. Gamlingay had an extremely poor epiphyte flora in the middle of the 20th century, perhaps a combination of its proximity to the Bedfordshire brickpits as well as its partial coniferisation. Madingley was distinctly more epiphyte-rich in this period. The start of the recovery in the late 20th century is clear at Gamlingay and Hayley, but Madingley was poorly recorded in these years. The epiphytes of Monks Wood in Huntingdonshire show a similar history to those of these Cambridgeshire woods (Preston & Walker 2005).

Confirmation of the poor epiphyte flora at Hayley is provided by the bryophyte list published by Rackham (1975), who recorded the habitats of all the Wood's bryophytes. We can thus tell whether or not the common, ecologically wide-ranging species were growing epiphytically. The only species which he listed from bark and which grew above the level of the coppice stools were the liverworts Lophocolea bidentata, L. heterophylla and Metzgeria furcata and the mosses Dicranoweisia cirrata, Dicranum scoparium, Plagiothecium curvifolium and Tetraphis pellucida. All but two of these, Lophocolea bidentata and Metzgeria furcata, are calcifuges. Only Metzgeria is a member of our Epiphytes cluster although two other Epiphytes were recorded on coppice stools in Rackham's list, Frullania dilatata ('one recent record') and Radula complanata. During the periods of high SO$_2$ pollution, some epiphytes were able to persist only close to ground level in sheltered places (Adams & Preston 1992). Bryum moravicum was not listed by Rackham as it was not then recognised as a species but it had already been collected (as B. capillare) at Hayley.

One of the themes of Oliver Rackham's work is that no ancient woodlands are identical, all have their special features. At Hayley fallen oaks provide

Table 8.5 The number of species in each habitat cluster in Gamlingay, Hayley and Madingley Woods.

| Cluster | Hayley | Gamlingay | Madingley |
|---|---|---|---|
| Arable | 6 | 6 | 4 |
| Ruderal | 7 | 10 | 6 |
| Calcicole | 2 | 3 | 3 |
| Built | 2 | 3 | 1 |
| Water | 7 | 5 | 2 |
| Shade | 9 | 8 | 9 |
| Common | 13 | 12 | 13 |
| Epiphyte | 11 | 11 | 14 |
| Acid & Fen | 13 | 15 | 6 |
| Woodland | 34 | 32 | 21 |
| Total | 104 | 105 | 79 |

Table 8.6 Occurrence of species in the epiphyte cluster, plus Dicranoweisia cirrata, in Gamlingay (Gam), Hayley (Hay) and Madingley (Mad) Woods, 1940–2017.

| Species | 1940–69 | | | 1970–99 | | | 2000–17 | | |
|---|---|---|---|---|---|---|---|---|---|
| | Gam | Hay | Mad | Gam | Hay | Mad | Gam | Hay | Mad |
| Metzgeria furcata | • | • | • | • | • | • | • | • | • |
| Dicranoweisia cirrata | • | • | • | • | • | • | | • | • |
| Brachytheciastrum velutinum | | • | • | • | • | • | • | | • |
| Bryum moravicum | | • | • | • | • | • | | • | • |
| Frullania dilatata | | • | • | • | | | • | • | • |
| Radula complanata | | • | • | | • | | • | • | • |
| Orthotrichum affine | | | • | • | • | | • | • | • |
| Zygodon viridissimus | | | • | • | • | | | • | • |
| Campylopus introflexus | | | | • | • | | • | • | • |
| Ulota bruchii | | | | | • | | • | • | • |
| Cololejeunea minutissima | | | | | | | • | • | • |
| Cryphaea heteromalla | | | | | | | | • | |
| Metzgeria violacea | | | | | | | • | | • |
| Orthotrichum lyellii | | | | | | | | | • |
| Orthotrichum pulchellum | | | | | | | | | • |
| Orthotrichum striatum | | | | | | | | • | |

a special feature of bryological interest. These died almost a century ago; they now lie like felled giants on the woodland floor, their wood decorticated but iron-hard (Figure 8.18). They support a colony of *Nowellia curvifolia* which has itself been present for over 50 years. At Gamlingay the sand-lens is the special feature. In 2016 a glade which had been extended on this soil some four years earlier had large and spectacular patches of male and female *Polytrichastrum formosum* as well as *Campylopus introflexus, C. pyriformis* and *Polytrichum juniperinum*.

## Secondary and new woods

New woods start with almost no bryophytes that can survive in woodland. There may be *Brachythecium rutabulum, Fissidens taxifolius, Kindbergia praelonga* and *Oxyrrhynchium hians*, but almost all other species must immigrate. In the period of our survey, the most rapid new colonists were *Amblystegium serpens, Bryum capillare, Hypnum cupressiforme, Orthotrichum affine, Orthotrichum diaphanum* and *Rhynchostegium confertum*. Colonisation by epiphytes need not in principle be slow. We know from Cambridgeshire orchards that trees aged about 40 years can acquire a substantial diversity of epiphytes. Closed-canopy woodlands are different, because their interiors are dark and the upper branches of their trees are too exposed to provide much shelter. *Rhynchostegium confertum* can establish on tree-boles, but few other species are able to thrive.

The rate at which woodland bryophytes enter a new wood depends on its size and whether or not there are ancient woods in the vicinity. Chippenham Fen has 23 species in the Woodland habitat cluster, more than any other site that is not ancient woodland (Table 8.7). The woods were planted about 1800, and now have numerous stumps and fallen logs. The size of the wooded area has been sufficient to offset the lack of proximity to ancient woods. Wicken Fen is the third richest new woodland, with 17 woodland species. It did not develop its scrub woodland ('carr') till late in the 19th century (Friday, Walters & Lock 1997) and it also is not near ancient woodland. Here again the extensive size of the woodlands was a major factor in its accumulation of species.

**Figure 8.18** One of the cohort of decorticated oaks at Hayley Wood which died in the 1920s, photographed in March 2017. They still support a colony of *Nowellia curvifolia* which was first discovered on them in 1962. Photo: Peter Leonard.

**Table 8.7** Recent woodland with 10 or more species in the Woodland habitat cluster.

| Recent Woods | Feature | Date of planting or colonisation | Count |
|---|---|---|---|
| Chippenham Fen | Fen | Planted c. 1800 | 23 |
| Croxton Park | Park | South Lodge Plantation planted 1818–1826; Turtlow Plantation 1826–1836 | 19 |
| Wicken Fen | Fen | Natural colonisation, from late 19th and early 20th centuries | 17 |
| Hildersham Hall | Park | Planted between 1810 and 1820 | 15 |
| Devil's Dyke nr Stetchworth | Earthwork | Wooded by 1785, adjoins ancient woodland at S end | 15 |
| Wimpole Hall | Park | Planted in 18th and early 19th centuries | 13 |
| Gamlingay, Heath Plantation | Plantation | Planted between 1843 and 1887 | 13 |
| Barrington, Hill Plantation | Disused chalk pit | On 1st edition OS map (1836) | 13 |
| Gray's Moor Pits nr March | Disused gravel pit | Natural colonisation, after 1950 | 11 |
| Hardwick, Whitepits Plantation | Plantation | On 1st edition OS map (1836) | 11 |
| Wandlebury | Park | Planted in 18th or early 19th century; basic pattern of planting on 1st edition of OS map (1836) | 11 |
| Arrington Decoy Pond | Plantation | Pond dug c. 1730 (S. Damant, pers. comm.) and on an 1828 estate map | 11 |
| Wort's Causeway beechwood | Plantation | Planted c. 1840 | 10 |

The woodlands of Croxton Park are the second richest non-ancient site with 19 woodland species. The presence of *Plagiochila asplenioides* is particularly noteworthy. The park was created and planted in the early 19th century, and there is no indication on earlier maps of the presence of woodland here before it was imparked. The nearest ancient wood, Eltisley Wood, is less than 1 km away but this does not have many ancient woodland bryophytes (Preston & Hill 2016); the nearest known *Plagiochila* population is in Gransden Wood, Hunts., 3.5 km away.

Gray's Moor Pits is one of the less rich sites, supporting 11 species. It is a small and rather isolated site in Fenland which was worked for railway ballast but has become colonised by willow scrub since 1950 (Figure 8.19). No Woodland species were recorded when the site was first visited, in 1959 and 1960, but surprisingly eight of the Woodland species were present by 1967, including four which persisted (*Atrichum undulatum, Aulacomnium androgynum, Dicranella heteromalla, Lophocolea heterophylla*) and four which have not been seen since (*Eurhynchium striatum, Mnium hornum, Orthodontium lineare* and *Pohlia wahlenbergii*). Three Woodland species have been added to the list since then, *Fissidens bryoides* (1987), *Plagiothecium nemorale*

**Figure 8.19** Sallow carr in Gray's Moor Pits, February 2013. This site was open and had a rich pioneer flora in 1959. Photo: Jonathan Graham.

(1987) and *Fissidens exilis* (2013). Clearly the pattern of colonisation involves both establishment and extinction; it does not simply involve the gradual accumulation of Woodland species over time.

Despite the complex pattern of colonisation at Gray's Moor, we can conclude from the 13 sites in Table 8.7 that recent woodland generally seems to take about 150 years to acquire a moderate number of species in the Woodland habitat cluster. The main exception is Wicken Fen, which as a result of its large size and moist soil took perhaps only 70 years. The Shade plants that colonise most rapidly and are among the 20 most frequent species in recent woodland are *Lophocolea bidentata*, *L. heterophylla*, *Fissidens taxifolius*, *Plagiomnium undulatum* and *Thamnobryum alopecurum*. Of the 20 most frequent species in ancient woods (Table 8.3), *Cirriphyllum piliferum*, *Eurhynchium striatum*, *Isothecium alopecuroides* and *Mnium hornum* colonise relatively slowly. The slowest to colonise are *Atrichum undulatum*, *Homalia trichomanoides*, *Plagiothecium nemorale* and *Thuidium tamariscinum*.

## Summary

Broad-leaved woodland is an uncommon habitat in Cambridgeshire and conifer woodland is rare (a few woods have been or were previously planted with conifers but there are no large conifer plantations). The ancient woods have been well studied by bryologists, particularly in the west of the county. Only a few woods were grubbed out in the 20th century and the surviving woods have often retained the same boundaries for many centuries. Ancient woods in the county are almost all on Boulder Clay and show rather little variation in their flora. They are characterised by numerous specialist species which are ecologically heterogeneous and exploit the wide range of different microhabitats in ancient woodland, including moist, acidic substrates which are otherwise rare in the county. Recent woods are gradually colonised by these specialists over a period of about 150 years. The main change in the woodland bryophyte flora since 1980 has been the very marked increase in the epiphytic flora. A few calcifuges have declined. Numerous small new woods have been planted in recent years.

# 9

# Orchards

Cambridgeshire was not noted historically as a fruit-growing county, although for centuries orchards played their part in the domestic economy of larger houses, monasteries and the more spacious Cambridge colleges. King's College, for example, was founded in 1441 and by 1468/69 it was obtaining 52 gallons of juice from the apples in its own orchard (Willis & Clark 1886). It was not until the 1870s that extensive commercial orchards began to be planted in the county in response both to agricultural depression, which reduced the profitability of standard crops, and to the relatively recent ability of growers to distribute their produce by rail. There was an increase in market gardening at the same time and in the same areas, both locally and nationally (Thirsk 1997).

The area of orchards in the county reached a peak in the 1930s, with over 4,400 hectares grown in 1935 (DEFRA statistics). By then, orchards were regarded as one of the county's distinctive features (Pettit 1941). The area declined only slowly in the 1950s and 1960s but much more steeply after entry into the EEC in 1973, when growers found that their apples could not compete with varieties bred for yield rather than taste and grown in warmer European countries. On average, over 100 hectares of orchards were grubbed up annually in the county between 1975 and 1985, the years of the 'Golden Delicious' apple. By 2000 the area of orchards had been reduced to 1,060 hectares and the fall has continued since, to 602 hectares by 2016. The fate of 134 orchards mapped in administrative Cambridgeshire on the 1:25,000 Millennium Edition maps but lost by 2005 was studied by the East of England Apples and Orchards Project (2005). They found that 42% had become arable, 22% grassland (mainly for horses) and 13% residential development.

The two largest areas of orchards were around Wisbech and about Cottenham and Histon north of Cambridge (Figure 9.1). In Wisbech commercial fruit farming began in the 1850s but at first it was both small in scale and apparently rather rough-and-ready; one of the early growers harvested his fruit by shaking the trees (Wright & Ward 1929). It began to expand in the 1880s. The Land Utilisation Survey of the Isle of Ely, which included both the Wisbech area and the smaller concentration on the Lower Greensand soils of the Haddenham ridge to the south, found that in 1936 70% of the orchard area was devoted to apples and 26% to plums, with only 3% pears and 1% cherries (Melbourne 1940). In many orchards in this area (29% of the area in 1945) soft fruit was grown below the trees (Figure 9.3), a practice which was much less common in Cambridgeshire south of the Isle (6%). The orchards of Cottenham and Histon were dominated by the firm of Chivers. The Chivers family first produced jam in a barn in 1873 and opened a small factory at Histon in 1875; thereafter the enterprise expanded rapidly and Chivers were the first British firm to begin commercial canning of fruit, in 1894 (Horridge undated). In addition to the medium-sized or large commercial orchards in these and other areas, many farms had a small area (less than one hectare) of orchard immediately by the farmhouse; these are mapped in meticulous detail on older Ordnance Survey maps.

## The traditional orchards of East Anglia

Many descriptions of the wildlife of orchards draw a sharp contrast between traditional and modern commercial orchards. 'Traditional management eschews large-scale alteration of the environment, instead favouring the natural balance of predator and prey'; by contrast 'modern intensive orchards contain small, short-lived trees managed with pesticides, herbicides and fertilisers. This increases productivity but greatly reduces any opportunity for wildlife' (People's Trust for Endangered Species undated). Traditional orchards are regarded as havens for wildlife (Maddock 2008, Rotherham 2008, Wedge & Robertson 2010) and have been described lyrically by Sinden (1989) who regards modern orchards as 'hardly worthy of the name, with their close-packed ranks of bush-trees ... growing in bare, herbicide-scorched earth'.[4] This dichotomy has been supported by detailed studies of Herefordshire orchards (Robertson *et al.* 2012).

Robin Stevenson has argued that the apple orchards of East Anglia never fitted this picture of the traditional orchard (Stevenson 2006, Stevenson & Rowntree 2009). He has pointed out that in order to eliminate pests which threaten dessert and cooking apples, the trees were sprayed with a sequence of

---

4 The Local Habitat Action Plan (Cambridgeshire and Peterborough Biodiversity Partnership 2008) provides a more realistic description of the habitat than the romantic and generalised picture often painted by national organisations.

**Figure 9.1** The distribution of orchards in Cambridgeshire at their maximum extent, as mapped on the Ordnance Survey 1:25,000 First Series (Provisional) maps, surveyed 1937–53 and published in 1951–57. Symbols of increasing size indicate estimated areas of <1, 1–5 and >5 hectares in each 1-km square.

**Figure 9.2** The distribution of bryophyte records from Cambridgeshire orchards, 2000–18.

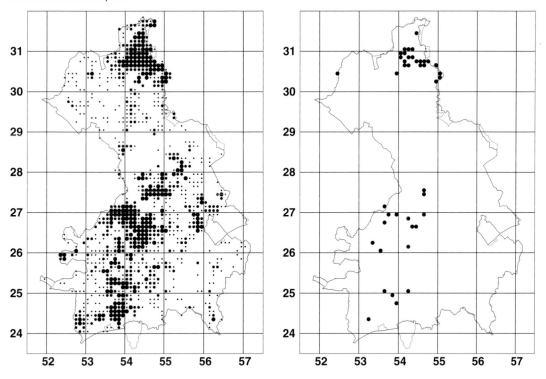

**Figure 9.3** Bush fruit cultivated below the trees in an orchard in the Wisbech area, 1930. Photo: Lilian Ream (Z062, Lilian Ream Trust, Wisbech).

chemicals which would have eliminated almost all mosses from them (Figure 9.4). Even the shape of the trees, which were pollarded at a height of about one metre ('half-standards') and pruned to maintain open crowns, was in part designed so that they would be easily accessible to the sprayer.

No-one reading the advice offered to fruit-growers in the heyday of our orchards can fail to be convinced by Stevenson's argument. The Cambridge zoologist Cecil Warburton, in a pamphlet *Orchard and bush-fruit pests and how to combat them* (1902), recommended eliminating bark crevices in which the

**Figure 9.4** Spraying in an orchard in the Wisbech area, 1959. Photo: Lilian Ream (Z068, Lilian Ream Trust, Wisbech).

codling moth and other pests might overwinter by scraping tree trunks to remove all loose bark and then scrubbing a dressing of some suitable insecticide into the cracks with a stiff brush. In would be interesting to know whether this advice was followed, even in the days of abundant agricultural labour before the First Word War. However, there is no doubt that the trees were sprayed. Warburton specifically recommended a solution of caustic soda (sodium hydroxide) and 'crude potashes', mixed with soft soap, for application in winter 'to kill hibernating insects and their eggs, or to clean tree-trunks smothered by moss and lichen'. Sanders (1919) 'up-to-date remedies' include spraying trees with paraffin emulsion in autumn and with lime-sulphur wash in winter against aphids, and a spray with arsenate of lead after the fall of the blossom to kill the larvae of several moths, including codling moth. Lime-sulphur was also used as a fungicide. Photographs published in the *Cambridge Chronicle* on 23 February 1921 show workers using Heron's Demon Sprayer to spray a mixture of lime and salt in a Chivers orchard at Histon. The trees and ground are so white that they resemble 'a scene after a snowstorm', illustrating Ingram & Robertson's (1999) view that 'the floor of apple orchards could become like a desert with the weight of toxic material applied to the trees and incidentally to the soil below'. Tar-oil washes were introduced in the early 1920s – in the Wisbech area they were first employed in the 1922–23 winter (Wright & Ward 1929) – and they rapidly became popular for use against aphids and psyllids. They could only be used in winter as they are toxic to foliage, but this gave them the additional advantage that 'the tar oils kill lichen and mosses, and therefore serve admirably as tree cleaners' (Martin 1956). By the 1950s, DDT was recommended for routine use alongside lime-sulphur, as a replacement for tar-oil wash (Martin 1956, Morgan & Marsh 1956), but the latter continued to be used in East Anglian orchards until the mid 1970s (Stevenson *et al.* 2017).

Stevenson (2006) has cited similar advice on pest control from other authors. Can we be sure that orchard growers followed the advice? Wright & Ward (1929) reported that the more up-to-date growers followed the recommended spraying regimes in the Wisbech area. However, many growers sprayed haphazardly, sometimes dispensing with a winter or summer wash, especially if they did not expect a crop that year ('a short-sighted policy'). There were also 'still men who refuse to spray at all' ('it is important that this attitude should be remedied', they commented tartly). Despite this variation in practice, it is clear that the management of Cambridgeshire's orchards in the first half of the 20th century was intensely antagonistic towards bryophytes, both deliberately (as they were regarded as refuges for pests) and as a by-product of other pest-control procedures. And of course even the unsprayed orchards were subject, like other habitats in the county, to the prevailing high concentrations of $SO_2$.

## Bryological records from orchards

Proctor's flora (1956) makes no mention of orchards, despite the large area then present in the county. One cited record, *Cryphaea heteromalla* collected by Haviland & Lister on an apple tree in Histon in 1881, might have come from an orchard. However, at least three orchards were visited by the collectors recruited by Harold Whitehouse to improve the 10-km square coverage of the county in preparation for the 1964 flora. W. Jackson's *Oxyrrhynchium hians* 'under grass by an orchard' at Manea in 1959 might have been a casual collection but Margaret Anderson clearly spent more time in an orchard near Over in 1960 as she collected 12 terrestrial bryophytes, but no epiphytes. Finally P.J. Bourne collected *Brachythecium rutabulum*, *Ceratodon purpureus*, *Hypnum cupressiforme*, *Oxyrrhynchium hians* and '*Pottia* sp.' from an orchard at Upwell in 1963. The first three (very common) species may have been growing as epiphytes. These few records of mundane species are consistent with the hypothesis that the managed orchards in the 20th century were of very little bryological interest. Local growers (cited by Stevenson *et al.* 2017) say that the current moss cover has developed in the last 40 years.

It was in the 1990s that we began to realise the potential of old orchards as habitats. On a bryological excursion in 1996 we visited a neglected orchard at Wilburton, recording 24 species including *Frullania dilatata*, *Orthotrichum lyellii* and *Ulota crispa sens. lat.* The following year a stop at a derelict orchard at Coldham produced a list of 21 species including more *Orthotrichum lyellii* and *Zygodon viridissimus*. Finally, in December 1999, Robin Stevenson arranged for us to visit a large disused orchard at Rummers Lane, Wisbech St Mary, for the last excursion of the millennium. We still have vivid memories of picking our way between the trees on this winter day, disturbing flocks of migrant thrushes which had been attracted by masses of fallen fruit. We listed 38 species with numerous epiphytes including *Platygyrium repens*, *Syntrichia laevipila* and *Ulota phyllantha*.

The sites from which we have orchard records since 2000 are mapped in Figure 9.2. Robin Stevenson has carried out detailed studies of the epiphytic bryophytes in some of the remaining orchards in the county (and in West Norfolk), particularly in the Wisbech area (Figure 9.5). He has studied some sites which are still in commercial production and others which are now disused (Lush *et al.* 2009, Stevenson 2006, Stevenson & Rowntree 2009, Stevenson *et al.* 2017). The distinction between the two categories is not absolute. Commercial orchards have now reduced spraying to a minimum, because of an increasing awareness of the dangers of pesticide sprays, their increasing cost and the development of more sophisticated methods of pest control, including the use of pheromone traps for insect pests. In addition, some of the orchards surveyed had recently reduced or suspended management (including pruning). Rather than simply listing species at sites, Robin has recorded orchards tree by tree, recording the number of trees in his samples on which each species is found. This technique is facilitated by the low size of the trees and their open crowns, as each tree can be surveyed thoroughly. We have been able to draw on Robin's records from 951 apple trees in 14 orchards, 173 pear trees in five orchards and 44 plum trees in one orchard in Cambridgeshire. There are few records from plum trees as Robin found that their epiphytes were too limited to repay such a detailed survey. The account below is largely based on the records of apple and pear trees from the county in this remarkable dataset. We also refer to a study of the epiphytic flora of Bramley's Seedling apples (colloquially known as Bramleys) by Whitelaw & Burton (2015) which incorporates records from three Hertfordshire orchards and from 20 trees (10 planted *c.* 1900 and 10 *c.* 1930) in one orchard in Cambridgeshire, at Haddenham.

**Figure 9.5** Robin Stevenson near Reffley Wood, King's Lynn, Norfolk, August 2006. Photo: Mark Hill.

# Orchard epiphytes

The species recorded on more than 1% of apple or pear trees surveyed by Robin Stevenson are listed in Table 9.1. *Hypnum cupressiforme* is the dominant bryophyte of Cambridgeshire's orchards. Whitelaw & Burton (2015), like Stevenson, found that it was the most frequent species in their orchards. It grew in large quantities on most of the trees they surveyed and it accounted for almost 50% of the total bryophyte cover.

All the species in the Common habitat cluster recognised in Chapter 6 have been recorded as orchard epiphytes except for *Bryoerythrophyllum recurvirostrum* (a surprising absentee), the terrestrial species *Calliergonella cuspidata* and *Oxyrrhynchium hians* and the very rare and non-epiphytic *Plagiomnium cuspidatum*, a poor fit in the Common group. Of the 36 members of the 'Epiphyte' cluster, 30 have been recorded at least once on this sample of orchard trees; in fact the delimitation of this cluster is based to a significant degree on the presence of species in the orchard tetrads. Thirteen of the 15 most frequent members of the Epiphyte cluster in the county were present on 1% or more of the trees of at least one of the two orchard hosts. *Radula complanata* was less frequent than would be expected from its wider range as an epiphyte, recorded on *c.* 0.5% of the trees of each host, and *Metzgeria violacea* was not found on the sampled trees. Both these are more commonly found on trees in moister habitats. The three most frequent species in the Built cluster in the county, *Grimmia pulvinata*, *Syntrichia montana* and *Tortula muralis*, plants normally found on concrete, brick or stone, are surprisingly frequent as orchard epiphytes. Bryophytes of the Woodland cluster are poorly represented, with only three species listed in Table 9.1 (and they are less frequent on orchard trees than the three species of the Built environment).

Not surprisingly, some of the county's increasing epiphytes were recorded at low frequency (<1%) on the sampled trees: *Cololejeunea minutissima*, *Leucodon sciuroides*, *Orthotrichum pulchellum*, *O. stramineum*, *O. striatum* and *O. tenellum*. Other rare orchard epiphytes are frequent in other habitats in the county, namely *Isothecium alopecuroides* (four sampled trees), *Pseudoscleropodium purum* (one), *Radula complanata* (six), *Schistidium crassipilum* (one) and *Syntrichia ruralis* (one, although perhaps sometimes recorded as *S. montana*). Three species, *Hypnum jutlandicum* (one), *Platygyrium repens* (one) and *Sciuro-hypnum populeum* (one), also occur in other habitats in the county, although much less frequently. However, a remarkable feature of the recent surveys of orchards has been the discovery of very rare epiphytes which have presumably colonised from a long distance (Figure 9.6). Of these, *Hypnum cupressiforme* var. *heseleri* (one tree), *Orthotrichum obtusifolium* (one), *Pterigynandrum filiforme* (one), *Pylaisia polyantha* (eight) and *Sanionia uncinata* (one) are only known from orchards in the county and *Orthotrichum speciosum* (two) has only one site outside orchards, an ancient wood. In addition, *Antitrichia curtipendula*

**Table 9.1** Species recorded on more than 1% of the 951 apple or 173 pear trees surveyed by Robin Stevenson in Cambridgeshire orchards, 2003–2013. For details of the habitat clusters, see Chapter 6. Ellenberg R values are an indication of species' substrate preference, ranging from 2 (acid) to 8 (basic); see Table 8.1.

| Species | Cluster | R | % apple trees | % pear trees |
|---|---|---|---|---|
| *Amblystegium serpens* | Common | 7 | 54 | 40 |
| *Aulacomnium androgynum* | Woodland | 3 | 0 | 6 |
| *Brachytheciastrum velutinum* | Epiphyte | 6 | 7 | 9 |
| *Brachythecium rutabulum* | Common | 6 | 64 | 58 |
| *Bryum argenteum* | Ruderal | 6 | 1 | 9 |
| *Bryum capillare* | Common | 7 | 51 | 28 |
| *Bryum dichotomum* | Ruderal | 7 | 0 | 14 |
| *Bryum moravicum* | Epiphyte | 6 | 8 | 1 |
| *Campylopus introflexus* | Epiphyte | 2 | 1 | 14 |
| *Ceratodon purpureus* | Common | 5 | 11 | 30 |
| *Cryphaea heteromalla* | Epiphyte | 6 | 3 | 0 |
| *Dicranoweisia cirrata* | Common | 4 | 43 | 69 |
| *Dicranum scoparium* | Acid | 3 | 0 | 1 |
| *Frullania dilatata* | Epiphyte | 6 | 6 | 7 |
| *Funaria hygrometrica* | Ruderal | 6 | 0 | 2 |
| *Grimmia pulvinata* | Built | 8 | 23 | 18 |
| *Homalothecium sericeum* | Common | 7 | 16 | 2 |
| *Hypnum cupressiforme* var. *cupressiforme* | Common | 4 | 77 | 74 |
| *Hypnum cupressiforme* var. *resupinatum* | Common | 4 | 26 | 18 |
| *Isothecium myosuroides* | Woodland | 4 | 2 | 2 |
| *Kindbergia praelonga* | Common | 5 | 10 | 24 |
| *Leptodictyum riparium* | Water | 7 | 3 | 1 |
| *Leskea polycarpa* | Water | 7 | 2 | 1 |
| *Lophocolea heterophylla* | Woodland | 4 | 1 | 1 |
| *Metzgeria furcata* | Epiphyte | 5 | 2 | 3 |
| *Orthotrichum affine* | Epiphyte | 6 | 64 | 61 |
| *Orthotrichum diaphanum* | Common | 7 | 74 | 55 |
| *Orthotrichum lyellii* | Epiphyte | 6 | 7 | 7 |
| *Rhynchostegium confertum* | Common | 7 | 40 | 29 |
| *Syntrichia laevipila* | Common | 6 | 5 | 1 |
| *Syntrichia montana* | Built | 8 | 24 | 9 |
| *Syntrichia papillosa* | Epiphyte | 6 | 8 | 1 |
| *Syntrichia virescens* | Epiphyte | 6 | 3 | 2 |
| *Tortula muralis* | Built | 8 | 4 | 6 |
| *Ulota bruchii** | Epiphyte | 5 | 7 | 16 |
| *Ulota phyllantha* | Epiphyte | 5 | 1 | 3 |
| *Zygodon conoideus* | Epiphyte | 6 | 3 | 1 |
| *Zygodon rupestris* | Epiphyte | 6 | 4 | 1 |
| *Zygodon viridissimus* | Epiphyte | 6 | 3 | 0 |

\* *Ulota crispa sens. lat.* was also recorded from 1% of apples and 1% of pears.

**Figure 9.6** Rare colonists of orchards. (a) *Hypnum cupressiforme* var. *heseleri*, Elm, March 2007. (b) *Orthotrichum obtusifolium*, Elm, January 2008. (c) *Pterigynandrum filiforme* (with *Hypnum cupressiforme* var. *cupressiforme*), Elm, April 2010. (d) *Sanionia uncinata*, Wisbech, December 2004. Photos: Robin Stevenson.

has been recorded in an orchard but not in Stevenson's sample of individual trees. The Boreal-montane *Pterigynandrum filiforme* is otherwise almost unknown in lowland England (it has two sites in West Suffolk) and *Hypnum cupressiforme* var. *heseleri* is known from only one other site in Britain, an orchard in West Norfolk where it was discovered two years before it was found at the Cambridgeshire site.

### Differences in epiphytes between host species and cultivars

It is clear from Table 9.1 that the epiphytes of orchard apples and pears are broadly similar. However, three of the more calcicolous species (*Bryum capillare, Homalothecium sericeum, Syntrichia montana*) are much more frequent on apples than pears. The same is true of *Syntrichia papillosa* which, though not normally regarded as a calcicole, was also associated with *Homalothecium sericeum* and *Syntrichia montana* in Whitelaw & Burton's (2015) analysis. They suggest that these species are more frequent on trees which have thicker trunks and are planted further apart. Conversely, several relatively calcifuge mosses are more frequent on pears (*Campylopus introflexus, Ceratodon purpureus, Dicranoweisia cirrata, Kindbergia praelonga, Ulota bruchii*). Another feature of Table 9.1 is the higher frequency of the ruderal species *Bryum argenteum* and *B. dichotomum* on pears, perhaps because all the pears were recorded in working orchards.

The mean number of epiphyte taxa recorded per tree was similar for apples (6.7) and pears (6.3), but much lower for the one stand of plums studied (2.7). Values for a single cultivar in one orchard varied from 3.3 to 10.3 for apples and 3.5 to 9.6 for pears. The varieties of *Hypnum cupressiforme* are treated as separate taxa in calculating these figures.

Cambridgeshire's orchards often included a mixture of cultivars, in part to insure against the failure of any one cultivar to fruit in a particular year. In many surviving orchards Bramleys are the dominant variety, but some include rows of dessert apples growing between them and others include blocks of different cultivars (Figure 9.7). In an analysis which examined the variation in the epiphytic flora of seven apple cultivars in five orchards in Cambridgeshire and Norfolk, Stevenson *et al.* (2017) found that 16% of the variation could be attributed to the orchard and 4% to the cultivar (80% was unexplained by the model). Howgate Wonder had a very poor epiphyte flora (and in many cases supported no epiphytes at all) whereas Bramleys (which, like Howgate Wonder, is a relatively large tree) and Cox were richer.

Whitelaw & Burton (2015) found that there was a high degree of overlap between the flora of the Bramleys in the different orchards they studied in Hertfordshire and Cambridgeshire, but that the differences between orchards were greater when frequency and bryophyte cover were taken into account. Tree characteristics, namely height, trunk girth and distance to nearest neighbour, accounted for 10% of the variation in their dataset. Tree age was not an important factor.

## Numerical analysis of Stevenson's orchard survey

The sample data listing the total number of trees on which each species was found in each orchard were analysed as follows. Counts were converted to a 1–10 scale so that orchards where many trees were counted were not given bigger weight. The resulting frequency table was clustered by spherical k-means clustering of species and orchards into four classes of species and four classes of orchards (Tables 9.2, 9.3). For the species, the main contrast is between those in cluster 1, characterised by *Homalothecium sericeum*, *Syntrichia papillosa* and *Bryum moravicum* (mostly obligate epiphytes) and those in cluster 2, characterised by *Grimmia pulvinata*, *Ceratodon purpureus* and *Bryum argenteum* (mostly ruderals and species of the built environment). Cluster 3 is intermediate with both epiphytes and ruderals moderately well represented. Clusters 3 and 4 are less species rich, cluster 4 especially so. In this cluster only *Hypnum cupressiforme*, *Bryum capillare* and *Dicranoweisia cirrata* were as common as in the other clusters; most other species were rarer.

There is, therefore, wide variation in the number of species per tree. Within the more species-rich orchards, there was an additional distinction between those orchards with a preponderance of the *Homalothecium sericeum-Syntrichia papillosa* species cluster, whose members were scarce on pears, and those with a preponderance of the *Grimmia pulvinata-Ceratodon purpureus* species cluster, which included both pears and apples.

**Table 9.3** Orchard data sorted by spherical k-means into four clusters of orchards and four clusters of species. Values for the species are mean frequencies, measured on a scale from 0 to 10. Values in italics represent under-representation of groups, and in bold represent high representation. Species present in fewer than 10 samples are omitted unless they are found in more than 50% of samples in one of the clusters.

| | Cluster | | | |
|---|---|---|---|---|
| | 1 | 2 | 3 | 4 |
| Number of orchards | 11 | 7 | 16 | 5 |
| Number samples of apples (Bramley's Seedling) | 11 (3) | 4(1) | 14(7) | 3(1) |
| Number samples of pears, plums | 0,0 | 3,0 | 1,1 | 2,0 |
| *Brachythecium rutabulum* | 7.5 | 9.1 | 5.7 | 2.4 |
| *Orthotrichum diaphanum* | 8.0 | 9.1 | 6.9 | 3.4 |
| *Amblystegium serpens* | 7.3 | 7.6 | 4.3 | 1.4 |
| *Orthotrichum affine* | 8.6 | 6.4 | 6.3 | 5.0 |
| *Rhynchostegium confertum* | 3.7 | 5.0 | 3.2 | 1.4 |
| *Syntrichia montana* | 2.8 | 2.9 | 1.6 | 0.4 |
| *Frullania dilatata* | 1.1 | 1.1 | 0.6 | 0.4 |
| *Orthotrichum lyellii* | 1.0 | 1.3 | 0.8 | 1.0 |
| *Kindbergia praelonga* | 2.0 | 2.9 | 0.6 | 1.0 |
| *Hypnum cupressiforme var. resupinatum* | 2.5 | 4.1 | 2.1 | 1.0 |
| *Ulota bruchii* | 1.4 | 2.1 | 0.9 | 0.8 |
| *Brachytheciastrum velutinum* | 1.7 | 1.1 | 0.6 | 0.2 |
| *Metzgeria furcata* | 0.6 | 0.6 | 0.5 | - |
| *Cryphaea heteromalla* | 0.6 | 0.3 | 0.3 | - |
| *Ulota phyllantha* | 0.6 | 0.6 | 0.2 | - |
| *Leskea polycarpa* | 0.4 | 0.6 | 0.3 | 0.2 |
| *Hypnum cupressiforme var. cupressiforme* | 9.0 | 5.0 | 9.5 | 9.8 |
| *Bryum capillare* | 6.2 | 3.9 | 5.4 | 4.0 |
| *Dicranoweisia cirrata* | 3.4 | 4.7 | 5.4 | 7.0 |
| *Isothecium myosuroides* | 0.5 | - | 0.4 | 0.8 |
| *Grimmia pulvinata* | *1.5* | **3.4** | 2.1 | 0.2 |
| *Ceratodon purpureus* | *0.9* | **3.0** | 1.3 | 1.4 |
| *Bryum argenteum* | - | **1.0** | 0.3 | - |
| *Campylopus introflexus* | - | **4.3** | 0.4 | 1.0 |
| *Leptodictyum riparium* | 0.1 | **0.6** | 0.3 | - |
| *Syntrichia virescens* | 0.3 | **0.9** | 0.7 | - |
| *Tortula muralis* | 0.3 | **1.1** | 0.4 | - |
| *Bryum dichotomum* | - | **1.7** | - | - |
| *Homalothecium sericeum* | **2.7** | *0.6* | 1.9 | 0.8 |
| *Syntrichia papillosa* | **1.8** | *0.4* | 1.3 | - |
| *Bryum moravicum* | **0.9** | *0.1* | 1.3 | - |
| *Zygodon rupestris* | **0.5** | *0.1* | 0.8 | 0.8 |
| *Syntrichia laevipila* | **0.6** | *0.3* | 0.6 | 0.8 |

**Table 9.2** Orchard clusters, showing fruit grown and mean number of species per tree. For further details of these clusters, see Table 9.3.

| Orchard cluster | 1 | 2 | 3 | 4 |
|---|---|---|---|---|
| Bramley's Seedling Apples | 3 | 1 | 7 | 1 |
| Other apples | 8 | 3 | 7 | 2 |
| Pears | - | 3 | 1 | 2 |
| Plums | - | - | 1 | - |
| Total number of orchards in cluster | 11 | 7 | 16 | 5 |
| Mean number of species per tree | 8.3 | 8.6 | 6.9 | 4.6 |

## Conclusions

The commercial orchards of Cambridgeshire were rather a transient, 20th-century feature, increasing massively in area from the 1870s to the 1930s and decreasing greatly from the 1970s. In their heyday they were intensively managed and they almost certainly had few epiphytic bryophytes. The remaining orchards are now less intensively managed and the semi-standard habit of the trees means that entire trees are accessible to the bryologist. They now support a richer epiphyte flora. We do not have the evidence to track this colonisation in orchards, but it presumably started at the same time as the more general spread of epiphytes in the county in the late 1980s. Epiphytic bryophytes differ according to orchard and host tree, but the extent of these differences is rather limited, reflecting the relatively homogeneous nature of the habitat. Intensive surveys have shown that several rare epiphytes are now present in orchards at very low frequency. These are almost certainly long-distance colonists and their occurrence is a striking example of the dispersal ability of bryophytes. Whether such species would also have been found elsewhere if over 1000 non-orchard trees (including their upper branches) had been examined systematically is an open question.

**Figure 9.7** Grenadier apple trees in an orchard at Popple Lane, Leverington, November 2007. Photo: Robin Stevenson.

# 10

# Wetland and calcifuge species

## The species

The largest group of species identified in the cluster analysis (Chapter 6) is, rather surprisingly, made up of some bryophytes of calcareous fens and others found in wet or dry, acidic habitats. The reason for this mixture will become apparent in this chapter. In short, there are few wetlands and few acidic habitats in the modern county, and the surviving calcareous fens have (or have had) a surprisingly large number of calcifuge species. These are a result of the acidification of fen peat at Wicken and to some extent at Chippenham, where decaying logs also provide an acidic substrate. Most of the species can be separated into two groups by applying Ellenberg values for 'reaction', i.e. substrate pH (Hill *et al.* 2007). The Acid group, with R values 1, 2, 3 or 4, comprises 49 species (Table 10.1). The Fen group, with R values 6, 7 or 8, comprises 15 species (Table 10.2). The 10 species for which R=5 have been divided into four that are strict calcifuges (*Hookeria lucens, Pohlia lescuriana, P. lutescens, Pseudephemerum nitidum*) and the remaining six which are not. The epiphyte *Frullania tamarisci* has R=4, and is arbitrarily included in the Fen group.

There are only five widespread (or formerly widespread) species in the cluster and the Frescalo analysis shows clear evidence for the decline of four of these since the 1980s, *Dicranum scoparium, Plagiothecium denticulatum, Pohlia nutans* and *Polytrichum juniperinum*; the decline of *P. nutans* in woodland is illustrated in Figure 8.4. The cluster has the highest percentage of species not seen since 1999 (43%) and many of the extant species are rare or very rare. The wetland calcicoles have lost proportionately fewer species (32%) than the calcifuges (47%), but the percentage of extinct wetland calcicoles is nevertheless higher than that

**Table 10.1** Species of acidic habitats included in the Acid & Fen habitat cluster. Species which have not been recorded in the recent survey are not italicised and the date of the last record is given. Ellenberg R values are an indication of species' substrate preference ranging from 1 (extreme acidity, mainly bog species) to 5 (moderately acid). CWG signifies whether species have been found at Gamlingay or Chippenham Fen or Wicken Fen in the period 1950–2017 or (lower case letters) were last seen there before 1950; the number of other 1950–2017 sites is indicated in a separate column.

| Species | R | Sites | Visits | Last record | CWG | Other sites | Species | R | Sites | Visits | Last record | CWG | Other sites |
|---|---|---|---|---|---|---|---|---|---|---|---|---|---|---|
| *Dicranum scoparium* | 3 | 64 | 131 | | CWG | 53 | *Calypogeia muelleriana* | 2 | 2 | 3 | | G | 1 |
| *Pohlia nutans* | 2 | 40 | 83 | | CWG | 33 | *Racomitrium ericoides* | 4 | 2 | 3 | 1961 | | 2 |
| *Polytrichastrum formosum* | 3 | 35 | 70 | | CWG | 27 | *Racomitrium lanuginosum* | 2 | 2 | 3 | 1984 | | 2 |
| *Plagiothecium denticulatum* | 4 | 23 | 46 | | CWG | 14 | *Sphagnum denticulatum* | 2 | 2 | 3 | | WG | |
| *Polytrichum juniperinum* | 3 | 22 | 38 | | WG | 19 | *Cephaloziella hampeana* | 2 | 2 | 2 | 1968 | G | 2 |
| *Hypnum jutlandicum* | 2 | 16 | 33 | | CWG | 9 | Hookeria lucens | 5 | 1 | 3 | 1975 | W | |
| *Campylopus flexuosus* | 2 | 13 | 28 | | CWG | 6 | Dicranella cerviculata | 2 | 1 | 2 | 1968 | | 1 |
| *Campylopus pyriformis* | 2 | 12 | 29 | | CWG | 4 | Racomitrium heterostichum | 2 | 1 | 2 | 1961 | | 1 |
| *Cephalozia bicuspidata* | 2 | 11 | 25 | | CWG | 7 | *Bryum bornholmense* | 3 | 1 | 1 | | G | |
| *Calypogeia fissa* | 3 | 10 | 30 | | CWG | 5 | Calypogeia arguta | 4 | 1 | 1 | 1988 | G | |
| *Polytrichum commune* | 2 | 9 | 14 | | CWG | 3 | Cephaloziella rubella | 2 | 1 | 1 | 1934 | g | |
| *Plagiothecium undulatum* | 2 | 7 | 8 | | CWG | 3 | Diplophyllum albicans | 2 | 1 | 1 | 1988 | G | |
| *Dicranum montanum* | 3 | 6 | 14 | | CG | 3 | *Fossombronia wondraczekii* | 4 | 1 | 1 | 1988 | G | |
| Pleurozium schreberi | 2 | 6 | 9 | 1999 | WG | 3 | *Pohlia lescuriana* | 5 | 1 | 1 | | G | |
| *Pellia epiphylla* | 4 | 5 | 14 | | CWG | 1 | *Sphagnum russowii* | 2 | 1 | 1 | | W | |
| *Sphagnum palustre* | 3 | 4 | 15 | | Wg | | Archidium alternifolium | 4 | - | - | 1788 | g | |
| *Polytrichum piliferum* | 3 | 4 | 4 | | G | 4 | Bartramia pomiformis | 4 | - | - | 1838 | g | |
| *Sphagnum subnitens* | 3 | 3 | 15 | | cWg | | Lophozia ventricosa | 2 | - | - | 1820 | g | |
| *Sphagnum fimbriatum* | 3 | 3 | 13 | | WG | | Odontoschisma sphagni | 1 | - | - | 1820 | g | |
| *Sphagnum squarrosum* | 4 | 3 | 13 | | Wg | | Philonotis fontana | 4 | - | - | 1838 | g | |
| *Leucobryum glaucum* | 2 | 3 | 7 | | CW | | Pogonatum aloides | 3 | - | - | c. 1830 | g | |
| *Polytrichastrum longisetum* | 3 | 3 | 7 | 1991 | W | 2 | Pogonatum nanum | 3 | - | - | 1829 | g | |
| *Aulacomnium palustre* | 3 | 3 | 6 | | Wg | 1 | Sphagnum papillosum | 1 | - | - | 1824 | g | |
| *Pohlia lutescens* | 5 | 3 | 5 | | G | 1 | Sphagnum tenellum | 1 | - | - | c. 1800 | g | |
| Sphagnum fallax | 2 | 3 | 5 | 1988 | WG | | Sphagnum teres | 4 | - | - | 1824 | g | |
| *Pseudephemerum nitidum* | 5 | 3 | 4 | | G | | Splachnum ampullaceum | 4 | - | - | 1841 | g | |
| Rhytidiadelphus loreus | 2 | 2 | 5 | 1989 | W | | | | | | | | |

for the species in any other habitat cluster, including the Calcicole species of dry calcareous habitats (18%).

Most of the species in the Acid and Fen cluster occur in Chippenham and Wicken Fens or at Gamlingay (Table 10.3). The fate of these is considered in the analysis that follows. There are seven other sites with seven or more species in the cluster. The two richest are Hayley Wood and Little Widgham Wood which share six calcifuge species (*Campylopus flexuosus, Dicranum scoparium, Plagiothecium denticulatum, Pohlia nutans, Polytrichastrum formosum, Polytrichum juniperinum*) and two wetland species (*Chiloscyphus pallescens, Rhizomnium punctatum*). A few of the more frequent calcifuges, and some calcifuge species classified in the Woodland cluster (Chapter 8), can be found in the relict areas of high-level gravels such as the Observatory Gravels at the Cambridge Observatory (*Atrichum undulatum, Mnium hornum, Polytrichastrum formosum*), Hildersham Furze Hills (*Dicranum scoparium*) and even a disused gravel pit on the Gog Magog Hills (*Atrichum undulatum*).

We start the site accounts by outlining what we know of the Cambridge 'moors', lost wetlands from which there are a few significant records of mosses made by the early bryologists and which doubtless supported many more.

## The lost wetlands

### The Cambridge 'moors'
The 'moors' were the richest plant habitats within easy reach of botanists living in Cambridge in the 17th and 18th centuries. They stretched in an arc from Teversham, east of the town, clockwise though Fulbourn, Cherry Hinton and Shelford to Trumpington south-west of Cambridge. They were at the northern edge of the exposed chalk, situated on the Lower Chalk below the junction with the Middle Chalk. They were presumably fed by springs from the Chalk, although as far as we know no one has attempted a detailed reconstruction of their hydrology. The springs at Cherry Hinton are described by Wareham & Wright (2002), and Hawkins (1990) illustrated the probable natural drainage of Teversham, Fulbourn and Wilbraham Fens, fed by a series of springs from the chalk to the south.

Hinton Moor was common land, an intercommon between Cambridge and Hinton parish (Hesse 2007). It was an easy walk from Cambridge and thus the best known of these sites. Ray (1660: 35) found *Cirsium dissectum* along 'the foot-way from Cambridge to Cherry-hinton', and on reaching 'the next field to Cherry-hinton church through which the foot-path from Cambridge lies' he saw *Vinca minor*.[5]

**Table 10.2** Species of basic wetland habitats included in the Acid & Fen habitat cluster. Species which have not been recorded in the recent survey are not italicised and the date of the last record is given. Ellenberg R values are an indication of species' substrate preference ranging from 5 (moderately basic) to 8 (strongly basic). CWG signifies whether species have been found at Gamlingay or Chippenham Fen or Wicken Fen in the period 1950–2017 (or lower case letters) were last seen there before 1950; the number of other 1950–2017 sites is indicated in a separate column.

| Species | R | Sites | Visits | Last record | CWG | Other sites |
|---|---|---|---|---|---|---|
| *Rhizomnium punctatum* | 5 | 31 | 89 | | CWG | 26 |
| *Riccardia chamedryfolia* | 6 | 30 | 34 | | CWG | 23 |
| *Campylium protensum* | 6 | 22 | 64 | | CWG | 17 |
| *Bryum pseudotriquetrum* | 6 | 22 | 43 | | CWg | 19 |
| *Ricciocarpos natans* | 7 | 22 | 40 | | cW | 16 |
| *Fissidens adianthoides* | 6 | 15 | 57 | | CW | 12 |
| *Brachythecium salebrosum* | 6 | 15 | 17 | | CW | 12 |
| *Chiloscyphus pallescens* | 6 | 11 | 45 | | CWG | 8 |
| *Plagiomnium elatum* | 6 | 10 | 43 | | CW | 6 |
| *Climacium dendroides* | 5 | 9 | 17 | | CWg | 4 |
| *Bryum pallens* | 6 | 6 | 8 | | CW | 4 |
| Riccardia multifida | 5 | 5 | 5 | 1988 | CWG | 1 |
| *Campylium stellatum* | 6 | 2 | 3 | | CWg | |
| Palustriella commutata | 8 | 2 | 3 | 1960 | C | |
| *Plagiomnium ellipticum* | 5 | 2 | 2 | | CW | 1 |
| Loeskeobryum brevirostre | 5 | 1 | 4 | 1989 | W | |
| Calliergon giganteum | 6 | 1 | 1 | 1942 | | |
| *Frullania tamarisci* | 4 | 1 | 1 | | W | |
| Ephemerum cohaerens | 5 | - | - | | C | |
| Palustriella falcata | 6 | - | - | 1929 | w | |
| Preissia quadrata | 7 | - | - | 1832 | | |
| Scorpidium revolvens | 6 | - | - | 1829 | g | |

**Table 10.3** Sites with at least seven species in the Acid and Fen Cluster.

| Site | Acid | Fen | Since 2000 | Comment |
|---|---|---|---|---|
| Gamlingay | 44 | 9 | 20 | Acid bogs and woodland |
| Chippenham Fen | 15 | 16 | 20 | Fen with planted woodland and carr |
| Wicken Fen | 26 | 17 | 23 | Fen with carr and now some former arable |
| Hayley Wood | 10 | 3 | 6 | Ancient wood |
| Little Widgham Wood | 8 | 2 | 6 | Ancient wood |
| Whittlesford | 2 | 6 | 0 | None since 1959; formerly calcareous springs |
| Hardwick Wood | 6 | 1 | 0 | Ancient wood, now relatively open |
| Botanic Garden | 4 | 3 | 5 | Garden with introduced substrates |
| March | 7 | 0 | 7 | Disused railway sidings, visited 2001 |
| Whittlesey | 2 | 5 | 5 | Disused clay pits |

5 The story that the geologist Adam Sedgwick 'shot snipes' on this path in 1802, included as a note in E.B. Cowell's copy of Babington's *Flora* (Cambridge University Library, classmark Adv.d.78.16), is irresistible, though slightly spoilt by the knowledge that in 1802 Sedgwick was still a schoolboy in Yorkshire.

The flowering plants he recorded from the moors are listed by Oswald & Preston (2011: 44) and allow us to visualise their habitats. The vegetation must have included short, calcareous fenland communities supporting *Anagallis tenella, Epipactis palustris, Parnassia palustris, Pinguicula vulgaris* ('on all the moores ... plentifully'), *Triglochin palustris* and *Valeriana dioica*, with *Sagina nodosa* 'near the watery places' and *Cladium mariscus* and *Liparis loeselii* 'in the watery places'. *Butomus umbellatus, Nymphaea alba* and *Potamogeton natans* must have grown in these waters. The presence of *Drosera intermedia, Epilobium palustre, Eriophorum angustifolium* and *Potentilla erecta* suggests that there was some more acidic ground. Ray's records of *Asperula cynanchica, Astragalus danicus* and *Hippocrepis comosa* 'on the drier part' of the moors shows that the wetland communities graded into chalk grassland. Similarly *Spiranthes spiralis* was found 'on the skirts of Teversham Moor' and *Aquilegia vulgaris* 'in a little thicket' there.

The only bryophyte recorded by Ray from Hinton Moor was *Polytrichum commune*, but Vernon recorded bryophytes on Teversham, Hinton and Trumpington Moors. The Martyns added just one or two records but Relhan found rather more; he also knew Fulbourn, Shelford and the more distant Sawston Moor. Inevitably, given the state of bryological knowledge at the time and the absence of localised specimens, the only records we can match to current species are those of the more distinctive bryophytes. Those recorded from Hinton Moor fit the picture of the vegetation we have deduced from the vascular plants. *Aneura pinguis, Bryum pseudotriquetrum, Calliergonella cuspidata, Campylium stellatum, Cratoneuron filicinum, Fissidens adianthoides* and *Scorpidium scorpioides* would have grown in the calcareous wetlands, with *Conocephalum conicum* by the shaded sides of water courses, *Funaria hygrometrica, Physcomitrium pyriforme* and perhaps *Pohlia melanodon* on disturbed ground and *Splachnum ampullaceum* on dung. The records of *Aulacomnium palustre, Mnium hornum, Philonotis fontana, Polytrichum commune* and *Sphagnum* spp. add to the evidence for more acidic areas. There must clearly have been very many more species than these. It is particularly frustrating that we do not have the evidence to identify the *Sphagnum* species, the thallose liverwort recorded on Hinton and other moors by Relhan as *Marchantia hemisphaerica* (probably *Preissia quadrata*), Vernon's *Muscus palustris terrestri similis* etc. (sometimes interpreted as *Palustriella falcata*, which would not be unlikely) and several of Relhan's pleurocarpous mosses.

Hinton Moor was drained soon after enclosure in 1810. Cambridge has expanded to incorporate Cherry Hinton; the Moor is now largely built over and most of the water courses are covered up. Shelford Moor survived for a few years longer than Hinton Moor but Great Shelford was enclosed in 1835 and both Shelford Moor and the nearly Trumpington Moor have been obliterated.

Further from Cambridge, much modified remnants of semi-natural vegetation survived into recent decades, or still persist. Hawkins (1990) showed that the drainage of Wilbraham, Fulbourn and Teversham Fens had already been modified in medieval times to provide power for water mills. Major drainage works followed the parliamentary enclosure of the parishes between 1797 and 1815. The wetland vegetation in those areas of Fulbourn Fen and Teversham Fen which were included in the Wilbraham Fens SSSI in 1951 was not pristine fenland but had developed after the drainage of these areas had deteriorated during the agricultural depressions of the late 19th and early 20th centuries and the interwar years. A renewed drying out of the area became apparent by the early 1960s as a result of restoration of the drainage and a general lowering of the water table (Cambridgeshire and Isle of Ely County Council Planning Department 1965). The current SSSI excludes the land in Fulbourn and Teversham, much of which is now arable farmland. Further south, vegetation which is probably not too dissimilar to that of the drier areas of the former 'moors' persists in the current Fulbourn Fen SSSI (a different site to that described above) and in Sawston Hall Meadows SSSI.

### Other lost sites

It is clear from vascular plant records that other wetlands had a rich flora but we know little or nothing about their bryophytes. Burwell Fen and Thriplow are good examples. Burwell Fen, a calcareous fenland south of Wicken, was drained in 1840; a specimen of *Preissia quadrata* collected there in 1832 is the sole bryophyte record and a tantalising glimpse of what must have been an interesting bryophyte flora. The flora of Thriplow before enclosure (Thriplow Common/Heath, Ninewells and the Peat Holes) is known mainly from the manuscript volumes of G.N. Maynard. *Parnassia palustris* and *Pinguicula vulgaris* grew by calcareous springs and streams at Ninewells, *Pulsatilla vulgaris* was abundant on heathy land nearby, *Calluna vulgaris* grew in profusion on Thriplow Heath and *Drosera anglica, D. rotundifolia* and *Eriophorum vaginatum* were found in wet areas which must have been more acidic (Crompton 1959). The Heath was drained and ploughed *c.* 1842 but some of the more interesting plants survived by the springs. We have no bryophyte records from Thriplow before enclosure, but *Palustriella commutata* survived long enough to be recorded by Paul Richards *c.* 1928. Thriplow Peat Holes is an SSSI.

## Chippenham Fen

Chippenham Fen, though it lies close to the eastern edge of the county, is our nearest surviving equivalent to the Cambridge 'moors'. Like the moors, it rests on the Lower Chalk just below the junction with the Middle Chalk, and the shallow depression in which it lies is spring-fed by calcareous water. It was actually called 'Chippenham Moor' by botanists until the late 19th century. Many of the plants of calcareous wetland which were recorded from the moors have also been found at Chippenham (Oswald & Preston 2011). Peat cutting at the site is documented from the 12th century onwards (Wareham & Wright 2002) and presumably it was responsible for lowering the surface of the land. The current landscape owes much to the work of John Tharp (1744–1804), who owned extensive sugar plantations in Jamaica. He bought the Chippenham Park estate in 1791 at a time when the agricultural improvers described the Moor as 'drowned, and in a very deplorable state' and producing 'little else than sedge, which is cut for thatch, litter, or fuel' (Vancouver 1794). Contemporary accounts credited Tharp with lowering the water table by five feet (Young 1805), and he planted areas of woodland which survive (in a much modified state) as Forty Acre Plantation and the Jerusalem Plantations. In an elegant study of tree rings, Kassas (1951) showed that conditions remained good for tree growth for the first four decades of the 19th century but deteriorated from 1840 to 1860, presumably because Tharp's drainage ditches were not maintained. There were further drainage works in the First and Second World Wars (1918, 1942), again reflected in the improved growth of established trees. Ash trees also began to colonise the fen vegetation in 1885 (Kassas 1952). There was a further wave of colonisation after 1918 and a third wave of colonisation followed the renewed drainage of the site in 1942. The site became a National Nature Reserve in 1963 and water levels can now be regulated by a system of sluices and dams. The fen vegetation is maintained by a combination of mowing and grazing, and a small herd of water buffalo was introduced in 2001 (Figure 10.1). Currently, the fen is grazed by water buffalo and cattle, as well as muntjac deer. There has been a recent, very thorough survey of the vascular plants (Leslie 2015).

Chippenham Fen was scarcely mentioned by the early Cambridgeshire botanists, but the site came into prominence with the discovery of Cambridge Milk-parsley *Selinum carvifolia* there in 1882. There was one early bryophyte record, Relhan's (1786) *Campylium stellatum sens. lat.*, and a few records in the late 19th and early 20th centuries (see Chapter 3). These included *Sphagnum subnitens*, which grew with *Drosera rotundifolia*. The first list of bryophytes from the Fen was made by R.A. Lewin and P.M. Priestley in 1941 and several bryologists visited the site in the 1950s and 1960s. The first bryophyte excursion took place in 1975 and was notable for the discovery of *Nowellia curvifolia*, found by Brian Huntley and Harold Whitehouse in Forty Acre Wood. After this Chippenham became a regular venue, with further excursions in 1976, 1977, 1981, 1985, 1986, 2001, 2004 and 2009 and a British Bryological Society field meeting in 2017.

### Bryophyte changes since 1950
There is little trend in the records (Figure 10.2) except for a marked increase in ruderals and arable species (not shown in the figure) after the introduction of buffalo to the site in 2001. *Bryum pallens* and

**Figure 10.1** Water buffalo (*Bubalus bubalis*) at Chippenham Fen NNR, July 2007. Photo: Ruth Angrave (Natural England).

*Physcomitrium pyriforme* also appeared, and remarkably *Ephemerum cohaerens* in 2017. The woodlands were little visited during the 1950s and but were the focus of attention in the 1970s, when wetland species were poorly recorded. During the 1990s the site was hardly visited; only *Campylium stellatum sens. lat.*, *Orthotrichum affine* and *O. lyellii* were recorded. Bryophytes of the Woodland Cluster were well represented from 1960 onwards, with *Lepidozia reptans*, *Nowellia curvifolia*, *Herzogiella seligeri* and *Tetraphis pellucida* notably persistent. Several species of the Acid cluster were apparently casuals: *Dicranum montanum*, *Leucobryum glaucum*, *Plagiothecium undulatum* and *Polytrichum commune*.

Most wetland species persisted, but these are not a very numerous group even though the site is a fen. *Palustriella commutata* disappeared after 1960 because the calcifying springs were drying up. *Campyliadelphus elodes* was refound after an absence of 57 years. Here as at Wicken Fen this small and inconspicuous plant may merely have eluded bryologists' eyes. The discovery of *Plagiomnium ellipticum* in 2017 is enigmatic. It was in an area grazed by buffalo, but it was poorly understood by local bryologists in the 20th century, and may previously have been misidentified as *P. affine*.

One slightly puzzling feature of Chippenham is the poverty of the epiphyte flora, which does not show the marked increase we have noted at many other sites.

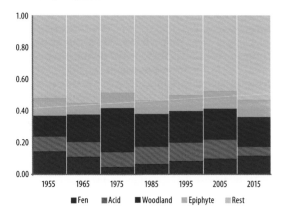

**Figure 10.2** Proportions of fenland species, calcifuges, woodland species and epiphytes in Chippenham Fen in the period 1950–2017. There were almost no records in the 1990s, so the values are interpolated as the mean of 1980s and 2000s.

## Wicken Fen

Wicken Fen, like Chippenham, was not known to the early Cambridge botanists. Until the early 19th century the Cambridge 'moors' were the sites to which they went to see plants of calcareous wetlands, and after their destruction Bottisham Fen and Burwell Fen were the places known to Henslow, Jenyns and their contemporaries in the 1820s and 1830s. It was only after Burwell Fen was drained in 1840 that botanists turned to Wicken (Rowell 1997). Wicken probably survived because of the importance of its main crop, sedge (*Cladium mariscus*), formerly used for fuel, thatching and for a surprisingly wide range of other purposes. It was first highlighted as a botanical site by Babington (1860) who described it as the only Fenland spot he knew in the county 'in which the ancient vegetation continues undisturbed and the land is sufficiently wet to allow of its coming to perfection' whereas steam drainage had reduced the rest of the Fens to 'a pattern in farming'. Babington included a complete list of the vascular plants he knew at the Fen in his flora, and after that botanical records continued to accumulate (Friday, Moore & Ballard 1997). Wicken also became a famous entomological site, and it was the entomologists who led the moves to preserve the Fen. J.C. Mobberly bought two acres of the Fen in 1893 and sold them to the National Trust in 1899. Wicken thus became the first of the National Trust's reserves, and its holding was greatly increased in 1911 when another entomologist, G.H. Verrall, bequeathed the 220 acres he had acquired by piecemeal purchases to the Trust. The flora and fauna of the Fen became well documented, thanks in large part to the link that the reserve developed with Cambridge University. Knowledge of the Fen was initially summarised in *The natural history of Wicken Fen* (Gardiner 1925–32, Gardiner & Tansley 1923), which included a chapter on the bryophytes (Richards 1932), and later in books edited by Friday (1997) and Friday & Harley (2000).

The colonisation of Wicken Fen by bushes started in the second half of the 19th century. One of the major constituents of the fen carr (scrub), *Frangula alnus*, does not appear in Babington's (1860) list for Wicken but he collected it there in 1861 and by 1898 it was abundant. Yapp (1908) detected at Wicken 'all the features of a drying-up marsh ... it may almost be said to be verging on another forest period'. Bushes, including *Frangula*, *Rhamnus cathartica*, *Salix* and *Viburnum opulus*, were few in the western part of the Fen but formed 'large and continuous thickets' to the east. *Frangula* was the commonest species and its stands were 'so dense that practically all other vegetation is excluded. The great number of seedlings and young plants of various ages which are found not only bordering these thickets, but elsewhere on the Fen, bears witness to the rapid rate at which this species is increasing'. (Yapp perhaps failed to appreciate the importance of mowing in suppressing the woody vegetation, a factor later established by Godwin.)

The drying of the Fen was accentuated by the installation of reliable pumping equipment at Upware in the 1940s. Hydrological studies later showed that much water was being lost from the Fen until the leaky northern boundary was sealed in 1987–88 (Lock & Bennett 1993); a new waterproof bank was constructed along the eastern margin of the reserve in 1990–91 (Lock *et al.* 1997).

Lock *et al.* (1997) documented the 'continuous battle against the relentless progress of succession' waged by successive site managers for much of the 20th century. Despite attempts to clear carr manually, and experiments with burning and herbicide treatments (Anon. 1963), the majority of the Fen was still covered by woody vegetation at the end of the century (Friday, Walters & Lock 1997). Fen vegetation was restricted to fields which were cut for reed, sedge or 'litter' (mixed vegetation). Lock *et al.* (1997) clearly thought that the best that could be done was to maintain the status quo. 'Scrub clearance continues today but at a very much reduced rate ... there is little enthusiasm for further large-scale scrub clearance ... it is perhaps time to adopt a more positive attitude to this habitat on the Fen'.

Rather than following Lock's recommendation, the National Trust celebrated the centenary of the Wicken reserve by developing plans for drastic scrub clearance in order to restore herbaceous vegetation to much of the Fen (Colston & Friday 1999). Most of the scrub was cleared in 2000–04 (Figure 10.3), leaving only three large blocks. In Verrall's Fen (but not Sedge Fen) the area from which the scrub had been cleared was grazed from 2001 by Konik ponies (Figure 10.4) and also, from 2012, by Highland cattle (Stroh & Croft 2015). It is this change in management that has allowed the large area of scrub to be cleared, as it made it possible to avoid a continuing commitment to cut unfeasibly large areas of vegetation.

In addition to changes to the management of the historic fenland area, the Wicken reserve has been extended in recent decades by the incorporation of former agricultural land, starting with over 60 ha of Baker's Fen in 1992 (Barratt *et al.* 1999). These have been developed as wet pastures with new ditches and scrapes (Figure 10.5).

**Figure 10.3** Clearing the fen carr at Wicken Fen, *c.* 2002. Photo: Martin Lester (National Trust).

**Figure 10.4** Konik ponies, introduced to graze the land cleared of scrub, Verrall's Fen, Wicken Fen, April 2008. Photo: Pete Stroh.

**Figure 10.5** Recent extensions to Wicken Fen, viewed from the north in April 2013. Baker's Fen, on the left, was incorporated into the reserve in 1992. Behind it lies Burwell Fen, a calcareous fen until the 1840s; it has been arable until recently but parts of it are now being restored as a wetland habitat. Photographed from a drone operated by Martin Lester (National Trust).

### Bryophyte changes since 1950

Whereas Chippenham Fen was relatively stable after 1950, the changes at Wicken Fen were spectacular. Before 1960 the Fen had been regarded as bryologically rather poor. Richards (1932) listed only 23 species, although they included fen specialists such as *Ricciocarpos natans* (Figure 10.6), *Bryum pseudotriquetrum*, *Campyliadelphus elodes*, *Campylium stellatum*, *Fissidens adianthoides*, *Oxyrrhynchium speciosum*, *Palustriella falcata* (as *P. commutata*) and *Plagiomnium elatum* as well as three colonists of ground burnt in a recent fire. Then in 1963 J.M. Lock found an area of young fen carr, perhaps 25 years old, in which the surface peat had become acidic, with pH locally as low at 4.2 (Lock 1964). Twelve calcifuge species had become established, of which *Hookeria lucens*, *Polytrichum commune*, *Sphagnum fimbriatum* and *Tetraphis pellucida* were reported in a note added in proof to *A flora of Cambridgeshire* (Perring *et al.* 1964). *Tetraphis* proved to be a casual and was never refound. *Hookeria* lasted for 12 years, but most of the other species persisted for decades.

After the discovery of these interesting species, the carr at Wicken received many visits from bryologists. Leslie (1974) surveyed the Godwin Plots I–V in detail; these 20 × 20 m experimental plots had been established by Harry Godwin in 1927 to study the effects of the frequency of mowing on the fen vegetation but had developed into fen carr after the experiment was discontinued in 1940 (Friday *et al.* 1999). The presence of numerous calcifuges in these well studied areas was additional evidence that they were relatively recent colonists. By 1975 five *Sphagnum* species were known from Wicken. The main habitats of the calcifuges were decaying tussocks of *Molinia* killed by shading in fen carr, raised ridges of peat which stood above the winter water level in areas of long-disused peat cuttings and the entire peat surface of the Fen in areas of carr which were too high to be flooded in the 1970s and 1980s (Lock 1990).

The colonisation of *Sphagnum* species at Wicken was interpreted as the start of a natural succession which had become familiar from the analysis of pollen and macrofossils in postglacial peat deposits, the replacement of fen carr by raised bog (Lock 1990). Godwin himself had been a pioneer of such studies and he illustrated the generalised succession, and examples from specific sites, in his popular work *Fenland* (1978). As far as we know, none of us realised at the time that the process was almost certainly being greatly accelerated by the acidifying effects of $SO_2$ pollution.

In retrospect the 1970s proved to be the high point of calcifuge occupancy (Figure 10.7). The extreme drought of 1976 may have killed off *Hookeria lucens*. Calcifuges were lost in the 1980s because of fire, scrub death and flooding (Lock 1990). One particularly rich area was accidentally burnt, killing the *Frangula* canopy. There was widespread die-back of *Frangula* in the 1980s, possibly due to fungal infection. The waterproofing of some of the fen banks in 1987–89 increased the amount of winter flooding which raised the pH. In spite of this, there were some areas in the south of the fen which retained acid peat on the surface. Tussocky *Sphagnum* was partly protected because it grew clear of the peat surface. The programme of widespread scrub clearance was instigated in 2000, but there was sufficient scrub remaining in 2003 for us to record six *Sphagnum* species. Since that date no *Sphagnum* has been seen and the calcifuges have almost all disappeared (Table 10.4). There are eight calcifuge survivors: *Atrichum undulatum*, *Aulacomnium androgynum*, *Campylopus introflexus*, *Dicranum scoparium*, *Hypnum jutlandicum*, *Plagiothecium curvifolium*, *P. denticulatum* and *P. nemorale*. Most of these are frequent in long-established woodland and

**Figure 10.6** *Ricciocarpos natans* at Wicken Fen, October 2005. Photo: Robin Stevenson.

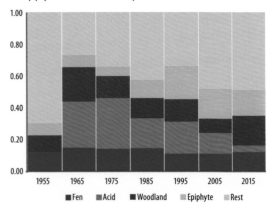

**Figure 10.7** Proportions of fenland species, calcifuges, woodland species and epiphytes in Wicken Fen in the period 1950–2017.

■ Fen  ■ Acid  ■ Woodland  ▨ Epiphyte  ▨ Rest

will probably persist indefinitely in Wicken Fen. The carr also supports some calcifuge species in the Woodland habitat cluster, such as *Mnium hornum* (Figure 10.8).

The increase in epiphytes at Wicken in the 1980s and 1990s can be seen in Figure 10.7, and in the moist fen carr they may be as luxuriant as anywhere in the county. Scrub clearance seems to have eliminated *Frullania tamarisci*, *Hypnum andoi*, *O. stramineum*, *O. tenellum* and *Zygodon viridissimus*. Except for *F. tamarisci* these species are likely to recolonise the site in places where carr is still tolerated.

As at Chippenham, *Bryum pallens* (Figure 10.9) has appeared in the grazed areas. The extension of the site to include former arable fields in the 'Wicken Vision' area has also added arable and ruderal species to the Wicken list. While some of these would have been present before conversion to grassland, *Riccia cavernosa* (Figure 10.10) and *Aphanorrhegma patens* are probably newcomers, taking advantage of seasonally flooded pools to complete their life cycle.

## Gamlingay

Gamlingay was a magnet for Cambridgeshire botanists from the time of John Ray until the First World War (Chapter 3). They were attracted by the complex of acidic habitats on the Woburn Sands. This area extends across the county boundary to Potton and Sandy in Bedfordshire, although it was not the habit of the Cambridgeshire botanists to venture into the neighbouring county. A remarkably detailed map of Gamlingay prepared by Thomas Langdon for Merton College, Oxford in 1602 shows that in many ways Gamlingay was a typical Cambridgeshire village, with a nucleus of houses and small, hedged fields ('closes')

**Table 10.4** Transient species in the carr at Wicken Fen 1963–2003.

**Liverworts**

| | |
|---|---|
| *Calypogeia fissa* | *Pellia epiphylla* |
| *Cephalozia bicuspidata* | *Riccardia multifida* |
| *Chiloscyphus pallescens†* | |

**Mosses**

| | |
|---|---|
| *Aulacomnium palustre* | *Polytrichastrum longisetum* |
| *Brachythecium salebrosum†* | *Polytrichum commune* |
| *Campylopus flexuosus* | *Polytrichum juniperinum\** |
| *Campylopus pyriformis* | *Rhytidiadelphus loreus* |
| *Dicranella heteromalla* | *Rhytidiadelphus triquetrus†\** |
| *Hookeria lucens* | *Sphagnum denticulatum\** |
| *Hylocomium splendens†\** | *Sphagnum fallax\** |
| *Leucobryum glaucum* | *Sphagnum fimbriatum* |
| *Loeskeobryum brevirostre†* | *Sphagnum palustre* |
| *Orthodontium lineare* | *Sphagnum russowii\** |
| *Plagiothecium undulatum* | *Sphagnum squarrosum* |
| *Pleurozium schreberi* | *Sphagnum subnitens* |
| *Pohlia nutans* | *Tetraphis pellucida\** |
| *Polytrichastrum formosum* | |

†Not calcifuge; \*Found only once.

**Figure 10.8** *Mnium hornum*, one of the few remaining calcifuges in the carr at Wicken Fen, perched above the calcareous ground-water, March 2018. Photo: Chris Preston.

**Figure 10.9** *Bryum pallens* on wood left behind after scrub clearance at Wicken Fen, April 2008. Photo: Robin Stevenson.

**Figure 10.10** *Riccia cavernosa*, a recent colonist of former arable land now incorporated into the nature reserve, Wicken Fen, October 2005. Photo: Robin Stevenson.

surrounded by strip-cultivated open fields, and with woodland at the edge of the parish. However, to the south-west of the village lies Greate Heathe and Little Heathe, with the Park of the Burgoyne family on its north side and Broome Woode (now White Wood) to the north-west (see Oswald & Preston 2011). The Park was later acquired by Sir George Downing and a new house built there in 1712–13 (but demolished in 1776).

As with the Cambridge moors, the flowering plants can be used to throw light on the habitats which were present at these sites. There were bogs on the Great Heath which supported *Carex canescens, C. dioica, Comarum palustre, Drosera rotundifolia, Erica tetralix, Hammarbya paludosa* ('in great plenty' according to Martyn 1732), *Hypericum elodes, Narthecium ossifragum, Potamogeton polygonifolius* and *Utricularia minor. D. rotundifolia* was one of the species described by Ray as growing 'in a moorish place where they digge turfes'. Relhan (1788) reported *Utricularia minor* from 'Gamlingay quaking Bogs'. Some of these species, such as *C. palustre*, extended into bogs within the Park (Martyn 1732). The bogs were drained in 1843 (Babington 1860: 44). *Hammarbya* was still present in 1848 when Henslow's party found it 'in a little patch of remaining bog' (Babington 1897: 144) but was 'nearly extirpated in 1855', the last record (Babington 1860). Babington (1860) was also the last to see *Vaccinium oxycoccos*, 'formerly abundant' but 'confined in 1859 to one small spot by the stream flowing to the site of the old pond'. By the time that he visited Gamlingay in 1862, he found that 'the last bit of bog was bearing a crop of potatoes. Every spot is so thoroughly under cultivation now that the botanizing is poor' (Babington 1897: 199). By 1898, West reported that not only had the bogs gone but 'there is none of the original open heath left' (West 1898).

The Great Heath and nearby sandy areas also supported calcifuges of wet or dry heaths, such as *Calluna vulgaris, Carex echinata, C. pilulifera, Erica cinerea, Genista anglica, Hypericum pulchrum, Jasione montana, Juncus squarrosus, Moenchia erecta, Nardus stricta, Ornithopus perpusillus, Polygala serpyllifolia, Solidago virgaurea, Teesdalia nudicaulis* and *Viola canina*. This flora has faded away gradually; most species survived into the 20th century and a few (*Calluna vulgaris, Carex echinata, Ornithopus perpusillus*) have been seen in recent years.

Great Heath Plantation (or Wood) is the one remaining site of botanical interest on the site of the former Great Heath. It was planted sometime between the drainage of the Bogs in 1843 and the publication of the first edition of the Ordnance Survey Six Inch map in 1887, although the first vascular plant records were not made here until the early 20th century (1908 onwards). There is also a meadow to the south. There was some continuity between the flora of the Heath and that of this site; *Carex rostrata* and *Hypericum elodes* were last seen *c.* 1930 in the Wood and *Potamogeton polygonifolius* in a spring in the meadow which was 'now very dry' when the plant was last seen in 1952. White Wood survives in a much modified state. It is difficult to reconstruct the former nature of White Wood from the species recorded there before 1860, which are ecologically heterogeneous, but it must have been very different from the current wood which is a mixed plantation of mainly broad-leaved trees with large patches of *Rhododendron*. Both Great Heath and White Woods were notified as SSSIs in the 1950s but are no longer scheduled as such. Also on the Woburn Sands (but not, as is sometimes claimed, on the site of the Great Heath) is Cinques Common, a Wildlife Trust reserve which was the last locality at Gamlingay for some other calcifuges such as *Genista anglica* (*c.* 1932) and *Viola canina* (1961), and where *Calluna vulgaris* still persists. An application in 1964 to use the lower parts of the site as a rubbish dump was refused (Cambridgeshire and Isle of Ely County Council Planning Department 1965), but some semi-natural vegetation at Gamlingay was lost to a playing field (Kerr 1975). Gamlingay Wood, north of the village, is on Boulder Clay rather than Woburn Sands (although part of it lies on a 'sand lens').

### Bryophytes lost before 1950

The bryophytes in the Acid and Fen cluster which were last recorded before 1843 include both calcifuge and calcicole wetland species which were presumably lost when the Bogs were drained. These are the calcifuge bog liverworts *Lophozia ventricosa* and *Odontoschisma sphagni* and mosses *Philonotis fontana, Sphagnum papillosum, S. squarrosum, S. tenellum, S. teres* and *Splachnum ampullaceum*. The calcicoles are *Bryum pseudotriquetrum, Campylium stellatum* and *Scorpidium revolvens. Aulacomnium palustre* persisted until 1881, *Sphagnum subnitens* until 1913 and *Sphagnum palustre* was last seen in Great Heath Plantation in 1930. Two species of moist habitats (*Archidium alternifolium, Climacium dendroides*), last recorded before 1843, might also have been lost when the bogs were drained. It is less easy to know why *Bartramia pomiformis* (recorded from White Wood), *Pogonatum aloides* and *P. nanum*, plants of dry ground, did not persist for longer. However, all three have suffered major declines in central southern England, possibly in response to changing hedgerow management and loss of sand pits. The inconspicuous *Cephaloziella rubella* was collected from Great Heath Plantation in 1934.

**Figure 10.11** Inspecting the only known patch of *Sphagnum* (*S. denticulatum*) in Cambridgeshire. Gamlingay Heath Plantation, March 2018. Photo: Chris Preston.

**Figure 10.13** *Pseudotaxiphyllum elegans* (with axillary branchlets). Gamlingay Heath Plantation, March 2018. Photo: Jeff Scott.

**Figure 10.12** Proportions of fenland species, calcifuges, woodland species and epiphytes at Gamlingay in the period 1950–2017. The 1980s peak in acid records was due to an exceptional excursion to Great Heath Plantation in 1988.

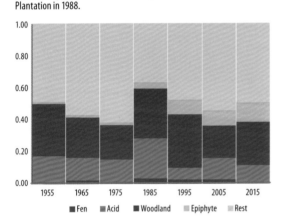

### Bryophyte changes since 1950

In the second half of the 20th century 10 calcifuges were confined to Gamlingay or had only one other site elsewhere (Table 10.1): *Calypogeia arguta, C. muelleriana, Diplophyllum albicans, Fossombronia wondraczekii, Pohlia lescuriana, P. lutescens, Pseudephemerum nitidum, Sphagnum denticulatum* (Figure 10.11), *S. fimbriatum* and *S. fallax*. All of them grew in or by Great Heath Plantation. *Pohlia lutescens* and *Pseudephemerum nitidum* were also found in other Gamlingay localities. Five of these species were seen during the recent survey, and *Bryum bornholmense* was added to the list in 2018. Of the remainder, *Fossombronia wondraczekii* has a persistent spore bank and may perhaps reappear at very infrequent intervals. The rest may persist in small niches in Great Heath Plantation, or may recolonise from long distances when conditions become suitable. There is no long-term trend in the number of species (Figure 10.12), which peaked in 1988 when there had been disturbance of soil close to the wood.

White Wood still has a strongly calcifuge flora which includes *Atrichum undulatum, Aulacomnium androgynum, Campylopus pyriformis, Dicranella heteromalla, Dicranum tauricum, Mnium hornum, Orthodontium lineare, Plagiothecium curvifolium, Pohlia nutans, Polytrichastrum formosum* and *Pseudotaxiphyllum elegans* (Figure 10.13). Some of the tree trunks support plentiful *Dicranum montanum*, which was first found here in 1955 and is now present as a large and persistent population. This is the only Cambridgeshire site where *D. montanum* does not appear to be a casual.

Gamlingay Wood (see Chapter 8) is not rich in calcifuge species. *Cephalozia connivens, Herzogiella seligeri* and *Tetraphis pellucida* have occurred there, possibly as casuals. *Hypnum jutlandicum* became locally abundant under conifers but has subsequently declined.

### Conclusions about changes at Chippenham, Wicken and Gamlingay

The loss of bryophyte species as a result of the destruction or deterioration of Cambridgeshire's wetlands before 1950 comes as no surprise. After 1950 the bryophyte records reveal a more interesting story. In the absence of major environmental change, there has been a small but fairly steady flow of casual species which do not establish permanent populations. At Gamlingay 15 calcifuge species were seen since 1950 that were seemingly not persistent (*Calypogeia arguta, Cephalozia connivens, Cephaloziella hampeana,*

*Diplophyllum albicans, Fossombronia wondraczekii, Herzogiella seligeri, Hypnum andoi, Lepidozia reptans, Plagiothecium undulatum, Pleurozium schreberi, Polytrichum commune, Polytrichum piliferum, Sphagnum fallax, Sphagnum fimbriatum, Tetraphis pellucida*). At Chippenham Fen there were eight (*Campylopus fragilis, Dicranum montanum, Dicranum tauricum, Fissidens bryoides, Hypnum andoi, Leucobryum glaucum, Plagiothecium undulatum, Polytrichum commune*). At Wicken Fen there were five (*Polytrichum juniperinum, Sphagnum fallax, Pellia epiphylla, Sphagnum russowii, Tetraphis pellucida*). At Wicken Fen the relatively large extent of moist acid peat allowed many more species to increase for a while and persist at the site. Moreover, the fen was visited regularly by bryologists, and the acid areas were specially sought out. Visits to Gamlingay were relatively infrequent, especially to the most distinctively acid site, Gamlingay Heath Plantation. Had visits been more regular, several species might have been seen to be persistent over one or two decades. Nevertheless, it is clear that most of Cambridgeshire's calcifuge species are in a state of flux, constantly reinvading, persisting for a while, and then vanishing.

# 11

# The Chalklands

## The Cambridgeshire chalk

The main habitats of calcicolous species are calcareous grassland and chalk pits. Up to about 1800, extensive chalk grassland was managed as sheepwalk in south-east Cambridgeshire, extending from Thriplow Heath in the south to Newmarket Heath in the north (Coombe 1987). However, much of this grassland would have been underlain by the relatively deep soils typical of much of the Cambridgeshire chalk rather than very shallow rendzinas (Chapter 2) and it might therefore have been of limited bryological interest. John Ray's records suggest that even in the 17th century the distribution of the least competitive flowering plants of chalk grassland turf was very restricted. The only sites he knew for *Neotinea ustulata, Pulsatilla vulgaris, Tephroseris integrifolia* and *Thesium humifusum* were on Gog Magog Hills and Newmarket Heath (including the Devil's Dyke), whereas he recorded rather more competitive species such as *Anthyllis vulneraria, Campanula glomerata* and *Filipendula vulgaris* much more widely (Oswald & Preston 2011). The rarer species were later found in a few more sites (Crompton 2001) but the evidence suggests that they were found only as limited populations, particularly in places where there were steeper gradients such as prehistoric tumuli (Bartlow Hills) or the linear post-Roman earthworks, Devil's Dyke (Figure 11.1) and Fleam Dyke (Malim 1997). The calcicolous bryophytes are likely to have been similarly restricted, although open habitats would have been available on trackways and in places where chalk was extracted and burnt

**Figure 11.1** Calcareous grassland on the Devil's Dyke, looking south-east from TL615617, May 2017. The obsessive neatness of the background scene is characteristic of equestrian Newmarket. Photo: Peter Leonard.

for lime or quarried for building stone ('clunch'). Most of the sheepwalk was ploughed up after enclosure, though small remnants persisted at Quy Fen, Great Wilbraham Common, Fulbourn Fen and Shepreth L-Moor. Larger areas remained on ancient monuments, beside the Roman Road and on the Gog Magog Golf Course, on the Fleam Dyke and Devil's Dyke, and on Newmarket Heath. Clearly the surviving chalkland sites were already relict habitat patches by the start of the modern recording period in 1927. Our records from them are analysed in this chapter.

## The chalk species

The cluster analysis (Chapter 6) identified a large group of 51 Calcicole species. These are listed in Table 11.1 and mapped in Figure 11.2.

On the basis of their preference for calcareous grassland, chalk pits and other habitats, the more frequent Calcicoles can be divided into four categories, (a) *chalk-pit species* with more sites in chalk pits than chalk grassland, (b) species occurring about equally in chalk pits and chalk grassland, (c) *chalk-grassland specialists* with more sites in chalk grassland than chalk pits, and (d) *non-*

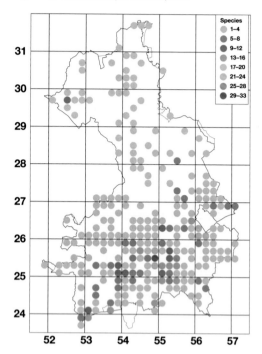

**Figure 11.2** Coincidence map of Calcicole species.

Species
- 1–4
- 5–8
- 9–12
- 13–16
- 17–20
- 21–24
- 25–28
- 29–33

**Table 11.1** Species in the Calcicole habitat cluster. Ellenberg R values are an indication of species' substrate preference ranging from 4 (moderately acid) to 9 (substrates with free calcium carbonate); see Table 8.1. Species which have not been recorded in the recent survey are not italicised. For details of the clustering analysis, and the definition of a site, see Chapter 6.

| Species | R | Sites | Visits | Species | R | Sites | Visits |
|---|---|---|---|---|---|---|---|
| Pseudoscleropodium purum | 6 | 236 | 444 | Encalypta vulgaris | 8 | 8 | 23 |
| Didymodon fallax | 7 | 162 | 322 | Campylophyllum calcareum | 8 | 7 | 37 |
| Homalothecium lutescens | 8 | 126 | 276 | Ditrichum gracile | 7 | 7 | 26 |
| Aneura pinguis | 6 | 64 | 101 | Aloina rigida | 8 | 6 | 9 |
| Rhynchostegium megapolitanum | 7 | 55 | 68 | Brachythecium glareosum | 8 | 6 | 6 |
| Ctenidium molluscum | 7 | 36 | 135 | Entodon concinnus | 8 | 5 | 22 |
| Tortula lanceola | 8 | 33 | 47 | Lophozia perssonii | 9 | 5 | 22 |
| Leiocolea turbinata | 8 | 32 | 105 | Tortella inflexa | 9 | 4 | 13 |
| Aloina aloides | 8 | 30 | 49 | Leiocolea badensis | 8 | 4 | 5 |
| Campyliadelphus chrysophyllus | 8 | 29 | 94 | Weissia sterilis | 8 | 3 | 9 |
| Fissidens dubius | 7 | 28 | 84 | Tortella tortuosa | 7 | 2 | 15 |
| Weissia longifolia var. angustifolia | 7 | 26 | 64 | Tortella inclinata | 9 | 2 | 13 |
| Microbryum curvicollum | 9 | 24 | 71 | Trichostomum brachydontium | 7 | 2 | 8 |
| Microbryum rectum | 7 | 24 | 65 | Pterygoneurum lamellatum | 9 | 2 | 5 |
| Tortula subulata agg. | 7 | 24 | 43 | Aloina brevirostris | 9 | 2 | 4 |
| Aloina ambigua | 7 | 24 | 33 | Rhodobryum roseum | 6 | 2 | 4 |
| Seligeria calcarea | 9 | 23 | 65 | Pottiopsis caespitosa | 8 | 2 | 2 |
| Weissia brachycarpa | 6 | 21 | 65 | Seligeria donniana | 8 | 2 | 2 |
| Seligeria calycina | 9 | 20 | 72 | Trichostomum crispulum | 8 | 1 | 9 |
| Pterygoneurum ovatum | 8 | 18 | 35 | Bryum torquescens | 7 | 1 | 3 |
| Abietinella abietina | 8 | 14 | 60 | Neckera crispa | 9 | 2 | 6 |
| Weissia controversa | 6 | 14 | 19 | Plasteurhynchium striatulum | 9 | 1 | 1 |
| Tortula vahliana | 9 | 11 | 42 | Rhytidium rugosum | 7 | 1 | 1 |
| Didymodon acutus | 8 | 11 | 17 | Scleropodium touretii | 6 | 1 | 1 |
| Hylocomium splendens | 4 | 9 | 16 | Scorpiurium circinatum | 7 | 1 | 1 |
| Encalypta streptocarpa | 8 | 8 | 34 | | | | |

*specialists* found mainly in the wider countryside (Table 11.2). Several of the sites in the wider countryside are also on the chalk, for example the parklands of Wandlebury, Hildersham Hall and Pampisford Hall, the tracks of disused railways, and some recent woods, especially beechwoods.

The specialists that favour chalk pits are colonists of disturbed ground or cliffs. The *Microbryum* and *Weissia* species favouring grassland require small-scale disturbance, such as rabbit burrows or slippage on steep slopes. *Abietinella abietina* (Figure 11.3a) also requires some disturbance, typically trampling. Only *Fissidens dubius* occurs regularly in the interstices of stable turf. The habitat distinction between chalk pits and chalk grassland is not a sharp one. For example, the disused clunch pit at Orwell has been restored to chalk grassland, while the nearby Hill Plantation is a clunch pit that has been planted with trees. The range of habitats of species may also have changed over time. *Microbryum rectum* (Figure 11.3b) is less frequent now in stubble fields than formerly, judging by Proctor's (1956) account.

Of the generalists that occur in the wider countryside, *Encalypta streptocarpa* and *E. vulgaris* were confined to the chalk, mainly in beech woods or on banks of railways. The others occur in a range of habitats, with *Aneura pinguis* and *Didymodon fallax* often on clay and *Homalothecium lutescens* and *Rhynchostegium megapolitanum* on well-drained tracksides and ditch banks. The most frequent of all the Calcicoles is *Pseudoscleropodium purum*, which occurs widely in unimproved permanent grassland and has a marked preference for churchyard lawns.

Most of the rarer Calcicoles are also specialists of chalk pits and chalk grassland. *Leiocolea badensis, Lophozia perssonii, Aloina brevirostris, A. rigida, Brachythecium glareosum* and *Pterygoneurum lamellatum* occurred mainly in chalk pits. *Bryum torquescens, Ditrichum gracile, Entodon concinnus, Seligeria donniana, Tortella inclinata, T. inflexa, T. tortuosa* and *Trichostomum brachydontium* occurred mainly in

**Table 11.2** Numbers of sites in which the more frequent calcicoles were recorded, categorised by habitat. Species are in four groups according to their preference for chalk pits, chalk grassland and other habitats. Totals here are for site+habitat combinations and are therefore larger than the site totals in Table 11.1.

| | Chalk Pit | Chalk Grass | Church | Recent wood | Halls & Parks | Other | Total |
|---|---|---|---|---|---|---|---|
| Number of sites with at least one calcicole | 42 | 19 | 81 | 35 | 17 | 347 | 541 |
| **(a) Favouring chalk pits** | | | | | | | |
| Leiocolea turbinata | 14 | 4 | | 3 | 2 | 18 | 41 |
| Seligeria calcarea | 14 | 2 | 2 | 1 | 3 | 6 | 28 |
| Tortula vahliana | 8 | | | | 2 | 6 | 16 |
| **(b) Chalk pits and chalk grassland** | | | | | | | |
| Ctenidium molluscum | 12 | 9 | | 3 | 1 | 26 | 51 |
| Tortula lanceola | 13 | 7 | 1 | 2 | 2 | 20 | 45 |
| Campyliadelphus chrysophyllus | 14 | 11 | | | | 11 | 36 |
| Pterygoneurum ovatum | 7 | 6 | | 1 | | 11 | 25 |
| Seligeria calycina | 9 | 5 | | 4 | 1 | 5 | 24 |
| Didymodon acutus | 3 | 3 | | | | 6 | 12 |
| **(c) Favouring chalk grassland** | | | | | | | |
| Weissia longifolia var. angustifolia | 5 | 9 | | 2 | 2 | 20 | 38 |
| Microbryum rectum | 5 | 8 | 2 | | 3 | 18 | 36 |
| Fissidens dubius | 8 | 10 | | 3 | 5 | 8 | 34 |
| Microbryum curvicollum | 6 | 11 | | 1 | 1 | 13 | 32 |
| Weissia brachycarpa | 1 | 11 | 1 | | 1 | 14 | 28 |
| Abietinella abietina | 2 | 10 | | 2 | | 10 | 24 |
| Weissia controversa | | 5 | | | 2 | 9 | 16 |
| **(d) Mainly in wider countryside** | | | | | | | |
| Pseudoscleropodium purum | 26 | 13 | 69 | 19 | 11 | 147 | 285 |
| Didymodon fallax | 26 | 11 | 6 | 10 | 9 | 154 | 216 |
| Homalothecium lutescens | 28 | 12 | 23 | 8 | 6 | 82 | 159 |
| Aneura pinguis | 6 | 1 | | 2 | 2 | 72 | 83 |
| Rhynchostegium megapolitanum | 3 | 8 | 11 | 2 | 2 | 37 | 63 |
| Aloina aloides | 6 | | 2 | 2 | 1 | 22 | 33 |
| Tortula subulata agg. | 3 | 3 | | 9 | 5 | 11 | 31 |
| Aloina ambigua | 5 | | | | 1 | 21 | 27 |
| Encalypta vulgaris | 1 | 2 | | 1 | 1 | 6 | 11 |
| Encalypta streptocarpa | | 2 | | 4 | 2 | 3 | 11 |

**Figure 11.3** Calcicole mosses with contrasting reproductive strategies, both photographed on the Devil's Dyke. (a) *Abietinella abietina*, which never fruits (February 2017, Peter Leonard), (b) *Microbryum rectum*, fruiting abundantly (February 2015, Robin Stevenson).

grassland. *Pottiopsis caespitosa* and *Trichostomum crispulum* occurred in both. Away from these habitats *Campylophyllum calcareum*, *Hylocomium splendens* and *Scleropodium touretii* were found mainly in woodland on the chalk. *H. splendens* is not a calcicole in western and northern Britain, but became restricted to calcareous sites near London, probably as a result of acid rain (Farmer *et al.* 1992). It appears to be similarly restricted in Cambridgeshire, although its single Wicken Fen occurrence may have been on soil that was becoming acidic. Two of the remaining three species, *Rhodobryum roseum* and *Rhytidium rugosum*, were found in sandy grassland, and *Plasteurhynchium striatulum* was a colonist in wooded former gravel workings. *Neckera crispa* and *Scorpiurium circinatum* grew on imported limestone and never spread from their original substrates.

In the analysis that follows, 'chalk specialists' are defined as the Calcicoles other than most of the generalists. Not all 'chalk specialists' have their main occurrence in chalk pits and chalk grassland. The list also includes *Campylophyllum calcareum*, *Encalypta streptocarpa*, *E. vulgaris*, *Hylocomium splendens* and *Scleropodium touretii*.

## Overview of the chalkland sites

For this analysis, chalk sites are defined as those from which at least four chalk specialists are recorded, but excluding the Botanic Garden, which is not on the chalk. In the decades when bryophyte excursions were held on Saturday afternoons, sites were often chosen because of their proximity to Cambridge. More than half of excursions to chalk sites were to the Gogs, the Devil's and Fleam Dykes and the Cherry Hinton chalk pits. In the decades since 2000, the choice of chalk sites was similar but with fewer excursions to the Gogs (Figure 11.4). We surveyed the Devil's Dyke and Fleam Dyke systematically by 1-km square, recording Devil's Dyke in 2003–08 and in 2014–18 and Fleam Dyke in 2010–13.

In Table 11.3 the 29 chalk sites with five or more chalk specialists are compared for their pattern of loss or persistence of chalk specialists. Some sites are composites, composed of separate locations in the same quadrant. Thus the rich site 'Fulbourn SE' is a composite; pre-1980 records are from the formerly excellent disused railway site at Worsted Lodge; later records are from another part of the disused railway and a disturbed roadside nearby. Likewise the site 'Babraham' is a composite with

**Figure 11.4** Visits to chalk sites per decade. Only visits on which at least 10 species were recorded are shown. The sites are those shown in Table 11.3: Gogs sites – Wandlebury, Wort's Causeway Beechwood, Roman Road, Gog Magog, Fulbourn SE; Dykes – Devil's and Fleam Dykes; Cherry H – Cherry Hinton chalk pits; Others – other chalk sites listed in Table 11.3.

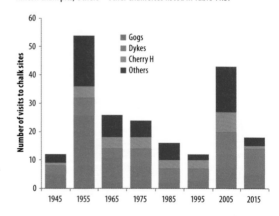

**Table 11.3** Main chalk sites, with counts of chalk specialists; sites with less than five specialists have been excluded. Site trends: – and – – deterioration minor and major; 0 little change; + improvement; ? no information on change.

| Site name | Quadrant | Chalk specialists | Lost since 1989 | Trend | Comment on change |
|---|---|---|---|---|---|
| Devil's Dyke central | TL66SW | 24 | 4 | 0 | Good survival |
| Fleam Dyke central | TL55SW | 24 | 8 | – | Loss of *Abietinella* etc. |
| Cherry Hinton chalk pits | TL45NE | 20 | 5 | 0 | Condition improved by East Pit landscaping |
| Fulbourn SE | TL55SW | 17 | 11 | – – | Worsted Lodge railway lost |
| Gog Magog | TL45SE | 17 | 10 | – – | Little Trees chalk pit scrubbed up |
| Devil's Dyke nr Swaffham Prior | TL56SE | 15 | 4 | – | Loss of *Abietinella, Weissia sterilis* |
| Devil's Dyke NW | TL56NE | 12 | 0 | ? | Few records before 1990 |
| Fleam SE | TL55SE | 12 | 0 | ? | No data before 2000 |
| Roman Road W | TL45SE | 12 | 11 | – – | No visits after 1990; deteriorated |
| Wandlebury | TL45SE | 11 | 8 | – – | Most open-ground spp. gone by 1980 |
| Ickleton pit | TL44SE | 9 | 3 | 0 | Loss of *Ctenidium, Tortula lanceola* |
| Orwell pit | TL35SE | 9 | 2 | + | Good condition after scrub removed |
| Roman Road Fulbourn | TL55SW | 9 | 6 | – – | Poor condition after 1965 |
| Wort's Causeway Beechwood | TL45SE | 9 | 5 | – | Loss of open-ground species |
| Babraham | TL55SW | 8 | 5 | – – | Chalk pits, railway scrubbed over |
| Barrington Hill Plantation | TL35SE | 8 | 7 | – – | Trees matured; *T. vahliana* appeared |
| Morden Grange pit N | TL24SE | 8 | 2 | ? | Few pre-2000 records (1960 only) |
| Fleam Dyke Fulbourn | TL55NW | 7 | 2 | – | Loss of *Entodon, C. chrysophyllus* |
| Harlton pit | TL35SE | 7 | 4 | – – | Now heavily shaded by trees |
| Quy Fen | TL56SW | 7 | 6 | – – | Only *C. chrysophyllus* surviving |
| Fulbourn | TL55NW | 6 | 4 | – – | Chalk species Teversham Fen 1960 |
| Gt Wilbraham Common | TL55NW | 6 | 4 | – – | Visited 1977; deteriorated by 2005 |
| Haslingfield pit | TL45SW | 6 | 0 | + | *T. vahliana* newly found 2005 |
| Litlington chalk pit | TL34SW | 6 | 2 | 0 | Little change |
| Orwell | TL35SE | 6 | 3 | – | Disused chalk pit overgrown 1956 |
| Pampisford Hall | TL54NW | 6 | 2 | 0 | *Hylocomium splendens* until 1978 |
| Barrington pit | TL35SE | 5 | 1 | 0 | Surprisingly few chalk specialists |
| Great Wilbraham pit | TL55NE | 5 | 5 | – – | Pit has been filled in |
| Gt & Lt Eversden | TL35SE | 5 | 3 | – – | Quarry filled in, planted with trees |

a different locality, Babraham Corner, visited in 2003. The calcicole bryophytes recorded before 1990 are compared in the table to those recorded subsequently. The balance is strongly negative, with 18 sites deteriorating, six showing little change and two possibly improving after conservation work. Three sites were insufficiently recorded before 1990 for us to assess change.

### Reasons for the decline of calcicoles

The main reasons for the loss of calcicole species, detailed below, are 1) under-grazing of large sites; 2) cessation of quarrying in larger pits; 3) plant succession in smaller chalk pits which had already been abandoned by 1927, and in disused railway cuttings; and 4) total habitat destruction.

The number of sheep in the county declined precipitously between 1875 and 1950 (Preece & Sparks 2012: 172) and wild rabbits became increasingly important as grazing animals. Following the myxomatosis outbreak of 1954–55, which almost exterminated rabbits, the ancient monuments were little grazed. They were rapidly invaded by scrub and coarse grasses, to the detriment of mosses in chalk turf. In 1959 conservation volunteers began programmes of scrub clearance in an attempt to save some of remaining grassland (Cambient 1960, Grubb & Key 1975). However, this was not enough to save the bryophyte flora of the Roman Road. The grassland at this site, a narrow track running through arable fields and lacking steep banks, deteriorated so greatly that bryologists almost stopped visiting it. Flat chalk grassland at Great Wilbraham Common and Quy Fen also deteriorated. Fleam Dyke became badly overgrown by scrub but Devil's Dyke was less seriously affected, as it is a larger site and a local farmer, John Clarke, and the Jockey Club ensured that some stretches remained open (Cambridgeshire and Isle of Ely County Council Planning Department 1965). Short turf was also maintained by trampling on the well-used footpath along the top. Subsequently others have contributed to the work of maintaining the chalk grassland on Devil's Dyke, including Butterfly Conservation (Lea 2011) and the County Council tenant farmers at Ditch Farm. In recent years small work parties have been replaced by more extensive programmes of clearance on the Dykes, and sheep grazing has also been reintroduced to some sections of the Devil's Dyke (Baker 2018, Leslie 2011). The result has been that both on the Fleam Dyke and Devil's Dyke, conditions suitable for mosses of short turf and open disturbed chalk soil gradually improved again.

The large chalk quarries have gradually been closed, and thus the number of sites for species requiring freshly disturbed chalk has fallen. Clunch was last quarried at Burwell in 1962. The two biggest pits, East Pit, Cherry Hinton and Barrington (Figure 11.5), were quarried for cement till 1984 and 2008 respectively. East Pit was colonised by scrub until this was removed by the Wildlife Trust in 2010–11 (Figures 11.6, 11.7). The only quarries which are still worked are at Steeple Morden. Morden Grange pit either improved or was better recorded. Station Quarry was visited for the first time in 2004.

**Figures 11.5** Fieldwork in Barrington Cement Works, December 2006. Simon Damant, Jonathan Graham and Mark Hill are the men in hard hats. Photo: Robin Stevenson.

**Figure 11.6** Dense *Buddleja davidii* scrub in East Pit, Cherry Hinton, December 2008. The scrub had a species-poor ground flora and few epiphytes. Photo: Jonathan Graham.

**Figure 11.7** East Pit, Cherry Hinton after scrub clearance by the Wildlife Trust, March 2012. Photo: Jonathan Graham.

The state of the small parish pits was a concern of the Naturalists' Trust in its earliest years. In its first annual report, in 1958, the Cambridgeshire and Isle of Ely Naturalists' Trust described them as 'increasingly valuable in a highly arable countryside as reservoirs for characteristic plants and animals', especially on the chalk, but commented that the 'complete neglect and abandonment of these pits means either a gradual reversion to blackthorn or hawthorn scrub, or, too frequently, a degeneration into uncontrolled and unsightly rubbish dumps' (Cambient 1958). This neglect or infilling has continued. A typical example is Wood Ditton Pit, a chalk pit which was 'visited annually for teaching purposes' until in 1965 it was reported that 'there has been tipping recently, mainly of sewage, and … it is now unlikely to be visited by any but the most devoted geologists' (Cambridgeshire and Isle of Ely County Council Planning Department 1965). Some of the smaller pits from which bryophytes were recorded in the 1950s or early 1960s now no longer exist (e.g. at Foxton, Great Wilbraham, Little Eversden and Steeple Morden). Harlton pit and Harston Hill pit reverted to scrub or woodland and lost light-demanding species. Little Trees Hill on Gog Magog Hills also lost the species of open chalk. Similarly the railway cuttings which run across the Fleam and Devil's Dykes became overgrown.

One of the best sites up to 1960, an old railway cutting near Worsted Lodge, deteriorated thereafter and ceased to be visited long before the A11 was upgraded to dual carriageway in 1992, making the line less accessible. However, some new chalk grassland has been sown at Wandlebury and on Magog Down (the latter site incorporates a small chalk pit), and a new road cutting was cut through the chalk at Royston. Cuttings along operational railway lines may also be refuges for calcicole bryophytes (Holland Hall Cutting at Melbourn is scheduled as an SSSI for its flowering plants) but they are inaccessible.

## Species trends at six frequently visited sites

For the six frequently visited chalk sites, a more detailed analysis is possible. In the terminology of Table 11.3, these were Devil's Dyke central (16 visits with at least 10 species recorded) and near Swaffham Prior (10), Fleam Dyke central (14), Cherry Hinton chalk pits, comprising Limekiln Close, East Pit and West Pit (27), Wandlebury (19) and Wort's Causeway Beechwood (14). Grouping these into the three Dyke sites, the chalk pits, and the two Gogs sites (Wandlebury and the Beechwood), the greater frequency of visits to the Gogs in the period 1944–1969 is obvious (Table 11.4). Averaging over the groups, the mean list length grew from about 25 in the first two periods to 34.8 in 1990–2017, with most of the increase coming from the Built, Common and Epiphyte clusters, which between them increased by eight species. Ruderals increased by 1.3 species, and were partly offset by the Calcicoles, which decreased by 0.6 species.

The differences in Built, Common and Ruderal species are at least partly the result of a different recording culture in 1990–2015, when species lists were more complete. The increase in Epiphytes is likely to be real. The decrease in Calcicoles is relatively small, as most of the lost chalk specialists were rare and not included in many lists. However, when visits are made repeatedly to particular sites, bryologists may know what to look for. For example, Harold Whitehouse used to search for *Entodon concinnus* in the lawn at Wandlebury, to show it to students. It was last found there in 1973.

The increase in Common species was not entirely the result of lists being more complete in the later period. Scrubbing-up of grassland was also a factor. For example, *Dicranoweisia cirrata* was regularly reported from Wandlebury and the Wort's Causeway Beechwood in the 1950s but there are no records from the other sites till 1977. In the 1949–1969 period, *Amblystegium serpens* was regularly found in the Gogs sites and Cherry Hinton chalk pits, but only once in the chalk grassland sites. From the 1970s onwards it was found regularly on the Fleam Dyke and Devil's Dyke, where it was common on elders in scrub.

**Table 11.4** Mean numbers of species in lists from selected chalk sites, categorised by species clusters (Chapter 6) and by time period: Period 1 1944–1969; Period 2 1970–1989; Period 3 1990–2017.

| Sites | Fleam & Devil's Dykes | | | Cherry Hinton Chalk Pits | | | Gogs Sites | | |
|---|---|---|---|---|---|---|---|---|---|
| Period | 1 | 2 | 3 | 1 | 2 | 3 | 1 | 2 | 3 |
| Calcicole | 13.1 | 9.6 | 10.6 | 9.1 | 7.8 | 7.8 | 4.8 | 3.8 | 4.0 |
| Common | 4.6 | 5.6 | 9.0 | 6.3 | 5.5 | 8.3 | 7.2 | 8.6 | 10.6 |
| Ruderal | 3.8 | 3.5 | 4.3 | 6.0 | 5.6 | 6.0 | 2.4 | 1.6 | 5.1 |
| Built | 1.1 | 1.6 | 3.6 | 1.3 | 1.4 | 3.7 | 3.2 | 3.0 | 6.5 |
| Epiphyte | 0.3 | 1.8 | 3.7 | 1.3 | 1.4 | 1.8 | 0.5 | 0.8 | 4.4 |
| Other | 1.8 | 2.3 | 4.4 | 4.8 | 2.6 | 3.5 | 6.4 | 5.0 | 7.3 |
| List length | 24.6 | 24.4 | 35.6 | 28.6 | 24.3 | 31.1 | 24.4 | 22.8 | 37.9 |
| No. of visits | 8 | 14 | 18 | 8 | 8 | 11 | 17 | 5 | 8 |

The same factor, of scrubbing up, had a major impact on the Epiphytes. *Orthotrichum affine* was frequently found in Cherry Hinton pits in 1949–1969. Very probably chalk dust from the pit ameliorated the effects of acid rain. It started to appear in the other sites after 1975. Acid rain, or rather the lack of it, accounts for the total disappearance of *Pohlia nutans*, which was a characteristic feature of the bases of beech trees, which were acidified by rainwater flowing down their trunks. It was last seen at Wandlebury in 1984 and in the Wort's Causeway Beechwood in 1983.

Finally, it is worth drawing attention to the apparent increase in *Eurhynchium striatum*. It first appeared at Wandlebury in 2002 and in the Cherry Hinton chalk pits in 2001. At Wandlebury it may have been introduced with planted trees, or spread into newly planted sites. It was found on the Devil's Dyke and Fleam Dyke in the 1940s, but there were no further records till 1994. It seems to be rather rare on the Cambridgeshire chalk. We found it in Orwell pit in 2000, but failed to refind it after scrub clearance in 2015. It is such a characteristic plant of chalk grassland elsewhere in Britain that its scarcity in this habitat in Cambridgeshire is remarkable.

## Conclusions

Many calcicoles have declined since the 1950s. Chalk grassland specialists were hit by the myxomatosis epidemic coupled with a lack of sheep grazing. Many other chalk specialists are dependent on regular disturbance, as on steep railway banks and in quarries. Quarrying of chalk in the county has nearly ceased. Scrubbing up of chalk pits and chalk grassland can be arrested by conservation management, which in the absence of sheep grazing is labour-intensive.

# 12

# Arable land

Arable agriculture is the predominant land-use on all soil types in Cambridgeshire (Figure 2.11). There is a suite of small mosses which rapidly reproduce by spores or vegetative propagules and which can be found in stubble fields. Harold Whitehouse was one of a small group of bryologists who led the study of the vegetatively reproducing species in the 1960s and 1970s, and he passed his interest in them on to us. We have done our best to ensure that the arable species have been covered during the recent survey of the county (Figure 12.1), but they inevitably remain under-recorded. Whereas woods or churchyards can be recorded throughout the winter, and are limited in number, most arable land in the county is only accessible for a few days or weeks between the harvest and the ploughing of the field for the next crop. Visiting even one stubble field in every tetrad in autumn would be an impossible task for anyone recording bryophytes in their spare time. We have had to rely on occasional visits to stubble fields in autumn followed by visits to those unploughed fields (or marginal strips alongside fields) which we have been able to find when surveying the wider countryside in winter. We report our results in this chapter, setting them in the context of earlier work in the county.

## History of arable fieldwork in the county

The first arable fields to attract the attention of bryologists were those on the chalk on the south-east side of Cambridge. H.N. Dixon collected *Microbryum curvicollum* from a chalky fallow field by the Roman Road in 1881 and *M. rectum* from a less precisely localised fallow field ('Cambridge') in 1882. A.W. Graveson also recorded *M. rectum*, and *M. davallianum*, from a cultivated field in Cherry Hinton in 1914. In February 1934 Eustace Jones and Paul Richards found *Microbryum davallianum* and *Weissia longifolia* in a sainfoin field near Comberton, presumably on clay. In the following month Jones discovered *Ephemerum recurvifolium* in five more localities, four of which were arable fields, the other being a temporary pasture. He did not make lists for these fields. The first arable list with more than four species was made by Harold Whitehouse near Dry Drayton in 1956; *Fissidens incurvus* and *Weissia longifolia* var. *longifolia* indicate a field that had been left fallow for several months. The only other arable list from the 1950s was by Whitehouse, David Coombe and Coombe's student Margaret Anderson near the Hoffer Brook, Newton, in 1958. Coombe had discovered *Lythrum hyssopifolia* at the site four days previously, and had evidently invited Whitehouse to identify bryophytes on a second visit. This was the first of many such visits to wet arable sites near Fowlmere,

**Figure 12.1** Recording bryophytes in an arable field on National Trust land at Wimpole Hall, February 2018. Photo: Peter Leonard.

Newton and Whittlesford, some of which supported populations of *Lythrum hyssopifolia*. This area is distinguished below as the *Lythrum* area.

In 1960, Whitehouse began an intensive study of mosses that produce tubers, growing them in pure culture on agar. He encouraged P.J. Bourne to collect specimens from arable fields. The first sample of *Dicranella staphylina* was collected by Bourne in November 1960 near Thorney. A field near Papworth St Agnes proved especially interesting, and was visited three times, producing *Acaulon muticum, Bryum gemmilucens, Ephemerum minutissimum* and *Trichodon cylindricus*. The BBS party stopped briefly at a stubble field in Horningsea during the Society's Autumn Meeting in 1961 to see *Bryum klinggraeffii* and *Ephemerum recurvifolium* (Dickson 1962). However, the arable

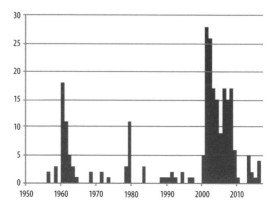

**Figure 12.2** Number of arable visits per year 1950–2017; visits with list length less than four are excluded.

habitat was not visited on student excursions and Whitehouse always maintained that calcareous stubble fields were much less interesting than those on acidic soils. Consequently he did not survey the Cambridgeshire arable as thoroughly as one might have expected. There were few arable records from 1960 till 1978 and 1979, when Preston and Whitehouse made an intensive study of the *Lythrum* hollows (Preston & Whitehouse 1986b). A surge in arable field recording started in 2000 and lasted throughout the decade (Figure 12.2). Before 2000 there were only three lists from arable fields in Fenland; from 2000 to 2017, 65 lists were made there. This recent fieldwork included visits to 76 arable fields which were recorded in the county for the BBS Survey of the Bryophytes of Arable Land (SBAL) in the winters from 2001/02 to 2004/05. This systematic survey required the collection of information on soil type, pH and bryophyte abundance, and we have often drawn on it for the species' accounts in this flora.

**Figure 12.3** A hollow with abundant *Lythrum hyssopifolia* in an arable field near New Farm, Whittlesford, August 2008. The bryophytes in the hollow included *Aphanorrhegma patens, Riccia cavernosa* and *R. glauca*. Photo: Chris Preston.

## Species of arable land

The cluster analysis (Chapter 6) identified a group of 23 Arable specialists (Table 12.1). The commoner species usually grow on circumneutral or basic soils; the rarer ones other than the *Riccia* species are calcifuges. Species which normally reproduce sexually in arable fields (14) outnumber those reproducing vegetatively by tubers (eight) or bulbils (one).

A list of the 20 most frequent species in the SBAL fields (Table 12.2), the most intensively surveyed fields in our survey, shows that the arable flora is dominated by Arable specialists (10) and species from the Ruderal cluster (seven), a group of species which are more widely distributed in disturbed habitats (see Chapter 14). There are also two species from the Common cluster and one Shade species; the latter, *Fissidens taxifolius*, is a colonist of set-aside or fallow fields.

## Trends in the species of arable land

For most of the 20th century, only occasional records were made from arable fields (Table 12.3). Systematic listing of species in arable fields did not begin until 1956 (see above). Because of the very uneven pattern of recording, we cannot infer anything about changes in the arable field flora of Fenland. Away from the fens, the period 1956–1999 was so dominated by recording of the *Lythrum* hollows that this category of records also needs to be distinguished if change is to be understood.

Lists from the period 2000–15 are longer than those from 1956–99, averaging 8.2 species as opposed to 4.5 species. The Arable cluster mosses *Dicranella schreberiana* and *D. staphylina* were more frequently recorded, as were the Ruderals *Bryum argenteum*, *B. dichotomum*, *B. ruderale* and *Funaria hygrometrica*. There were also more frequent records of *Brachythecium rutabulum*, *Kindbergia praelonga*, *Oxyrrhynchium hians* and *Pohlia melanodon*. The three pleurocarps are more typical of the fallow assemblage *Brachythecium rutabulum-Fissidens taxifolius* of Preston *et al.* (2010) and may represent the early stages of fields left unploughed under the Set-aside scheme. It is also possible that Whitehouse excluded pleurocarps from

**Table 12.1** Species in the Arable habitat cluster. Species which have not been recorded in the recent survey are not italicised. The normal mode of reproduction in arable fields is stated. Ellenberg R values are an indication of species' substrate preference ranging from 5 (moderately acidic) to 8 (strongly basic); see Table 8.1. Note that this table is not restricted to longer lists, but is the total for all occurrences.

| Species | Reproduction | R | Sites | Visits |
|---|---|---|---|---|
| *Phascum cuspidatum* | Spores | 7 | 365 | 563 |
| *Bryum rubens* | Tubers | 6 | 296 | 460 |
| *Microbryum davallianum* | Spores | 7 | 149 | 219 |
| *Bryum klinggraeffii* | Tubers | 6 | 128 | 170 |
| *Dicranella staphylina* | Tubers | 6 | 109 | 149 |
| *Bryum violaceum* | Tubers | 6 | 105 | 122 |
| *Dicranella schreberiana* | Tubers | 6 | 77 | 102 |
| *Tortula truncata* | Spores | 6 | 74 | 98 |
| *Leptobryum pyriforme* | Tubers | 6 | 59 | 78 |
| *Microbryum floerkeanum* | Spores | 8 | 43 | 55 |
| *Trichodon cylindricus* | Tubers | 5 | 32 | 43 |
| *Aphanorrhegma patens* | Spores | 7 | 27 | 32 |
| *Ephemerum recurvifolium* | Spores | 8 | 24 | 26 |
| *Weissia longifolia* var. *longifolia* | Spores | 5 | 21 | 23 |
| *Riccia glauca* | Spores | 6 | 13 | 26 |
| *Bryum subapiculatum* | Tubers | 5 | 8 | 10 |
| *Riccia cavernosa* | Spores | 7 | 6 | 14 |
| *Riccia sorocarpa* | Spores | 5 | 6 | 10 |
| *Acaulon muticum* | Spores | 5 | 3 | 5 |
| *Riccia subbifurca* | Spores | 5 | 3 | 8 |
| *Weissia squarrosa* | Spores | 5 | 2 | 3 |
| *Sphaerocarpos michelii* | Spores | 5 | 2 | 3 |
| *Bryum gemmilucens* | Bulbils | 5 | 1 | 1 |

**Table 12.2** The 20 most frequent species in the 76 arable fields surveyed for the SBAL project in Cambridgeshire, 2001–05. The normal mode of reproduction in arable fields is stated; bracketed modes are uncommon in arable fields. For the habitat clusters see Chapter 6; for the meaning of R values, see Table 12.1.

| Species | Habitat cluster | Reproduction | R | Number of fields |
|---|---|---|---|---|
| *Phascum cuspidatum* | Arable | Spores | 7 | 70 |
| *Barbula unguiculata* | Ruderal | (Spores) | 7 | 63 |
| *Bryum dichotomum* | Ruderal | Bulbils | 7 | 54 |
| *Bryum klinggraeffii* | Arable | Tubers | 6 | 52 |
| *Bryum rubens* | Arable | Tubers | 6 | 51 |
| *Dicranella staphylina* | Arable | Tubers | 6 | 45 |
| *Bryum violaceum* | Arable | Tubers | 6 | 44 |
| *Bryum argenteum* | Ruderal | Bulbils | 6 | 39 |
| *Funaria hygrometrica* | Ruderal | Spores | 6 | 37 |
| *Brachythecium rutabulum* | Common | - | 6 | 33 |
| *Barbula convoluta* | Ruderal | Tubers | 7 | 31 |
| *Dicranella varia* | Ruderal | (Tubers) | 7 | 26 |
| *Dicranella schreberiana* | Arable | Tubers | 6 | 22 |
| *Microbryum davallianum* | Arable | Spores | 7 | 22 |
| *Fissidens taxifolius* | Shade | (Tubers) | 7 | 15 |
| *Trichodon cylindricus* | Arable | Tubers | 5 | 15 |
| *Microbryum floerkeanum* | Arable | Spores | 8 | 14 |
| *Tortula truncata* | Arable | Spores | 6 | 13 |
| *Oxyrrhynchium hians* | Common | - | 6 | 12 |
| *Bryum ruderale**  | Ruderal | Tubers | 7 | 11 |

*Morphologically typical plants (see species account).

his lists when they were present in only small quantity, because they were adventives.

The greater length of 2000–15 lists is partly due to more intensive searching during the SBAL project. During 2000–05, average list length was 10.0. It fell to 7.1 in the period 2006–17. *Dicranella staphylina* may perhaps have increased. It was regarded as a mild calcifuge like *Tortula truncata* in the 1960s. By 1979 it was present in four of the 10 2 × 2 m quadrats (pH 7.8–7.9) recorded in the *Lythrum* hollows by C.D.P., something then regarded (perhaps erroneously) as rather a peculiar feature of this base-rich site. It is now found elsewhere on the chalk, although it is still more frequent in non-calcareous fields (see the species account). The increase of *D. schreberiana* cannot be explained in this way; it was only recognised in the county in 1959 and it was probably overlooked in the earlier period. The increase in ruderal species is probably real and accords with our memory of change. It is possible that ruderals have found it easier to establish following cessation of stubble burning in 1993.

**Table 12.3** Species recorded in arable fields per decade, including those from fields with short list length.

| Decade | Visits | Species | List length |
|---|---|---|---|
| 1930s | 2 | 4 | 2.0 |
| 1940s | 3 | 6 | 2.0 |
| 1950s | 18 | 51 | 2.8 |
| 1960s | 78 | 317 | 4.1 |
| 1970s | 20 | 188 | 9.4 |
| 1980s | 17 | 48 | 2.8 |
| 1990s | 16 | 79 | 4.9 |
| 2000s | 189 | 1653 | 8.7 |
| 2010s | 25 | 116 | 4.6 |
| Total | 368 | 2462 | 6.7 |

## Trends in species' assemblages

To compare Cambridgeshire with other parts of Britain, lists were assigned algorithmically to the assemblages recognised by Preston *et al.* (2010) using the cosine measure of similarity (Table 12.4). Changes are hard to ascertain. The species list for the *Dicranella staphylina-Riccia glauca* assemblage, which contains several calcifuges, is based on records from one field visited several times near Papworth St Agnes, and single fields near Ashley, Chatteris, Knapwell, Thorney and Willingham. Two of the species lists ascribed to this assemblage in the *Lythrum* hollows near Fowlmere appear to be incomplete, with three *Riccia* species and a list length of four. A third list of eight species may also be incomplete, but it included *Riccia glauca, R. sorocarpa* and *Tortula truncata*. Soil pH generally rose in England and Wales between 1978 and 2003, partly as a result of cessation of acid rain coupled, on acidic arable land, with agricultural liming (Kirk *et al.* 2010). The species of this assemblage, especially *Riccia glauca* and *R. sorocarpa*, require a period of autumn stubble to ripen their spores. The assemblage was always rare in Cambridgeshire as, apart from the dubious occurrences near Fowlmere, it does not occur on chalk or chalky Boulder Clay. It is likely to be declining, but we do not have data to prove this.

*Lythrum hyssopifolia* and its characteristic associates are still present in some of the hollows south of Cambridge, though the characteristic vegetation is well developed only after wet winters when the hollows flood (Figure 12.3). This, and the short season in late summer when the hollows are accessible between harvest and ploughing, makes them difficult to monitor. Bryophyte lists from the area mostly fall in the *Barbula unguiculata-Bryum klinggraeffii* assemblage, but are distinguished by the high frequency of *Riccia cavernosa, R. glauca, Microbryum davallianum* and *Pohlia melanodon*.

The *Bryum dichotomum-Marchantia polymorpha* assemblage is characterised by a high proportion of ruderal species, notably *Bryum argenteum, B. dichotomum* and *Funaria hygrometrica*. It is concentrated in

**Table 12.4** Numbers of arable visits with at least 4 recorded species, in 4 periods, assigned to assemblages defined by Preston *et al.* (2010). Values in brackets are visits to the Fowlmere and Chippenham areas, noted for *Lythrum hyssopifolia*.

| Assemblage | 1950–59 | 1960–79 | 1980–99 | 2000–17 | Total |
|---|---|---|---|---|---|
| B. *Dicranella staphylina-Riccia glauca* | | 5 | (2) | 5 (1) | 10 (3) |
| C. *Barbula unguiculata-Bryum klinggraeffii* | 1 (3) | 28 (13) | 6 (1) | 67 (16) | 102 (33) |
| D. *Phascum cuspidatum-Microbryum davallianum* | 1 | 2 (3) | | 22 (1) | 25 (4) |
| E. *Bryum dichotomum-Marchantia polymorpha* | | 3 (1) | 2 | 39 (1) | 44 (2) |
| F. *Brachythecium rutabulum-Fissidens taxifolius* | | 1 | 2 | 15 | 18 |
| Total | 2 (3) | 39 (17) | 10 (3) | 148 (19) | 199 (42) |

Fenland (26 of 46 occurrences). In the national survey this assemblage had mean pH 6.9, 0.5 units lower than pH 7.4 noted for the *Barbula unguiculata-Bryum klinggraeffii* assemblage. *Trichodon cylindricus* was found in 26 of the 46 Cambridgeshire lists, suggesting that Cambridgeshire samples also had relatively low pH. There are only six pre-2000 records of the assemblage so change cannot be assessed. The assemblage may have increased at the expense of the *Dicranella staphylina-Riccia glauca* assemblage, because rapidly-colonising ruderals rather than *Riccia* species are favoured by regimes in which stubbles are ploughed before winter. They are also favoured by high nutrient levels.

The fallow assemblage *Brachythecium rutabulum-Fissidens taxifolius* was found only three times before 2000, so that for this also change cannot be reported. The assemblage probably decreased when set-aside was phased out in 2009. In the landscape of the 2010s, assemblages of this type may be found when grass leys are sown after arable cropping or in bare areas among direct-drilled *Brassica* crops.

## Summary

Arable bryophytes are small and only specialist bryologists record them. Although a few fruiting mosses were recorded between the 1880s and the 1950s, the study of the vegetatively reproducing, tuber-bearing species (a significant minority of the arable specialists) did not begin until the late 1950s. Systematic lists of species in arable fields started at the same time. There are therefore considerable limitations in the extent to which the database can be used to assess change. Nevertheless, there is no evidence for major changes in the arable flora. We can probably conclude that if there have been changes, these have been rather subtle. They include a possible increase in non-specialist, ruderal species.

# 13

# Parks and gardens

Cambridgeshire as a county is not well provided with stately homes and their accompanying parkland. Simon Jenkins lists just three in *England's thousand best houses* (2003), Anglesey Abbey and Wimpole Hall (National Trust) and Madingley Hall (Cambridge University), though he adds some urban houses and Cambridge colleges. There are certainly more great houses in both Norfolk and Suffolk, including the seats of monarchs, dukes, marquesses and earls. Unlike most of our neighbouring counties, we no longer have any deer parks. The high value of agricultural land in Cambridgeshire has presumably discouraged magnates from acquiring large land holdings and setting them aside as unproductive parkland, and Fenland has not attracted those wanting to develop sporting estates.

Though they are less numerous and less grand than in neighbouring counties, Cambridgeshire's large houses and their surrounding parks and gardens have nevertheless been visited on many bryophyte excursions. Individual venues have varied in popularity over the years, with some sites visited frequently for a period simply because good relationships had been established with their owners. Hildersham Hall and Pampisford Hall were more popular before 1970 than in later years, as was Wandlebury because of its proximity to Cambridge. We first visited the Wimpole estate in 1998 but we have returned to it frequently, encouraged by Simon Damant of the National Trust. We did not go to Anglesey Abbey until 2007. By contrast Madingley Hall, as a University property, has been recorded at intervals throughout the post-war years. A rather different site, also covered in this chapter, is the Cambridge University Botanic Garden which was a very popular venue in the 20th century. There has been no excursion there since 1991 but it has been recorded by individual bryologists, including Jonathan Graham who carried out a systematic bryophyte survey (Graham 2011). Domestic gardens are a very under-recorded habitat, but a survey of such gardens in Cambridge is currently underway and will provide some information on their bryophytes.

## Diversity of the parkland flora

The 16 parks and gardens from which more than 40 species have been recorded are listed in Table 13.1. The components of the Parks and gardens flora are analysed in Table 13.2. The Parks profile closely matches the average of Open country, Towns and Recent woodland. This is hardly surprising as the parks and gardens usually include buildings and some estate woodland.

The totals for parks are higher than those for other habitats except fens, reflecting our experience that an excursion to a hall and its parkland often provides a good species list. The average numbers of rare species in parks are similar to those in several other habitats (Table 13.2). Open country sites and churches have fewer rare species and fens have many more. The richness of Cambridge inflates the value for towns. The figures for individual parks (Table 13.1) show that three are particularly rich in rare species. The chalkland rarities formerly found at Wandlebury have been discussed in Chapter 11. At Hildersham Hall the rare species grew in various habitats including watersides (*Dialytrichia mucronata*, *Riccia cavernosa*) and both a lawn (*Entodon concinnus*, *Thuidium assimile*) and beech woodland (*Plagiomnium cuspidatum*, *Scleropodium touretii*) on chalk. Several of the Botanic Garden rarities are plants of introduced substrates and these are described later in this chapter.

**Table 13.1** The parks and gardens from which more than 40 bryophyte species have been recorded. Rare species are defined as those with fewer than 10 sites. Visits are counted only if they resulted in 10 or more species records.

| Site name | Number of visits | Number of species | Number of rare species |
|---|---|---|---|
| Anglesey Abbey | 2 | 63 | 1 |
| Botanic Garden, Cambridge | 12 | 112 | 11 |
| Bottisham Park E | 1 | 50 | 0 |
| Childerley Hall | 1 | 60 | 0 |
| Chippenham Park | 1 | 58 | 1 |
| Croxton Park | 3 | 60 | 0 |
| Hildersham Hall | 7 | 97 | 7 |
| Landwade Park | 1 | 46 | 0 |
| Longstowe Hall | 3 | 71 | 2 |
| Madingley Park | 10 | 85 | 2 |
| Pampisford Hall | 7 | 87 | 2 |
| Sawston Hall | 2 | 67 | 3 |
| Swaffham Prior House | 1 | 60 | 0 |
| Wandlebury | 16 | 108 | 7 |
| Wilbraham Temple | 1 | 51 | 0 |
| Wimpole Hall | 5 | 115 | 1 |

**Table 13.2** The percentage occurrence of species in Parks & gardens, compared with those in some other habitats. The species clusters are those defined in Chapter 6; rare species are those with fewer than 10 sites. Only sites with at least 40 recorded species are included.

| Habitat group | Parks & gardens | Open country | Towns | Recent woods | Ancient woods | Churches | Chalk pits | Fens |
|---|---|---|---|---|---|---|---|---|
| Arable | 5.0 | 7.0 | 5.4 | 2.3 | 2.7 | 4.5 | 5.5 | 5.7 |
| Ruderal | 14.5 | 21.6 | 19.9 | 8.2 | 5.1 | 14.0 | 13.4 | 10.1 |
| Calcicole | 5.6 | 2.9 | 3.5 | 4.4 | 1.4 | 3.7 | 20.3 | 5.4 |
| Built | 20.3 | 17.0 | 23.9 | 8.3 | 2.6 | 35.5 | 10.7 | 5.1 |
| Water | 5.6 | 5.9 | 4.8 | 5.2 | 3.5 | 2.1 | 2.7 | 7.5 |
| Shade | 9.8 | 7.9 | 7.1 | 10.6 | 11.9 | 8.8 | 9.1 | 6.7 |
| Common | 18.3 | 22.2 | 20.8 | 23.1 | 19.0 | 26.0 | 20.6 | 16.4 |
| Epiphyte | 10.4 | 10.5 | 12.3 | 17.0 | 16.9 | 4.9 | 10.4 | 13.1 |
| Acid & Fen: Acid | 1.4 | 1.2 | 0.3 | 3.4 | 4.7 | 0.0 | 0.0 | 10.9 |
| Acid & Fen: Fen | 1.3 | 0.8 | 0.3 | 1.3 | 1.3 | 0.0 | 1.8 | 7.9 |
| Woodland | 7.9 | 3.0 | 1.7 | 16.1 | 31.0 | 0.6 | 5.4 | 11.3 |
| Number of sites | 16 | 19 | 10 | 19 | 32 | 18 | 11 | 9 |
| Species per site | 73 | 47 | 61 | 52 | 59 | 45 | 57 | 77 |
| Rare species per site | 2.4 | 0.5 | 2.4 | 2.1 | 2.3 | 0.2 | 2.3 | 9.4 |

## Madingley Hall and Wimpole Hall

These two parks are geologically similar, both including extensive stretches of Gault and Boulder Clay with a sliver of Lower Chalk between them. Madingley Hall (Figure 13.1) is a Tudor building, begun by the Henrician lawyer John Hynde in the 1540s and probably completed by his son in the 1590s. By the 18th century it had passed by marriage to the Cotton family. Sir John Hynde Cotton commissioned Capability Brown to landscape the park in 1756–57 and he created the sinuous lake in the grounds. Terraces and

**Figure 13.1** Ornamental stonework at Madingley Hall, January 2016. Photo: Peter Leonard.

gardens were laid out around the house in the decade before the First World War (Royal Commission on Historical Monuments 1968). The estate was bought by the University in 1948.

Wimpole Hall and its park are larger and grander than Madingley. The Hall has as its nucleus a house begun by Thomas Chicheley c. 1640 on the site of an earlier house and an ancient park. Chicheley's house was extensively extended by later owners, particularly by the Earls of Hardwicke in the 18th and 19th centuries. The present walled garden dates from the 1790s and the inner red brick walls survive, surrounded by a wall of Gault brick which was added in the 19th century and is of more bryological interest. The park includes Cobb's Wood, a small ancient secondary wood on the site of the abandoned village of Wratworth. A monumental elm avenue extending southwards from the house was planted in the 1720s by Charles Bridgeman and cut through the existing landscape in dramatic fashion. Both Capability Brown (who 'serpentized' the fish ponds in 1767–72) and Humphry Repton had hands in the later development of the park, which included woodland plantings (Royal Commission on Historical Monuments 1968). The estate remained in the Yorke family until it was relinquished by the 5th Earl of Hardwicke in 1894. He had already acquired the nickname 'Champagne Charlie' and accumulated vast debts by the time that he inherited the earldom in 1873 and he proceeded headlong into bankruptcy. The last private owners were Captain George Bambridge and his wife Elsie, daughter of Rudyard Kipling; on her death in 1978 the widowed Mrs Bambridge left the house to the National Trust. By then most of the elms had died of disease. The park went on to lose many more trees, hedges and other landscape features to a programme of agricultural improvement which was inflicted on 'one of the finest parkland areas in the country' (Taylor 1973) by the National Trust soon after it acquired the estate; this has since become a notorious example of historic mismanagement (Rackham 1986). Despite this, the Park retains much wildlife interest including an important barbastelle bat population (for which it is an SSSI) and some rare saproxylic invertebrates (Damant 2005).

The first bryophytes explicitly recorded from Madingley Park were two common species, *Brachythecium rutabulum* and *Fissidens taxifolius*, collected by A.C. Sturdy in 1904. Paul Richards recorded a few species in 1949 and the first bryophyte excursion visited the Hall in 1951. It was followed by five more between 1957 and 1985. There were no excursions to Wimpole Hall while it was owned by the Bambridges, perhaps because Mrs Bambridge was known to be eccentric and reclusive (Jenkins 2003), but Harold Whitehouse recorded 18 species by the Avenue in 1960 (presumably on the stretch which runs alongside a public footpath), including *Homalothecium sericeum*, *Syntrichia laevipila* and *Zygodon viridissimus* on the trees and *Drepanocladus aduncus* in the central Basin. We visited both parks in the recent survey.

The visits to Madingley Hall in the 20th century were too irregularly spaced to allow us to analyse the flora by decade, but the 20th- and 21st-century records for species in the habitat clusters, and the 21st-century records from Wimpole, are compared in Table 13.3. The composition of the modern flora is broadly similar for the two sites except for the much richer representation of Woodland species at Wimpole. The richest site is the oldest wood, Cobb's Wood (12 species) but The Gloucesters, an estate plantation, is almost as rich (nine). *Anomodon viticulosus*, *Cirriphyllum piliferum*, *Eurhynchium striatum*, *Homalia trichomanoides*, *Isothecium alopecuroides*, *Neckera complanata*, *Orthodontium lineare* and *Porella platyphylla* are found in both but Cobb's Wood also has four additional species on decaying wood (*Aulacomnium androgynum*, *Dicranum tauricum*, *Lophocolea heterophylla*, *Plagiothecium nemorale*) compared to one additional species, *Fissidens bryoides*, in The Gloucesters. The richness of the secondary woods at Wimpole has already been

**Table 13.3** Number of species in each habitat cluster recorded from Madingley Hall and Wimpole Hall.

| No. | Cluster name | Total in county | Madingley Hall 1950–1999 | Madingley Hall 2000–2018 | Wimpole Hall 2000–2018 |
|---|---|---|---|---|---|
| 1 | Arable | 23 | 3 | 3 | 7 |
| 2 | Ruderal | 25 | 10 | 10 | 12 |
| 3 | Calcicole | 51 | 2 | 0 | 3 |
| 4 | Built | 31 | 16 | 16 | 17 |
| 5 | Water | 31 | 3 | 4 | 7 |
| 6 | Shade | 13 | 8 | 9 | 10 |
| 7 | Common | 16 | 13 | 14 | 14 |
| 8 | Epiphyte | 34 | 4 | 13 | 19 |
| 9 | Acid & Fen | 75 | 5 | 0 | 2 |
| 10 | Woodland | 41 | 6 | 3 | 17 |

**Figure 13.2** *Pseudocrossidium revolutum* fruiting on the stonework at Madingley Hall, January 2016. Photo: Peter Leonard.

noted (Chapter 8). Common, Shade and Built-environment species are well represented at both sites. The Built-environment species include the largest population of *Leucodon sciuroides* in the county on the Gault bricks of the garden wall. At Madingley there is a population of *Leptobarbula berica* that is known to have been present since 1951 and much *Pseudocrossidium revolutum* (Figure 13.2). The records summarised in Table 13.3 exclude the churchyards which are found at the heart of the Wimpole estate and at the edge of Madingley Park; their inclusion would add more species to the Built list, especially at Madingley. By contrast, the only Calcicole species in these parks are the three most widespread plants in the cluster (*Didymodon fallax, Homalothecium lutescens, Pseudoscleropodium purum*). Changes in the bryophyte flora at Madingley between the middle of the 20th century and the start of the 21st include the threefold increase in the number of Epiphytes and the loss of calcifuge species in the Acid and Fen and Woodland clusters. The increase in Epiphytes is a symptom of a wider change but the loss of the calcifuges is largely due to the disappearance of casual populations of *Atrichum undulatum, Mnium hornum, Pohlia nutans* and three *Racomitrium* species, all recorded in 1961 on clinker on a sewage works which has long since been demolished. Another calcifuge, *Polytrichastrum formosum*, was recorded here and elsewhere in the Park but was last seen in 1967.

## Cambridge Botanic Garden: bryophytes on introduced substrates

Five hundred tons of Carboniferous Limestone from a low-altitude quarry in Westmorland were imported to the University Botanic Garden in 1951–53 and 1957 during its major post-war expansion and reconstruction (Figure 13.3). With characteristic prescience, Harold Whitehouse recorded the bryophytes on the limestone soon after it arrived (1955, 1957). He found many species which were not previously known from the Garden as well as commoner species which were already present in other habitats (e.g. *Bryum capillare, Hypnum cupressiforme, Tortula muralis*). Here we concentrate on the species which were recorded in the 20th century in the Garden only from the Carboniferous Limestone; details of the others are given by Preston & Whitehouse (1992b).

**Figure 13.3** Cambridge University Botanic Garden, showing the rock garden constructed in the 1950s using Carboniferous limestone from Westmorland, January 2011. Photo: Jonathan Graham.

Fourteen species listed on the incoming limestone by Whitehouse and confined to that substrate in the Garden survived for over 50 years and were still present in 2008–2011 (Table 13.4). All of these are native to Cambridgeshire, although *Tortella tortuosa* is apparently extinct at its native sites and is currently known only from the Garden. Six species have failed to persist but of these only *Neckera crispa* was recorded after 1957. *N. crispa* survived until 1973; it is not native to East Anglia and may be outside its climatic limits here. *Trichostomum crispulum* was first recorded on the limestone in 1980 and was presumably overlooked initially. *Orthotrichum cupulatum* was not recorded until 1986, even though fruiting plants are easily recognised. It must either have been overlooked earlier or have colonised the limestone as part of its massive expansion in the county which started in the mid 1980s.

Other introduced substrates are less well documented than the Carboniferous Limestone but also contribute to the diversity of the Garden bryoflora. The moist, shaded soft limestone and sandstone rocks in the Water Garden, which date from the original development of the Garden in the 19th century (Parker 2006), support a mixed population of *Gyroweisia tenuis*, *Leptobarbula berica* and *Tortula marginata* which is unique in the county. All three are now known to have been present since the 1950s, although *Leptobarbula* was not recognised until 1986. *Rhynchostegium murale* is also well established here. The population of *Leiocolea turbinata*, found recently on imported chalky soil, may prove to be more transient.

Introduced substrates also support calcifuge species. *Mnium hornum*, found on acidic sandstone imported from the Weald, has been recorded since the 1950s but *Calypogeia fissa* and *Cephalozia bicuspidata* were only discovered on this sandstone in 2010–11 (Graham 2011). *Calypogeia muelleriana* on an *Osmunda* tussock (1973) was certainly a casual, as were *Pohlia annotina* and *Polytrichastrum formosum* on glazing bars (1982) and *Polytrichum commune* in guttering (2014), all three on the outside of glasshouses. *Campylopus introflexus* was initially found on the 'bog oak' displayed in the Garden in 2008 and has also colonised the acidic sandstone, where it may persist.

**Table 13.4** Species imported on Carboniferous Limestone to Cambridge Botanic Garden. Only species which were confined to this habitat in the Garden in the 20th century are listed.

**Recorded in 1955–57 and still present in 2008–2011**

| | |
|---|---|
| Anomodon viticulosus | Neckera complanata |
| Bryoerythrophyllum recurvirostrum[1] | Orthotrichum anomalum |
| Cirriphyllum crassinervium | Porella platyphylla |
| Ctenidium molluscum | Rhynchostegiella tenella |
| Encalypta streptocarpa | Syntrichia montana |
| Fissidens dubius | Tortella tortuosa |
| Homalothecium sericeum | Weissia controversa |

**No longer present (with last record)**

| | |
|---|---|
| Homalia trichomanoides (1955) | Pleuridium acuminatum[2] (1955) |
| Neckera crispa (1973) | Scapania aspera (1957) |
| Plagiomnium affine[2,3] (1957) | Thamnobryum alopecurum[1] (1957) |

**First seen on limestone after 1957**

| | |
|---|---|
| Orthotrichum cupulatum (1986 onwards) | Trichostomum crispulum (1980) |

**Notes:**
1 Also found on sandstone elsewhere in Garden in 2010–11.
2 Seen in 1955–57 on soil on limestone rather than on the rock itself.
3 Also found in lawn elsewhere in Garden in 2010–11.

# 14

# The built environment

## Species of the built environment

Cambridgeshire is a rural county but it is certainly not a wilderness. In addition to the main towns and larger villages, shown on the land cover map (Figure 2.11), smaller villages and settlements occur throughout the county. The cluster analysis (Chapter 6) identified one group of 31 species which are characteristically found in built-up areas. These are listed in Table 14.1 and mapped in Figure 14.1. For comparison, the county's churches and chapels are mapped in Figure 14.2. Most of the species of the Built-environment cluster grow on calcareous stonework or brickwork and are thus dependent on a habitat which would not have been available in the county, or would have been very much rarer, before these materials were used for buildings. They presumably expanded their range greatly in the last millennium. Another group of 25 species, the Ruderals, comprises species which occur in a wide range of disturbed habitats (Table 14.2, Figure 14.3). These and the Common species cluster (Table 14.3, Figure 14.4) are most conveniently dealt with in this chapter although many of them are frequent both in built-up areas and in the wider countryside, and some are actually commoner in the open countryside. These are rather less exacting calcicoles than the Built-environment species and a few of the species are calcifuges. The Common, Built-environment and Ruderal species have higher mean frequencies than any of the other habitat groups (Chapter 6).

The records we inherited from built-up areas are less amenable to analysis than those of some other habitats. For many years Cambridgeshire bryologists usually recorded these species only rather casually,

**Figure 14.1** Coincidence map of Built-environment species.

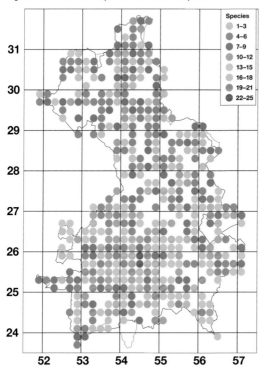

**Figure 14.2** Medieval churches (solid symbols) and later churches and chapels (circles) in Cambridgeshire. If both are present, only the medieval churches are mapped. Based on data taken from Bradley & Pevsner (2014) and Ordnance Survey maps.

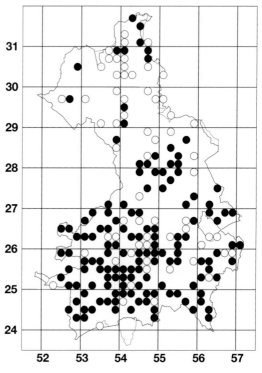

**Table 14.1** Species in the Built-environment habitat cluster. Ellenberg R values are an indication of species' substrate preference ranging from 2 (acid) to 9 (substrates with free calcium carbonate); see Table 8.1. 'Masonry' has been used in this table to cover both stonework and brickwork. All species have been recorded in the recent survey. Counts of site visits are for those visits on which at least 10 species were recorded. For details of the clustering analysis, and the definition of a site, see Chapter 6.

| Species | R | Typical habitat(s) | Sites | Visits |
|---|---|---|---|---|
| Tortula muralis | 8 | Masonry | 476 | 910 |
| Grimmia pulvinata | 8 | Masonry | 416 | 726 |
| Syntrichia montana | 8 | Masonry; roofs | 376 | 586 |
| Syntrichia ruralis sens. str. | 8 | Masonry; roofs | 365 | 581 |
| Didymodon vinealis | 8 | Masonry | 289 | 480 |
| Rhytidiadelphus squarrosus | 5 | Lawns | 246 | 396 |
| Schistidium crassipilum | 8 | Masonry | 244 | 348 |
| Bryum radiculosum | 8 | Masonry | 226 | 301 |
| Lunularia cruciata | 7 | Shaded soil | 202 | 395 |
| Orthotrichum anomalum | 8 | Masonry | 195 | 285 |
| Didymodon rigidulus | 8 | Shaded masonry | 183 | 243 |
| Didymodon luridus | 8 | Shaded stonework; chalky soil | 174 | 256 |
| Didymodon sinuosus | 7 | Shaded masonry; streamsides | 164 | 263 |
| Didymodon insulanus | 6 | Shaded stonework; shaded ground | 125 | 189 |
| Rhynchostegiella tenella | 8 | Shaded masonry | 105 | 143 |
| Rhynchostegium murale | 7 | Stonework | 79 | 108 |
| Pseudocrossidium revolutum | 8 | Masonry | 71 | 120 |
| Orthotrichum cupulatum | 8 | Stonework | 56 | 69 |
| Didymodon nicholsonii | 7 | Lightly shaded asphalt and concrete | 52 | 59 |
| Didymodon umbrosus | 8 | Shaded masonry | 32 | 44 |
| Tortula marginata | 8 | Shaded masonry | 30 | 50 |
| Gyroweisia tenuis | 7 | Moist masonry | 19 | 25 |
| Fissidens gracilifolius | 7 | Shaded masonry and chalk rock | 17 | 27 |
| Hygrohypnum luridum | 7 | Shaded masonry | 17 | 20 |
| Leucodon sciuroides | 7 | Masonry; epiphyte in orchards | 16 | 26 |
| Eucladium verticillatum | 9 | Moist masonry | 13 | 17 |
| Grimmia dissimulata | 9 | Stonework | 9 | 16 |
| Leptobarbula berica | 8 | Shaded masonry | 7 | 25 |
| Grimmia lisae | 6 | Stonework | 2 | 4 |
| Grimmia trichophylla | 2 | Stonework | 1 | 3 |
| Plagiochila porelloides | 6 | Beechwood on chalk | 1 | 3 |

**Table 14.2** Species in the Ruderal habitat cluster. For explanation of columns, see Table 14.1. Species which have not been recorded in the recent survey are not italicised; the record of *Pohlia annotina* was not included in a list with 10 or more species, and therefore has a count of zero for sites and visits.

| Species | R | Typical habitat(s) | Sites | Visits |
|---|---|---|---|---|
| Barbula unguiculata | 7 | Disturbed ground | 503 | 1093 |
| Bryum argenteum | 6 | Disturbed or trampled ground | 430 | 843 |
| Bryum dichotomum | 7 | Disturbed or trampled ground | 396 | 746 |
| Barbula convoluta | 7 | Disturbed or trampled ground | 395 | 758 |
| Funaria hygrometrica | 6 | Disturbed ground | 369 | 621 |
| Pseudocrossidium hornschuchianum | 7 | Trampled ground | 291 | 487 |
| Dicranella varia | 7 | Moist soil | 268 | 506 |
| Marchantia polymorpha | 6 | Disturbed or trampled ground | 236 | 411 |
| Brachythecium albicans | 6 | Well-drained soil and open grassland | 208 | 308 |
| Bryum ruderale | 7 | Trampled ground | 197 | 260 |
| Didymodon tophaceus | 8 | Moist soil | 129 | 195 |
| Syntrichia ruraliformis | 7 | Trampled ground | 126 | 159 |
| Brachythecium mildeanum | 6 | Well-drained soil and open grassland | 88 | 101 |
| Tortula protobryoides | 7 | Lightly trampled ground; disturbed soil | 70 | 84 |
| Bryum gemmiferum | 7 | Moist or disturbed soil | 61 | 72 |
| Bryum caespiticium | 6 | Brick walls; railway clinker | 30 | 34 |
| Tortula modica | 6 | Disturbed soil | 20 | 21 |
| Bryum algovicum | 7 | Well-drained sandy or gravelly ground | 15 | 17 |
| Bryum pallescens | 6 | Moist, metal-polluted substrates | 11 | 13 |
| Bryum archangelicum | 7 | Disturbed soil | 5 | 6 |
| Cephaloziella divaricata | 2 | Railway ballast; granite hoggin | 4 | 4 |
| Pogonatum urnigerum | 3 | Granite hoggin | 2 | 7 |
| Hennediella heimii | 7 | Salt-laden soil | 2 | 2 |
| Lophozia excisa | 5 | Railway clinker | 1 | 1 |
| Pohlia annotina | 4 | Glazing bars on greenhouse | - | - |

rather than on organised excursions. When C.D.P. suggested to Harold Whitehouse that it might be interesting to have an excursion to look round the historic buildings of Cambridge, Harold rejected the idea on the grounds that we would make ourselves 'objects of public ridicule'. Furthermore, built-up areas are not as well defined as relict sites such as chalk pits, fens or woods and often they cannot be identified by place names attached to earlier records. We can assume that a specimen labelled 'Gamlingay Wood' was collected in the wood but a specimen labelled 'Gamlingay' might have been collected anywhere in the parish. When we started our recording project in 2000, we were unconcerned about ridicule and made frequent records in towns and villages outside the curtilage of churchyards. Thus, the records from towns and villages are almost all in the period of our survey.

## Habitats of species in villages, towns and churchyards

Predictably there is a concentration of records from the Built-environment cluster in towns, villages, churchyards and cemeteries (Table 14.4). Halls and parks have a slightly lower proportion, and 'Open

**Figure 14.3** Coincidence map of Ruderal species.

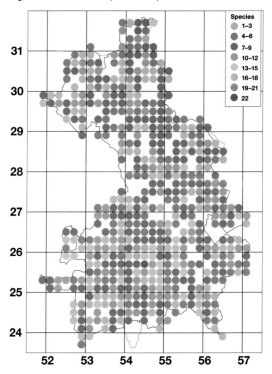

| Species | |
|---|---|
| ● | 1–3 |
| ● | 4–6 |
| ● | 7–9 |
| ● | 10–12 |
| ● | 13–15 |
| ● | 16–18 |
| ● | 19–21 |
| ● | 22 |

**Figure 14.4** Coincidence map of Common species.

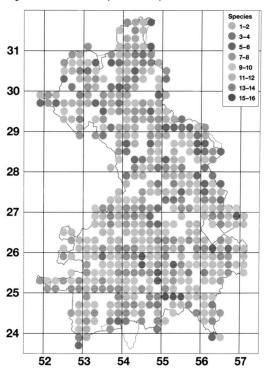

| Species | |
|---|---|
| ● | 1–2 |
| ● | 3–4 |
| ● | 5–6 |
| ● | 7–8 |
| ● | 9–10 |
| ● | 11–12 |
| ● | 13–14 |
| ● | 15–16 |

**Table 14.3** Species in the Common habitat cluster. All the species have been recorded in the recent survey. For explanation of columns, see Table 14.1.

| Name | R | Typical Habitat(s) | Sites | Visits |
|---|---|---|---|---|
| Brachythecium rutabulum | 6 | Nearly ubiquitous | 603 | 1357 |
| Bryum capillare | 7 | Walls; roofs; trees | 561 | 1147 |
| Amblystegium serpens | 7 | Shaded walls; trees; banks | 560 | 1155 |
| Kindbergia praelonga | 5 | Shaded grass; woodland | 552 | 1127 |
| Hypnum cupressiforme | 4 | Walls; roofs; trees | 537 | 1140 |
| Orthotrichum diaphanum | 7 | Masonry; base-rich bark | 521 | 974 |
| Rhynchostegium confertum | 7 | Shaded walls; trunks | 497 | 944 |
| Oxyrrhynchium hians | 6 | Soil; grass | 480 | 992 |
| Ceratodon purpureus | 5 | Asphalt, thatch, wood | 421 | 832 |
| Homalothecium sericeum | 7 | Masonry; base-rich bark | 385 | 697 |
| Calliergonella cuspidata | 7 | Grass; woodland rides | 378 | 719 |
| Dicranoweisia cirrata | 4 | Rotting wood | 292 | 559 |
| Syntrichia laevipila | 6 | Tree trunks and branches | 109 | 172 |
| Bryoerythrophyllum recurvirostrum | 7 | Roofs; paths; woodland | 97 | 153 |
| Plagiomnium affine | 6 | Thin turf | 27 | 43 |
| Plagiomnium cuspidatum | 7 | Woodland soil; rotting wood | 5 | 15 |

**Table 14.4** Relative frequency of species from Built, Ruderal and Common habitat clusters in lists from various landscape settings; values are the percentage of visits in lists of length 10 or more made in each setting after 1920.

| Landscape setting | Total records | Built | Ruderal | Common | Others |
|---|---|---|---|---|---|
| Village and town | 3235 | 27% | 25% | 30% | 18% |
| Church and cemetery | 6415 | 38% | 13% | 34% | 15% |
| Halls and parks | 3011 | 21% | 14% | 26% | 39% |
| Arable fields | 1461 | 1% | 27% | 8% | 65% |
| Open countryside | 4429 | 17% | 25% | 31% | 27% |
| The rest | 19,660 | 6% | 10% | 28% | 55% |
| All settings | 38,211 | 16% | 15% | 29% | 41% |

countryside', which may include buildings such as farm houses outside villages, have about half as many. Churchyards have the highest proportion of species from the Built cluster but a lower proportion of Ruderals. Species in the Common habitat cluster are not well represented in arable fields, but otherwise make up about 30% of all records.

If we compare the bryophytes of towns and villages with those of churchyards and cemeteries, the top 20 species are all mosses (Table 14.5). The most frequent mosses in towns and villages are *Bryum argenteum* and *Ceratodon purpureus*, which can be found on almost any asphalt surface. They are markedly less frequent in churchyards. These two are closely followed by *Brachythecium rutabulum, Bryum capillare, Grimmia pulvinata, Orthotrichum diaphanum* and *Tortula muralis*, which are equally common in churchyards. The tendency that is apparent in Table 14.5 for Ruderals to be more frequent in villages and towns and for Built-environment species to be more frequent in churchyards is clearly exemplified. An apparent exception is *Syntrichia ruralis*, which is attributed to the Built-environment cluster. However *S. ruralis* was a borderline case in the original clustering; it could equally well have been ascribed to either the Ruderal or Common habitat clusters.

## Analysis of the churchyard data

There was very little recording in churchyards before the 1980s. Bryologists tended to visit a single churchyard to see the characteristic species of calcareous stonework. Coton church (Figures 14.5, 14.6), an easy walk or cycle ride from Cambridge, was an early favourite; it was included on Henslow's excursions (Chapter 3) and then visited by Haviland & Lister (1880), Dixon (1882), Graveson (1914), Jones (1932), Richards (1942, 1943), Warburg (1945) and Whitehouse (1955) before the recent survey. Trumpington church was known to Relhan and Henslow but it was not visited again until 1941. It became a favourite venue for excursions in the 1950s and 1960s.

Regular recording in churchyards started in 1987, had a lull in the mid 1990s and then picked up again from 1997 onwards (Figure 14.7). Before the 1980s, complete lists were often not made, and species of the built environment were emphasised. Coton churchyard is an extreme case; the nine bryologists who visited it in the 19th and 20th centuries have left records of just five species, *Grimmia pulvinata, Orthotrichum anomalum* (collected by most), *Rhynchostegium murale*,

**Table 14.5** Relative frequency of species in the Village and town landscape setting compared with that for Churchyard and cemetery. The top 20 species are shown for each group; relative frequencies are calculated as a proportion of records in lists with 10 or more records.

| Name | Cluster | Village and town | Churchyard and cemetery |
|---|---|---|---|
| **In top 20 for both groups** | | | |
| Amblystegium serpens | Common | 2.8% | 3.1% |
| Barbula convoluta | Ruderal | 2.9% | 2.1% |
| Barbula unguiculata | Ruderal | 2.9% | 2.4% |
| Brachythecium rutabulum | Common | 3.3% | 3.6% |
| Bryum argenteum | Ruderal | 3.6% | 2.4% |
| Bryum capillare | Common | 3.4% | 3.9% |
| Calliergonella cuspidata | Common | 2.1% | 2.7% |
| Didymodon vinealis | Built | 2.1% | 3.4% |
| Grimmia pulvinata | Built | 3.4% | 3.6% |
| Hypnum cupressiforme | Common | 2.3% | 3.1% |
| Kindbergia praelonga | Common | 2.4% | 3.5% |
| Orthotrichum diaphanum | Common | 3.0% | 2.8% |
| Syntrichia montana | Built | 2.6% | 3.5% |
| Tortula muralis | Built | 3.4% | 3.9% |
| **In top 20 only for Village and town** | | | |
| Ceratodon purpureus | Common | 3.6% | 1.8% |
| Bryum dichotomum | Ruderal | 2.9% | 1.6% |
| Syntrichia ruralis s. str. | Built | 2.8% | 1.9% |
| Pseudocrossidium hornschuchianum | Ruderal | 2.5% | 1.1% |
| Oxyrrhynchium hians | Common | 2.3% | 1.9% |
| Funaria hygrometrica | Ruderal | 2.0% | 1.3% |
| **In top 20 only for Churchyard and cemetery** | | | |
| Schistidium crassipilum | Built | 1.9% | 2.1% |
| Rhynchostegium confertum | Common | 1.9% | 2.8% |
| Rhytidiadelphus squarrosus | Built | 1.7% | 2.6% |
| Homalothecium sericeum | Common | 1.5% | 3.4% |
| Bryum radiculosum | Built | 1.5% | 2.2% |
| Orthotrichum anomalum | Built | 1.1% | 2.2% |
| Didymodon rigidulus | Built | 1.1% | 2.4% |

**Figure 14.6** *Orthotrichum anomalum* on the churchyard wall, Coton, March 2017. The wall along the north side of the churchyard does not appear on Relhan's painting but now supports a rich bryophyte flora. The earliest of several specimens of *O. anomalum* from this church was collected in 1830. Photo: Peter Leonard.

**Figure 14.5** The younger Richard Relhan's watercolour of Coton church from the south, c. 1800. Reproduced by kind permission of the Syndics of Cambridge University Library.

*Schistidium crassipilum* and *Syntrichia montana*. After 1987, complete lists were normally made, and the balance between the categories of species was similar. Our analysis is based on records from churchyards and cemeteries made between 1927 and 2017, considering only visits when at least 10 records were made.

Because of the short period during which churchyard recording has been popular, it is impossible to report on long-term trends. Chi-squared tests, comparing species counts in the period 1980–1999 with those from 2000–15, indicate no significant difference. The proportion of epiphyte records rose from 1.8% in 1980–99 to 2.4% in 2000–17 but this was such a poorly represented group that the difference was not significant.

It is of interest to document the most frequent species in churchyards and cemeteries (Table 14.6). For this enumeration, frequencies are out of the 255 lists where at least 10 species were recorded. The average list length was 25.2. Two of the species in Table 14.6 normally occur in lawns: *Calliergonella cuspidata* and *Rhytidiadelphus squarrosus*. The Ruderals, together with *Ceratodon purpureus* and *Syntrichia ruralis*, grow on paths. *Plagiomnium undulatum* typically grows among grass on the north side of churches. *Phascum cuspidatum* is found in flower beds and on recently dug graves. *Fissidens taxifolius* and *Oxyrrhynchium hians* grow on the ground, often where it is disturbed and shaded. The remaining species, in the Built and Common clusters, are found on masonry and gravestones.

In a subsidiary analysis, we looked at the flora of different types of churches. Fen churches, defined as those with altitude 0–5 m, were distinguished from upland churches. Upland churches include those such as Ely Cathedral on high fen islands. Churches were also categorised by date, medieval and modern. These are easy distinguished as very few churches were built between 1500 and 1800. Modern churches have dates of dedication from 1837 to 1878, except for the Guyhirn Chapel of Ease (1660) and Six Mile Bottom (1933). Cemeteries date from 1843 to 1960.

The length of lists from cemeteries and medieval churches was similar. Modern churches averaged about six fewer species. Much of the difference is attributable to the presence of limestone walls and gravestones in ancient churchyards. Five frequent species (asterisked in Table 14.6), *Didymodon luridus, D. rigidulus, Homalothecium sericeum, Orthotrichum anomalum*

**Table 14.6** Frequency (%) of species in churchyards and cemeteries, categorised by location and date of construction: FM Fenland modern; UM Upland modern; FA Fenland ancient; UA Upland ancient; Cem Cemetery. Species found on fewer than 40% of all visits are not listed.
\* Frequency in ancient churchyards greater than twice that in modern churchyards
† Frequency in modern churchyards greater than 10% more than ancient churchyards

| | FM | UM | FA | UA | Cem |
|---|---|---|---|---|---|
| Number of visits | 17 | 8 | 45 | 167 | 18 |
| Average list length | 20.3 | 20.9 | 25.0 | 26.7 | 25.5 |
| **(a) Built** | | | | | |
| Tortula muralis | 94 | 100 | 100 | 99 | 94 |
| Grimmia pulvinata | 94 | 75 | 89 | 95 | 78 |
| Syntrichia montana | 65 | 63 | 91 | 91 | 78 |
| Didymodon vinealis | 47 | 75 | 82 | 92 | 67 |
| Rhytidiadelphus squarrosus | 47 | 38 | 51 | 72 | 61 |
| Didymodon rigidulus* | 24 | 38 | 62 | 68 | 33 |
| Orthotrichum anomalum* | 12 | 13 | 47 | 67 | 28 |
| Bryum radiculosum | 53 | 63 | 69 | 52 | 33 |
| Schistidium crassipilum | 35 | 38 | 62 | 54 | 50 |
| Syntrichia ruralis s. str.† | 53 | 63 | 53 | 40 | 94 |
| Rhynchostegiella tenella* | 12 | 13 | 44 | 51 | 6 |
| Didymodon luridus* | 6 | | 44 | 46 | 28 |
| **(b) Ruderal** | | | | | |
| Barbula unguiculata | 47 | 75 | 53 | 60 | 94 |
| Bryum argenteum† | 65 | 75 | 64 | 56 | 89 |
| Barbula convoluta† | 53 | 75 | 56 | 53 | 44 |
| Bryum dichotomum | 24 | 50 | 42 | 40 | 61 |
| **(c) Common** | | | | | |
| Bryum capillare | 94 | 100 | 100 | 98 | 89 |
| Brachythecium rutabulum | 88 | 100 | 89 | 90 | 89 |
| Kindbergia praelonga | 88 | 88 | 93 | 88 | 83 |
| Homalothecium sericeum* | 41 | 38 | 91 | 95 | 44 |
| Amblystegium serpens | 82 | 50 | 82 | 80 | 78 |
| Hypnum cupressiforme | 94 | 63 | 71 | 80 | 89 |
| Orthotrichum diaphanum | 82 | 50 | 64 | 69 | 78 |
| Rhynchostegium confertum | 76 | 63 | 78 | 70 | 39 |
| Calliergonella cuspidata | 47 | 50 | 58 | 71 | 83 |
| Oxyrrhynchium hians | 47 | 63 | 36 | 51 | 44 |
| Ceratodon purpureus† | 65 | 38 | 49 | 41 | 83 |
| **(d) Others** | | | | | |
| Plagiomnium undulatum | 24 | 38 | 51 | 57 | 33 |
| Fissidens taxifolius† | 59 | 38 | 42 | 47 | 61 |
| Phascum cuspidatum | 47 | 38 | 38 | 44 | 56 |

**Figure 14.7** Numbers of species records per year in churchyards and cemeteries, 1980–2015.

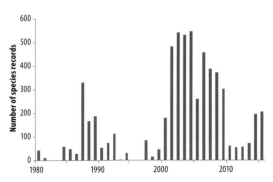

**Figure 14.8** Swaffham Prior churchyard, February 2017. Photo: Peter Leonard.

and *Rhynchostegiella tenella*, were twice as common in medieval as in modern churchyards. Between them they account for a difference of 2.2 species in list length. In the other direction, *Barbula convoluta*, *Bryum argenteum*, *Ceratodon purpureus*, *Fissidens taxifolius* and *Syntrichia ruralis* were slightly commoner in modern churchyards. These account for a difference in list length in the opposite direction of 0.5. It is notable that these species reflect the differences between churchyards and cemeteries on the one hand and towns and villages on the other. Modern churches have a flora more like the general flora in towns and villages.

Differences between Fenland and upland lists were much smaller than differences between those from ancient and modern churchyards. Among the species with less than 40% frequency, *Lophocolea bidentata* and *Bryum rubens* were rarer in Fenland churchyards. *Orthotrichum cupulatum* was commoner. With these minor exceptions, lists from Fenland churches were similar to those from the rest of the county.

Stevenson (2003) studied 258 churches in Norfolk and recorded an average of 16 species, considerably fewer than our average of 25. The 11 most frequent species in his sample are almost identical to those in our upland ancient churchyards (Table 4.6), the only difference being that his 11th species, *Rhynchostegium confertum*, is 13th in our list and is replaced in the Cambridgeshire dataset by *Rhytidiadelphus squarrosus*.

Finally, homage should be paid to the richest of all the churchyards, Swaffham Prior, extraordinary for including two churches (Figure 14.8). We found 46 species there in 2007. Two of them, *Aloina aloides* and *Bryum violaceum*, were found in no other churchyard. *Microbryum rectum* was found in just one other. *Bryoerythrophyllum recurvirostrum*, *Cratoneuron filicinum*, *Dicranella varia*, *Fissidens incurvus*, *Rhynchostegium megapolitanum*, *Syntrichia papillosa* and *Tortula protobryoides* were found on less than 5% of other churchyard visits. We were interviewed by a church warden for the parish magazine, who featured our visit under the heading 'Bryologists invade the village' (Everitt 2007). He reported that we were very jolly people who appeared to go away happy, but we failed to convey to him the truly exceptional nature of his churchyard.

# 15

# Epiphytes

## The epiphyte cluster

One of the clusters identified in Chapter 6 includes 34 primarily epiphytic species. They are listed in Table 15.1 and their distribution is mapped in Figure 15.1. As the coincidence map shows, this group of epiphytic species is especially frequent in the orchards around Wisbech (see Chapter 9) but the commoner species also occur as epiphytes in woods and in other habitats. Although most of the species are mainly or exclusively epiphytic, *Campylopus introflexus* is more frequent on other acidic substrates and *Bryum donianum* is not an epiphyte but is found on one stream bank. Other habitat clusters also include epiphytes. Some of the most frequent epiphytic species are included in the Common cluster (Chapter 14); these also grow in other habitats. Epiphytes found primarily in woods are found in the Woodland and Shade clusters (Chapter 8) and a few which usually grow on masonry but also occur fairly frequently on trees

**Figure 15.1** Coincidence map of species in the Epiphyte cluster.

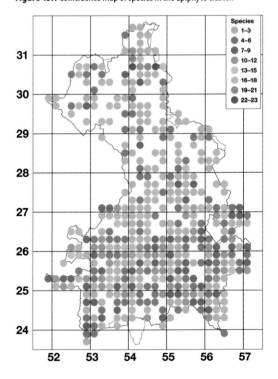

**Table 15.1** Species in the Epiphyte habitat cluster. All species have been recorded in the recent survey. The modes of reproduction are those observed in Cambridgeshire; uncommon or rare modes are bracketed. Species known to possess the capacity to produce protonemal gemmae are indicated by † and these observations are taken from Blockeel *et al.* (2014). Counts of site visits are for those visits on which at least 10 species were recorded. For details of the clustering analysis, and the definition of a site, see Chapter 6.

| Species | Reproduction | First Cambs record | Sites | Visits |
|---|---|---|---|---|
| *Orthotrichum affine* | Spores† | 1881 | 343 | 585 |
| *Metzgeria furcata* | (Spores, gemmae) | 1802 | 282 | 579 |
| *Frullania dilatata* | | 1729 | 234 | 404 |
| *Zygodon viridissimus* | (Spores), gemmae† | 1928 | 204 | 330 |
| *Syntrichia virescens* | (Spores)† | 1965 | 177 | 232 |
| *Radula complanata* | Gemmae, spores | 1729 | 160 | 261 |
| *Bryum moravicum* | Gemmae† | 1941 | 137 | 214 |
| *Cryphaea heteromalla* | Spores† | 1729 | 136 | 176 |
| *Campylopus introflexus* | Spores, leaves | 1965 | 121 | 172 |
| *Brachytheciastrum velutinum* | Spores | 1796 | 116 | 169 |
| *Ulota bruchii* | Spores† | 1881 | 112 | 155 |
| *Metzgeria violacea* | Gemmae | 1953 | 89 | 128 |
| *Orthotrichum lyellii* | Gemmae† | 1911 | 80 | 112 |
| *Ulota phyllantha* | Gemmae† | 1986 | 49 | 57 |
| *Syntrichia papillosa* | Gemmae | 1952 | 44 | 67 |
| *Orthotrichum pulchellum* | Spores | 1990 | 35 | 48 |
| *Cololejeunea minutissima* | Gemmae | 2007 | 32 | 35 |
| *Zygodon conoideus* | (Spores), gemmae† | 1991 | 31 | 37 |
| *Orthotrichum stramineum* | Spores | 1994 | 19 | 19 |
| *Orthotrichum tenellum* | Spores, gemmae† | 2000 | 18 | 21 |
| *Orthotrichum striatum* | Spores | 1821 | 11 | 16 |
| *Zygodon rupestris* | Gemmae† | 1932 | 9 | 13 |
| *Rhynchostegiella litorea* | Spores | 1960 | 6 | 10 |
| *Sciuro-hypnum populeum* | Spores | 1960 | 5 | 5 |
| *Ulota crispa* | Spores | 1990 | 5 | 5 |
| *Pylaisia polyantha* | Spores | 2004 | 4 | 9 |
| *Orthotrichum speciosum* | Spores | 2008 | 2 | 2 |
| *Sanionia uncinata* | | 2004 | 2 | 3 |
| *Antitrichia curtipendula* | | 2006 | 1 | 2 |
| *Bryum donianum* | † | 2004 | 1 | 1 |
| *Metzgeria consanguinea* | Gemmae | 2015 | 1 | 1 |
| *Orthotrichum obtusifolium* | Gemmae† | 2007 | 1 | 2 |
| *Orthotrichum pumilum* | Spores† | 2017 | 1 | 1 |
| *Pterigynandrum filiforme* | | 2010 | 1 | 2 |

Species
● 1–3
● 4–6
● 7–9
● 10–12
● 13–15
● 16–18
● 19–21
● 22–23

are included in the Built-environment cluster (Chapter 14).

The growth of trees and shrubs means that new epiphyte habitat constantly becomes available for colonisation, and most epiphytes either fruit freely or produce copious vegetative propagules or in some cases do both. The reproductive structures we have seen in Cambridgeshire are shown in Table 15.1. Protonemal gemmae are difficult to observe and they are probably found on more moss species than those indicated in the table. *Frullania dilatata* (Figure 15.2) is anomalous as it is now a common epiphyte but we have not seen sporophytes in the county in recent years and it lacks specialised vegetative propagules. Although it is dioicous, it fruits freely in western Britain (where it is often very much more abundant than in Cambridgeshire) and many plants in the county have probably come in from wind-blown spores; once here, it perhaps spreads by vegetative fragments.

**Figure 15.2** *Frullania dilatata*, an increasing epiphyte, growing with *Hypnum cupressiforme* at Cobb's Wood, Wimpole, February 2018. Photo: Peter Leonard.

## The recent expansion of epiphytes

We have already noted the increase of epiphytes in woods (Chapter 8), in chalkland sites (Chapter 11) and at Wicken Fen (Chapter 10) and Madingley Hall (Chapter 13). The Epiphyte cluster includes most of the species which have contributed to this expansion. Species which were already present in the county in the middle of the 20th century and were described by Whitehouse (1964) as rare (*Cryphaea heteromalla*), occasional (*Radula complanata*) or even frequent (*Frullania dilatata, Orthotrichum affine*) have increased very markedly in recent decades (Figure 15.3a, b). However, almost half of the species in the cluster (16 of the 34) have been discovered in the county since 1985 and 11 of these were first found from 2000 onwards. The increase of two of these newcomers, *Orthotrichum pulchellum* and *Ulota phyllantha*, is shown in Figure 15.3c. The increase in epiphytes is a local illustration of a national trend (Hill & Preston 2014, Pescott *et al.* 2015). The main causal factor is the reduction in $SO_2$ pollution, but it is possible that changes in climate, particularly warmer winters, may also have contributed in some cases (Bates & Preston 2011). Two epiphytes which have certainly not increased in frequency are *Brachytheciastrum velutinum* and *Bryum moravicum*. The Frescalo results suggest that *Bryum moravicum* appeared to increase until the 1990s, but then decreased (Figure 15.3d). It is tempting to suggest that the initial rise reflected the increasing knowledge of the species after it was described in 1973, but the pattern is very similar to the well-known epiphyte *Dicranoweisia cirrata*. The latter (assigned in our analysis to the Common habitat cluster) is known for its tolerance of $SO_2$ pollution.

## Host preferences

The number of epiphytic species recorded on the main tree and shrub hosts is listed in Table 15.2. This table includes records of 48 of the commoner epiphytic bryophytes, the 18 species in the Epiphyte habitat cluster which are recorded in 20 or more sites and an additional 30 species from other habitat clusters. The occurrence of the 15 species in the Epiphyte cluster which are known from fewer than 20 sites is also noted. The total number of bryophyte species recorded from the most productive hosts is rather similar, with 40–51 of the 63 bryophytes recorded on eight of the hosts (apple, ash, elder, field maple, hawthorn, pear, sycamore and willow). However, if the figures for the major hosts are examined it is clear that ash, elder and willow are particularly important hosts in the wild, as is apple in orchards. The intensive study of orchard apples is reflected in the high number of rare species recorded on them. The least productive of the commoner tree species is lime, which is not uncommon as a roadside tree but rarely has any specialist epiphytes.

In addition to the most frequent hosts, bryophytes can be found on a wide range of cultivated trees and shrubs, as shown by the list of the hosts of species such as *Frullania dilatata, Metzgeria furcata, Orthotrichum affine* and *Syntrichia virescens* in Appendix 3.

The frequency of the 48 commoner epiphytes on the 16 hosts listed in Table 15.2 was analysed by Detrended Correspondence Analysis (DCA), treating epiphytes as objects to be classified and their

**Figure 15.3** Trends in the frequency of epiphytes in Cambridgeshire, 1950–2017. For explanation of the method, see Chapter 7.

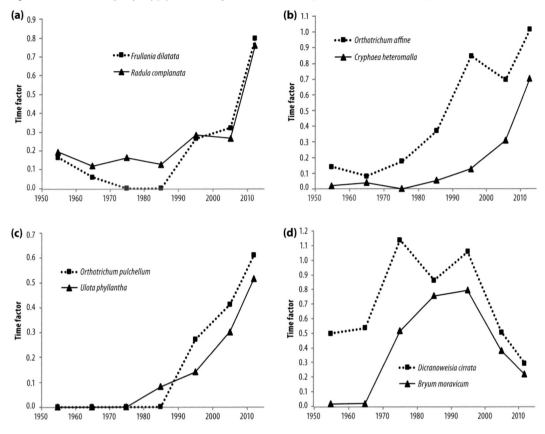

**Table 15.2** The number of epiphytic bryophyte species recorded on some of the most frequent trees and shrubs in Cambridgeshire. For the distinction between the 48 common and 15 rare epiphytes, see text. A major host is one with 10% or more of the host-tetrad records, a minor host has less than 10%. Scientific names of the host species are given in Appendix 3.

| Host | Common epiphytic bryophytes (n=48): major host | Common epiphytic bryophytes (n=48): minor host | Rare epiphytic bryophytes (n=15) | Total number of bryophytes recorded (n=63) |
|---|---|---|---|---|
| Apple | 24 | 15 | 11 | 50 |
| Ash | 34 | 11 | 6 | 51 |
| Beech | 0 | 33 | 0 | 33 |
| Birch | 1 | 20 | 1 | 22 |
| Elder | 25 | 16 | 1 | 42 |
| Elm | 0 | 38 | 1 | 39 |
| Field maple | 6 | 31 | 3 | 40 |
| Hawthorn | 11 | 29 | 3 | 43 |
| Hazel | 0 | 21 | 0 | 21 |
| Lime | 0 | 15 | 0 | 15 |
| Oak | 5 | 28 | 2 | 35 |
| Pear | 5 | 30 | 5 | 40 |
| Poplar | 0 | 29 | 0 | 29 |
| *Prunus* | 3 | 29 | 0 | 32 |
| Sycamore | 3 | 38 | 2 | 43 |
| Willow | 32 | 13 | 4 | 49 |

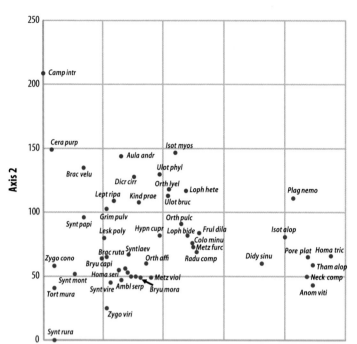

**Figure 15.4** DCA ordination of bryophyte epiphytes according to their hosts. There are four unlabelled species just above *Amblystegium serpens*. These are, in order from left to right: *Rhynchostegium confertum*, *Syntrichia latifolia*, *Cryphaea heteromalla* and *Orthotrichum diaphanum*.

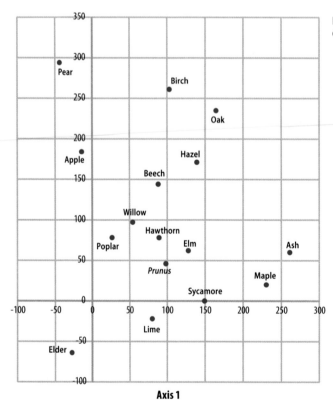

**Figure 15.5** Tree species corresponding to the ordination of epiphytes in Figure 15.4.

**Figure 15.6** A massive ash coppice stool in Hayley Wood, March 2017. Such stools support a characteristic suite of uncommon epiphytes including *Anomodon viticulosus, Homalia trichomanoides, Neckera complanata* and *Porella platyphylla*. Photo: Peter Leonard.

percentage occurrence on tree host species as attributes (Figure 15.4). The first axis represents a gradient from scrub and orchards to ancient woodland. The second axis is a gradient from base-rich to acid bark. *Porella platyphylla, Anomodon viticulosus, Homalia trichomanoides, Neckera complanata* and *Thamnobryum alopecurum* form one obvious group of species of base-rich bark in ancient woodland; all are species of our Woodland and Shade habitat clusters. At the other end of the axis, in base-rich but more open habitats, are species which are often found on masonry (*Homalothecium sericeum, Syntrichia montana, S. ruralis, S. virescens, Tortula muralis, Zygodon viridissimus*). The third axis (not shown) distinguishes species of wet places from the rest: those with third-axis scores greater than 100 were *Cololejeunea minutissima, Leptodictyum riparium, Leskea polycarpa, Lophocolea bidentata, Metzgeria violacea* and *Syntrichia latifolia*.

The corresponding ordination of trees (Figure 15.5) contrasts elder, apple and pear, plants of open habitats, on the low end of the first axis with ash and field maple at the high end (Figure 15.6). The second axis contrasts elder, lime (surprisingly) and sycamore at the basic end of the axis with pear, birch and oak which have relatively acid bark.

# 16

# Aquatic and waterside species

The 31 species assigned to the Aquatic and waterside habitat cluster in Chapter 6 are listed in Table 16.1 and their distribution is mapped in Figure 16.1. They have a rather diffuse distribution in the county, but there are concentrations along the Rivers Granta and Cam and the River Great Ouse and Ouse Washes, as well as Chippenham Fen, Wicken Fen and Gray's Moor Pits.

The species in this cluster differ in the extent to which they are found by water. Eight aquatic or semi-aquatic species are confined to watersides in Cambridgeshire. The most tolerant of these species to exposure, *Cinclidotus fontinaloides* (Figure 16.2), is sometimes found away from water in wetter regions of Britain and Ireland. *Dialytrichia mucronata*, a Mediterranean-Atlantic species which is much rarer in the county than it is in some other areas of southern Britain, is also confined to watersides in Cambridgeshire but sometimes found in other habitats elsewhere. *Leptodictyum riparium*, although normally found in wet places, can sometimes grow as an epiphyte in our orchards and (rarely) in other habitats. The two species of silty substrates, *Leskea polycarpa* and *Syntrichia latifolia*, typically dry out for long periods even in their waterside habitats and they too are occasionally found well away from water. The rarer *Scleropodium cespitans* similarly grows on tarmac in two sites. *Cratoneuron filicinum* and *Pohlia melanodon* are often found in damp habitats away from water, and it is not unusual to find *P. melanodon* in arable fields. *Hennediella macrophylla* is not found in wet places but riversides often provide the rather bare, shaded soil on which it grows and it perhaps spreads along them. Some of the rarest species, recorded from just 1–2 sites, are only placed in this cluster as they happened by chance to occur in disused pits (*Bryum intermedium, B. creberrimum*) or by water bodies (*Hedwigia ciliata sens. lat.*).

Not unexpectedly, some species in other habitat clusters are ecologically similar to the Aquatic and waterside species. *Ricciocarpos natans* shares the same lemnoid life-form as *Riccia fluitans* but it is classified as a Fen species as it is rarer than *R. fluitans* in ditches in arable Fenland. *Campyliadelphus elodes, Drepanocladus polygamus* and *Scorpidium scorpioides* are also allied to the Fen species. *Aphanorrhegma patens* and *Riccia cavernosa* are treated as Arable species as they grow in winter-flooded hollows in arable fields as well as on seasonally exposed mud in other habitats. They are similar in their ecology to *Bryum tenuisetum*. *Physcomitrium pyriforme* differs as it fruits in spring rather than in autumn in habitats which are wet in winter but not flooded for long periods.

Unlike the Acid and fen species, the proportion of extinct Aquatic and waterside species is low. The only plants which have been lost from the county are *Scorpidium scorpioides*, which is really a species of mires, the weedy *Bryum creberrimum*, recorded only once, and *Riccia rhenana*, a true aquatic but an introduced species. Few of the surviving species show well-marked trends in their frequency in the county. *Drepanocladus aduncus* and *Fontinalis antipyretica* have declined because of the loss of some of the smaller water bodies in which they grew, and the characteristic habitat of *Physcomitrium pyriforme*, grazed wet grassland and watersides, is less frequent than it was. However, many of the remaining species in the cluster are well adapted to the rather eutrophic waterside habitats still available in the county.

**Figure 16.1** Coincidence map of species in the Aquatic and waterside cluster.

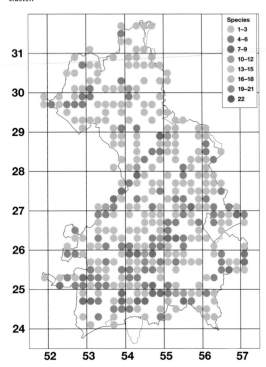

Species
- 1–3
- 4–6
- 7–9
- 10–12
- 13–15
- 16–18
- 19–21
- 22

**Table 16.1** Species in the Aquatic and waterside habitat cluster. Species which have not been recorded in the recent survey are not italicised. For details of the clustering analysis, and the definition of a site, see Chapter 6. Species that grow in or on water but may be exposed at times of low water are described as Aquatic or semi-aquatic.

| Species | Typical waterside habitat(s) | Typical water bodies | Sites | Visits |
|---|---|---|---|---|
| Leptodictyum riparium | Unsilted substrates in flood zone | Various; often small ponds | 191 | 343 |
| Pohlia melanodon | Moist soil | Various | 191 | 309 |
| Cratoneuron filicinum | Many moist or wet habitats | Various | 161 | 275 |
| Drepanocladus aduncus | Many wet habitats | Various | 95 | 142 |
| Syntrichia latifolia | Silty substrates in flood zone | Streams, rivers | 81 | 122 |
| Leskea polycarpa | Silty substrates in flood zone | Streams, rivers | 74 | 126 |
| Platyhypnidium riparioides | Aquatic or semi-aquatic | Streams, rivers | 64 | 97 |
| Fontinalis antipyretica | Aquatic or semi-aquatic | Various | 56 | 109 |
| Oxyrrhynchium speciosum | Eutrophic substrates | Ditches, disused pits | 47 | 72 |
| Brachythecium rivulare | Wet or swampy ground | Various | 38 | 58 |
| Riccia fluitans | Aquatic or semi-aquatic | Fenland ditches | 27 | 49 |
| Conocephalum conicum | Soil, masonry | Rivers, streams, ditches | 24 | 55 |
| Physcomitrium pyriforme | Disturbed mud | Various | 24 | 38 |
| Hygroamblystegium varium | Various damp substrates | Various | 14 | 15 |
| Scleropodium cespitans | Tree bases | Rivers, washland | 11 | 12 |
| Fissidens crassipes | Aquatic or semi-aquatic | Streams, rivers | 10 | 20 |
| Hennediella macrophylla | Trampled or disturbed, shaded soil | Rivers | 9 | 12 |
| Hygroamblystegium humile | Various damp substrates | Various | 8 | 10 |
| Cinclidotus fontinaloides | Aquatic or semi-aquatic | Rivers | 7 | 15 |
| Dialytrichia mucronata | Tree bases | Small rivers | 6 | 12 |
| Rhynchostegiella curviseta | Soil, masonry | Streams, rivers | 5 | 6 |
| Drepanocladus polygamus | Wet ground | Fens, disused pits | 3 | 11 |
| Campyliadelphus elodes | Wet ground | Fens | 3 | 12 |
| Riccia rhenana | Aquatic or semi-aquatic | Disused pits | 3 | 12 |
| Bryum intermedium | Open ground | Disused pit | 2 | 2 |
| Fissidens fontanus | Aquatic or semi-aquatic | River Nene | 2 | 2 |
| Hedwigia ciliata sens. lat. | Trees and worked wood | Disused pit, fen lode | 2 | 3 |
| Rhynchostegiella teneriffae | Aquatic or semi-aquatic | Streams, rivers | 2 | 3 |
| Bryum tenuisetum | Exposed mud | Washland | 1 | 1 |
| Bryum creberrimum | Sandy soil | Disused pit | 1 | 1 |
| Scorpidium scorpioides | Base-rich fens | Disused pit | 1 | 4 |

**Figure 16.2** Mark Hill and Björn Beckmann confirming the presence of *Cinclidotus fontinaloides* on the silty Gault Bridge over the New Bedford River at Sutton Gault, August 2008. Photo: Chris Preston.

# 17

# Casual occurrences, extinct species and introductions

## The concept of native casuals

In considering the origin of flowering plants, botanists often make a primary division between native and introduced species, then divide the introductions into those that are naturalised and persist as self-perpetuating populations in the wild, and those that are casual. The casuals are introduced as seed or as vegetative material and individuals plant(s) survive, but do not reproduce; the casual population therefore disappears when the pioneer individuals die. The term may also be used to cover populations which die out after a few years even though the pioneers may produce a few progeny. There is often a tacit assumption that native populations are self-perpetuating, accompanying the explicit recognition that introduced populations may be either self-perpetuating or casual.

Bryologists do not normally have to worry whether populations are native or introduced. There are very few introduced bryophytes. In part this is because the bryophyte flora of the northern hemisphere has less regional differentiation than the flowering plant flora, and in part because bryophytes are not grown by horticulturists and few have been transported along the trading pathways which have accidentally brought us so many flowering plants. However, some bryophytes may be *native casuals*, populations which arrive by natural dispersal but do not persist. This has become particularly clear after the fall in $SO_2$ concentrations, as some epiphytes have been recorded in new sites only as single individuals, or in very small numbers, rather than as self-sustaining populations. Four such *Orthotrichum* species have been added to the British flora recently, *O. acuminatum* and *O. rogeri* initially as single tufts and *O. patens* and *O. scanicum* as several tufts on a single tree (Blockeel & Fisk 2018, Blockeel *et al*. 2014, Bosanquet 2015). All except *O. rogeri* have since been found in further sites. Bosanquet (2012) has applied birding terminology to the native casuals, describing them as vagrants. Some well dispersed vascular plants also come into this category, though this has rarely been recognised. Examples include some occurrences of coastal species such as Oysterplant, *Mertensia maritima*, and of the Lizard Orchid, *Himantoglossum hircinum*, which in Britain has 'a high turnover of populations with a high proportion of new records and a high proportion of populations disappearing from the records' (Carey 1999).

The detailed study of Cambridgeshire bryophytes in the 20th century allows us to identify several species which are native casuals. Some are known from just one site; others are recurrent casuals with more than one casual population. However, we need detailed knowledge of the circumstances to identify such populations. This is not always available – if all we know of a record is the label on a 19th-century herbarium specimen, we lack such knowledge. However, in assessing the bryophytes which have not been refound since 2000 it is useful to bear in mind the concept of the native casual, so that we can distinguish, when possible, the loss of established populations from the disappearance of those species which are 'easy come, easy go'.

## Species not recorded in the 2000–2018 survey

There are 57 species which have been recorded from the county but which we have been unable to refind in our survey. These amount to 17% of the total flora; by comparison, Preston (2000) estimated that 13% of native flowering plants of the county had become extinct by 2000. The bryophytes which we have failed to refind can be divided into several groups, listed below.

One sizeable group of species are those last recorded in the complex of habitats on the Woburn Sands at Gamlingay. These include nine species of wet ground, listed below with the date of the last record:

*Lophozia ventricosa* (1820)  
*Odontoschisma sphagni* (1820)  
*Philonotis fontana* (1838)  
*Scorpidium revolvens* (1829)  
*Sphagnum fallax* (1988)  

*Sphagnum papillosum* (1824)  
*Sphagnum tenellum* (c. 1800)  
*Sphagnum teres* (1824)  
*Splachnum ampullaceum* (1841)

Of these, *P. fontana* and *S. ampullaceum* were also recorded on the 'moors' near Cambridge, *S. fallax* was one of the calcifuge colonists of Wicken Fen in the 1970s and the rest were known only from Gamlingay. There are also nine species of moist or dry habitats which were known only from Gamlingay:

*Anthoceros punctatus sens. lat.* (1833)
*Archidium alternifolium* (1788)
*Bartramia pomiformis* (1838)
*Calypogeia arguta* (1988)
*Cephaloziella rubella* (1934)

*Diplophyllum albicans* (1988)
*Fossombronia wondraczekii* (1988)
*Pogonatum aloides* (*c.* 1830)
*Pogonatum nanum* (1829)

The three species last seen in 1988 were recorded only once, on a single excursion when we were able to examine a newly cut ditch side; *Pohlia lescuriana* was also found with them but was rediscovered in 2018 on freshly disturbed soil nearby.

The largest group of species are 13 taxa formerly recorded from disturbed, acidic soil, especially in arable fields or in woodland, or as colonists of railway ballast or clinker (Figure 17.1):

*Acaulon muticum* (1965)
*Bryum creberrimum* (1959)
*Bryum gemmilucens* (1960)
*Cephaloziella hampeana* (1968)
*Fossombronia pusilla* (1995)
*Lophozia excisa* (1973)
*Pleuridium acuminatum* (1951)

*Pleuridium subulatum* (1993)
*Pohlia annotina* (1982)
*Racomitrium ericoides* (1961)
*Racomitrium heterostichum* (1961)
*Racomitrium lanuginosum* (1984)
*Weissia rostellata* (1965)

**Figure 17.1** A typical habitat for casual calcifuges in Cambridgeshire, the disused railway line alongside Hayley Wood in Cambridgeshire, recorded on a bryophyte excursion on 10 February 1968 and documented by Oliver Rackham. *Lophozia excisa* was discovered, new to the county, on this excursion. The disputed *Polytrichum* was recorded here on other occasions as *P. juniperinum*. Reproduced by kind permission of the Master and Fellows of Corpus Christi College Cambridge (*Rackham red notebook* 130: 9912–13).

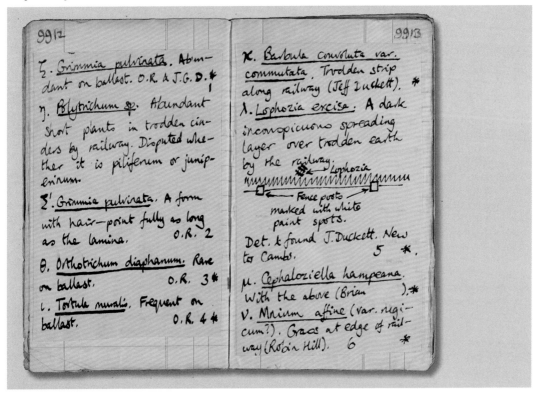

This list includes several native casuals, including *B. creberrimum*, *L. excisa*, *P. annotina*, as well as *C. hampeana* in some of its sites and *R. lanuginosum* in at least at one of its two localities. The populations of *R. ericoides*, *R. heterostichum* and *R. lanuginosum* at Madingley probably also fall into this category, although we cannot completely rule out the possibility that they were introduced on the clinker on which they grew.

A further set of nine species were recorded in acidic habitats such as peat or decaying wood in fens or woodland, including six, marked 'w', which colonised Wicken Fen during the calcifuge invasion:

Campylopus fragilis (1977)           Dicranella cerviculata (1968)
Cephalozia connivens (1989)          Hookeria lucens (w, 1975)
Loeskeobryum brevirostre (w, 1989)   Rhytidiadelphus loreus (w, 1989)
Pleurozium schreberi (w, 1999)       Riccardia multifida (w, 1978)
Polytrichastrum longisetum (w, 1991)

Of these, *L. brevirostre* is anomalous in that it is not normally calcifuge. *P. schreberi* was last seen at Wicken but it had earlier been recorded on soil, and on one occasion on a decaying log, in several woods. *C. fragilis*, *C. connivens* and *D. cerviculata* are fairly clear examples of native casuals, as is the Wicken colonist *Hookeria lucens* (which failed to survive the 1975/76 droughts). The other Wicken colonists are less clear-cut examples, as they might have survived longer had the management of the Fen not changed. (Similarly the Madingley *Racomitrium* species might have persisted if their sewage works had not been demolished.)

Two further species, *Plagiothecium laetum* (1991) and *Ptilidium pulcherrimum* (1980), are calcifuge epiphytes. The former is closely related to *P. curvifolium* and might be overlooked, but *P. pulcherrimum* was a recurrent native casual, recorded in four sites.

There are fewer lost calcicoles but the following five species formerly grew in calcareous wetlands on the 'moors' or in fens:

Calliergon giganteum (1942)          Preissia quadrata (1832)
Palustriella commutata (1960)        Scorpidium scorpioides (1957)
Palustriella falcata (1929)

A further seven species grew on disturbed ground, in open turf on the chalk or on sand over chalk:

Aloina brevirostris (1989)           Rhodobryum roseum (1955)
Entodon concinnus (1973)             Rhytidium rugosum (1930)
Leiocolea badensis (1977)            Scleropodium touretii (1953)
Pterygoneurum lamellatum (1970)

Finally there are three species which are introductions which have failed to persist. *Neckera crispa* (1973) and *Scorpiurium circinatum* (1961) are native elsewhere in Britain and Ireland and were introduced on rockery stones brought from their native range to build rock gardens. *Riccia rhenana* (1988) is an aquatic which has been introduced from Europe.

The dates of the last records of the above 57 species are plotted in Figure 17.2 and show a remarkably bimodal pattern. The peak in the 1820s and 1830s reflects habitat destruction following parliamentary enclosure, and especially the loss of the acid bogs and drier habitats at Gamlingay. The 1820s and 1830s were also decades when many flowering plants were recorded in the county for the last time, for similar reasons (Figure 17.3; Preston 2000). The available data must under-estimate the scale of the bryophyte losses in the early 19th century, as the habitats at Gamlingay must have supported more species than were recorded at the time, and we have only a very fragmentary knowledge of the bryoflora of calcareous wetlands such as the 'moors' near Cambridge and Burwell Fen. After 1841 there was a period of over 80 years with no last records of bryophytes, not surprisingly as there was so little bryophyte recording then (Chapter 3). It is possible that some of the species last recorded in the 1820s and 1830s survived into this period. The second peak towards the end of the 20th century has at least three components. Some of the species are established mosses which have almost certainly been lost because of environmental changes such as the deterioration of chalk grassland (e.g. *Entodon concinnus*), the cessation of quarrying at Cherry Hinton (e.g. *Aloina brevirostris*) and the changing management at Wicken which has restored calcareous fen vegetation in areas which were acidifying fen carr (e.g. *Rhytidiadelphus loreus*). A second group of species are rare calcifuge ephemerals of very sporadic occurrence (e.g. *Fossombronia pusilla*, *F. wondraczekii*,

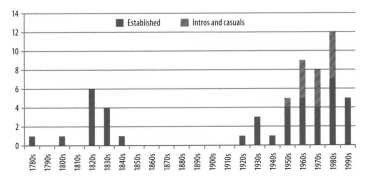

**Figure 17.2** Last dates for the 57 bryophyte species not refound in the recent survey, plotted by decade. Species identified as introductions or native casuals in the text are distinguished.

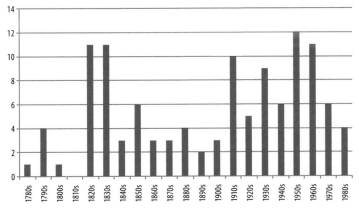

**Figure 17.3** Last dates for 115 native vascular plant species regarded by Preston (2000) as extinct in Cambridgeshire, plotted by decade. Five species last recorded before 1780 are excluded from this total, as are all species last recorded after 1989.

*Pleuridium subulatum*); the probability of finding these in any one year is low but we would expect some to be rediscovered in the future. Finally there are the native casuals detected during periods of intensive and well-documented bryological recording in the second half of the 20th century.

We can conclude that the last records of bryophytes will be concentrated in periods when bryologists are most active, not because bryologising causes extinction but because it is in these periods that rare species are most likely to be recorded.

**Native casuals recorded in the 2000–2018 survey**

A number of species we have recorded during the recent survey are almost certainly native casuals. The most obvious examples are the tiny tufts of the rupestral species *Hedwigia ciliata*, seen in Cambridgeshire on an elder, and *H. stellata*, found on a wooden bench. Both *Antitrichia curtipendula* and *Frullania tamarisci* grew as single patches on trees which were chopped down shortly after their bryophytes were discovered. Other epiphytes recorded (so far) on only a single tree are *Hypnum cupressiforme* var. *heseleri*, *Orthotrichum pumilum* and *Pterigynandrum filiforme*. *Cephalozia lunulifolia* has been seen on only one rotting tree stump. However, small populations can sometimes spread – *Orthotrichum obtusifolium*, initially recorded from one apple tree in an orchard, has now colonised a nearby tree. It is difficult to imagine that *Plasteurhynchium striatulum* will survive for many years in the county, as the concrete lump on which it grows differs so greatly from its normal habitat. *Pogonatum urnigerum* (Figure 17.4) has spread since it was first detected

**Figure 17.4** *Pogonatum urnigerum* on granite hoggin in a car park in West Cambridge, November 2014. Photo: Peter Leonard.

on granite hoggin at two sites landscaped for Cambridge University, but the habitat may not last for long. Some native casuals are casuals because they colonise short-lived habitats.

Our recent fieldwork suggests that some wetland species, *Brachythecium rivulare*, *Bryum pseudotriquetrum* and *Polytrichum commune*, have both established and casual populations. The same may be true of *Brachythecium salebrosum*; its non-woodland populations are certainly casual, but it may be established in some wet woodlands.

## Introduced bryophytes

Porley & Hodgetts (2005: 97) list 18 bryophytes which have been introduced to Britain and Ireland. The two commonest, *Campylopus introflexus* and *Orthotrichum lineare*, are both well established in Cambridgeshire. We also have established populations of *Hennediella macrophylla* and *H. stanfordensis*, but *Riccia rhenana* has not been seen since 1988 (and appears to be declining nationally). Porley & Hodgetts and Blockeel *et al.* (2014) also suggest that *Didymodon umbrosus* is probably introduced. *Platygyrium repens* has certainly spread in Britain in recent decades and it may have colonised naturally from western Europe, where it is also becoming more frequent (Blockeel *et al.* 2014).

In addition to the species which have been introduced to Britain, a few mosses have been introduced to Cambridgeshire from native sites elsewhere in Britain or Ireland. *Neckera crispa* and *Scorpiurium circinatum* are listed above as species which have failed to persist. *Grimmia trichophylla* is confined to a single acidic rock, brought from Cheviot, and *Tortella tortuosa* is apparently extinct as a native species but persists as an introduction on Carboniferous limestone in Cambridge Botanic Garden.

# 18

# Biogeography of the Cambridgeshire Flora

Earlier chapters have discussed habitat clusters which are based on the distribution of species in Cambridgeshire. This chapter looks at our bryophytes in relation to their wider range. They can be divided into floristic elements which distinguish species by their occurrence in major biomes and by the extent to which they extend eastwards from western Ireland. The major biomes are Arctic-montane, Boreal-montane, Temperate and Southern or Mediterranean; some species occur in two biomes (Boreo-arctic, Boreo-temperate, Southern-temperate) or even three (Wide-boreal in Arctic, Boreal and Temperate, Wide-temperate in Boreal, Temperate and Southern). The eastern limits are Hyperoceanic, Oceanic, Suboceanic, European, Eurosiberian, Eurasian and Circumpolar. Mediterranean-Atlantic species are exceptional as they are found in the Southern biome in much of Europe but extend north in western Europe into the Temperate zone, and Submediterranean-Subatlantic species have a similar but rather broader distribution. For further details of this classification see Hill & Preston (1998) or the summaries in Blockeel *et al.* (2014) or Hill *et al.* (2007).

The number of Cambridgeshire species in the different floristic elements is set out in Table 18.1, and in Table 18.2 these values are expressed as a proportion of the total number of species in the British and Irish flora. The absence of Arctic-montane species and the poor representation of the Boreo-arctic Montane and Boreal-montane elements is no surprise. Similarly the virtual absence of Hyperoceanic species is to be expected; the only such species, *Cololejeunea minutissima*, has spread out of this limited range in recent years in both Britain and Europe and it now has a more or less Mediterranean-Atlantic distribution. The species in the Wide-boreal and Wide-temperate elements are particularly well represented in Cambridgeshire. These elements include some bryophytes which are not only widespread at a continental scale but also very frequent in Britain (e.g. *Bryum argenteum, Ceratodon purpureus, Funaria hygrometrica*). The largest elements in the flora, in Cambridgeshire as in Britain and Ireland as a whole, are the Circumpolar Boreo-temperate and European Temperate, a reflection of our position in the Temperate biome. Southern-temperate species are less well represented overall than the Boreo-temperate and Temperate elements, but this is because we lack so many Hyperoceanic and Oceanic members of the group. The more widespread Southern-temperate European and Circumpolar species are particularly well represented and we have just over half the Submediterranean-Subatlantic species.

The species in each floristic element which have not been seen in the county since 2000 are compared with those which have been discovered in the county in recent years in Table 18.3. This reveals a remarkable turnover in the members of the northernmost elements. There are 26 Boreo-arctic and Boreal-montane species of which 15 are extinct and seven have been seen in the county for the first time since 2000. Only *Lophozia perssonii, Abietinella abietina, Aloina rigida* and *Plagiomnium*

**Table 18.1** The number of bryophyte species in different floristic elements recorded from Cambridgeshire. The full names of the eastern limit categories are Hyperoceanic, Oceanic, Suboceanic, European, Eurosiberian, Eurasian and Circumpolar. A zero value is given if the element is represented in Britain and Ireland but not in Cambridgeshire.

| Major biome category | Hype | Ocea | Subo | Euro | Esib | Easi | Circ | Total |
|---|---|---|---|---|---|---|---|---|
| Arctic-montane | | 0 | 0 | 0 | 0 | 0 | 0 | 0 |
| Boreo-arctic Montane | | | 0 | 0 | 0 | | 16 | 16 |
| Boreal-montane | | 0 | 0 | 2 | 1 | 0 | 7 | 10 |
| Wide-boreal | | | | 1 | 1 | | 17 | 19 |
| Boreo-temperate | | 1 | 9 | 22 | 1 | 2 | 58 | 93 |
| Wide-temperate | | | | 2 | 2 | | 11 | 15 |
| Temperate | 0 | 3 | 18 | 64 | 3 | 1 | 22 | 111 |
| Southern-temperate | 1 | 1 | 0 | 16 | 3 | 2 | 17 | |
| Mediterranean | | | 15 | 22 | | | | 37 |
| Total | 1 | 20 | 50 | 107 | 10 | 5 | 148 | 341 |

**Table 18.2** The percentage of British and Irish species in each floristic element recorded from Cambridgeshire. For abbreviations, see Table 18.1. The table is based on the British and Irish totals given by Hill & Preston (1998) updated to take into account the additional species (and a few deleted species) listed by Blockeel *et al.* (2014).

| Major biome category | Hype | Ocea | Subo | Euro | Esib | Easi | Circ | Total |
|---|---|---|---|---|---|---|---|---|
| Arctic-montane | | 0 | 0 | 0 | 0 | 0 | 0 | 0 |
| Boreo-arctic Montane | | | 0 | 0 | 0 | | 14 | 12 |
| Boreal-montane | | 0 | 0 | 3 | 25 | 0 | 10 | 5 |
| Wide-boreal | | | 100 | 100 | | | 89 | 95 |
| Boreo-temperate | | 50 | 43 | 44 | 50 | 50 | 57 | 52 |
| Wide-temperate | | | | 100 | 100 | | 79 | 83 |
| Temperate | 0 | 14 | 53 | 64 | 75 | 33 | 79 | 54 |
| Southern-temperate | 3 | 6 | 0 | 70 | 60 | 67 | 85 | 37 |
| Mediterranean | | | 25 | 52 | | | | 37 |
| Total | 2 | 16 | 38 | 40 | 53 | 36 | 35 | 33 |

*ellipticum* have been recorded in both millennia, and two of these maintain a precarious existence dependent on chalk quarrying or other large-scale disturbance. Some of the extinct species were probably permanent members of wetland plant communities before they were destroyed by drainage in the early 19th century (e.g. *Preissia quadrata*, *Scorpidium revolvens*); this was certainly true of *Splachnum ampullaceum* which is so conspicuous that it was recorded by several bryologists even though its last site was drained in the 1840s. *Entodon concinnus* was a familiar member of the chalk grassland flora until the 1970s. However, other northern species recorded in the 20th century were casuals (e.g. *Lophozia excisa*, *Ptilidium pulcherrimum*, *Racomitrium lanuginosum*).

**Table 18.3** Cambridgeshire species in each major biome category which have not been seen since 2000 ('Extinct') and those which have been seen in that period for the first time ('New'). Species found both before and after 2000 are signified as 'Persisting'.

| Major biome category | Extinct | New | Persisting | Total |
|---|---|---|---|---|
| Boreo-arctic Montane | 10 | 4 | 2 | 16 |
| Boreal-montane | 5 | 3 | 2 | 10 |
| Wide-boreal | 2 | 0 | 17 | 19 |
| Boreo-temperate | 19 | 7 | 67 | 93 |
| Wide-temperate | 1 | 0 | 14 | 15 |
| Temperate | 13 | 8 | 90 | 111 |
| Southern-temperate | 2 | 1 | 37 | 40 |
| Mediterranean | 5 | 2 | 30 | 37 |
| Total | 57 | 25 | 259 | 341 |

The newly discovered northern species comprise one which has already been lost (*Sphagnum russowii*), one which is currently well established but in a habitat which is unlikely to be present for very long (*Pogonatum urnigerum*), the inconspicuous *Seligeria donniana* and four rare epiphytes (*Orthotrichum obtusifolium*, *O. speciosum*, *Pterigynandrum filiforme*, *Sanionia uncinata*).

The decline of the established northern flora in southern Britain is a feature of floristic change over recent centuries. It has been documented for vascular plants in detailed studies of individual counties (e.g. Boon 1998, Preston 2000, Walker & Preston 2006) and for both bryophytes and vascular plants at the national scale (Hill & Preston 2015). The reason for the loss of the bryophytes is that they grew in unproductive habitats with low nutrient levels, just those habitats which have been destroyed by agricultural improvement. Though the decline of northern species is well known, the turnover which is so apparent in Cambridgeshire has not, as far as we know, been identified in previous studies.

Table 18.4 shows the biogeographical composition of the habitat clusters recognised in Chapter 6. They show that there are concentrations of Boreo-arctic and Boreal species in Acid and Fen and Calcicole clusters, the two which have suffered most losses. The species in the Woodland and Epiphyte habitat clusters are predominantly drawn from the Boreo-temperate and Temperate elements, not surprisingly in view of their association with broad-leaved trees, the defining feature of the Temperate zone. By contrast, the Calcicole cluster includes many species of open habitats and is unusual in having both relatively high percentages of Boreo-arctic and Boreal species and a particularly high number of Southern and Mediterranean species, with a correspondingly low representation of the common Boreo-temperate and Temperate elements. The Shade cluster has a more southern composition than that of the Woodland cluster. The Arable flora is predominantly Temperate and the species of the Built cluster have the most southerly affinities.

**Table 18.4** Taxa in the habitat clusters in each major biome category. The taxa tabulated here include the aggregates and intraspecific taxa recognised in the cluster analysis, hence the total of 338 taxa rather than the 341 species in Tables 18.1–18.3.

| Cluster | Bor-arc | Bor-mon | Wide-bor | Bor-temp | Wide-temp | Temp | South-temp | Med | Total |
|---|---|---|---|---|---|---|---|---|---|
| Acid & Fen: Fen | 3 | 0 | 4 | 10 | 0 | 2 | 1 | 0 | 20 |
| Acid & Fen: Acid | 3 | 2 | 10 | 22 | 1 | 13 | 1 | 1 | 53 |
| Woodland | 0 | 2 | 1 | 19 | 0 | 18 | 0 | 1 | 41 |
| Epiphyte | 2 | 2 | 0 | 6 | 0 | 17 | 3 | 4 | 34 |
| Ruderal | 2 | 0 | 1 | 10 | 4 | 5 | 3 | 0 | 25 |
| Calcicole | 4 | 4 | 2 | 7 | 1 | 11 | 10 | 12 | 51 |
| Water | 1 | 0 | 0 | 7 | 1 | 14 | 5 | 3 | 31 |
| Common | 0 | 0 | 1 | 4 | 1 | 7 | 2 | 1 | 16 |
| Arable | 0 | 0 | 0 | 2 | 2 | 13 | 3 | 3 | 23 |
| Shade | 0 | 0 | 0 | 1 | 1 | 6 | 3 | 2 | 13 |
| Built | 0 | 0 | 0 | 4 | 4 | 4 | 10 | 9 | 31 |
| Total | 15 | 10 | 19 | 92 | 15 | 110 | 41 | 36 | 338 |

# 19

# Species accounts

## Explanation of the text

The taxonomy, nomenclature and sequence of species follow Hill *et al.* (2008). Synonyms which fell into disuse before 1950, including pre-Linnaean names, are included in the species accounts when we cite works using them, but later synonyms are listed in the index and cross-referenced to the current name.

In addition to the accounts of all species accepted from the county, we have provided full accounts of four infraspecific taxa (*Marchantia polymorpha* subsp. *ruderalis*, *Weissia longifolia* var. *angustifolia*, *Syntrichia ruralis* var. *ruraliformis* and *Hypnum cupressiforme* var. *heseleri*) in addition to the type of these species. Notes on other infraspecific taxa are given in the species accounts.

In the headings, the names of species which have not been recorded from the county in the recent survey are preceded by an obelus (†).

The **first paragraph** of the account describes the habitat and distribution of the taxon in the county *in the recent survey period* (January 2000–March 2018). Where relevant, we refer to Robin Stevenson's survey of apple and pear trees in orchards, and the BBS Survey of the Bryophytes of Arable Land (SBAL), both described in Chapter 4. Other statistics in the accounts, such as those on the host preferences of epiphytes, were calculated in 2017 and thus exclude records made after March 2017. In calculating statistics such as host or substrate preferences we have usually aggregated records into tetrads, to avoid an overemphasis on frequently visited sites. This first paragraph is sometimes omitted if there is only a single record of a species made in the county which dates from before 2000.

The **second paragraph** starts with the first acceptable record of the plant from the county. We do not necessarily cite the exact wording of a published record or a herbarium label. The paragraph goes on to discuss trends in the distribution of the species by comparing earlier records to those made recently. In doing this we sometimes draw on the Frescalo analysis described in Chapter 7.

The **third paragraph** begins with the sexuality of the species. This information is taken from Blockeel *et al.* (2014) and employs the following terms:

- autoicous: antheridia and archegonia borne in separate inflorescences on the same plant
- dioicous: antheridia and archegonia borne on separate plants
- monoicous: antheridia and archegonia borne on the same plant; monoicous plants may be autoicous, paroicous, pseudodioicous or synoicous
- paroicous: antheridia naked in the axils of the leaves immediately below the female inflorescence
- pseudodioicous: antheridia and archegonia borne on plants which are apparently separate but have actually arisen from protonema which has grown from a single spore
- rhizautoicous: antheridia and archegonia borne in separate inflorescences, with the male shoots attached to the female by rhizoids
- synoicous: antheridia and archegonia borne in the same inflorescence.

The references to the presence of sporophytes, gemmae and tubers which follow refer, unless otherwise stated, to plants in Cambridgeshire. The percentage of tetrads in which sporophytes have been recorded is based on data gathered in the recent survey. Information on the timing of sporophyte maturation is drawn from all available records but the vast majority of these were made recently. As we have done very little bryology in the summer months, our records of the times of maturity of summer-fruiting species are often inadequate.

Other observations are sometimes given in a **fourth paragraph**.

Full details of all our records are publicly available on the National Biodiversity Network Atlas website. We have not therefore felt the need to cite full grid references, only tetrads or quadrants, and we have been sparing in naming individual recorders (especially as many records were made communally on bryophyte excursions). We have often used 'we' in phrases such as 'we have recorded this species from …' to refer to all recent recorders rather than just C.D.P. and M.O.H. We have omitted altitudinal data as this is of little relevance in such a lowland county; some species have restricted altitudinal ranges in the county but these just reflect the restricted altitudinal occurrence of habitats such as ancient woodland.

## Explanation of the maps

The distribution of all but the rarest species is shown on two maps. The basemap shows the vice-county boundary as a solid line. Where it differs from the vice-county boundary, the boundary of the administrative county in the middle of the 20th century, the area covered by previous bryophyte floras (Proctor 1956, Whitehouse 1964), is shown as a dotted line.

The map of 5 × 5 km squares (also known as 5-km squares or quadrants) shows the relationship between records made before 2000 to those made in the recent survey:

● first recorded from 2000 onwards
■ recorded both before 2000 and from 2000 onwards
○ last recorded between 1950 and 1999
× last recorded before 1950.

The second is a more usual map of 2 × 2 km squares (also known as 2-km squares or tetrads) which gives preference to the records made in the recent survey:

● recorded from 2000 onwards
○ last recorded before 2000.

The tetrads are identified by letters according to a standard system, shown in Figure 19.1.

Many historic records can be allocated to a quadrant but not to a tetrad; these appear only on the quadrant maps. A few modern records can be allocated to a quadrant but not a tetrad, or *vice versa*. The number of records in the different categories is shown below the maps.

**Figure 19.1** The alphabetical labelling of the tetrads in a 10-km square.

| | | | | | |
|---|---|---|---|---|---|
| 8,9 | E | J | P | U | Z |
| 6,7 | D | I | N | T | Y |
| 4,5 | C | H | M | S | X |
| 2,3 | B | G | L | R | W |
| 0,1 | A | F | K | Q | V |
| | 0,1 | 2,3 | 4,5 | 6,7 | 8,9 |

# ANTHOCEROTOPHYTA (HORNWORTS)

## ANTHOCEROTOPSIDA

### ANTHOCEROTACEAE

#### †*Anthoceros punctatus sens. lat.*
First and only record: Gamlingay, TL25SW, 1833, J.S. Henslow, CGE. Henslow (1835) added the species to the Cambridgeshire list in the second edition of *A catalogue of British plants*. We have failed to find mature antheridia in the specimen, and hence cannot identify it as *A. agrestis* (which normally grows in arable fields) or *A. punctatus sens. str.* (which often grows on open ground in other habitats). The latter was found in 2006 just across the county boundary, on the floor of Sandy Heath Quarry, Bedfordshire, TL24E (Boon & Outen 2011). Henslow's plant is unlikely to have been collected from an arable field.

Monoicous. The Cambridgeshire specimen, collected in May, is fruiting, and although Henslow noted that the fruits were unripe when collected, one appears to be on the point of dehiscence.

# MARCHANTIOPHYTA (LIVERWORTS)

## MARCHANTIOPSIDA

### SPHAEROCARPACEAE

#### *Sphaerocarpos michelii*
*Sphaerocarpos michelii* is well established on sandy paths at Anglesey Abbey, a National Trust property, where the population is centred on the Rose Garden, TL56B. In March 2008 green female plants and small, strongly vinous-tinged male plants were frequent to abundant along 30 metres of hoggin path here, and scattered for a further 25 metres, growing with *Barbula unguiculata*, *Bryum argenteum*, *B. dichotomum* and *Pseudocrossidium hornschuchianum*. The path is treated with 'Roundup' and weeded by hoeing. It was recorded at the second site, an arable field at Ashley, TL76A, in the winter of 2006–07, intimately mixed with *Bryum klinggraeffii*, *B. violaceum*, *Dicranella staphylina* and *Trichodon cylindricus* on sandy loam (pH 6.4); *Riccia glauca* and *R. sorocarpa* grew nearby.

First record: Barnwell gravel pit, TL45U (Relhan 1802: 441, as *Sphaerocarpus terrestris*; see Appendix 2). Not seen again in the county until it was found at Ashley in 2006 (BBSUK) and Anglesey Abbey in 2007. The plants were presumably introduced to Anglesey Abbey, perhaps on visitors' feet or with 'as-raised' hoggin for the paths. In England *S. michelii*, a Mediterranean-Atlantic species, was until recently known almost exclusively from cultivated land but it has now begun to spread onto paths and tracks (Blockeel *et al.* 2014), similar habitats to those in which it grows in the Mediterranean lands.

Dioicous. Only identifiable in fruit; spores ripe March.

### LUNULARIACEAE

#### *Lunularia cruciata*
A plant of more or less semi-natural habitats by water and a weed elsewhere. It grows on soil and wood (including logs and worked timber) above the water-level on the banks of ditches, streams and rivers and on damp ground by lakes and ponds. Away from water *Lunularia* grows on damp, shaded stonework and brickwork, especially at the base of walls, in the cracks between paving stones or cobbles, on at least slightly shaded, trampled ground and disturbed soil below hedges and in gardens, churchyards, orchards and farmyards and on limestone and sandstone in garden rockeries. We have recorded it in 22% of the churchyards we have visited. It was abundant in secondary woodland at Madingley Brick Pits, TL46A, in 2005, growing in

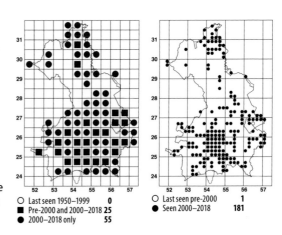

○ Last seen 1950–1999    0
■ Pre-2000 and 2000–2018  25
● 2000–2018 only          55

○ Last seen pre-2000      1
● Seen 2000–2018          181

places where leaves do not settle. It is sometimes found on ground treated with herbicide or as a weed in plant pots, although it is much less frequent as a weed of pots than *Marchantia polymorpha*.

First record: At the water's edge, Byron's Pool, Trumpington, TL45H, R.H. Compton (Evans 1913; see Appendix 2). *L. cruciata* may well be native by rivers and streams in Britain, as it was used to plug the seams of a Bronze Age canoe excavated at Brigg, Lincolnshire (Dickson 1973). The records suggest that in Cambridgeshire it colonised urban habitats fairly rapidly in the 20th century. It was first recorded from Cambridge city at the Botanic Garden, TL45N, in 1928 and elsewhere in the city in the 1940s, over 250 years after the first record there of *Marchantia polymorpha*. By the next decade it was 'very common in and about Cambridge' (Proctor 1956).

Dioicous. Most plants lack sex organs, but both sexes occur in the county and have been reported from adjacent gardens in Holbrook Road, Cambridge, TL45S. Fruits have not been recorded. Populations in Counties Cork and Kerry, where plants do fruit, seem to be more variable morphologically than those in Cambridgeshire; some, for example, have reddish-tinged margins to the thalli (Bosanquet & Preston 2010). Gemmae are always present except sometimes on plants with sex organs.

## MARCHANTIACEAE

### *Marchantia polymorpha* subsp. *polymorpha*
This subspecies is very much rarer than subsp. *ruderalis*. The only recent record based on microscopic examination of the ventral scales, made by R.A. Finch in 2002, is from a disused orchard south-west of Cottenham, TL46I. These plants grew on a plastic sheet on which plant pots were standing, a habitat in which we would expect subsp. *ruderalis*. Plants with a strong black median line along the thallus, found by the edge of a lake at Papworth Everard, TL26W, and by a pond at Milton Park and Ride, TL46R, have also been reported as subsp. *polymorpha* but we think that they were probably subsp. *ruderalis*, which can mimic subsp. *polymorpha* in wet conditions (Paton 1999).

First record: Amongst *Juncus* at the edge of Gray's Moor Pits, TF40A, J.G. Duckett and E.R.B. Little, 1967, BBSUK, conf. D.G. Long, 1993. Not seen thereafter until the recent survey. Wicken and Chippenham Fens are perhaps too calcareous for this subspecies, which is recorded from wet ground in more acidic sites in neighbouring counties (e.g. Sandy Heath Quarry, Bedfordshire; Holme Fen, Huntingdonshire; Tuddenham Heath, West Suffolk).

Dioicous. The specimen from Gray's Moor Pits has a few gemmae cups but no sex organs.

### *Marchantia polymorpha* subsp. *ruderalis*
Common and locally abundant as a weed of built-up areas, growing on railway clinker, gravelly and chalky paths, trampled ground, damp concrete and tarmac, cobbled areas and pavements, and in gardens and college courts. As a street weed it is found in places where it escapes heavy trampling, such as the angle between the pavement and an adjoining wall, or in crevices between cobbles or paving stones; these sites also retain moisture for slightly longer after rain. Jonathan Shanklin recommends searching for it between the block paving often currently used for house drives. It is noticeably more luxuriant in such habitats in wet summers (e.g. 2012, 2016) than after long, dry spells. It often infests plant pots, and is a notoriously

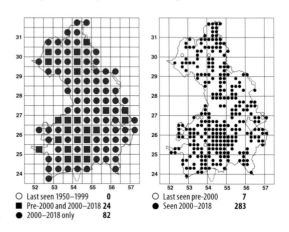

○ Last seen 1950–1999     0
■ Pre-2000 and 2000–2018   24
● 2000–2018 only        82

○ Last seen pre-2000     7
● Seen 2000–2018     283

difficult species to control in nurseries (Fausey 2003). It is less frequent than *Lunularia* in churchyards (we have found it in 7% of those surveyed). It is uncommon in the open countryside, growing on brickwork, soil and wood on the sides of lakes, ponds, streams and ditches, and on nearby dredgings. Tiny *Riccia*-like plants 5–10 mm in diameter with only 1–4 gemmae cups were found on ditch sides at the Ouse Washes, TL59A, in 2002. It occasionally grows in stubble fields on gravelly, sandy, silty and peaty soils in Fenland, but it was seen in just one of the 76 arable fields surveyed for the SBAL project (and only a single thallus was found in that field). It has also been recorded on cleared ground in secondary woodland at Madingley Hall, TL36V, cleared scrub at Wicken Fen, TL57K, and on ground trampled by water buffalo at Chippenham Fen, TL66P. Its tolerance of chemical weed-killers must account for its abundance on sprayed ground beneath electric fences, in orchards and elsewhere. Although it is traditionally a plant of bonfire sites, we made such records in only five tetrads in our recent survey.

First record: 'Hepatica stellata … *Star headed Liverwort. On the north side of Peterhouse chappel abundantly, observed by Mᵣ Dent'* (Ray 1663; see Appendix 2). It was still present in 2016 in the court around Peterhouse chapel, TL45N. Vernon, though a fellow of Peterhouse, recorded it from Caius College, TL45P, in his annotated Ray (1696: 40, as *Lichen petraeus stellatus*) and Relhan (1785: 420) found it 'Near the Water-engine, in the Garden of Pembroke College', TL45P. In the north, Skrimshire collected it 'under a North Wall in my Father's Garden at Wisbech' in 1795 (WBCH) but added that it was 'Not very frequent in this Neighbourhood'. There were also early records from more natural habitats, including Bottisham Fen, TL56SW (L. Jenyns, 1825, BTH). It was abundant at Wicken Fen in 1930 and 1957 after fires but not seen there again until it was found by a bonfire site in 1972. All records of *M. polymorpha* except those of subsp. *polymorpha* are mapped here as subsp. *ruderalis*. The Frescalo analysis suggests that it has increased in frequency since the 1990s.

Dioicous. Antheridiophores and archegoniophores frequent. Male plants have been reported from 35 tetrads since 2000, female plants from 38 and both sexes from 26. Capsules appear to be rare, but although they are bright yellow, they are borne on the lower side of the archegoniophores and are easily overlooked; dehiscence has been noted in June, August. Gemmae are always present; they are splash-dispersed and can be transported up to 1.6 m by water from automatic sprinklers in nurseries (England & Jeger 2005).

### †*Preissia quadrata*
First and only record: Burwell Fen, TL56NE, 1832, C.E. Broome (as *Marchantia*), BTH, det. D.G. Long. *P. quadrata* is frequent in calcareous districts in northern Britain. In south-east England it was a rare plant of calcareous fens but it has declined almost to extinction and it survives now only in the New Forest. Relhan's records of *Reboulia hemisphaerica* from wet places on Sawston Moor, TL44NE, Hinton Moor, TL45NE, and Fulbourn Moor, TL55NW (1788: 18, as *Marchantia hemisphaerica*; 1802: 442) may have been based on *Preissia*, but there are no vouchers. Elsewhere in East Anglia, it was collected at Whittlesey Mere, Huntingdonshire, in 1826 (CGE) and it survived in Norfolk and Suffolk until the 1950s.

Dioicous. Broome's specimen, collected on 28 May, has capsules with mature spores.

## CONOCEPHALACEAE

### *Conocephalum conicum*
On shaded soil, brickwork and stonework at the edge of ditches, streams and rivers, usually on more or less vertical surfaces just above the normal water level. It also grows on the ground in wet woodland at Hildersham Alder Carr, TL54P, and Chippenham Fen, TL66P, but not in the boulder-clay woods where it presumably cannot cope with the summer-droughted soils. Most of its sites are by streams arising from the chalk and their associated ditch systems. *C. conicum* grows above the *Pellia endiviifolia* zone when these two grow on the same stream bank. *Lunularia cruciata* often grows in similar habitats, but is much commoner and colonises eroding banks more rapidly. Although there are some large *Conocephalum* populations in the county, as at Dernford Fen, TL45Q, and Chippenham Fen, others are small.

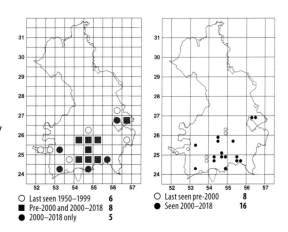

| | |
|---|---|
| ○ Last seen 1950–1999 | 6 |
| ■ Pre-2000 and 2000–2018 | 8 |
| ● 2000–2018 only | 5 |

| | |
|---|---|
| ○ Last seen pre-2000 | 8 |
| ● Seen 2000–2018 | 16 |

First record: Hinton Moor, TL45NE (Relhan 1785: 421, as *Marchantia conica*); Relhan (1820: 471) added Shelford Moor, TL45SE, and there is an unlocalised fruiting specimen from Relhan in Skrimshire's herbarium (WBCH). It was not seen again until Rhodes (1911) found it at Thriplow, TL44NW, where it still grows. We have refound it in many of its 20th-century sites, but we have searched in vain by a wood at Shepreth, TL34Y, and at two sites by the Cam north of Cambridge, TL46V, W, places where it was recorded in the 1950s or 1960s. It was also known to Proctor (1956) as an occasional invasive weed of pots in Cambridge Botanic Garden, TL45N, but has not been recorded in this habitat since (though it is still present by the stream there). The Frescalo analysis suggests that it has declined since the 1970s. The presence of two species of *Conocephalum* in Britain has recently been recognised (Blackstock *et al.* 2005); the Cambridgeshire populations we have checked since 2006 are all *C. conicum sens. str.* rather than *C. salebrosum* and we have assumed that all the records refer to this species, which is much the commoner segregate in south-east England.

Dioicous. Mature capsules seen once (6% tetrads), in March.

## RICCIACEAE

### *Riccia cavernosa*

A habitat specialist, confined to winter-flooded ground where it often grows with *Aphanorrhegma patens*. It was found in the recent survey by parkland lakes, fenland meres and farm reservoirs, on the beds of summer-dry ponds, in disused gravel pits and in hollows in arable fields. In arable fields on chalk soils at Fowlmere, Thriplow and Whittlesford, TL44, it is an associate of *Lythrum hyssopifolia*, germinating from dormant spores after winters which are sufficiently wet to flood hollows in the fields and kill the autumn-sown cereal crops (Preston & Whitehouse 1986b). It is most frequent in the lowest part of these hollows, where the flooding is most prolonged. Despite its large spores and cleistocarpous capsules, *R. cavernosa* can clearly

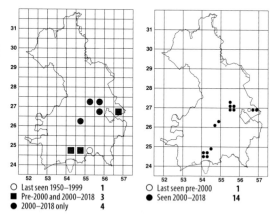

○ Last seen 1950–1999   1
■ Pre-2000 and 2000–2018   3
● 2000–2018 only   4

○ Last seen pre-2000   1
● Seen 2000–2018   14

colonise new sites. By 2005 it was locally abundant or even dominant over hundreds of square metres at Baker's Fen, Wicken, TL56U, 57Q, which was arable until 1993–94 when it was converted to grassland and managed for conservation. It was most abundant in a low-lying drainage channel, growing with *Drepanocladus aduncus, Crassula helmsii, Gnaphalium uliginosum, Juncus bufonius, Persicaria maculosa, Poa trivialis, Ranunculus sceleratus* and *Rorippa palustris* as well as *Aphanorrhegma patens*. (It has never been recorded in the adjacent semi-natural vegetation of Wicken Fen.) In 2009 it was found in vehicle ruts on peaty soil at Kingfishers Bridge wetland, TL57L. This is another ex-arable site, and *R. cavernosa* grew in an area by the lake from which the topsoil was completely removed in 1995 (Tomkins 1998). It is absent from the Ouse Washes, which lack extensive open mud. *R. cavernosa* does not seem able to thrive in the small niches occupied there by *Aphanorrhegma patens*.

First record: An extensive carpet growing with *Aphanorrhegma patens* [and *Leptobryum pyriforme*] on the floor of a dried-up pond at Hildersham Hall, TL54NW, R.E. Parker, 1952, BBSUK, CGE (see Appendix 2). It was first found in the *Lythrum hyssopifolia* hollows at Whittlesford, TL44P, by D.E. Coombe in 1958.

Monoicous. Capsules frequent (43% tetrads), August–November. The generation time from spore to spore can be as short as three weeks in Alaska (Seppelt & Laursen 1999).

### *Riccia fluitans*

The narrow, bifurcating fronds of *R. fluitans* grow intermeshed in masses which float on the surface of the water in ditches dividing arable fields in Fenland. They are sometimes mixed with *Lemna* species and *Ricciocarpos natans*. We have also found them on mud and on mossy concrete 'sandbags' at the water's edge. Unusually, both *R. fluitans* and *Ricciocarpos natans* were found in 2007 in an organically farmed field at Holt Fen, TL57H, which had been temporarily flooded to control eelworms and slugs. *R. fluitans* seems to be most frequent in the area east of Ely and Littleport, TL68, where it has been seen at the edge of the River Lark as well as in the usual ditch habitats. South of Fenland, the only recent record is from the lake at Madingley Hall, TL36V.

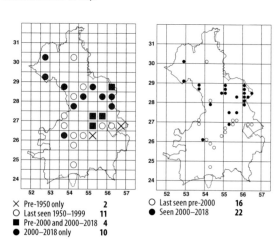

✕ Pre-1950 only   2
○ Last seen 1950–1999   11
■ Pre-2000 and 2000–2018   4
● 2000–2018 only   10

○ Last seen pre-2000   16
● Seen 2000–2018   22

First record: Baitsbite, TL46W, J.S. Henslow, CGE, undated but reported from Cambridgeshire by Henslow (1835). It was rediscovered in a ditch by the River Cam at Baitsbite by T.G. Tutin in 1929 and last seen there (in a newly cleaned ditch) in 1959. The maps show a marked lack of correspondence between recent and older records, and it is difficult to assess trends in the distribution of this species. Plants must be dispersed from site to site by water and perhaps by birds. Populations probably fluctuate in abundance in response to successional changes and the slubbing out of the ditches in which they grow, but the species has only once been found fruiting in Britain (Hill *et al.* 1991) and so it is probably unable to survive prolonged periods of unfavourable habitat conditions. It largely disappears in winter, so most of the records since 1980 have been made in summer by botanists studying flowering plants. It declined markedly in the south of the county during the 20th century. Between 1910 and 1960 it was found in several sites around Cambridge and in the Cam valley to the north. Surprisingly, it also seems to have disappeared from Wicken Fen, TL56P, TL57K, where it occurred between 1957 and 1989 and where *Ricciocarpos natans* is flourishing.

Dioicous. Capsules not recorded; sex organs are rare and capsules very rare in Britain.

## †*Riccia rhenana*

An introduced plant which is morphologically close to *R. fluitans*, last seen in 1988.

First record: With *R. fluitans* in pools, Madingley brickpits, TL46A, E.A. George, 1959, BBSUK. It was found later that year both as an aquatic form on water and as a terrestrial form on mud carpeted with plant debris. It was recorded until 1966 and again in 1979 at these brickpits, which ceased to be worked in the 1890s (Coombe *et al.* 1990). Two days after its discovery at Madingley it was found on decaying vegetation at Gray's Moor Pits, TF40A, by B. Reeve; it was last seen at this gravel pit in 1960. These were the first sites in which the species was recorded in the wild in Britain (the only earlier record was from an artificial concrete pond in the grounds of Royal Holloway College, Surrey in 1952). The last Cambridgeshire site was by the flyover where the Oakington–Dry Drayton road crosses the A604 (now A14) road, TL36W, where it was discovered floating in the pond by H. Belcher and E. Swale in 1987 (det. J.A. Paton) and last seen on earth at the edge in 1988. Although *R. rhenana* is almost certainly a rare introduction to Britain, it is not clear how the plant is introduced and to what extent it spreads from established populations in the wild. It is notable that two of the three sites were discovered by algologists – like *R. fluitans*, this aquatic is not very likely to be found by bryologists in the normal course of their fieldwork.

Dioicous. Capsules are unknown both in Cambridgeshire and elsewhere.

## *Riccia sorocarpa*

*Riccia sorocarpa* has been recorded since 2000 in six arable fields, growing in wheat and barley stubble, game cover and rape direct-drilled into stubble. Four sites were on light, sandy or gravelly soils (pH 6.0, 7.4 measured at two sites) whereas two were on clay, including the acidic Oxford Clay at Papworth St Agnes, TL26S. It was recorded as 'occasional' and 'occasional-frequent' at Ashley, TL66V, TL76A, and there was an especially large population at Block Fen, Wimblington, TL48J, in 2008 when *R. sorocarpa* was abundant over several hundred square metres (and still present in 2012). By contrast, only a single tiny frond was seen at Westoe Farm, TL54X, and at Six Mile Bottom, TL55Y. *R. glauca* grew in five of the six fields (although in separate tetrads in a large

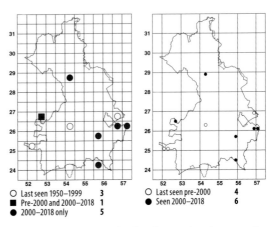

O Last seen 1950–1999   3
■ Pre-2000 and 2000–2018   1
● 2000–2018 only   5

O Last seen pre-2000   4
● Seen 2000–2018   6

field at Westoe Farm) and the only obvious difference in their ecology in Cambridgeshire is the absence of *R. sorocarpa* from seasonally inundated hollows on the chalk.

First record: With *R. glauca* and *Ephemerum minutissimum* in a stubble field near Papworth St Agnes, TL26S, P.J. Bourne, 1960, BBSUK, CGE. *R. sorocarpa* was also recorded in the next 40 years at Gamlingay, TL25A, F, Histon, TL46G, and Chippenham, TL66Z, also on clay or sandy soils.

Monoicous. Capsules frequent (67% tetrads), mature July, October, November.

## *Riccia glauca*

The best known sites for *R. glauca* in the county are the hollows of periglacial origin ('pingos') in chalky arable fields south of Cambridge, where it has been recorded with *Lythrum hyssopifolia* for several decades. These hollows flood in wet winters, killing the standing crop, and a characteristic community of spring-germinating annual flowering plants and ephemeral bryophytes develops as they dry out in spring. In the recent survey *R. glauca* was found in *Lythrum* hollows at Fowlmere, TL44D, I, Whittlesford, TL44P, and Thriplow, TL44H, and in similar vegetation without *Lythrum* near Dernford Fen, TL45Q (see *R. subbifurca*). *R. glauca* also grows with *Lythrum* in similar hollows at Chippenham, TL66T. Elsewhere there are scattered records of plants in fields where there is no evidence for seasonal water-logging. These include barley and wheat stubble fields, a marginal strip sown with bird-seed mix, an asparagus field and bare patches in a grass ley sown for horses. It grows in both acidic and basic

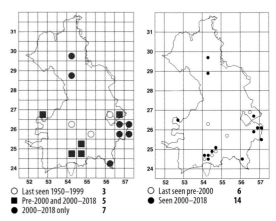

○ Last seen 1950–1999    3
■ Pre-2000 and 2000–2018   5
● 2000–2018 only          7

○ Last seen pre-2000    6
● Seen 2000–2018      14

conditions (pH 5.8, 7.8 measured at two sites) on sandy, gravelly and silty soils and Boulder Clay. The size of the populations in these fields is very variable – in some fields *R. glauca* was frequent but in the asparagus field only a single rosette was found.

First record: Damp hollow in arable field (among *Lythrum hyssopifolia*) near Chippenham Park Avenue, TL66NE, E.F. Warburg, 1941, OXF (see Appendix 2). The first population growing with *L. hyssopifolia* south of Cambridge was discovered by D.E. Coombe at Whittlesford, TL44P, in 1958. The plant community in these hollows was described by Preston and Whitehouse (1986b) and the published quadrats are the sole basis for the *Lythrum hyssopifolia-Juncus bufonius* community (OV36) described by Rodwell (2000). There is no evidence to suggest that terrestrial *Riccia* species were formerly more frequent in Cambridgeshire. Although E.W. Jones found the inconspicuous *Ephemerum recurvifolium* in six sites in the county in 1934, he never found *R. glauca* here.

Monoicous. Capsules frequent (57% tetrads), mature August–December.

## Riccia subbifurca

This is the rarest of the three *Riccia* species which grow with *Lythrum hyssopifolia* in the winter-flooded hollows in chalky arable fields south of Cambridge, although it may be frequent in such hollows in suitable seasons. Since 2000 it has been found in four hollows, three at Thriplow, TL44H, and one at Whittlesford, TL44P. It was also found in a winter-flooded area of an arable field on the northern edge of Dernford Fen, TL45Q, where there is no *L. hyssopifolia* but where *R. subbifurca* grows with many of its usual associates, including *R. glauca, Aphanorrhegma patens, Pohlia melanodon, Alopecurus myosuroides, Epilobium hirsutum, Juncus bufonius, Persicaria maculosa* and *Pulicaria dysenterica*. In the field it can be distinguished from *R. glauca* by its small, neat rosettes with narrow, non-overlapping thallus segments with a violet or blackish violet tinge along the margins.

First record: With *Lythrum hyssopifolia* in a dried-up pool in an arable field near Whittlesford, TL44P, D.E. Coombe, 1958 and C.C. Townsend, 1959, BBSUK, conf. J.A. Paton (see Preston and Whitehouse 1990). David Coombe first detected this species with *R. glauca* in the newly discovered *Lythrum* hollows in 1958 and suggested that it might be the plant then known to British bryologists as *R. warnstorfii*. He was unable to get definite confirmation of his identification from F. Rose and E.W. Jones but Townsend visited the site the following spring and concluded that it was indeed this species. In surveys of the *Lythrum* hollows in 1978–94 (Preston & Whitehouse 1990, 1995) it was found in five hollows at Fowlmere, TL44C, D, H and four hollows at Whittlesford, TL44P, but these sites were not surveyed as thoroughly in our recent survey. The soil pH was measured as 7.6–7.9. The Thriplow sites were first found in 2001. When S. Jovet determined material collected in 1979 at Whittlesford and Fowlmere as *R. subbifurca* it appeared that both species must be present, but it later transpired that all British material previously referred to *R. warnstorfii* is actually *R. subbifurca* (Paton 1990). J.G. Duckett collected the species in wet hollows in an arable field at Dernford Fen, TL45Q, in 1967 (CGE) but there was no further record from this area until 2008.

Monoicous. Capsules usually present (all tetrads), August–September.

## Ricciocarpos natans

Like the duckweeds (*Lemna* spp.), *Ricciocarpos natans* is an aquatic liverwort which floats on the water surface and reproduces by vegetative budding. It is known from scattered pits, ponds and ditches in Fenland. There was a massive population dominating the surface of the water along a 0.8–1 km stretch of field drain north of Ramsey Mereside, TL29V, in October 2006, growing with *Riccia fluitans, Lemna minor, L. trisulca, Myriophyllum verticillatum* and *Potamogeton natans*. At Wicken Fen, TL56P, it has been recorded in recent years in a reed-fringed ditch on Adventurers' Fen, and in the shallow water (*c.* 70 cm deep) of a restored reedbed where in places it covered more than 95% of the surface of the water in 2005. Adventurers' Fen is on the old reserve whereas the reedbed was restored in the 1990s by lowering the surface of an area which had become rank wet grassland. The discovery of *R. natans* in 2001 on mud by the lake at a newly created wetland at Kingfishers Bridge, TL57L, also shows its capacity to colonise new

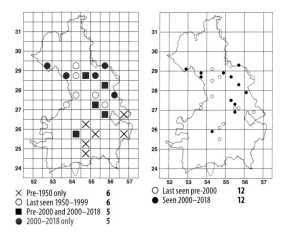

| | |
|---|---|
| ✕ Pre-1950 only | 6 |
| ○ Last seen 1950–1999 | 6 |
| ■ Pre-2000 and 2000–2018 | 5 |
| ● 2000–2018 only | 5 |

| | |
|---|---|
| ○ Last seen pre-2000 | 12 |
| ● Seen 2000–2018 | 12 |

sites, as does its presence in a temporarily flooded field at Holt Fen, TL57H (see *Riccia fluitans*). In addition to these records, the species still survives (2018) in a small ornamental pond at the British Antarctic Survey, Cambridge, TL45J, where it was introduced from Denbighshire in 2013 by Jonathan Shanklin.

First record: Sawston Moor, TL44NE, and in a pond, in a grove of oaks, near Hall Wood, Wood Ditton, TL65NE (Relhan 1793: 11, as *Riccia natans*). There are no later records from these sites, except perhaps for an imprecisely localised specimen from Newmarket in Dawson Turner's herbarium (BM), and there appears to have been a progressive loss of the more southern populations. These include Barton, TL45NW, where it was collected by C.C. Babington in 1831 (BM), and the stream running from Nine Wells to Shelford Moor, TL45SE, where it was known to Relhan (1820: 472) and collected by J.S. Henslow (Shelford Common, 1828, CGE; 1829, BM) and H.E. Lowe (Nine Wells, 1834, WARMS). The last record from the Cambridge area, excluding the recent introduction, was from Chesterton Ballast Pits, TL46Q, in 1942. By 1950 the species had become restricted as a native to Fenland. It was recorded at Chippenham Fen, TL66P, from 1904 to 1938. Records from Wicken Fen date from 1928 but it was seen there only sporadically until systematic observation in the mid 1980s showed that it was then present annually in a ditch near the windpump, TL57Q. It sometimes appeared as early as late May (presumably from fronds overwintering at the bottom of the ditch) but it increased in abundance towards the end of the season. The difficulties of assessing trends in the frequency of *Riccia fluitans* apply equally well to this species. However, the recent records made during the course of summer fieldwork in Fenland show that it is not quite so rare in the county as we thought at the start of the recent survey.

Sex organs and capsules have not been recorded in Britain.

Henslow put forward a curious theory about this plant to W.J. Hooker. In a postscript to a letter sent by R.T. Lowe to Hooker while he was staying with Henslow on 26 August 1828, and now with the *R. natans* specimens in BM, Henslow said that specimens of *R. natans* 'are found abundantly near here just now, but seem to him [Henslow] to be only a state and mere *fragment* of another plant probably *R. fluitans*'. An accompanying sketch showed *R. natans* plants as the tips of a hypothetical dichotomously branched thallus like that of *R. fluitans*, and suggested that 'Sowerby's fig. [in *English Botany*, a perfectly adequate illustration] must be a fiction'.

# JUNGERMANNIOPSIDA

## PELLIACEAE

### Pellia epiphylla

Although this is the text-book example of a common thalloid liverwort, it is replaced by *P. endiviifolia* in calcareous Cambridgeshire. It was seen in only three sites during the recent survey, growing on wet ground and rutted rides in White Wood, Gamlingay, TL25B (with *Atrichum undulatum* and *Polytrichastrum formosum*), Great Heath Plantation, Gamlingay, TL25F, and the North Quarter of Hayley Wood, TL25W.

First record: Gamlingay Bogs, TL25SW (Relhan 1793: 11, as *Jungermannia epiphylla*; see Appendix 2). It was seen again in 1861, according to Babington's annotated Relhan (1820), and at Great Heath Plantation, Gamlingay, TL25F, by R.H. Compton (Evans 1913). Fruiting plants of *P. epiphylla* were rediscovered at Great

Heath Plantation in 1958 (BBSUK, CGE). It was first found in Hayley Wood in 1966 and also recorded from Wicken Fen at the brick pits, TL57Q, and Godwin Plots, TL57K, during the calcifuge invasion (1972–74) and from Chippenham Fen, TL66P, between 1973 and 1985.

Monoicous. Capsules frequent (67% tetrads), February, March.

### Pellia neesiana

Moist or wet, acidic soils in woods over Woburn Sands and on the western Boulder Clay. Not found in the county until the recent survey, when it was discovered on damp ground by a stream in Great Heath Plantation, Gamlingay (see below). It was subsequently recorded on slightly raised ground at the edge of a winter-wet pond and on a pathside in Hayley Wood, TL25W, and on two rutted rides in Gamlingay Wood, TL25L. All three *Pellia* species were found in the North Quarter of Hayley Wood in 2003, on soil measuring pH 6.1 at the site for *P. neesiana*, pH 5.8 and 6.1 for *P. epiphylla* and pH 6.3 and 6.7 for the calcicole *P. endiviifolia*.

First record: Great Heath Plantation, Gamlingay, TL25F, M.O. Hill, 2002, BBSUK. This species was under-recorded nationally until the mid 20th century, probably because it was overlooked as *Pellia epiphylla*; this and its rarity as a calcifuge species explains its late discovery in Cambridgeshire.

Dioicous. Capsules not recorded. Both sexes have been recorded at Great Heath Plantation, male plants at Hayley Wood and female plants at Gamlingay Wood.

### Pellia endiviifolia

A plant of moist, calcareous, often shaded but sometimes exposed chalky, clay, sandy or peaty soils and chalky spoil, more rarely on gravel, damp brickwork and concrete, and on limestone and sandstone rocks in gardens. It grows on the banks of rivers, streams, chalk springs, ditches, lakes and ponds, on woodland rides and paths, and on the ground in wet secondary woodland, shaded paths in the gardens of large country houses, north-facing cuttings of disused railways, disused clay and gravel pits and both working and disused chalk quarries. At Chippenham Fen (but not Wicken) it is known from peaty soil on tracks and in grazed areas. There are no records from rivers north of the River Kennett, TL67Q; the sluggish Fenland rivers are clearly unsuitable for it.

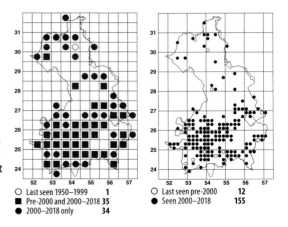

○ Last seen 1950–1999     1
■ Pre-2000 and 2000–2018  35
● 2000–2018 only          34

○ Last seen pre-2000      12
● Seen 2000–2018          155

First record: Trumpington, TL45SW, and Wicken, TL56/57, Rhodes (1911, as *P. epiphylla*). Although published as *P. epiphylla*, the records from these localities, and R.H. Compton's from Hobson's Conduit, Cambridge, TL45, and Bourn Brook, Grantchester, TL45SW (Evans 1913), must have been *P. endiviifolia*. Skrimshire almost certainly knew it at Wisbech, TF41SE, in 1795 (see Appendix 2, under *Lunularia cruciata*) and a later but fragmentary specimen collected by him at Bushy Place, Wisbech, TF41SE, in 1824 (WBCH) is probably this species. P.W. Richards was the first explicitly to record the species in the county, from Plot 576 (village end), Wicken Fen, TL57Q, in 1929 (CGE). The Frescalo analysis does not suggest that there has been any marked change in its frequency.

Dioicous. Capsules rare (9% tetrads), immature October–March, mature March, April. The characteristic finely branched thalli are frequently seen between October and early January and may act as vegetative propagules.

## FOSSOMBRONIACEAE

### †Fossombronia pusilla

On disturbed, acidic soil in the boulder-clay woods; not seen since 1995.

First record: Side of ruts, Gamlingay Wood, TL25SW, H.L.K. Whitehouse, 1957 (see Appendix 2); it was seen here until 1989. It was also recorded from a recently coppiced plot at Hayley Wood, TL25W, in 1985. In the eastern boulder-clay woods *F. pusilla* was discovered on the side of a rut in a ride in Ditton Park Wood, TL65T, in 1958 (BBSUK) and, with *Aphanorrhegma patens*, *Dicranella schreberiana* and *D. varia*, on the bank of a ditch at Lower Wood, Weston Colville TL65G, in 1995. This ephemeral species is only recorded sporadically when bryologists happen to encounter fruiting material on suitably disturbed acidic soil. The lack of recent records may reflect the low probability of such an event rather than the loss of the species.

Monoicous. Only identifiable with mature capsules, although if immature capsules are present they are easily grown on to maturity. Capsules recorded October, November, February.

### †*Fossombronia wondraczekii*

First and only record: with *Pohlia lescuriana* and *Pseudephemerum nitidum* on the side of a newly-cut ditch near Old Plantation Cottage, Great Heath Plantation, Gamlingay, TL25F, M.O. Hill, C.D. Preston *et al.*, 1988, BBSUK, CGE. Like *F. pusilla*, this is a calcifuge; it is the less frequent of the two species in East Anglia.

Monoicous. Only identifiable when mature capsules are present; capsules recorded October.

## METZGERIACEAE

### *Metzgeria violacea*

This epiphyte is most frequent in moist or wet woodland, fen carr, seasonally flooded, disused gravel pits, humid scrub and on trees by rivers, streams and pools. It is, however, also found in apparently less humid habitats in ancient woodlands, plantations and, very rarely, in orchards. In favourable situations it may be more abundant on some trees than *M. furcata*, from which it differs in its yellower green colour and the frequent gemmae on the erect, attenuate tips of the thalli. On 9 November 2003 plants growing in woodland near the lake at Wimpole Hall, TL35SW, were showing the characteristic blue colour which develops post-mortem. They had presumably been killed by that summer's drought and this

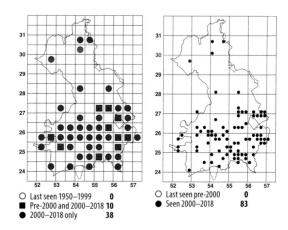

○ Last seen 1950–1999   **0**
■ Pre-2000 and 2000–2018 **10**
● 2000–2018 only **38**

○ Last seen pre-2000   **0**
● Seen 2000–2018 **83**

susceptibility may explain the lower frequency of the species in ancient, boulder-clay woods than in waterside woodlands. The most frequent hosts are willow (29% of tetrad records), elder (17%), blackthorn (12%), ash (11%), hawthorn (7%), sycamore (7%) and field maple (6%); the rarer hosts are listed in Appendix 3. It is recorded from only two orchards, both near Wisbech, TF40D, T; it is too infrequent in this habitat to have been recorded in Robin Stevenson's systematic survey of 951 individual apple trees.

First record: Rotten tree stump, swampy wood near Hildersham church [Hildersham Alder Carr], TL54P, R.E. Parker, 1953, BBSUK, conf. D.G. Long, 1977. This was the only site known until 1969, when it was discovered in woodland by the R. Snail near Fordham Abbey, TL66J. There was a gradual increase in the number of known sites in the next 30 years and a rapid expansion of range during the recent survey. This reflects a national increase in range over the same period. It persists in the sites in which it was first discovered, Hildersham Alder Carr and the Fordham Abbey woodland.

Dioicous. Capsules not seen; gemmae always present.

### *Metzgeria consanguinea*

First recorded during the recent survey growing with *M. violacea* on a dead branch of field maple in Madingley Wood (see below) and later found, also with *M. violacea*, on a waterside willow at Roswell Pits, TL58K.

First record: Madingley Wood, TL35Z, J.D. Shanklin, 2015, BBSUK. This species is easily overlooked when growing with *M. violacea*, or gemmiferous *M. furcata*. Like *M. violacea* it has increased nationally in recent years but it retains a markedly western distribution, and is much the rarer of the two species in eastern England.

Dioicous. Capsules not seen; gemmae always present.

### *Metzgeria furcata*

With the exception of a single occurrence on brickwork in South Lodge Plantation, Croxton, TL25NE, and two records from decaying logs, all our records of *M. furcata* are of epiphytic plants. However, its habitat range as an epiphyte is sufficiently great that it has been recorded since 2000 in more tetrads than any other liverwort in the county except *Marchantia polymorpha*. Its main hosts are hawthorn (19% of tetrad records), ash (17%), willow (14%) and field maple (10%), followed by elder (6%), *Prunus* spp., including blackthorn and cherry plum (6%), sycamore (5%), and numerous rarer hosts (Appendix 3). As the varied host list suggests, it is found in a wide range of habitats including ancient woods, long-established and recently planted secondary woodland, parklands, orchards, riversides and streamsides, chalk pits, fen carr and scrub. It needs a modicum of shelter, and is not found (for example) in exposed shelter belts or on urban street trees, but it otherwise spans the spectrum from relatively exposed places to humid, shaded and sheltered sites. Its shade tolerance perhaps explains its frequent occurrence in the interior of ancient woodland, where it is often much more abundant

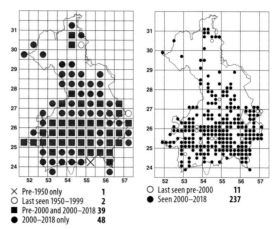

| | |
|---|---|
| ✕ Pre-1950 only | 1 |
| ○ Last seen 1950–1999 | 2 |
| ■ Pre-2000 and 2000–2018 | 39 |
| ● 2000–2018 only | 48 |

| | |
|---|---|
| ○ Last seen pre-2000 | 11 |
| ● Seen 2000–2018 | 237 |

on field maple than on other hosts, forming extensive sheets on its irregular, bossed trunks. It is sometimes abundant on some trees but absent from many other apparently suitable ones in the same site, suggesting that dispersal may be limiting its occurrence at this scale. In orchards it was recorded on 21 (2%) of the 951 apple trees surveyed by Robin Stevenson and on five (3%) of the 173 pears.

First record: Madingley Plantations, TL36SE, White Wood, Gamlingay, TL25SW and on beech trees at Wood Ditton, TL65NE (Relhan 1802: 441, as *Jungermannia furcata*). It was not seen again until P.G.M. Rhodes collected it from a tree at Madingley in 1908 (CGE). He regarded it as scarce in Cambridgeshire, 'only occurring at wide intervals and in small quantity' (Rhodes 1911) but he did little work in the boulder-clay woods so this description might refer primarily to the open countryside.

Dioicous. Capsules rare (4% tetrads), but they are both ephemeral and inconspicuous and so are probably overlooked; seen October, November, January–April. Gemmae are occasionally found on the thallus margins.

## ANEURACEAE

### *Aneura pinguis*
A pioneer species of open, moist, base-rich soils, predominantly over clay, including chalky clay (53% of tetrads with substrate records) and chalk (26%) but with 1–3 recorded occurrences on Corallian limestone, sand and gravel, railway clinker and even, at one site, damp hardboard. Most records are from active or disused chalk and clay pits, disturbed calcareous grassland, road cuttings and the sides of lakes, farm reservoirs, pools and ditches. Less frequent habitats include sand or gravel pits, a limestone spoil heap, ground in a newly planted woodland, a hole created by a wind-thrown tree in mature woodland, damp hollows in railway sidings, a building site and a 10 m wide ploughed but unsown strip at the edge of an arable field.

First record: On the sides of Madingley Bath,

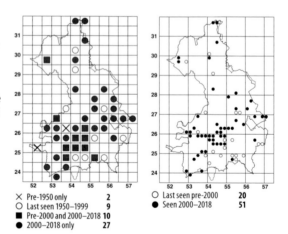

| | |
|---|---|
| ✕ Pre-1950 only | 2 |
| ○ Last seen 1950–1999 | 9 |
| ■ Pre-2000 and 2000–2018 | 10 |
| ● 2000–2018 only | 27 |

| | |
|---|---|
| ○ Last seen pre-2000 | 20 |
| ● Seen 2000–2018 | 51 |

etc., TL45E (Relhan 1785: 420, as *Jungermannia pinguis*). Relhan later noted it from Gamlingay Bogs, TL25SW (1802: 441) and Hinton Moor, TL45NE, the latter a Relhan manuscript record extracted by Babington into his annotated copy of Relhan (1820). The high proportion of tetrads with pre-2000 records doubtless reflects the pioneer habitats of the species; several older records are from chalk or gravel pits which have been filled in or no longer have any open ground suitable for the species. E.W. Jones' record from depressions in an old fallow field with 2–3 feet high hawthorns on clayey soil by the Mare Way at Eversden, TL35, not only illustrates the pioneer nature of the species but also the condition of farming on clay soils in 1933. The Frescalo analysis does not suggest that there has been any marked change in its frequency. *Aneura* is known from genetic analysis to consist of several somewhat cryptic microspecies. According to

D.G. Long, the common plant in our area is *A. pinguis sens. str.* However, Jones noted that the plants he found in 1933, at Mare Way and on wet clay by a pond at Childerley Hall, TL36K (CGE), lacked the normal greasy appearance and light green colour and were frequently branched, with crisped margins to the thallus; these plants are likely to have been one of the other microspecies.

Dioicous. Capsules occasional (20% tetrads), immature October–January, March, April.

### †*Riccardia multifida*

Recorded from four sites in the county between 1959 and 1988.

First record: Damp soil and decaying vegetation, Gray's Moor Pits, TF40A, B. Reeve, 1959, BBSUK, conf. J.A. Paton & T.H. Blackstock. The other records are: Great Heath Plantation, Gamlingay, TL25F, N.G. Hodgetts, 1988; Godwin Plot 3D, Wicken Fen, TL57K, A.C. Leslie, 1974, CGE, conf. H.J.B. Birks; by a pool, Chippenham Fen, TL66P, A.C. Leslie & J.S. Watson, 1975, CGE, conf. T.H. Blackstock. The records suggest an occurrence on more acidic substrates than *R. chamedryfolia*.

Usually autoicous. Immature sporophytes are present on the specimen collected at Chippenham Fen in February 1975 and gemmae are also recorded.

### *Riccardia chamedryfolia*

This is a smaller and much less conspicuous pioneer than *Aneura pinguis*, usually recorded on clay (eight of the 11 recent tetrads with records of substrate), more rarely on chalk, loam and peat. It is found in open areas in disused clay and chalk pits, by lakes, farm reservoirs, ponds and scrapes, on ditch banks and in disturbed rough grassland on calcareous clay. As well as growing in open substrates we have also found it amongst pleurocarpous mosses in thin *Calamagrostis epigejos* and *Phragmites australis* stands in a disused clay pit at Roswell Pits, TL58K, under vascular plants at the edge of the Cambridge Botanic Garden lake, TL45N, and in a very wet, highly calcareous species-rich fen meadow with extensive bryophyte cover over peat at Chippenham Fen, TL66P.

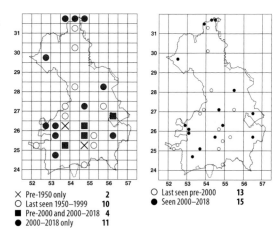

| | |
|---|---|
| ✕ Pre-1950 only | 2 |
| ○ Last seen 1950–1999 | 10 |
| ■ Pre-2000 and 2000–2018 | 4 |
| ● 2000–2018 only | 11 |

| | |
|---|---|
| ○ Last seen pre-2000 | 13 |
| ● Seen 2000–2018 | 15 |

First record: In a field of temporary pasture on heavy soil near Lolworth, TL36SE, E.W. Jones, 1934 (*Richards file*). Several older records suggest a wider habitat range than that recorded recently, including those from a fallow field at Barrington, TL35SE (1934), a clay ride in Gamlingay Wood, TL25L (1945, 1960) and on a dead branch (with *Bryum moravicum*) at ground level in fen carr at Wicken Fen, TL57K (1975). E.J.H. Corner's record of a large mass in a spring at Dernford Fen, TL45Q, in 1946 is supported by a 20 cm² specimen (NMW) which comprises a dense mass of stems and is quite unlike the habit of any material we have seen in the county. As with *Aneura pinguis*, there is little coincidence between the older and the recent records. The explanation doubtless lies in the pioneer habitats of the species, coupled in this case with its inconspicuousness. The Frescalo analysis does not suggest that there has been any marked change in its frequency.

Autoicous. Capsules rare (3% tetrads), immature November; gemmae usually present.

## PORELLACEAE

### *Porella platyphylla*

This uncommon liverwort is found on chalky soil in beech woods, as an epiphyte and on masonry. It is very frequent on the ground in the Beechwood Nature Reserve on the Gog Magog Hills, TL45X, where patches may cover hundreds of square centimetres, and locally abundant over a smaller area on a chalky roadside embankment at Chalkpit Plantation, Babraham, TL55A. It also grows in both these sites as an epiphyte on exposed roots and at the base of trees. Elsewhere it is found on the base of trees growing on old earthworks, boundary banks and by woodland rides in ancient woodland, in parkland and in parish boundary hedges, often on old pollards by streams, ditches, lakes or ponds, and on old coppice stools within woodland. It is usually confined to a few trees and many records result from deliberate searches of the largest trees or coppice stools for this species and the ecologically similar *Anomodon viticulosus*. However, it occurs in several places on the Wimpole Hall estate, TL35F, G, K. Ash is much the most frequent host (60% of tetrad records); the others are field maple (12%), beech (9%), sycamore (7%), oak (5%) and elder, elm and horse chestnut (all 2%). *Neckera complanata* is a particularly characteristic associate on tree bases and others include *Metzgeria furcata, Anomodon viticulosus, Bryoerythrophyllum recurvirostrum, Cirriphyllum crassinervium, Homalia trichomanoides, Homalothecium sericeum, Isothecium alopecuroides, Rhynchostegium confertum* and *Thamnobryum alopecurum*. On masonry it grows on oolitic limestone, brickwork and flint on old, often north-facing, walls of churches, churchyards and old parkland, and on a concrete drainpipe by a stream at Childerley Hall, TL36K. It has persisted since 1957 on Carboniferous limestone introduced from Westmorland to the Cambridge Botanic Garden, TL45N.

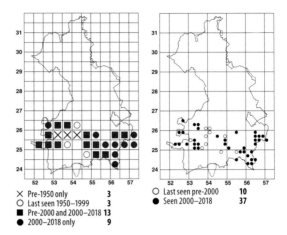

| | |
|---|---|
| ✕ Pre-1950 only | 3 |
| ○ Last seen 1950–1999 | 3 |
| ■ Pre-2000 and 2000–2018 | 13 |
| ● 2000–2018 only | 9 |

| | |
|---|---|
| ○ Last seen pre-2000 | 10 |
| ● Seen 2000–2018 | 37 |

First record: Madingley Wood, TL35/45, etc. (Relhan 1785: 419, as *Jungermannia platyphylla*); not seen there since. Relhan (1820: 469) added Chalk-pit Close, Cherry Hinton, TL45NE, where it was recorded until 1999. *P. platyphylla* has colonised woodland at the south end of the Devil's Dyke and the Gogs beechwood, which was planted on arable land *c.* 1840. However, it appears to be a very poor coloniser and as an epiphyte away from the chalk it is virtually restricted to a small number of old trees in 'ancient countryside'. Although it has not disappeared from many sites in the past 50 years, we think that it has become less frequent. Like *Anomodon viticulosus* (q.v.), it can be expected to continue to decline as the old trees on which it grows are lost from the landscape.

Dioicous. Capsules seen once (3% tetrads), immature in January.

## RADULACEAE

### *Radula complanata*

A shade-tolerant epiphyte which usually grows in sheltered or humid sites, especially in ancient and recent woodland, fen carr and disused chalk pits. It sometimes grows on bark as a pioneer colonist in the absence of other bryophytes but it is also found amongst pleurocarpous mosses at later stages of colonisation. Its requirement for more humid sites than *Frullania dilatata* is shown by its rarity in orchards, where Robin Stevenson recorded it on only five of the 951 apple trees and one of the 173 pear trees he surveyed. By contrast, it is abundant and notably luxuriant in dense carr at Wicken Fen, TL57Q. Its main hosts are ash (19% of tetrad records), hawthorn (18%), willow (16%), blackthorn (9%), field maple (9%) and sycamore (5%); there are numerous minor hosts (Appendix 3).

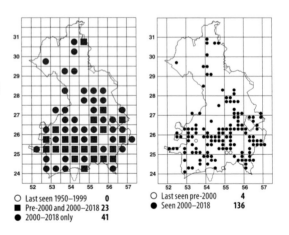

| | |
|---|---|
| ○ Last seen 1950–1999 | 0 |
| ■ Pre-2000 and 2000–2018 | 23 |
| ● 2000–2018 only | 41 |

| | |
|---|---|
| ○ Last seen pre-2000 | 4 |
| ● Seen 2000–2018 | 136 |

First record: Madingley Wood, TL35/45, J. Martyn (1729a: 16, as *Lichenastrum imbricatum majus*); published without the locality by T. Martyn (1763: 25, as *Jungermannia complanata*). The first collection is W. Skrimshire's fruiting specimen from the trunks of trees about Wisbech, 1795 (WBCH). The Frescalo analysis shows a modest increase since the 1980s and a more dramatic spread since 2000. There is similar evidence for an increase in frequency between 1995 and 2005 in industrial areas such as South Lancashire (Lowell 2009).

Paroicous. Capsules frequent (28% tetrads), noted late November–April, once in May, June and July (undehisced November–January, dehisced January–April). Gemmae common.

## FRULLANIACEAE

### Frullania tamarisci

First and only record: A single patch, with *Brachythecium rutabulum* and *Orthotrichum affine*, on the trunk of a sallow colonising fen vegetation north of Godwin Plots, Compartment 12, Wicken Fen, TL57K, R.A. Finch, 2003, BBSUK (see Appendix 2). By 2009 the scrub had been cleared. Unlike many other epiphytes which have been (re-)discovered in the county in recent years, this species does not seem to be undergoing a marked expansion in its range in eastern England.

Dioicous; capsules not recorded.

### Frullania dilatata

Epiphytic on well-illuminated to lightly shaded trees and shrubs in a wide range of habitats, including ancient and recent woodland, scrub, fen carr, parkland, orchards, disused clay and chalk pits and the open countryside. It is perhaps more frequent on trees in swamps, by pools, lakes and rivers and in sheltered scrub than in less humid habitats. However, it is much more frequent than *Radula complanata* in drier sites such as orchards, where it was recorded by Robin Stevenson on 57 (6%) of the 951 apple trees he surveyed and 12 (7%) of the 173 pears. It is usually restricted to scattered trees in its Cambridgeshire sites, rather than occurring in the abundance in which it grows in western Britain and

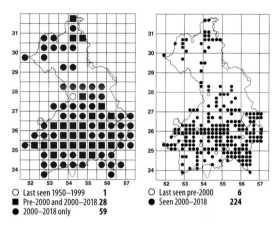

| | |
|---|---|
| ○ Last seen 1950–1999 | 1 |
| ■ Pre-2000 and 2000–2018 | 28 |
| ● 2000–2018 only | 59 |

| | |
|---|---|
| ○ Last seen pre-2000 | 6 |
| ● Seen 2000–2018 | 224 |

Ireland. We recorded it most frequently on ash (20% of tetrad records), hawthorn (15%), willow (14%), blackthorn (9%), field maple (7%) and oak (5%); the rarer hosts are listed in Appendix 3.

First record: Frequent on trees, J. Martyn (1729a: 16, as *Lichenastrum imbricatum minus*); published by T. Martyn (1763: 25, as *Jungermannia dilatata*) from Madingley Wood, TL35/45, and Moor Barns Thicket, TL45E. Skrimshire collected it in Wisbech, TF40NE, in 1795 (WBCH). Rhodes (1911) regarded the commoner liverworts, such as *Frullania dilatata* and *Metzgeria furcata*, as 'only occurring at wide intervals and in small quantity' (but see *M. furcata*). *F. dilatata* was recorded throughout the period of high air pollution in the 1950s and 1960s, and Proctor (1956) even described it as 'frequent on isolated trees and bushes' although Hill (1967) considered that it was uncommon and declining. Whitehouse's (1964) suggestion that it was particularly frequent on elders is not supported by his records. The Frescalo analysis shows a very similar trend to that of *Radula complanata*, a modest increase since the 1980s and a more dramatic spread since 2000.

Dioicous. Capsules rare (1% tetrads), recorded in November, January–March. In view of the current rarity of fruiting plants, it is interesting that Leonard Jenyns' specimen from a lime tree at Bottisham, TL56, collected in 1824 (BTH), is fruiting freely.

## LEJEUNEACEAE

### Cololejeunea minutissima

A recent colonist, now known as an epiphyte in ancient woodland, disused brick and gravel pits, by rivers, streams and ponds and more rarely in orchards and scrub away from water. Colonies vary from single small patches to the 40 or more small colonies discovered on four neighbouring willow trunks near a pond at Hoo Fen, Anglesey Abbey, TL56G, in 2011 or the large patches many square centimetres in area on a willow trunk overhanging shallowly flooded gravel workings at Milton Country Park, TL46V, in 2016. Most of the early records were from willow and this is still the most frequent host (31% of tetrad records) but it has now been joined by ash (23%), hawthorn (17%), sycamore (11%) and apple, blackthorn, field maple, hazel and *Prunus* sp. (all <10%). Associates include *Metzgeria furcata*, *M. violacea*, *Frullania dilatata*, *Radula complanata*, *Amblystegium serpens*, *Cryphaea heteromalla*, *Orthotrichum affine*, *O. diaphanum* and *Syntrichia virescens* in addition to those mentioned below.

First record: Frequent patches on one willow, with *Dicranoweisia cirrata* and *Hypnum cupressiforme*, in *Salix* scrub in low-lying, disused brick pit, Lattersey Local Nature Reserve, Whittlesey, TL29Y, C.R. Stevenson, 2007, BBSUK. It was found in four further Cambridgeshire sites in 2009 and four more in 2011 and it is now

fairly frequent in suitable habitats. Although
*C. minutissima* formerly had a Hyperoceanic
Southern-temperate distribution in Europe and a
coastal distribution in Britain, it has been spreading
rapidly in recent years. It was discovered in four
neighbouring counties within a year of its discovery
in Cambridgeshire (Bedfordshire and Hertfordshire
2006, North Essex and West Norfolk in 2008).
Although the individual stems of this liverwort are
indeed tiny, they form dense green patches which
are less inconspicuous than one might expect of a
species with the epithet *minutissima*.

Autoicous. Perianths always present; capsules
not yet seen though they are common nationally.
Gemmae frequent.

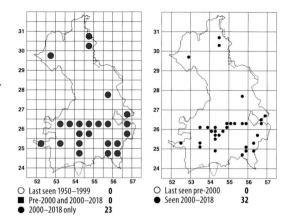

○ Last seen 1950–1999    **0**
■ Pre-2000 and 2000–2018   **0**
● 2000–2018 only        **23**

○ Last seen pre-2000    **0**
● Seen 2000–2018      **32**

### Lejeunea cavifolia

An extremely rare but persistent plant, confined to old coppice stools in ancient woods on Boulder
Clay. It is currently known from an ash stool by a ditch in East Quarter, Hayley Wood, TL25W, and from
an ancient ash stool in Basefield Wood, TL65N. At Hayley it grows with (or over) *Lophocolea bidentata*,
*Homalia trichomanoides*, *Isothecium alopecuroides* and *Kindbergia praelonga* and at Basefield with *Homalia
trichomanoides* below a zone of *Isothecium alopecuroides* and *Thamnobryum alopecurum*.

First record: Hayley Wood, TL25W, E.F. Warburg, 1941, BBSUK, OXF. It was rediscovered at Hayley in 1966
on the very same ash on which it is currently known; the tree was safeguarded by Oliver Rackham until his
death in 2015. There are single records from Borley Wood, TL54NE, in 1943 and from Little Widgham Wood,
TL65S ('on stumps') in 1946. Both woods were subsequently coniferised. M.C.F. Proctor found it on a stump
at Ditton Park Wood, TL65T, in 1952 and it was rediscovered at this site by C.D.P. in 1991, growing as several
patches around the lower parts of two adjacent coppiced ash stools. Searches for *L. cavifolia* during the
recent survey here and in the coniferised woods were unsuccessful. It was, however, discovered in Basefield
Wood in 2009, the first new site for the species in the county for over 40 years. *L. cavifolia* is frequent in
western Britain but rare in the Midlands and East Anglia.

Autoicous. Capsules not recorded.

## PTILIDIACEAE

### †Ptilidium pulcherrimum

Recorded as an epiphyte in four sites between 1946 and 1980.

First record: A few stems only, on a birch trunk in young plantation [south of Bulls Close] between
Madingley and Girton, TL46A, P.W. Richards, 1946, NMW (cf. Richards 1947b; see Appendix 2). *P.
pulcherrimum* was recorded again here by H.L.K. Whitehouse in 1956 (CGE), initially as a 'patch several
inches across' and by 1960 as 'about four scattered patches over an area three or four inches across, the
centre of the plant having died out'. Clearly only a single plant was known to Whitehouse. There is no
evidence that the species persisted for as long as this at the other three sites, on an oak trunk at Hardwick
Wood, TL35N, M.C. Anderson, 1961; on two oaks at Hayley Wood, TL25W, O. Rackham, 1966 and on the bark
of ash, Knapwell Wood, TL36F, C.D.P., 1980. At Hayley it was initially recorded in 1966 on the tops of two
fallen oaks with a single patch on each; these patches had 'substantially increased' by 1968 (*Rackham
notebooks, Red 130: 9916*) but no new colonies were discovered. The most plausible interpretation of the
ecology of this species is that the records in south-east England arise from long-distance dispersal of
spores. The species is abundant in the forests of northern Fennoscandia and some 685 million spores per
hectare of forest may be released in early spring (Söderström & Jonsson 1989). Wallace (1963) suggested
that 'it may be spreading in the British Isles. During the last thirty years it has been found in many localities
in central and southern England' but any such increase has long since stopped and there have been few
records in south-east England since 1990 (Blockeel *et al.* 2014). Its appearance and subsequent
disappearance are most likely to have been caused by changes in substrate acidity but the chance arrival of
spores may also have been a factor.

Dioicous. Capsules not recorded.

## LEPIDOZIACEAE

### Lepidozia reptans

A rare colonist of rotting wood, recorded since 2000 on decorticated oak logs and rotting oak stumps in at least four places in Hayley Wood, TL25W, on decaying conifer stumps at Little Widgham Wood, TL65S, and with *Cephalozia bicuspidata*, *Orthodontium lineare* and *Tetraphis pellucida* on rotting logs and stumps at Forty Acre Wood, Chippenham Fen, TL66P. It is similar in its ecology and rarity in the county to *Cephalozia bicuspidata*, *C. connivens*, *C. lunulifolia*, *Nowellia curvifolia*, *Herzogiella seligeri* and *Tetraphis pellucida*. *Orthodontium lineare* grows on similar substrates but can tolerate drier conditions and is much more frequent.

First record: On rotten tree stumps in damp woodland, Hayley Wood, TL25W, S.J.P. Waters, 1965, BBSUK. The Hayley population, and that at Chippenham (which was first recorded in 1976) are persistent, but there are only single records from Papworth Wood, TL26W, in 1971, Fulbourn Fen, TL55I, in 1972, White Wood, Gamlingay, TL25SW, in 1988 and Little Widgham Wood in 2008.

Autoicous. Capsules recorded once (33% tetrads), at Chippenham, dehiscing in April.

## LOPHOCOLEACEAE

### Lophocolea bidentata

*Lophocolea bidentata* grows in a wide range of moist, shaded, undisturbed or only lightly disturbed habitats. It is typically found in lawns, on soil by water bodies, in shelter belts, scrub and both ancient and recent woodland, and on shaded walls, brickwork and stonework. It often grows amongst pleurocarpous mosses. We have found it in 34% of the churchyards surveyed and in them its preference for shade is often apparent; it is most frequent in thin grassland and soil on the north side of the church, often growing with *Plagiomnium undulatum*. In wooded habitats it grows on moist ground, as an epiphyte and on rotting stumps and logs. We have few records of it growing epiphytically, on willow (32% of these

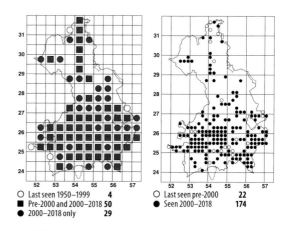

○ Last seen 1950–1999    **4**
■ Pre-2000 and 2000–2018 **50**
● 2000–2018 only    **29**

○ Last seen pre-2000    **22**
● Seen 2000–2018    **174**

tetrad records), hawthorn (30%), ash (25%), beech (5%) and blackthorn (5%). Although it frequently grows on decaying hardwoods, it is notably more abundant on conifer logs and stumps in sites such as Little Widgham Wood, TL65S, where both substrates occur together. There are a few records from unshaded habitats, e.g. in disused clay pits. It is not recorded from orchards.

First record: T. Martyn, 1760–61 (*Martyn letters*, as *Jungermannia bidentata*) and Martyn (1763: 25). The first localised records were made by R.H. Compton from Great Heath Plantation at Gamlingay, TL25F, Madingley Wood, TL35/45, and Kennett, TL66NE (Evans 1913). *L. bidentata* (89 tetrads) and *L. heterophylla* (90 tetrads) were recorded before 2000 in more tetrads than any other liverworts in the county. In our survey, from 2000 onwards, these two species were less frequent than two epiphytes, *Frullania dilatata* and *Metzgeria furcata*, and two weedy species, *Lunularia cruciata* and *Marchantia polymorpha*. The Frescalo analysis shows a steady decline in both species since the 1970s.

Autoicous. Capsules rare (8% tetrads), November, January–June, recorded on the ground in damp meadows and swampy woodland, on fallen logs in woodland and just above the water-level on mature willows in a disused, flooded gravel pit.

### Lophocolea heterophylla

*Lophocolea heterophylla* is more specialised in its habitat requirements than *L. bidentata*. The majority of records are from ancient or recent woodland and scrub, including fen woodland and carr, with other records from churchyards, gardens, orchards, parkland, open clay pits and stream banks. It favours shaded, acidic substrates but appears to be almost equally frequent on rotting wood (51% of tetrad records) and as an epiphyte on living bark (44%); there are also a few records from soil (4%) and worked wood (1%). Like *L. bidentata*, it is notably more abundant and fructiferous on decaying softwood than hardwood logs when both substrates can be compared at the same site (as at Kingston Wood, TL35H). As an epiphyte most records are from hawthorn (29% of tetrad records), ash (17%), birch (11%), oak (10%), willow (10%) and *Prunus* spp., including plum and blackthorn (8%); the relatively high proportion of occurrences on birch and oak indicate its preference for acidic substrates. There are a few records from other hosts (Appendix 3). It is often confined to tree bases and this is certainly true of its few occurrences as an epiphyte in orchards, where Robin Stevenson has recorded it from nine (1%) out of 951 apple trees surveyed and two (1%) of 173 pears. It is rare on the ground in woods, hedges, acidic grassland and disused clay pits (where it occurs in the open and in scrub), and on ditch sides. It tolerates pH 4.1 on peaty ground in Six Acre Plantation, TL68E. Records from a wooden bridge and an old railway sleeper provide rare examples of occurrences on artificial substrates.

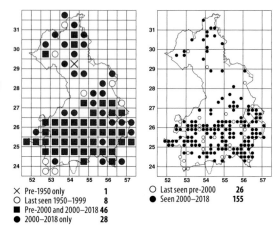

| | |
|---|---|
| ✕ Pre-1950 only | 1 |
| ○ Last seen 1950–1999 | 8 |
| ■ Pre-2000 and 2000–2018 | 46 |
| ● 2000–2018 only | 28 |

| | |
|---|---|
| ○ Last seen pre-2000 | 26 |
| ● Seen 2000–2018 | 155 |

First record: Beech coppice on Gogs, Babraham, TL55SW, P.G.M. Rhodes, 1905 (*Richards file*). In the mid 20th century *L. bidentata* and *L. heterophylla* were the only common leafy liverworts in the county and *L. heterophylla* was much the commoner species in woodland (Hill 1967). It was described as abundant on tree bases and rotting wood by both Proctor (1956) and Whitehouse (1964) and as 'often abundant' in these habitats by Hill (1967); it was so frequent that neither Whitehouse nor Hill listed all their records. This suggests that it is much less frequent now than it was in the mid 20th century, and just this pattern is shown by the Frescalo analysis.

Paroicous. Capsules frequent (34% tetrads), usually found on rotting logs and stumps, less frequent on shaded ground and on trees; noted November–May. Gemmae occur on epiphytic plants as well as those in other habitats.

## Chiloscyphus pallescens

A rare species in the western boulder-clay woods, growing on the woodland floor or on the sides of paths and rides, often in areas which are waterlogged in winter. In the recent survey it was recorded in Gamlingay Wood, TL25G, L, Hayley Wood, TL25W and Madingley Wood, TL45E. At Hayley the soil on which it grew in one wet and swampy area was distinctly acidic (pH 5.7). It is frequent in wet woodland at Chippenham Fen, TL66P, growing around the bases of trees or on the lower trunks in seasonally flooded areas.

First record: On damp soil in ride, Little Widgham Wood, TL65S, P.W. Richards, 1939, as *C. polyanthos* (see Appendix 2). Before 2000, *C. pallescens* was recorded from rotting wood and the base of *Molinia caerulea* tussocks as well as its current habitats. The Frescalo analysis suggests a marked decline in its frequency. We have failed to refind it in four woods in which it was recorded between 1958 and 1992, Longstowe Wood, TL35C, Overhall Grove, TL36G, Little Widgham Wood, TL65S and Ten Wood, Stetchworth, TL65NE. It is tempting to attribute its loss to the reduced frequency of spring flooding and the increased frequency of hot, dry summers in recent decades, changes to which Rackham (1999) attributes the decline of the primrose (*Primula vulgaris*) in the western boulder-clay woods. The reduction of 'acid rain' may also have acted against it. The other sites with last records in this period are Whittlesford Fen, TL44U, Dernford Fen, TL45Q, and Wicken Fen, TL57K, Q. It was very widespread at Wicken during the calcifuge invasion (first seen 1966, last recorded 1989).

Autoicous. Capsules recorded since 2000 only at Chippenham (20% tetrads), seen January, February, April.

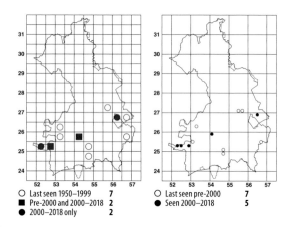

| | |
|---|---|
| ○ Last seen 1950–1999 | 7 |
| ■ Pre-2000 and 2000–2018 | 2 |
| ● 2000–2018 only | 2 |

| | |
|---|---|
| ○ Last seen pre-2000 | 7 |
| ● Seen 2000–2018 | 5 |

## PLAGIOCHILACEAE

### Plagiochila porelloides

A colony of some 10–20 small patches (the largest 50 cm² in area) was discovered during the recent survey on humic soil at the foot of a single beech tree in mature beech woodland, growing with *Ctenidium molluscum*, *Homalothecium lutescens* and *Hypnum cupressiforme* (see below).

First record: Beechwood Nature Reserve, Gog Magog Hills, TL45X, J.D. Shanklin, 2009, BBSUK. The beech wood was planted on arable land over chalk *c.* 1840 and was frequently visited by bryological excursions in the 1950s and 1960s. The *Plagiochila* must have arrived in the last two centuries and perhaps very much more recently. The wood is quite different from the woodland sites for *P. asplenioides* in the county.

Dioicous. Capsules not recorded.

### Plagiochila asplenioides

This handsome species, much the largest leafy liverwort in the county, is one of the most distinctive bryophytes of the boulder-clay woods. It is found in woodland interiors or on ditch banks and the sides of rides and ponds, often in low-lying areas where there is a high cover of large mosses such as *Eurhynchium striatum*, *Fissidens taxifolius*, *Kindbergia praelonga*, *Plagiomnium undulatum*, *Thamnobryum alopecurum* and *Thuidium tamariscinum*. We noted it as fairly frequent in the North and East Quarters of Hayley Wood, TL25W, in 2009, but at most sites it is at best occasional and often very scarce. It has the strongest preference for ancient woodland of any of the county's commoner bryophytes (Preston & Hill 2016); the only current site which is recent rather than ancient woodland is South Lodge Plantation, Croxton, TL25P, U, which was planted between 1818 and 1826.

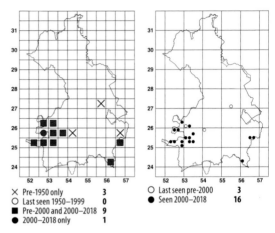

| | | |
|---|---|---|
| ✕ Pre-1950 only | 3 | |
| ○ Last seen 1950–1999 | 0 | |
| ■ Pre-2000 and 2000–2018 | 9 | |
| ● 2000–2018 only | 1 | |

| | | |
|---|---|---|
| ○ Last seen pre-2000 | 3 | |
| ● Seen 2000–2018 | 16 | |

First record: Madingley Wood, TL35/45, undated, BM (Herb. Sloane 285 f. 26, as *Muscus Trichomanes facie*). This early specimen was almost certainly collected by W. Vernon, who is known to have visited Madingley Wood (see *Fissidens taxifolius*); a letter from Vernon to Samuel Doody (1656–1706) is pasted into the front of the next volume, Sloane 286, and was sent 'With Two parcells of plants'. More than half of Madingley Wood was grubbed out in the 17th or 18th centuries, with the apparent loss of *Primula elatior* as well as *Plagiochila asplenioides* (Rackham & Coombe 1996). Relhan (1788: 19, as *Jungermannia asplenioides*) knew it from Wood Ditton, TL65NE, but there were no further records until P.C. Hodgson collected it at Wicken Fen, TL57K, in 1931 (CGE), the sole Fenland record. E.W. Jones found it in Buff Wood, TL25V, in 1934. We have rediscovered it since 2000 in all the woodlands in which it was recorded in the 20th century except Elsworth Wood, TL36A. However, it appears to be less common at Hayley now than it was in the 1960s, when Oliver Rackham remembered that it was very easy to collect material for teaching purposes. It may have become less frequent in woodlands during subsequent hot, dry summers. As a species which very rarely fruits in Britain, it presumably has little capacity for long-distance dispersal. It can spread over short distances through woodland: it was recorded in 1992 in The Triangle, an area of 19th-century secondary woodland adjacent to the ancient part of Hayley Wood.

Dioicous. Capsules not recorded.

## CEPHALOZIACEAE

Species of *Cephalozia* are widespread in acidic habitats in the north and west of Britain. *C. bicuspidata* is the most frequent, having broader habitat requirements than the others, and is the least rare of the three species recorded from Cambridgeshire. The other two species, and the related *Nowellia curvifolia* and *Odontoschisma sphagni*, have more specialised ecological requirements.

### Cephalozia bicuspidata

Found during the recent survey on rotting tree stumps and wood in three localities: Gamlingay Heath Plantation, TL25F, Madingley Wood, TL45E, and Chippenham Fen, in both Forty Acre Wood and

Compartment 9, TL66P. It grew with *Lepidozia reptans* at Chippenham Fen and with *Nowellia curvifolia* at Madingley Wood. It may have been introduced to Cambridge University Botanic Garden, TL45N, where it has been found on a sandstone boulder near the lake, growing with *Calypogeia fissa* and *Campylopus introflexus* (Graham 2011).

First record: Gamlingay Bogs, TL25SW (Relhan 1788: 20, as *Jungermannia bicuspidata*). The first localised record from Gamlingay Heath Plantation dates from 1949, and in the past it was found here on sandy soil as well as rotting wood (Proctor 1956). It was first found at Chippenham Fen in 1956. The maps suggest a marked decline in its frequency. Our failure to rediscover the species in the western

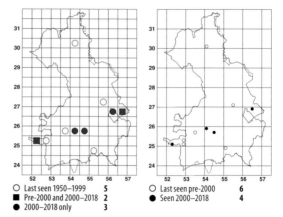

| | |
|---|---|
| ○ Last seen 1950–1999 | 5 |
| ■ Pre-2000 and 2000–2018 | 2 |
| ● 2000–2018 only | 3 |

| | |
|---|---|
| ○ Last seen pre-2000 | 6 |
| ● Seen 2000–2018 | 4 |

boulder-clay woods, Buff Wood, TL25V, Hayley Wood, TL25W, and Hardwick Wood, TL35N, is noteworthy. The absence of recent records from Wicken Fen, TL57K, is less surprising in view of the loss of most calcifuges from this site. The land-use at Mill Hill, Gamlingay, TL25F, has changed, Gray's Moor Pits, TF40A, was an early successional site which has become overgrown with scrub and there may have been insufficient habitat to maintain the colony on rotten wood at Pampisford Hall, TL54E.

Autoicous. Capsules frequent (50% tetrads), March, April. Gemmae frequent in the shade at Gamlingay Heath Plantation.

## Cephalozia lunulifolia

First and only record: With *Orthodontium lineare* on a rotting tree stump, Hardwick Wood, TL35N, C.D. Preston, 2005, BBSUK.

Dioicous. Capsules not recorded; gemmae frequent.

## †Cephalozia connivens

A very rare plant of decaying tree stumps in boulder-clay woods, recorded twice before the recent survey but not seen since 1989.

First record: On a heavily shaded and 'lusciously rotting' stump, with *Orthodontium lineare* and *Tetraphis pellucida*, Hayley Wood, TL25W, M.O. Hill, 1966, BBSUK. Only recorded subsequently from a decayed stump in Gamlingay Wood, TL25G, by P.W. Richards and H.L.K. Whitehouse in 1989.

Autoicous. Capsules not recorded. Gemmae are occasional nationally but have not been noted on our material.

## Nowellia curvifolia

British bryologists expect to see *Nowellia curvifolia* covering spongy, rotting logs in humid valleys in northern and western Britain. It is remarkable that there are two long-established populations in Cambridgeshire which survived 'the heat of six great summers' in the 20th century (Rackham 1999) including those of 1975 and 1976. In Hayley Wood, TL25W, an ancient boulder-clay wood, it grows in a sparse bryophyte cover with *Lophocolea heterophylla*, *Dicranum tauricum*, *Hypnum andoi* and *H. cupressiforme* on iron-hard, decorticated fallen trunks and branches of oaks in one area of the East Quarter. These appear to be the remains of trees killed by invasive elms (Rackham 1975: 105, 166–167) and Oliver Rackham told us that they had remained largely unchanged since he first saw them, with even the arching branches as well as the main trunks still present; they are clearly exceptionally resistant to decay. In 2003 *Nowellia* was seen on at least six separate logs and it was still present in 2017. In addition to climatic extremes, it has also survived the effects of the death of the invasive elms in this part of the wood. At Chippenham Fen *Nowellia* grows with *Herzogiella seligeri* on decaying conifer logs in Forty Acre Wood, TL66P. It was discovered at three further sites during the recent survey, growing with *Lophocolea heterophylla* and *Kindbergia praelonga* on four very soft, decorticated elm logs at Papworth Wood, TL26W, with *Lophocolea heterophylla* on a rotten sycamore at Decoy Pond, Arrington, TL35B, and with *Cephalozia bicuspidata* on two rotting logs at Madingley Wood, TL45E.

First record: Hayley Wood, TL25W, M.H. Martin, 1962, BBSUK (cf. Martin 1963). It was first discovered at Chippenham Fen in 1975 (CGE). The range of the species has expanded in southern England and Wales since 1950 (Blockeel *et al.* 2014).

Sexuality uncertain. Capsules seen in February at Hayley Wood and Madingley Wood (40% tetrads); gemmae also found when looked for microscopically (Papworth Wood).

### †*Odontoschisma sphagni*
First and only record: Marshy places, adhering to *Sphagnum 'latifolium'* (perhaps *S. papillosum*), Gamlingay Bogs, and Ditches, TL25SW (Relhan 1820, as *Jungermannia sphagni*). One of the commoner bog liverworts in Britain; like its characteristic habitat, this dioicous species has long since disappeared from Cambridgeshire.

## CEPHALOZIELLACEAE

*Cephaloziella* species are tiny liverworts and are therefore either pioneers of open habitats or stress-tolerant species which are able to persist in places where the growth of other plants is suppressed (e.g. by high concentrations of heavy metals). All three species recorded from Cambridgeshire are pioneer colonists of acidic substrates. Not surprisingly, therefore, records are few and far between. In addition to the records below, unidentifiable *Cephaloziella* stems were found by J.M. Lock at Wicken Fen in 1967 (Lock 1990) and by O. Rackham on a long-dead, fallen oak in a coppice plot at Hayley Wood, TL25W, in 2004 (CGE).

### †*Cephaloziella rubella*
First and only record: With *Polytrichastrum formosum* [as *Polytrichum gracile*, now *Polytrichastrum longisetum*, but voucher is *P. formosum*], Great Heath Plantation, Gamlingay, TL25F, E.W. Jones and P.W. Richards, 1934, CGE. E.W. Jones commented in 1955 that this material is miserable but that it includes individuals with paroicous inflorescences which could hardly be anything other than *C. rubella*.

Capsules not recorded.

### †*Cephaloziella hampeana*
Only three records, the last in 1968.

First record: In turf on sandy soil, Furze Hill, Hildersham, TL54P, M.C.F. Proctor, 1952, BBSUK, det. E.W. Jones. The vegetation of the Furze Hills was altered by sand extraction in the 1950s (Trist 1988). *C. hampeana* was also recorded from decaying wood, Gamlingay Wood, TL25SW, by H.J.B. Birks in 1965 (E) and from clinker on the disused railway alongside Hayley Wood, TL25W, by J.G. Duckett in 1968, the same site as that of another casual calcifuge, *Lophozia excisa*. It probably persisted at Hayley until 1973, when *Cephaloziella* sp. was recorded as an associate of the *Lophozia*.

Autoicous. Capsules not recorded. Gemmae are usually present, as on the Hildersham specimen.

### *Cephaloziella divaricata*
A colony of this species was discovered in 2008 by J.J. Graham and C.D.P. (det. D.G. Long), growing on the consolidated ballast of an old railway siding at the edge of Stanground Wash Nature Reserve, Peterborough, TL29D. Four patches were seen, the largest measuring 13.5 × 9.5 cm, in heavily rabbit-grazed open turf with *Brachythecium albicans*, *Ceratodon purpureus*, *Dicranum scoparium*, *Cladonia* sp. and scattered vascular plants including dwarf *Chamerion angustifolium*, *Centaurium erythraea*, *Hypericum perforatum* and *Pilosella officinarum*. It has also colonised crushed granite hoggin in the light shade of a planted birch on the Sidgwick Avenue site, Cambridge, TL45N, where frequent, scattered small patches were found with *Barbula convoluta*, *Ceratodon purpureus*, *Didymodon insulanus* and *Pogonatum urnigerum* in 2016.

First certain record: Gamlingay Cinques, TL25G, G. Halliday and H.L.K. Whitehouse, 1957, BBSUK (see Appendix 2). Not seen again until the recent survey.

Dioicous. Archegonia present September, December; capsules recorded February (Gamlingay Cinques). Gemmae also recorded.

## SCAPANIACEAE

### †*Lophozia ventricosa*
First and only record: Gamlingay Bogs, TL25SW, Relhan (1820: 468, as *Jungermannia ventricosa*). A dioicous species, frequent in a range of acidic habitats in northern and western Britain.

### †*Lophozia excisa*
A casual calcifuge in Cambridgeshire; not recorded since 1973.

First record: Clinker of abandoned railway by Hayley Wood, TL25W, J.G. Duckett and H.L.K. Whitehouse, 1968, BBSUK. Refound here with *Cephaloziella* sp. by H.L.K.W. in 1973, clearly the basis of Whitehouse's (1974) comment that 'it still flourishes there'. However, the site is small and the species has been searched for on several subsequent occasions without success.

Paroicous. Capsules not recorded. The usual mode of reproduction is by gemmae, although these were not explicitly recorded in Cambridgeshire.

### *Lophozia perssonii*
A rare plant of very disturbed chalk soil. The classic site for this nationally scarce species in the county is East Pit, Cherry Hinton, TL45X, where its tendency to fluctuate in numbers was well demonstrated in the recent survey. It was seen in small quantity between 2001 and 2007 on the floor of this disused chalk pit, always growing amongst more frequent *Leiocolea turbinata*. Other associates were *Aloina aloides*, *Bryum dichotomum* and *Didymodon fallax*. By 2008 the only plants which could be found grew with frequent *Leiocolea turbinata* on the surface of a chalk boulder. Large flakes were shed from the boulder in winter when it absorbed water like a sponge and subsequently froze; this prevented colonisation by more competitive species. Nearby boulders were completely shattered by freeze-thaw processes. In 2010–11 masses of *Buddleja davidii* scrub were cleared from the site and the floor of the pit reprofiled and by 2012 *L. perssonii* had responded. In particular, small but luxuriant patches, typically with 10–12 gemmiferous stems, were fairly frequent (with *L. turbinata*) in a large saucer-shaped hollow, especially in places where they were sheltered by *Reseda lutea* plants. Pilkington (2010) notes a similar need for some shelter in a large population on tank tracks in the military training areas of Salisbury Plain. Two small patches of *L. perssonii* were also found in an open area of the West Pit, Cherry Hinton, TL45X, in 2007, growing with *Aloina aloides*, *Dicranella varia*, *Didymodon fallax*, *Homalothecium lutescens* and *Oxyrrhynchium hians*. *L. perssonii* was discovered in two new sites during the recent survey: Station Quarry, Steeple Morden, TL33E, a working chalk pit, where it grew with *Leiocolea turbinata* and *Seligeria calcarea* on a crust of chalky soil over the rock; and Ickleton Pit, TL44W, a long-disused chalk pit where it was found in small quantity on a narrow path.

First record: On bare wet chalk soil on floor of chalk pit, Cherry Hinton, TL45X, 1966, H.J.B. Birks, BBSUK (cf. Paton & Birks 1968). This was only the third British locality for this species, which had been discovered in two quarries in Yorkshire the previous year. It was 'abundant on both sides of the road' when first found at Cherry Hinton, i.e. in both East and West Pit, but was not seen there between 1968 and 1983. It was again frequent in East Pit by 1986, colonising the wet chalky slurry created by the frequent passage of lorries across the floor of the pit. It declined in abundance after the pit ceased to be worked in the 1980s and even the more open areas of the quarry floor became encrusted with a mat of *Leiocolea turbinata*. *L. perssonii* was also discovered at Fleam Dyke, TL55M, by J. Dransfield in 1967, growing on the continually crumbling north-facing chalk side of a disused railway cutting; it was last seen here in 1988.

Dioicous. Immature perianths seen at Cherry Hinton; male inflorescences and capsules not seen. Gemmae always present.

### †*Diplophyllum albicans*
First and only record: One patch on shaded bank by ditch, Great Heath Plantation, Gamlingay, TL25F, C.R. Stevenson, 1988, BBSUK, CGE. This is one of the most frequent and distinctive liverworts in acidic areas of northern and western Britain, where it normally grows on shaded rocks and soil.

Dioicous. Capsules are frequent nationally and gemmae very common but neither were recorded from Cambridgeshire.

## CALYPOGEIACEAE

### *Calypogeia fissa*
This plant of acidic ground was found in four woods during the recent survey: with abundant *Dicranella heteromalla* on a ditch bank at the edge of Gamlingay Heath Plantation, TL25F; on a bank by a ride and a cleared glade in Gamlingay Wood, TL25L; with *Eurhynchium striatum*, *Dicranella heteromalla* and *Thuidium tamariscinum* on sandy clay soil on slightly raised ground in Out Wood, TL65M; and in wet woodland at Chippenham Fen, TL66P. Additionally, Graham (2011) found it growing in very small quantity, with *Cephalozia bicuspidata* and *Campylopus introflexus*, on a sandstone boulder near the lake in the Cambridge University Botanic Garden, TL45N, where it was presumably introduced.

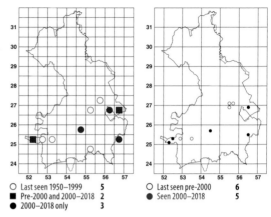

○ Last seen 1950–1999   **5**
■ Pre-2000 and 2000–2018   **2**
● 2000–2018 only   **3**

○ Last seen pre-2000   **6**
● Seen 2000–2018   **5**

First record: On soil in oak wood, Gamlingay Heath Plantation, TL25F, M.C.F. Proctor, 1953, BBSUK. It was first found at Wicken Fen, TL56P and 57K, in 1963, became one of the more widespread calcifuges during the 1970s and was last seen there in 1999. We have not refound it in several places where it was recorded in the 20th century: Hayley Wood, TL25W, Eversden Wood, TL35L and Hildersham Wood, TL54H. The Frescalo analysis shows a marked decline in its frequency.

Autoicous. Capsules not seen; gemmae recorded.

### *Calypogeia muelleriana*
A shade-tolerant calcifuge, found in the recent survey only on a streamside bank in Great Heath Plantation, Gamlingay, TL25F, in 2002.

First record: With *Mnium hornum* at the base of *Osmunda regalis* in the Water Garden, Cambridge Botanic Garden, TL45N, H.J.B. Birks, 1973, BBSUK. It had not been seen when this habitat was searched in 1955 or 1965 and Whitehouse (1974) thought that it was probably a natural colonist, but that the possibility of accidental introduction with cultivated plants could not be ruled out. It was never seen here again, but was subsequently found on wet ground in Great Heath Plantation by C.R. Stevenson in 1988.

Autoicous. Capsules not seen; gemmae recorded.

### †*Calypogeia arguta*
First and only record: With *Cephalozia bicuspidata* on wet ground in Great Heath Plantation, Gamlingay, TL25F, P.E. Jackson, 1988, BBSUK. This is the most distinctive member of the genus, and a frequent plant of crumbling acidic soil on banks in western Britain. Like *Diplophyllum albicans* and *Fossombronia wondraczekii*, it was seen on open, acidic soil at Great Heath Plantation in 1988 but has never been refound in the county.

Autoicous; capsules not recorded and rare nationally. Gemmae are the normal mode of reproduction, and are present on the Gamlingay specimen.

## MESOPTYCHIACEAE

### †*Leiocolea badensis*
Recorded sporadically between 1953 and 1977.

First record: Damp chalky soil on floor of derelict railway cutting near Worsted Lodge, TL55G, M.C.F. Proctor, 1953, BBSUK. The other records are: near chalk spring, Nine Wells, Great Shelford, TL45S, C.M. Pannell, 1977; amongst *Lophozia perssonii* and other bryophytes on wet chalk, East Pit, Cherry Hinton, TL45X, H.J.B. Birks, 1966, BBSUK and on chalk at same site, J.A. Paton, 1967, BBSUK; on chalky banks of the disused railway at Fleam Dyke, TL55M, J.C. Gardiner, 1973, CGE. With the exception of Worsted Lodge, where the record is based on a single specimen which was initially named *L. turbinata* and has only recently been redetermined, all these are sites where *L. turbinata* has also been recorded. The identity of the herbarium specimens has been kindly confirmed by T.H. Blackstock. It is difficult to account for the occasional records of *L. badensis* from the same habitats as *L. turbinata*, and difficult to know whether we have overlooked the species in the recent survey. There appears to be a broad overlap in their habitat requirements elsewhere in the British Isles.

Dioicous; capsules not recorded.

### Leiocolea turbinata

*Leiocolea turbinata* is a habitat specialist, confined to sparsely vegetated chalk soil, stones, boulders or rock faces. The largest populations are found as crusts on loose or semi-consolidated, disturbed chalk soil in active or recently disused chalk pits, including flat areas on the floor of chalk pits which are subject to flooding in wet weather. *L. turbinata* also grows in small open areas in north-facing chalk grassland or in turf on the steep sides of chalk pits, on steep chalky stream banks, railway and road cuttings, on the sides of ponds dug in chalky soil, on paths through otherwise closed vegetation and on heavily shaded, compacted soil, stones or rock on earthworks and in disused chalk pits.

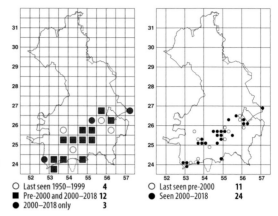

| | |
|---|---|
| ○ Last seen 1950–1999 | 4 |
| ■ Pre-2000 and 2000–2018 | 12 |
| ● 2000–2018 only | 3 |

| | |
|---|---|
| ○ Last seen pre-2000 | 11 |
| ● Seen 2000–2018 | 24 |

First record: Cherry Hinton chalk pit, TL45NE, P.G.M. Rhodes, 1908, CGE. However, Relhan's (1820: 468) record of the calcifuge *Solenostoma gracillimum* (as *Jungermannia gracillima*) from 'Dry Chalky places. Hinton, Chalk-pit Close' must refer to *Leiocolea turbinata*, which was not distinguished at the time. The ability of *L. turbinata* to grow in heavy shade gives it the ability to persist in disused chalk pits. Although almost all the pre-2000 records are from chalk substrates, it was recorded on calcareous Boulder Clay on a ditch bank beside Hardwick Wood, TL35N, by M.O.H. in 1966. The sites where the species has not been refound include several small chalk pits, a disused railway cutting where it may have been lost to vegetation succession and a cutting by an active railway which is now inaccessible, as well as one or two ditches and paths in the open countryside. The Frescalo analysis suggests a decline in its frequency since the 1970s.

Dioicous; capsules occasional (30% tetrads), December–April.

## BRYOPHYTA (MOSSES)

# SPHAGNOPSIDA

## SPHAGNACEAE

### Sphagnum

There are few available habitats for *Sphagnum* species in a county where the soils are as calcareous as those in Cambridgeshire. Unfortunately there are no specimens to support the first *Sphagnum* records, made by Vernon *c.* 1696 and J. Martyn *c.* 1729 in their annotated copies of Ray's floras and then by T. Martyn (1763: 24) and Relhan (1785: 394). The populations known to Relhan at Hinton Moor, TL45NE, and Teversham Moor, TL55NW, would have been lost with the agricultural improvement of these sites after parliamentary enclosure in the early 19th century. *Sphagnum* was first recorded at Gamlingay, TL25SW, by Vernon and one can only imagine how many species a modern bryologist might have been able to find growing there with *Hammarbya paludosa*, which Martyn (1763: 40, as *Ophrys palustris*) recorded 'On the upper parts of those Bogs which face the great house, among the *Sphagnum*, in great plenty'. *Sphagnum* species survived in Great Heath Plantation, Gamlingay, until 1930 but Proctor (1956) was unable to find any in this wood in 1952 and considered that they might have been exterminated by pigs kept here. Aggressive free-range swine were still present in 1975–77 (Leslie 1979) but they had gone by 1988 when tiny *Sphagnum* populations were rediscovered there.

Whitehouse (1964) knew no extant *Sphagnum* populations in the county when he wrote the main text of his bryophyte flora but a note added in proof (p. xvi) recorded the discovery of *S. fimbriatum* at Wicken Fen. *Sphagnum* species were prominent amongst the calcifuges which were subsequently discovered as colonists of the fen carr at Wicken, and they persisted longer than many of the others; in 2003 we recorded six species there. However, the extensive programme of scrub clearance in the following years may have eliminated all these species. We could certainly find no trace of *Sphagnum* in 2008 when we revisited the two areas where we had found them five years previously, and have not seen any species on subsequent visits.

### †*Sphagnum papillosum*

It is only recently that historic specimens of this species, a characteristic plant of peat bogs, have been identified from Cambridgeshire.

First and only record: Gamlingay Bogs, TL25SW, L. Jenyns, 1824, BTH (as *Sphagnum cymbifolium*), det. M.O.H. A specimen labelled Gamlingay was collected on the same occasion by Henslow (CGE).

Dioicous. The Cambridgeshire specimens, collected in August, are fruiting.

### *Sphagnum palustre*

*Sphagnum palustre* was still present in 2003 in at least two sites at Wicken Fen. There were large mounds in fairly open birch scrub in one rather small area of compartment 12, north of the Godwin Plots, TL57K, with *S. fimbriatum*, *S. squarrosum*, *S. subnitens*, *Cladium mariscus* and *Phragmites australis*. It also grew on Verrall's Fen between Malcarse Drain and New Dyke (compartment 2), TL56P and 57K, in pony-grazed birch/sallow carr with some open glades. At the latter site water of pH 5.4 was squeezed from a *Sphagnum* tussock.

First record: Gamlingay, C.E. Moss, undated, CGE (see Appendix 2). It was last seen at Gamlingay by P.W. Richards, in a bog in Great Heath Plantation, TL25F, in 1930. The first record from Wicken Fen was made in the Godwin Plots by S.M. Walters and H.L.K. Whitehouse in 1974 and by 1983 it was widely distributed at Wicken (Crompton & Whitehouse 1983).

Dioicous. Capsules not recorded.

Examination of Cambridgeshire specimens by M.O.H. has shown that both the Moss and Richards specimens from Gamlingay (BBSUK, CGE) are var. *palustre*, as is a specimen collected by Whitehouse from compartment 5, Wicken Fen, in 1989 (CGE). However, a small number of the cells of the latter are of the var. *centrale* type, suggesting that the varieties are not very distinct in Britain even though they are often treated as species by European bryologists. Material collected by C.D.P. from compartment 12 at Wicken in 2003 (BBSUK) is var. *centrale*.

### *Sphagnum squarrosum*

*Sphagnum squarrosum* persisted until 2003 in birch scrub in compartment 12, Wicken Fen, TL57K (see *S. palustre* above).

First record: Gamlingay, TL25SW, R. Relhan, herb. Skrimshire, WBCH, conf. M.O.H.; a specimen from Gamlingay in F.K. Eagle's herbarium (CGE) is dated 1806 and was probably also collected by Relhan. *S. squarrosum* was discovered in the Godwin Plots at Wicken Fen, TL57K, by A.C. Leslie in 1974 (CGE); by the 1980s it was widespread at Wicken and sometimes present as large cushions (Crompton & Whitehouse 1983, Preston & Whitehouse 1990).

Autoicous. Capsules known only on Relhan's specimen.

### †*Sphagnum teres*

One of the more base-demanding *Sphagnum* species, known from the county only as a single historic specimen.

First and only record: Gamlingay Bogs, TL25SW, L. Jenyns, 1824, BTH (as *S. cuspidatum*), det. M.O.H. Dioicous. Capsules not recorded.

### *Sphagnum fimbriatum*

*Sphagnum fimbriatum* was recorded at Wicken Fen in 2003 at the same sites as *S. palustre* (q.v.), in birch scrub in compartment 12, TL57K, and in birch/sallow carr in compartment 2, TL56P, 57K.

First record: Small patch on a low mound at base of an oak in *Frangula* carr, with *Atrichum undulatum*, *Dicranella heteromalla* and *Mnium hornum*, near the Brick Pits, Wicken Fen, TL57Q, J.M. Lock, 1963, CGE (cf. Lock 1964). Like several other *Sphagnum* species, it became widely distributed at Wicken and was sometimes present as large cushions (Crompton & Whitehouse 1983, Preston & Whitehouse 1990). The only other record is from Gamlingay Meadow (which adjoins Great Heath Plantation), TL25F, F.H. Perring, 1966.

Autoicous. Capsules recorded twice at Wicken, in December 1994 and May 1989.

### *Sphagnum russowii*

Seen once at Wicken Fen, growing with *Sphagnum subnitens* in mixed tussocks on the ground in pony-grazed birch carr with some open glades.

First record: Verrall's Fen between Malcarse Drain and New Dyke, Compartment 2, Wicken Fen, TL56P, M.O.H., 2003, BBSUK.

Dioicous. Capsules not present, and rare nationally.

### Sphagnum subnitens var. subnitens

*Sphagnum subnitens* was recorded at Wicken Fen in 2003 at the same sites as *S. palustre* (q.v.), in birch scrub in compartment 12, TL57K, and in birch/sallow carr in compartment 2, TL56P, 57K.

First record: With *Drosera rotundifolia*, Chippenham Fen, TL66P, A. Shrubbs, 1898, CGE. Rhodes (1911) said that *Sphagnum* was still present at Chippenham when he was writing but 'even there it is now nearly extinct'. The only other historic record of *S. subnitens* is from Gamlingay, TL25SW (Adamson in Evans 1913, as *S. acutifolium* var. *subnitens*). The first record from Wicken Fen was made in the Godwin Plots, TL57K, by S.M. Walters & H.L.K. Whitehouse in 1974 and by 1983 it was widespread there, sometimes growing as large cushions (Crompton & Whitehouse 1983, Preston & Whitehouse 1990).

Autoicous. Capsules recorded both at Wicken (April 2003 and May 1989, but unlikely to have been ripe by then) and at Chippenham (August 1898).

### Sphagnum denticulatum

A few stems of *Sphagnum denticulatum* were rediscovered at Great Heath Plantation, Gamlingay, TL25F, in 2002 (BBSUK), growing near a stream in deciduous woodland in a wet area of dead leaves which lacked a ground layer of vascular plants. We found a larger patch (30 × 15 cm) here when we revisited the site in 2018. In 2003 it was found with other *Sphagnum* species in pony-grazed birch/sallow carr on Verrall's Fen between Malcarse Drain and New Dyke, Compartment 2, Wicken Fen, TL56P, the first Wicken record.

First record: Gamlingay, TL25SW, J.S. Henslow, 1857, CGE, det. M.C.F. Proctor. This specimen has been re-examined by M.O.H. who regards it as intermediate between *S. denticulatum* and *S. inundatum*. It was subsequently collected at Gamlingay in 1881 (CGE, *fide* H.L.K. Whitehouse) and 1910 (NMW, det. M.O.H.) and the last record before the recent survey was from Great Heath Plantation, Gamlingay, by P.W. Richards in 1930 (BBSUK).

Dioicous. Capsules not recorded.

### †Sphagnum tenellum

First and only record: Gamlingay, TL25SW, R. Relhan, herb. Skrimshire, WBCH (as *Sphagnum capillifolium*), det. M.O.H.

Dioicous. The Gamlingay specimen is fruiting.

### †Sphagnum fallax

Recorded from both Gamlingay and Wicken Fen in the 20th century, but not seen during the recent survey.

First record: With *Sphagnum denticulatum*, Great Heath Plantation, Gamlingay, TL25F, P.W. Richards, 1930, NMW, conf. M.O.H. A single patch was refound by C.D.P. on damp ground in this wood in 1988 (CGE, det. M.O.H.). *S. fallax* was discovered at Wicken Fen by H.J.B. Birks in 1975, and described as widespread there by Crompton & Whitehouse (1983), but it could not be refound in 1989 and there are no subsequent records. Preston & Whitehouse (1990) suggest that it may have been eliminated by competition from vascular plants following the die-back from disease of *Frangula alnus*, a major component of the fen carr at Wicken. *S. fallax* does not form tussocks, unlike the other species of *Sphagnum* at Wicken which were widespread in the 1970s and persisted into the 21st century.

Dioicous. Capsules not recorded.

## POLYTRICHOPSIDA

## POLYTRICHACEAE

All the members of this family recorded in the county, especially the species of *Pogonatum*, *Polytrichastrum* and *Polytrichum*, are calcifuges. They are therefore all uncommon, but they provide good illustrations of the different niches available, or previously available, for calcifuges in the county.

### Atrichum undulatum var. undulatum

This mildly calcifuge moss forms vigorous patches on acidic ground in woodland, and is therefore frequent on the Woburn Sands. It is a rather local plant in the predominantly calcareous boulder-clay woods, where it grows in areas of more acidic soil (pH 5.7 at Lower Wood, Weston Colville, TL65G) or on decaying wood. Although most of its sites are ancient woods, it also grows in secondary woodland, as at Gamlingay Heath Plantation, TL25F, and Warrenhill Plantation, Newmarket, TL66R, in fen woodland and carr, at St Edmund's Fen, Wicken, TL57Q, and Chippenham Fen, TL66P, on gravelly soil under planted beeches at Cambridge

University Observatories, TL45J, sandy soil by a disused gravel pit in Telegraph Clump, Wandlebury, TL45W, and in the disused clay pits at Gray's Moor Pits, TF40A. Outside woodland it occurs in shaded grassland and stream banks at Gamlingay, TL25F, G, and on crushed granite hoggin below a planted tree in the West Residences car park, Cambridge, TL45J; it was also recorded from disused railway sidings at March, TL49E.

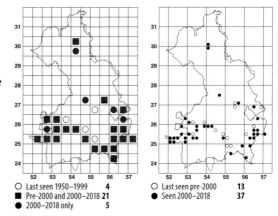

O Last seen 1950–1999    4
■ Pre-2000 and 2000–2018 21
● 2000–2018 only    5

O Last seen pre-2000    13
● Seen 2000–2018    37

First record: Gamlingay, TL25SW, W. Vernon, c. 1696 (Vernon's annotated Ray 1696: 29, as *Muscus capillaris majusculus, foliis longis cum aliqua latitudine, acutis, rugosis*). Vernon noted that the capsule was rostrate. Fruiting plants were collected at Gamlingay but not named by Henslow in 1829 (CGE). Some 20th-century records suggest that the species sometimes grew as a transient colonist of open habitats, including the single tuft on clinker at Madingley Hall sewage works, TL36V, and plants in sand and gravel pits at Bourn Bridge, TL54E and Chippenham, TL66NE. It was one of the first of the calcifuge colonists to be recorded at Wicken Fen, in 1959, and by the 1970s it was one of the most widespread.

Monoicous. Capsules frequent (62% tetrads); immature November, December, dehiscing February. Miles *et al.* (1989) have shown that *A. undulatum* has a markedly seasonal reproductive cycle, with gametangia developing early in the year and maturing in May and June, capsules developing during the summer and dehiscing during the winter, with spore release from the dehisced capsules continuing for several months until late May. However, development of the gametangia can be delayed by drought or unfavourable temperatures (Benson-Evans & Brough 1966) and it therefore seems likely that fruiting would be delayed or prevented by spring droughts, which are not infrequent in the Cambridgeshire woods.

### †*Pogonatum nanum*

A plant of open, dry soils which has declined very markedly in lowland England and has long been extinct in Cambridgeshire.

First record: Gamlingay, TL25SW, W. Vernon (Ray 1696: 28, as *Adiantum pileolo villoso minimum*, with the locality added in Vernon's annotated copy). This is the first British record. It was later collected at Gamlingay by J.S. Henslow in 1827 (a few plants mixed with *Polytrichum piliferum*) and 1829 (both CGE). The later specimen has been confirmed by M.O.H. as excellent and typical *P. nanum*. Relhan's record from the Gog Magog Hills (1786: 17, as *Polytrichum subrotundum*) is best treated as doubtful in the absence of a specimen.

Dioicous. Both specimens are fruiting.

### †*Pogonatum aloides*

First and only record: Gamlingay, TL25SW, J.S. Henslow, undated, CGE, conf. M.O. Hill. A common colonist of acidic soils on banks and ditch sides in northern and western Britain.

Dioicous. The Gamlingay specimen is fruiting.

### *Pogonatum urnigerum*

Unlike the two other, long-extinct *Pogonatum* species, *P. urnigerum* is apparently a recent arrival. A colony was discovered in 2014 extending for 8 m on hoggin of crushed granite on a raised strip along the side of a West Cambridge car park (see below). It grew best under young beech standards, perhaps because it was less trampled there. Another colony was found on the same substrate at the edge of planted birches by the Criminology Department, Sidgwick Avenue site, Cambridge, TL45N. This occupied a much smaller area when it was first found by Jonathan Shanklin in 2015, but by the end of 2016 it had spread so that shoots were frequent over an area of 4 × 3.5 m and scattered over 7 × 6 m. Granite hoggin is not usual in Cambridgeshire but it has clearly been used recently at these sites by contractors landscaping University grounds. The presence of *P. urnigerum* at both localities perhaps indicates that it was introduced with the material rather than a later colonist. It is frequent in similar habitats (e.g. forest tracks) in northern and western Britain.

First record: Car park, University West Residences, Cambridge, TL45J, S. Hartley, 2014, BBSUK.

Dioicous. Capsules not recorded. A specimen collected at the West Cambridge site shed most of its leaves soon after collection, suggesting that it might be the variant of this species with caducous leaves described by Long (1988). The leaves perhaps act as vegetative propagules.

### †*Polytrichastrum longisetum*
A rare calcifuge, not seen in the county since 1991.

First record: On a rotting stump in *Frangula* carr, Wicken Fen, TL57, J.M. Lock, 1963, CGE and Lock (1964) (see Appendix 2). The species became more widespread at Wicken, and there are specimens in CGE collected at St Edmund's Fen, TL57, in 1972 and from peat in the Godwin Plots, TL57K, in 1974. It was last reported from Wicken in 1979. Otherwise there are only two confirmed records, from the eastern boulder-clay woods: at the base of a beech tree in Great Widgham Wood, TL65S, in 1988 (C.R. Stevenson, conf. M.O.H.) and on ground near the main entrance to Ditton Park Wood, TL65T, in 1991 (P.W. Richards, CGE). The species was much over-recorded in Cambridgeshire in the 20th century, as the key character given in Dixon's *Student's Handbook of British Mosses* to distinguish it from *P. formosum* is unreliable. The available specimens have been revised by M.O.H. (Preston & Hill 2006).

Dioicous. Capsules not recorded.

### *Polytrichastrum formosum*
*Polytrichastrum formosum* is similar in its ecology to *Atrichum undulatum*, growing on acidic ground and on rotting stumps, but it is a more exacting calcifuge and is consequently rarer. It is frequent only on the Woburn Sands at Gamlingay but there was also a spectacular colony with large patches of both sexes on the 'sand lens' at Gamlingay Wood, TL25L, in April 2016, growing in a clearing which had been extended *c.* four years earlier. It is less frequent in the other western boulder-clay woods than on the sandier soils in the eastern woods (pH 4.3 at Great Wood, Kirtling, TL75C). Surprisingly, it has persisted for several decades below beech trees in the Beechwood reserve on the Gog Magog Hills, TL45X, which was planted *c.* 1840; although the soil

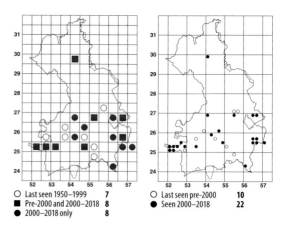

| | |
|---|---|
| ○ Last seen 1950–1999 | 7 |
| ■ Pre-2000 and 2000–2018 | 8 |
| ● 2000–2018 only | 8 |

| | |
|---|---|
| ○ Last seen pre-2000 | 10 |
| ● Seen 2000–2018 | 22 |

here is almost pure chalk, there are acidified, humic areas under the trees (pH 4.9). Other recent sites include gravelly soil under planted beeches at Cambridge University Observatories, TL45J, a hedge at the furthest edge of the Woburn Sands at Rampton, TL46E, disused railway sidings at March, TL49E, fen carr at Wicken, TL56P, and fen woodland at Chippenham, TL66P.

First record: Gamlingay, TL25SW, J.S. Tozer (Relhan (1820: 464, as *Polytrichum attenuatum*). Fruiting plants were collected (but not named) by Henslow from Gamlingay in 1829 (CGE). Like *Atrichum undulatum*, a single tuft of *Polytrichastrum formosum* was discovered on the clinker of the sewage works at Madingley Hall, TL36V, in 1961. It was first found at Wicken Fen in 1963 (Lock 1964) and it became one of the more widespread calcifuges there. Very small colonies of *Polytrichastrum* were found on rotting wood over neutral or calcareous substrates in the 20th century and were presumably able to colonise because of the prevailing levels of SO$_2$ pollution; we have not encountered such colonies in our survey. Such plants were named *P. longisetum* at the time but the surviving voucher shows that the three shoots on a rotten log at Copley Hill, TL55B, found by Harold Whitehouse in 1955 (CGE) were *P. formosum*, as was material collected from aluminium glazing bars on the outside of a glasshouse in Cambridge Botanic Garden, TL45N, in 1982 (NMW). Unfortunately we do not know the identity of the single shoot found on a rotten log at Adams Road Bird Sanctuary, Cambridge, TL45J, by Whitehouse in 1958 (no voucher survives) or the few stems found on a dark, damp old beech stump at Cracknow Hill, TL35Q, by M.O.H. in 1965 (the voucher in herb. M.O.H. is unidentifiable).

Dioicous. Capsules recorded once in the recent survey (5% tetrads), in the large Gamlingay Wood colony, and once before, in White Wood in August 1955.

### *Polytrichum commune* var. *commune*
The only recent records of this large moss are from guttering 10 m high on the Palm House at Cambridge Botanic Garden, TL45N, found and removed when the guttering was being cleaned out in 2014; from the disused railway sidings at Chesterton, TL46Q, in 2000 and from wet woodland in Compartment 9, Chippenham Fen, TL66P, in 2001.

First record: 'On Hinton Moor in the watery places' (Ray 1660: 4, as *Adianthum aureum majus*); Ray's subsequent comment (1670: 8), 'we once found it on Hinton-moor', TL45NE, suggests that it was rather rare there. This is normally a species of bogs and other acidic wetlands. It was first recorded 'In the Boggy Grounds at Gamlingay', TL25SW, by J. Martyn *c.* 1729 in his annotated copy of Ray (1660) and collected at Gamlingay by J.S. Henslow (1827, 1830, 1836), by G.D. Haviland and J.J. Lister (1881) and finally from Gamlingay Meadow (described then as a valley fen) by F.H. Perring and O. Rackham (1963). Otherwise the only records before the recent survey were of casual occurrences at Chesterton Ballast Pits, TL46Q (*c.* 1935) and Manea Pit, TL48Z (1965, 1968) and of plants recorded during the influx of calcifuges at Wicken Fen, TL56P, TL57K, between 1963 and 1989.

Dioicous. Henslow's specimens, collected in April and May, have immature capsules.

### Polytrichum piliferum

*Polytrichum piliferum* was recorded with *P. juniperinum* and *Hypnum jutlandicum* on a hard substrate at the disused railway sidings, March, TL49E, in 2001.

First record: Gamlingay Heath, TL25SW, Relhan (1820: 465); an undated specimen collected by Relhan at Gamlingay is in Skrimshire's herbarium at WBCH. It was collected again at Gamlingay by J.S. Henslow in 1827 (CGE) and rediscovered with *P. formosum* on a roadside in Gamlingay, TL25F, by A.C. Leslie in 1976 (Leslie 1979). H. Godwin found plants with *Brachythecium albicans*, *Ceratodon purpureus* and *Cladonia* sp. on the base of a derelict raised bog at Sutton Meadlands, TL47NW, in 1944; J.J. Graham and C.D.P. were unable to refind the species here in 2001 but a farmer told us that he had increased the pH of the arable land here from 3.5 to 6 or 7 by liming. The only other records are of plants growing 'in quantity' on cinders at the gasworks sidings, Coldham's Lane, Cambridge, TL45NE (C.C. Townsend, 1957), on a disused railway track near Earith, TL37X (P.J. Bourne, 1960) and in the Beechwood reserve on the Gog Magog Hills, TL45X (N.G. Hodgetts, 1983–84).

Dioicous. Henslow's specimen, collected in April, is fruiting.

### Polytrichum juniperinum

The largest populations seen in the recent survey were on railway ballast. At Stanground Wash Nature Reserve, Peterborough, TL29D, it is the most frequent bryophyte over several square metres, growing with *Brachythecium albicans* and *Ceratodon purpureus* on the heavily rabbit-grazed disused railway siding which runs alongside the current line. It was also recorded in the disused sidings at Chesterton, TL46Q, and March, TL49E; at the latter site it was abundant over many hundreds of square metres of open, clinkery ground in 2001 with species such as *Dicranum scoparium*, *Hypnum jutlandicum* and *P. piliferum*. It is also found on hoggin of crushed granite on raised strips between bays in a car park of the Cambridge University West Residences, TL45J, growing under young beech standards. The only

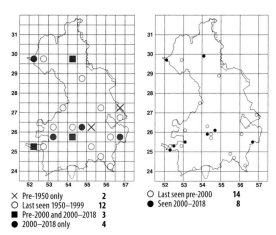

| | |
|---|---|
| ✕ Pre-1950 only | 2 |
| ○ Last seen 1950–1999 | 12 |
| ■ Pre-2000 and 2000–2018 | 3 |
| ● 2000–2018 only | 4 |

| | |
|---|---|
| ○ Last seen pre-2000 | 14 |
| ● Seen 2000–2018 | 8 |

other records are from a track in Gamlingay Heath Plantation, TL25F, a glade on the 'sand lens' at Gamlingay Wood, TL25L, a stump in Longstowe Park, TL35C, and with *Campylopus introflexus* on the rootplate of a fallen conifer in Little Widgham Wood, TL65S.

First record: Gamlingay Park, TL25SW, Relhan (1785: 397, as *Polytrichum commune* var. β). Richard Jackson had earlier added the name of the species to his annotated copy of Martyn's *Methodus* (1727a), perhaps on the basis of a Gamlingay record. It was recorded in at least six sites at Gamlingay between 1957 and 1988, including White Wood, TL25SW. It was known from the Hill of Health, TL45NW (Relhan 1820: 465, Preston 2018), presumably on gravelly soils, and there is a sequence of records from the sand hills at Hildersham, where it was found at Juniper Hill, TL54T, by Relhan (1820) and at the nearby Furze Hills, TL54P, between 1874 and 1988. *P. juniperinum* also appears to have been established along the Breckland fringe, as there are 20th-century records from Dullingham, TL65E, the Newmarket–Thetford road, TL66, Chippenham, TL66Z, and Isleham Plantation, TL67SE (both *P. juniperinum* and *P. piliferum* are frequent in Breckland). However, most of the other 20th-century records are single occurrences on railway land or in clay pits or other weedy habitats.

Dioicous. Capsules seen recently on the railway ballast at Stanground Wash and March (29% tetrads); immature September, April, dehiscing June.

# TETRAPHIDOPSIDA

## TETRAPHIDACEAE

### Tetraphis pellucida

The characteristic gemmae-bearing shoots of *Tetraphis pellucida* have been recorded recently on rotting stumps, branches and logs in three western boulder-clay woods (Hayley Wood, TL25W, Eversden Wood, TL35L, Hardwick Wood, TL35N) and at two sites on the eastern fringe of the county (Chippenham Fen, TL66P, Warrenhill Plantation, TL66R). At Hayley Wood in grows on old, decorticated oak trunks similar to those that support *Nowellia curvifolia* (q.v.).

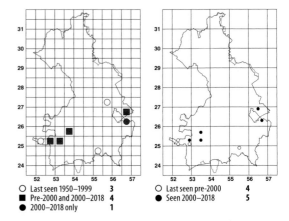

O Last seen 1950–1999   3
■ Pre-2000 and 2000–2018   4
● 2000–2018 only   1

O Last seen pre-2000   4
● Seen 2000–2018   5

First record: Stumps, Great Heath Plantation, Gamlingay, TL25F, M.C.F. Proctor, 1951 (*Whitehouse species file*; see Appendix 2). The other sites in which it has not been refound in recent years are Gamlingay Wood, TL25G, Buff Wood, TL25V, Hildersham Hall, TL54P and Wicken Fen, TL57Q. It was first recorded in the extant sites of Hayley Wood and Chippenham Fen in 1966, in Eversden Wood in 1964 and in Hardwick Wood in 1991.

Autoicous. Capsules seen at Eversden Wood (20% tetrads); immature February.

# BRYOPSIDA

## ENCALYPTACEAE

### Encalypta streptocarpa

The only recent occurrences of this calcicolous species in the wild are on chalky soils in beech woods near Royston, TL34Q, and on the Gog Magog Hills, TL45X. At the Gogs Beechwood reserve, which was planted on arable land *c*. 1840, it grows with *Porella platyphylla*, *Ctenidium molluscum* and *Hypnum cupressiforme*. *E. streptocarpa* also persists (with *Fissidens dubius*) on north-facing Carboniferous limestone rocks in Cambridge Botanic Garden, TL45N; it was recorded on these rocks soon after they were imported from Westmorland in the 1950s (Preston & Whitehouse 1992b).

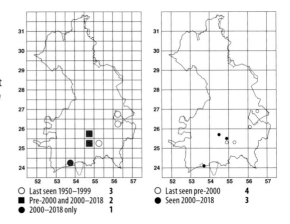

O Last seen 1950–1999   3
■ Pre-2000 and 2000–2018   2
● 2000–2018 only   1

O Last seen pre-2000   4
● Seen 2000–2018   3

First record: On ground under beeches by Cambridge–Newmarket road west of Devil's Dyke, TL66A, M.C.F. Proctor, 1951 (*Whitehouse species file*). Proctor discovered it in the Gogs beechwood a few days later (BBSUK). It was subsequently recorded on chalky ground under beeches near Wormwood Hill, Wandlebury, TL45W, by the Roman Road, TL45X, and at Chippenham Fen, TL66P. Outside beechwoods, it was known from a north-facing chalk bank in the old railway cutting at Worsted Lodge, TL55G, and as a few stems on introduced limestone rocks at 11 Chaucer Road, Cambridge, TL45N. In western Britain and Ireland it has a wider ecological range, and is often found on the mortar of old walls and bridges.

Dioicous. Capsules not recorded and very rare nationally; filamentous gemmae abundant in the leaf axils (Whitehouse 1964).

### Encalypta vulgaris

The two recent records of *Encalypta vulgaris* are from the top of the chalky railway cutting on the north side of the railway west of Mill Road, Great Wilbraham, TL55N, and (vegetative shoots) from disturbed chalky soil where scrub has been cleared on the Devil's Dyke south of the A1304 road, TL66F.

First record: Gog Magog Hills, TL45SE, Relhan (1785: 402, as *Bryum extinctorium*). The species has apparently been lost from this area, although it was known from several sites in the 20th century including under beeches at Wandlebury, TL45W (1957), the Gogs Beechwood reserve, TL45X (where it grew with *E. streptocarpa* and was recorded on at least nine occasions between 1951 and 1979), Cherry Hinton chalk pit, TL45Y (1986) and the banks of the old railway near Worsted Lodge, TL55G (1932–60). At the Devil's Dyke the only earlier records were in 1950 (two capsules only) and 1958. The decrease in Cambridgeshire reflects a wider decline in both Britain and Ireland (Blockeel *et al.* 2014).

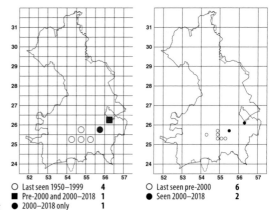

○ Last seen 1950–1999  4
■ Pre-2000 and 2000–2018  1
● 2000–2018 only  1

○ Last seen pre-2000  6
● Seen 2000–2018  2

Autoicous. Capsules usually present (only seen at one of the two recent sites but most earlier records are of fruiting plants); immature November.

## FUNARIACEAE

### *Funaria hygrometrica*
A weed of nutrient-rich, open or disturbed ground, including soil in infrequently tended garden beds, lightly trampled ground, asphalt and gravel paths and the cracks between paving stones, clinker at the edge of railway tracks, stream and lake dredgings, areas disturbed by animals (e.g. anthills, badger and rabbit diggings) and bonfire sites. It was found in 37 of the 76 arable fields recorded for the SBAL project, and it is a common weed of plant pots in gardens and garden centres. It can turn up occasionally on other substrates, such as moist concrete, tree bases and rotting wood. It reproduces and spreads by spores, readily colonising new sites. The even distribution across the county suggests that it does not have any marked soil preferences, and is recorded over chalk, clay, peat, sand and silt.

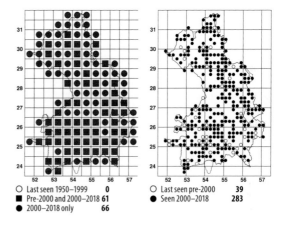

○ Last seen 1950–1999  0
■ Pre-2000 and 2000–2018  61
● 2000–2018 only  66

○ Last seen pre-2000  39
● Seen 2000–2018  283

First record: Hinton Moor, TL45NE, J. Davies (Ray 1696: 32, as *Adiantum medium palustre, foliis bulbi in modum se amplexantibus, capitulis erectis*; see Appendix 2). The plant was described by Vernon; unlocalised specimens from Leonard Plukenet's and Adam Buddle's herbaria (BM; Herb. Sloane 104 f. 49, 115 f. 33) confirm that this name was applied to *Funaria hygrometrica*. J. Martyn (1727a: 5, as *Bryum capitulis reflexis pyriformibus, calyptra quadrangulari foliis in bulbi formam congestis*) cited no localities but T. Martyn (1763: 24, as *Bryum hygrometricum*) published his father's records from Moor Barns Grove, TL45E, and Madingley Wood, TL35/45. There are several early 19th-century specimens including Skrimshire's which grew at Wisbech, TF41K, 'on my Garden Walk near the Arbour, at Bushy-Place' (1824, WBCH). Proctor (1956) described it as a very common weed and the quadrant map illustrates the improved coverage of Fenland in the recent survey. Records from Wicken Fen are sporadic, reflecting the occasional opening up of closed vegetation by fires in the 1930s and 1950s and scrub clearance more recently.

Autoicous. Capsules frequent (66% tetrads); often dehiscing asynchronously within a population and recorded in all months of the year.

### *Physcomitrium pyriforme*
Wet soil at the edge of rivers, streams, ditches, lakes and pools, dredgings dumped alongside such waters and wet, cattle-trampled soil in pastures. It is also recorded on peaty ground trampled by water buffalo at Chippenham Fen, TL66P, and in a flower bed by a lake in Cambridge Botanic Garden, TL45N, which had been flooded the previous winter. Associates include *Barbula unguiculata*, *Bryum dichotomum* and *Funaria hygrometrica* on dredgings, and *Bryum klinggraeffii* and *Pohlia melanodon* on cattle-trampled ditch sides.

First record: In water-filled ditches near Cambridge, W. Vernon, c. 1696 (Vernon's annotated Ray 1696: 29, as *Muscus capillaris parvus, capitulis magnis pyriformibus erectis, in pediculis brevibus*). Vernon noted that it fruited in May and June. Skrimshire's specimen from Walsoken Marsh (WBCH, as *Gymnostomum pyriforme*), cited by Proctor (1956) and Whitehouse (1964), is *Tortula modica* and was probably collected from vc 28. However, Relhan (1802: 424, as *Bryum py[ri]forme*) knew it from Cow [Coe] Fen, TL45N, Hinton Moor, TL45NE, and Moor Barns, TL45E. It was collected by Henslow from Coe Fen in 1825 and 1826 and by Lowe in 1834 (CGE), recorded there several times between 1941 and 1965 and refound in 2008. The 20th-century records, which are from similar habitats to the recent finds,

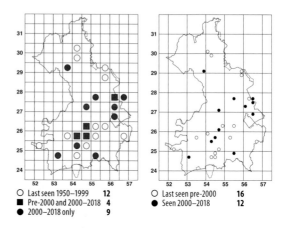

○ Last seen 1950–1999   **12**
■ Pre-2000 and 2000–2018   **4**
● 2000–2018 only   **9**

○ Last seen pre-2000   **16**
● Seen 2000–2018   **12**

suggest that the species has decreased in frequency and this is confirmed by the Frescalo analysis.

Autoicous. Usually only identified when fruiting (75% tetrads); capsules immature March–April, dehiscing May, June. The species is usually seen when fruiting in spring but a large population on the clayey bank of the River Lark at Isleham, TL67M, N, found in November 2008, was identified on the basis of the mature male inflorescences which were inconspicuous and had erecto-patent perigonial leaves and scarcely toothed basal marginal cells.

## Aphanorrhegma patens

A characteristic plant of winter-flooded, often cattle-trampled ground by lakes, ponds and ditches, on dredgings from rivers and ditches and in rutted lanes, depressions in gravel pits and hollows in arable fields. It is particularly frequent in washland areas (Ouse Washes, Nene Washes, Stanground Wash). It is a highly seasonal species, maturing in late summer and rarely seen after Christmas. It also varies in quantity from year to year; although favoured by dry summers, when water levels fall, it was difficult to find it in the Ouse Washes in the dry summer of 2006 except in shaded sites or deep hoofprints where the mud had remained sufficiently moist for it to grow to maturity. Its associates include *Riccia cavernosa*, *Bryum klinggraeffii*,

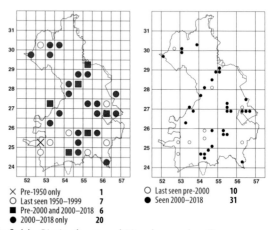

✕ Pre-1950 only   **1**
○ Last seen 1950–1999   **7**
■ Pre-2000 and 2000–2018   **6**
● 2000–2018 only   **20**

○ Last seen pre-2000   **10**
● Seen 2000–2018   **31**

*Leptobryum pyriforme*, *Pohlia melanodon* and, in arable fields, *Riccia glauca* and *Microbryum davallianum*. Like *Riccia cavernosa*, it has colonised newly created wetlands at Baker's Fen, Wicken, TL56U, and Kingfishers Bridge, TL57L. It is recorded over a range of soils including chalk, clay, peat, sand and silt.

First record: River bank, Grantchester, TL45H, J. Carpenter, 1941 (*Richards file*). The Ouse Washes populations were not discovered until 2002, as the site was scarcely visited by bryologists until then.

Paroicous or synoicous. Capsules usually present (93% tetrads), cleistocarpous; both immature and mature capsules seen between August and November, often mixed in the same population; disintegrating capsules seen in December.

## GRIMMIACEAE

### Schistidium crassipilum

*Schistidium crassipilum* is a plant of hard, exposed or shaded, base-rich substrates. It is recorded from churchyards in 84 tetrads (36% of tetrad records) and only from other sites in 152 (64%). In churchyards it usually grows on stonework, whereas in secular habitats concrete and cement are the usual habitats (62% of these tetrad records), with 9% from stonework, 9% from tarmac and 7% from asbestos roofs. It may be found on isolated concrete installations in otherwise arable landscapes. It also occurs occasionally on breeze blocks, brickwork, mortar and roof tiles, and we have single records from cobbles in a college courtyard, road chippings, an iron girder, an old telegraph pole edging a garden bed and as an epiphyte on a Conference pear, an elder and on exposed beech roots.

First record: Walls of Trumpington churchyard, TL45M, J.S. Henslow, 1821, CGE, as *Grimmia apocarpa* (see Appendix 2); still present in the churchyard in 2012. We have treated all Cambridgeshire *Schistidium* records as *S. crassipilum* as all the material we have checked is this species, which is much the commonest of the segregates of the *S. apocarpum* aggregate in southern England. It is more sensitive to $SO_2$ pollution than *Grimmia pulvinata* (Gilbert 1968, 1970) and it has increased in frequency and in habitat range in Cambridgeshire in recent decades. There were few mid 20th-century

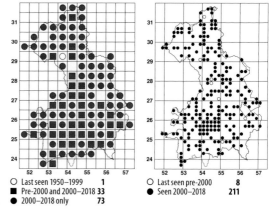

○ Last seen 1950–1999    1
■ Pre-2000 and 2000–2018   33
● 2000–2018 only        73

○ Last seen pre-2000     8
● Seen 2000–2018    211

records from Cambridge, although it was recorded regularly from the nearby Trumpington churchyard. It now occurs in numerous sites from the notional centre of the city, Great St Mary's churchyard, TL45P, outwards. The Frescalo analysis shows a marked increase since the 1980s.

Autoicous. Capsules very frequent (69% tetrads). The capsules follow a strict seasonal pattern, young green capsules developing slowly and synchronously from the autumn until they dehisce in March and April. Colonies often fruit freely but extensive swards can sometimes be found with very few fruits.

## Grimmia pulvinata

Very common on well-illuminated, dry, neutral and calcareous brickwork, stonework and concrete, particularly on wall tops, and on asbestos and tile roofs. It is usually confined to horizontal or sloping surfaces and, unlike *Tortula muralis*, it never seems to grow on the vertical sides of walls. It is recorded as an epiphyte in 72 tetrads, usually growing as small, isolated (but fruiting) tufts on exposed trees and shrubs. Most records are from apple (20% of tetrad records), elder (16%), ash (12%), willow (11%), pear (9%), hawthorn (6%) and poplar (5%), with 1–3 records from the species listed in Appendix 3. In orchards Robin Stevenson recorded it from a remarkable 222 (23%) of the 951 apple trees he surveyed and 31 (18%) of the 173 pears. It is also

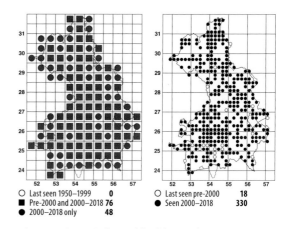

○ Last seen 1950–1999    0
■ Pre-2000 and 2000–2018   76
● 2000–2018 only       48

○ Last seen pre-2000    18
● Seen 2000–2018    330

recorded on a chalk quarry face, old planks and railway sleepers, iron girders, old rubberised matting, rotting wood, road chippings, dumped tarmac, gravel paths and the thatched top of a wall in Whittlesey, TL29T. It is a rapid colonist, commonly occurring on new substrates in suburbia and expanding villages.

First record: On walls everywhere, J. Martyn (1729b: 13, as *Bryum trichoides, hirsutie canescens, capitulis subrotundis, reflexis, in perbrevibus pediculis*); published without the habitat detail by T. Martyn (1763: 24, as *Bryum pulvinatum*). The first localised record was from Wisbech, TF40NE, in 1795 (WBCH) where Skrimshire described it as common. *G. pulvinata* remained common in Cambridge even during the period of maximum $SO_2$ pollution, and M.O.H. described a colony on Silver Street in 1965 growing on a concrete wall top in 'a really filthy place' and with its tufts 'filled with black dirt'. This ties in with its relative tolerance of $SO_2$ pollution in the Tyne valley at the period, when it persisted on asbestos roofs and concrete into the outer suburbs of Newcastle upon Tyne (Gilbert 1968, 1970). The records assembled by Whitehouse for the 1964 account include just one occurrence of *G. pulvinata* growing as an epiphyte, on the base of an elm in Cambridge, TL45J, and this was sufficiently surprising for the finder, M.C.F. Proctor, to note that despite the unusual habitat the plant was certainly this species. It has clearly increased in such habitats.

Autoicous. Capsules are almost always abundant (96% tetrads) and vary in age within a single tuft. We have no detailed observations of the time of dehiscence, but more detailed studies suggest that this takes place between April and July (Miles *et al.* 1989, Duckett & Pressel 2017), with the old capsules persisting for almost a year.

## Grimmia trichophylla

*Grimmia trichophylla* grows with fruiting *Dicranoweisia cirrata* on a rock from Cheviot in Boxworth churchyard, a memorial to R.C. Parker (d. 1955) and M. Parker (d. 1968). This colony, which in 2003 comprised 18 small tufts, may have been introduced on the acidic stone on which it grows.

First record: Boxworth churchyard, TL36M, C.D.P., 1992, CGE and R.D. Porley and C.D.P., 2003, BBSUK, conf. E. Maier. This is the only confirmed site in the county for the calcifuge *G. trichophylla sens. str.*; all other records are attributable to *G. lisae* or *G. dissimulata*, other members of the *G. trichophylla* aggregate (Porley *et al.* 2004).

Dioicous. Capsules not recorded and rare nationally; gemmae present.

## Grimmia lisae

Known from two churchyards, Sawston, TL44Z, and Balsham, TL55V, growing on stone ledges along the church walls and at Sawston also on the flat tops of 18th- or perhaps 17th-century oolitic limestone gravestones (see Porley *et al.* 2004). A large patch of this species at Balsham grows on a south-facing ledge fully exposed to the sun, with *Bryum capillare*, *Grimmia pulvinata*, *Orthotrichum diaphanum* and *Syntrichia montana*. Additional associates at Sawston include *Didymodon vinealis*, *Pseudocrossidium revolutum* and *Tortula muralis*.

First record: Detached plants lying on a cushion of *Syntrichia montana* on north wall of Balsham church, TL55V, H.L.K. Whitehouse, 1993, CGE, det. M.O.H. This was initially identified as *G. trichophylla*. In 2003, following the taxonomic revision of this species, the plant was refound at Balsham (growing *in situ*) and discovered at Sawston, and the identity of this material confirmed by the *Grimmia* expert Eva Maier. The presence of *G. lisae* rather than *G. dissimulata* in these Cambridgeshire sites is surprising; the nearest English locality for *G. lisae* mapped by Blockeel *et al.* (2014) is West Stoke, West Sussex, although it was discovered at Westcliff-on-Sea, South Essex, in 2015. The species is known from rocks, especially on sunny sea cliffs, in south-west England and Wales and on waterside rocks in North Wales and Scotland.

Dioicous. Capsules not recorded in Britain.

## Grimmia dissimulata

As small clumps or larger mats on flat or gently sloping calcareous stonework in churchyards, growing on ledges along church walls, buttresses, monuments, the tops of chest tombs and the coping stones of churchyard walls. The monuments on which it grows date from the 18th century to the 1860s. It grows in sites which are fully exposed to the sun or shaded to various degrees, with a range of associates including *Bryum capillare*, *Didymodon rigidulus*, *D. vinealis*, *Grimmia pulvinata*, *Homalothecium sericeum*, *Orthotrichum anomalum*, *O. cupulatum*, *Syntrichia montana* and *Tortula muralis* (Porley *et al.* 2004). It also grows outside churchyards on a dry concrete wall top at Newton, TL44J, and on both mortar and brickwork of old walls in

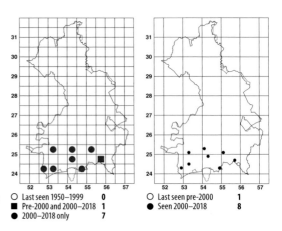

| | |
|---|---|
| ○ Last seen 1950–1999 | 0 |
| ■ Pre-2000 and 2000–2018 | 1 |
| ● 2000–2018 only | 7 |

| | |
|---|---|
| ○ Last seen pre-2000 | 1 |
| ● Seen 2000–2018 | 8 |

Babraham, TL55A. Colonies on church walls are vulnerable to the activities of excessively tidy parishioners, as at Linton, TL54T, where plants on a limestone window ledge had been scraped away between our visits in February 2002 and April 2003. At Haslingfield, TL45B, almost all the clumps discovered on a monument by M.O.H. in December 2002 had been dislodged by April 2003, in this case probably by birds seeking food in a very dry spring.

First record: Several brick walls and a brick-capped flint wall, Linton, TL54T, R.E. Parker, 1953 (*Whitehouse species file*, as *G. trichophylla*). Found by Parker immediately afterwards on a buttress at Linton church and a brick wall at Bartlow, TL54X; a specimen collected at Linton church later in 1953 by Mrs J. Appleyard is in NMW. *G. dissimulata* was confused with *G. trichophylla* until the species was described by E. Maier in 2002; material from Linton churchyard collected by R.D. Porley and C.D.P. in 2003 was kindly confirmed as this species by Maier. We have not rediscovered the plants found by Parker on walls in Linton and Bartlow villages.

Dioicous. Capsules not recorded in Britain.

## Racomitrium

The first report of the calcifuge genus *Racomitrium* in the county is Relhan's (1820) record of *R. canescens* (as *Trichostomum canescens*) on sandy, wet places at Gamlingay Heath, TL25SW. Unfortunately this taxon is now known to comprise three species and it is impossible to know which of these grew at Gamlingay; two of them, *R. elongatum* and *R. canescens*, are recorded from Breckland in Norfolk and Suffolk. The three species reported below are frequent on acidic substrates in northern and western Britain. They were all discovered on clinker at Madingley on 11 February 1961 by S.J.P. Waters. Other calcifuges here included *Atrichum undulatum*, *Mnium hornum*, *Pohlia nutans* and *Polytrichastrum formosum*. Whitehouse (1962) concluded that they had colonised the clinker (which was imported from the London area *c.* 1952) as wind-blown spores. The records below combine the original record with a count of the number of tufts made by Whitehouse when he revisited the site with Waters and J.H. Dickson on 20 May 1961. The filter-bed on which they were recorded has long since gone.

### †*Racomitrium heterostichum*

First and only record: One tuft on clinker on outside wall on north-east side of filter-bed, Madingley Hall sewage works, TL36V, S.J.P. Waters, 1961, BBSUK; later confirmed as *R. heterostichum sens. str.* by T.L. Blockeel (1991).
    Dioicous. Capsules not recorded.

### †*Racomitrium lanuginosum*

First record: Two groups of tufts on clinker on outside wall on north and north-west sides of filter-bed, Madingley Hall sewage works, TL36V, S.J.P. Waters, 1961, BBSUK. The only later record is from a horizontal concrete surface near ground level on the north side of Sawston Hall, TL44Z, where it was found by I.M. Turner in 1984 (CGE, NMW) but was not refound in 2001. The Sawston plant had rather short hair-points and was initially misidentified as *Grimmia trichophylla* (Whitehouse 1985).
    Dioicous. Capsules not recorded.

### †*Racomitrium ericoides*

First and only record: One group of tufts on clinker on outside wall on north-north-west side of filter-bed, Madingley Hall sewage works, TL36V, S.J.P. Waters, 1961, BBSUK, as *R. canescens* [*sens. lat.*]; later determined as *R. ericoides* by M.O.H. (Hill 1984).
    Dioicous. Capsules not recorded.

## SELIGERIACEAE

### *Seligeria calycina*

A tiny rupestral species with very fine leaves which give its patches a felt-like appearance and distinguish it from *S. calcarea*. Unlike that species, it is confined to detached lumps of chalk. These may be found on old spoil banks in chalk quarries, earthworks and old clunch pits, and in nearby hedgerows, scrub and secondary woodland. It also grows on chalk lumps in grassland on Fleam Dyke, TL55, and it is locally frequent on both loose and half-buried stones in grassland on both the north- and south-facing slopes of the Devil's Dyke, TL56, 65 and 66, as well as in nearby scrub.

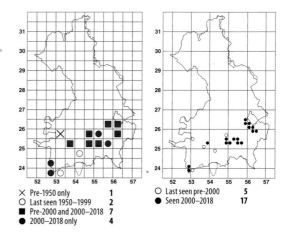

| | |
|---|---|
| ✕ Pre-1950 only | 1 |
| ○ Last seen 1950–1999 | 2 |
| ■ Pre-2000 and 2000–2018 | 7 |
| ● 2000–2018 only | 4 |
| ○ Last seen pre-2000 | 5 |
| ● Seen 2000–2018 | 17 |

    First record: On pieces of chalk protruding from surface deep among the grass tussocks, Devil's Dyke, frequent, E.W. Jones, 1932, NMW. The ability of this species to survive in overgrown habitats has presumably enabled it to persist when many chalk species of more open habitats have declined.
    Autoicous. Capsules usually present (all tetrads). Emergent setae noted October, December–February, green capsules December–April but one population seen in November had emergent setae and both green and freshly dehisced capsules.

## Seligeria calcarea

On chalk rock and large detached chalk boulders in chalk quarries and on steep-sided road cuttings, as well as on chalk stones in the open and in scrub in active and disused chalk pits and (rarely) on friable, recently disturbed chalk soil in chalk pits. It is much rarer than *S. calycina* on chalk in grassland on the Devil's Dyke, TL56W. We have also found it on lumps of oolitic limestone fallen from a balcony at Longstowe Hall, TL35C, and on hard, shaded stone at the base of steps leading down to the crypt at Westry church, TL39Z.

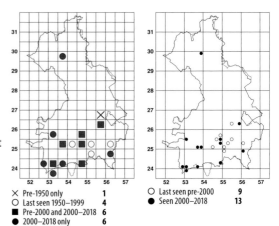

| | | |
|---|---|---|
| ✕ Pre-1950 only | | 1 |
| ○ Last seen 1950–1999 | | 4 |
| ■ Pre-2000 and 2000–2018 | | 6 |
| ● 2000–2018 only | | 6 |
| | | |
| ○ Last seen pre-2000 | | 9 |
| ● Seen 2000–2018 | | 13 |

First record: On chalky rocks near Newmarket Heath, TL66, Dickson (1790: 3, as *Bryum calcareum*), the first British record. Smith (1794) gave the finders as Dickson and the Norfolk botanist James Crowe. Relhan (1793: 9) reported the species from chalk pits by Gog Magog Hills, TL45SE, and at Babraham, and Henslow collected it (as *Weissia calcarea*) from chalk pits in Reach, TL56NE, in 1822 (CGE). It was still present in the chalk pit at Babraham, TL55A, in 1964. The sites at which this species has not been refound in the recent survey include a few small chalk pits as well as Fleam Dyke, TL55M (last seen 1998) and two places where it grew on masonry. It was seen on oolitic limestone fallen from a wall at Pampisford Hall, TL54E, in 1990 and on detached masonry on the south side of the church at West Wratting, TL65B, in 1988.

Autoicous. Capsules very frequent (85% tetrads). Immature capsules noted October–February, colonies with a mixture of green, brown and freshly dehisced capsules December–January, a mixture of immature and mature capsules in March and freshly dehisced capsules in March.

## Seligeria donniana

Recorded twice, on a chalk pebble in a rabbit hole in south-facing chalk grassland on the Devil's Dyke, where R.J. Fisk added it to the county list in a serendipitous piece of bryological fieldwork in 2005, and covering many square centimetres on the vertical, north-facing side of a table tomb in Stetchworth churchyard, with *Fissidens gracilifolius* and *Tortula muralis*, TL65P, where it was found by N. Jardine in 2009.

First record: Devil's Dyke, TL66A, R.J. Fisk, 2005, BBSUK.

Autoicous. Capsules seen at both sites; swollen and green at Stetchworth in March, dehiscing on the Devil's Dyke in February.

## ARCHIDIACEAE

### †*Archidium alternifolium*

First and only record: Gamlingay Bogs, TL25SW, Relhan (1788: 18, as *Phascum alternifolium*). In a letter to J.E. Smith (5 September 1800), Relhan says it was 'found by me on Gamlingay Bogs, and shown there to Mr. Griffith' (*Smith letters*). Mr Griffith was presumably the bryologist and lichenologist J. Wynne Griffith of Garn near Denbigh. *A. alternifolium* is a northern and western species in Britain; it has been lost from numerous sites along the fringes of its range.

## FISSIDENTACEAE

### *Fissidens*

As with other genera, we have taken information on the sexuality of *Fissidens* species from standard reference works, summarised by Blockeel *et al.* (2014). According to the books, several of the smaller species (*F. exilis, F. gracilifolius, F. incurvus, F. viridulus*), in addition to being autoicous or sometimes synoicous, are sometimes dioicous. We have not examined the sexuality of the Cambridgeshire plants systematically, but casual observations suggest that they are usually autoicous. The occurrence in the county of dioicous populations of such freely fruiting species seems unlikely, and we have omitted reference to the dioicous states.

### *Fissidens viridulus*

*Fissidens viridulus* is most frequent on chalky and clayey soil on river, stream and ditch banks, sometimes extending onto streamside dredgings. Another characteristic habitat is soil in disused chalk and clunch pits or in scrub (or places where scrub has been cleared) on chalk earthworks, including disturbed soil around rabbit burrows or badger setts. It is also recorded from clay soil in brick pits, and soil in ancient woodland, on rutted woodland rides, in plantations, on trackside banks, paths and the vertical cut edges of lawns. It sometimes grows with *F. incurvus*, and in mixed stands it clearly differs from that species in its smaller fronds and smaller as well as erect capsules which appear to mature slightly earlier.

First record: Clay bank in an old railway cutting, Babraham, TL55F, M.C.F. Proctor, 1951 (*Whitehouse species file*; see Appendix 2). Proctor (1956) knew of no further records, but it was found in a further four sites in 1957 and it has been recorded frequently since then.

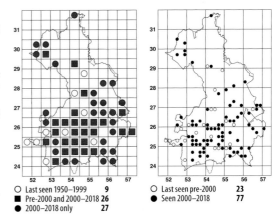

○ Last seen 1950–1999 **9**
■ Pre-2000 and 2000–2018 **26**
● 2000–2018 only **27**

○ Last seen pre-2000 **23**
● Seen 2000–2018 **77**

Autoicous or synoicous. Only identifiable in fruit; capsules are produced copiously, immature November–April, dehiscing October–April.

## Fissidens gracilifolius

On pieces of chalk in scrub and woodland on chalk earthworks, in old chalk pits and in disused railway cuttings, and on the deeply shaded stonework and brickwork at the base of church walls and on the north-facing side of tombs.

First record: On old bricks under trees in disused railway cutting, Babraham, TL55F, D.E. Coombe and M.C.F. Proctor, 1951, BBSUK. In the next 30 years only three further sites were discovered (cf. Crompton & Whitehouse 1983), but more systematic coverage of churchyards resulted in more records from 1988 onwards.

Autoicous. Capsules very frequent (73% tetrads); immature October, dehiscing October, December–February(–March).

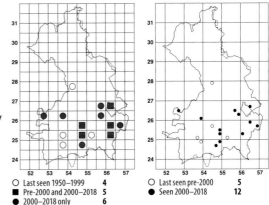

○ Last seen 1950–1999 **4**
■ Pre-2000 and 2000–2018 **5**
● 2000–2018 only **6**

○ Last seen pre-2000 **5**
● Seen 2000–2018 **12**

## Fissidens incurvus

The commonest small *Fissidens* species in the county, found on soil in ancient woodland and recent plantations, on river, stream and ditch banks, in open chalk grassland and chalk scrub, disused clay, chalk and gravel pits and in stubble and set-aside fields, grass leys, the vertical cut edges of lawns and neglected flower beds. It is most frequent on clay and chalky soils and rarely if ever seen on peat. Eight of the 10 SBAL fields in which we found it were on clay soils. It often grows with the larger *F. taxifolius*, which is very similar in its habitat requirements but fruits much less freely.

First record: Near Cambridge, TL45, J.S. Henslow, 1821, CGE (as *Dicranum bryoides*), det. M.O.H. and C.D.P. It was not recognised as a species distinct from *F. bryoides* until much later (see Appendix 2 under *F. bryoides*). When he found it in Kingston Wood, TL35SW, in 1914 the undergraduate A.W. Graveson modestly noted in his diary 'not recorded from Cambridgeshire so may be a mistake', but his identification was surely correct (it still grows in the wood). The first record of the modern era was made by P.W. Richards and T.G. Tutin at Over Wood, TL64J, in 1932 (NMW) and it was still present there in 2006.

○ Last seen 1950–1999 **1**
■ Pre-2000 and 2000–2018 **39**
● 2000–2018 only **64**

○ Last seen pre-2000 **15**
● Seen 2000–2018 **170**

Autoicous. Only identifiable in fruit; capsules are produced abundantly, immature October–March, dehiscing December–April.

### *Fissidens bryoides* var. *bryoides*

Although *Fissidens bryoides* is a very frequent species in much of Britain, its occurrence in Cambridgeshire is restricted by its requirement for base-poor soils (pH 5.0–5.4 has been measured at four sites in the county). It is concentrated in the ancient boulder-clay woods, where it grows on soil on the woodland floor and on banks, by paths and on ditch sides. It is more frequent on the sandier Boulder Clay of the eastern woods than in the west. It is also recorded from beech plantations and sandy streamsides in southern Cambridgeshire. At its isolated Fenland sites it grows in three disused clay pit complexes, Whittlesey, TL29N, Lattersey LNR, TL29Y, and Gray's Moor Pits, TF40A, and on a ditch side near Tydd St Giles, TF31X.

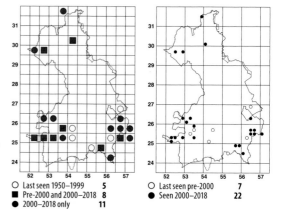

| | |
|---|---|
| ○ Last seen 1950–1999 | 5 |
| ■ Pre-2000 and 2000–2018 | 8 |
| ● 2000–2018 only | 11 |

| | |
|---|---|
| ○ Last seen pre-2000 | 7 |
| ● Seen 2000–2018 | 22 |

First record: Borley Wood, TL54NE, E.F. Warburg, 1943; still present here in 2006. Until well into the 1930s the commoner *F. incurvus* was included in the concept of *F. bryoides* (see Appendix 2) and Proctor (1956) was insufficiently ruthless in purging the records of the latter. Whitehouse (1964) was the first to appreciate how uncommon *F. bryoides* is in calcareous Cambridgeshire.

Autoicous. Capsules very frequent (86% tetrads); immature November–February, dehiscing February–April.

A population of *Fissidens* grew with *Rhynchostegiella teneriffae* on the damp, highly shaded brickwork of a tunnel carrying a stream into Newnham Mill Pond, Cambridge, TL45N. Specimens collected in 1985 and 1991 by C.D.P. and H.L.K. Whitehouse have been examined by M.F.V. Corley and M.O.H. who have been unable to identify them as any species other than *F. bryoides*. However, the habitat is so unlikely for this species that we suspect that they must represent some other taxon. We have been unable to revisit the locality recently as it is only accessible when the water level in the River Cam is lowered by the Conservators.

### *Fissidens crassipes*

An aquatic species, growing on concrete, stonework, brickwork or (rarely) on ironwork, stones and tree bases at or near the normal water level, sometimes in deeply shaded sites such as the underside of concrete culverts. All recent records are from the Cam valley, where it grows by a clear, canalised chalk stream in Melbourn village, TL34X, and further down the valley on the side of the sluggish, eutrophic River Cam and its rather more rapidly flowing sluices and tributaries. The largest population we know is at the Mill Pit, Mill Lane, Cambridge, TL45P, where large masses grow in the rapidly flowing waters of a sluice. At most sites it is present in much smaller quantity.

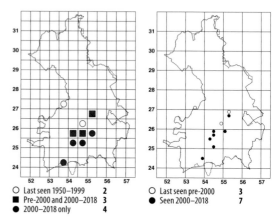

| | |
|---|---|
| ○ Last seen 1950–1999 | 2 |
| ■ Pre-2000 and 2000–2018 | 3 |
| ● 2000–2018 only | 4 |

| | |
|---|---|
| ○ Last seen pre-2000 | 3 |
| ● Seen 2000–2018 | 7 |

First record: On brick walls in the water, in ditch and in the main stream, The Backs, Cambridge, TL45P, P.W. Richards, 1928, NMW. By 1937 Richards reported that the species was extinct at the first site where he had seen it, St John's College, but survived elsewhere (*BBS ledger*). M.O.H. noted its continued presence along The Backs in 1965. The only record outside the Cam valley is from the stonework of a sluice near Swavesey, TL37K, in 1961. Its apparent absence from other Fenland sites is surprising.

Described as dioicous, autoicous or rarely synoicous. Capsules frequent (43% tetrads); immature November, dehiscing March.

## Fissidens exilis

*Fissidens exilis* is the smallest and most inconspicuous of the county's *Fissidens* species, but its numerous, tiny fruits attract attention even when they are found amongst the leaves of the much larger *F. taxifolius*, with which it often grows. It is found on patches of open soil in ancient woodland, often in areas where leaves do not accumulate such as banks, ditch sides and raised mounds formed by old rootplates, or in disturbed sites on deer tracks or the sides of rides and paths. It is a calcifuge, found on the more acidic or sandy Boulder Clays or in areas of surface acidification (pH 5.1 at Madingley Wood, TL35Z). Its requirement for non-calcareous soil explains its very strong association with ancient woodland (Preston & Hill 2016) but it is also recorded from stubble and set-aside fields on Ampthill Clay at Knapwell, TL36G, and Boxworth, TL36M, and from a recently exposed clay bank at Gray's Moor Pits, TF40A.

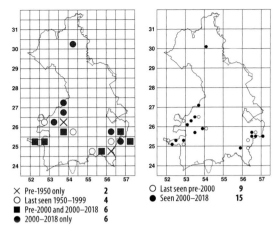

| | |
|---|---|
| ✕ Pre-1950 only | 2 |
| ○ Last seen 1950–1999 | 4 |
| ■ Pre-2000 and 2000–2018 | 6 |
| ● 2000–2018 only | 6 |

| | |
|---|---|
| ○ Last seen pre-2000 | 9 |
| ● Seen 2000–2018 | 15 |

First record: Abundant on clay on edges and in cleared parts, Over Wood, TL64J, P.W. Richards and T.G. Tutin, 1932, NMW. *F. exilis* has not suffered from the taxonomic confusion which has affected the recording of some of the county's other small *Fissidens* species. The very imperfect match between 20th- and 21st-century records is likely to be a result of the difficulty of refinding the species and its presumably rather transient occurrence in some of its disturbed microhabitats.

Autoicous. Only likely to be recorded in fruit; capsules brown and more or less mature December–March; dehiscing February–March.

## Fissidens taxifolius var. taxifolius

One of the most distinctive and frequent of the county's mosses, found on soil in primary and ancient secondary woodland, plantations, in scrub and chalk grassland, on river and stream banks, ditch sides, path sides, disused chalk, clay and gravel pits, in churchyards, cemeteries and gardens (where it grows in flower beds as well as less disturbed habitats) and in stubble and set-aside fields. It is equally frequent on acidic and basic soils but it rarely grows on peat and in Fenland it is often found on restricted areas of clay soil. It grew in 15 of the 76 SBAL fields we sampled, of which 10 were on clay. The pH readings ranged from 5.3 on sand at Gamlingay, TL25L, to 8.2 on chalky Boulder Clay at Croxton Park, TL25U.

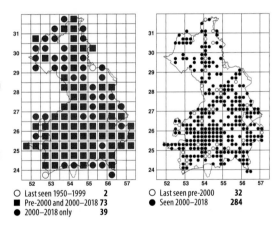

| | |
|---|---|
| ○ Last seen 1950–1999 | 2 |
| ■ Pre-2000 and 2000–2018 | 73 |
| ● 2000–2018 only | 39 |

| | |
|---|---|
| ○ Last seen pre-2000 | 32 |
| ● Seen 2000–2018 | 284 |

First record: Madingley Wood, W. Vernon, *c.* 1696 (Vernon's annotated Ray 1696: 35, as *Muscus Filicifolius seu pennatus minor, pinnulis plurimis ad mediam costam, latiusculis, crebris*). Vernon also recorded it from Cherry Hinton but this plant might have been *F. dubius*. The identity of the plant in Madingley Wood is more secure; Relhan (1820: 441, as *Dicranum taxifolium*) knew it here and it was still present in TL35Z and 45E in 2006. Rhodes (1911) described it as common and this is certainly true in the south of the county.

Autoicous. Capsules are less frequent than on the smaller terrestrial *Fissidens* (23% tetrads), swollen, green September–February; brown, January–February; dehiscing February–April. Tubers have been found on plants in set-aside fields at Gamlingay, TL25L, Graveley, TL26M, and Boxworth, TL36M, and in a field of rape direct-drilled into stubble at Conington, TL36I. However, most arable populations in Cambridgeshire appear to lack tubers; we looked for them in material from 14 fields in the SBAL survey and detected them in just two collections. Whitehouse (1966a) found that tuber-bearing material from Witchford, TL47Z, continued to produce tubers in cultivation, whereas plants without tubers cultivated from Madingley Wood remained tuberless.

## Fissidens dubius

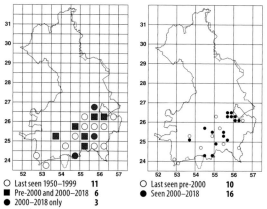

*Fissidens dubius* and *F. adianthoides* are closely related. On the Devil's Dyke, *F. dubius* grows in south-facing chalk grassland at its best site in the county (TL56, 66) whereas *F. adianthoides* is found in the more mesic, north-facing grassland and differs, even in the field, in having broader fronds and occasional fruits. The other native sites for *F. dubius* are in chalk grassland on Fleam Dyke, TL55M, in disused chalk pits and on chalky soil at the edge of an old lawn. Unusually, we found it growing as dense masses on the decaying stumps of old laburnum bushes in Crishall Grange Plantation, TL44L, and as a single patch on the trunk of a very mature elder in the railway cutting by Fleam Dyke,

○ Last seen 1950–1999  **11**
■ Pre-2000 and 2000–2018  **6**
● 2000–2018 only  **3**

○ Last seen pre-2000  **10**
● Seen 2000–2018  **16**

TL55M. It has survived for over 50 years on imported Carboniferous limestone rocks in Cambridge Botanic Garden, TL45N, and it also occurs on stonework by a calcareous stream at Swaffham Prior House, TL56R.

First record: Hildersham Furze Hill, TL54P, F.Y. Brocas, 1874, SWN. There is clear evidence for the decline of *F. dubius*, which appears to have been lost from the Furze Hills, where it was last recorded in 1952, as well as from the lawns at Hildersham Hall, TL54P, and Wandlebury, TL45W, and chalk grassland by the Roman Road on the Gog Magog Hills, TL45X, as well as from several chalk pits.

Autoicous or dioicous. Capsules not recorded in Cambridgeshire, although it fruits freely in some areas of Britain.

## Fissidens adianthoides

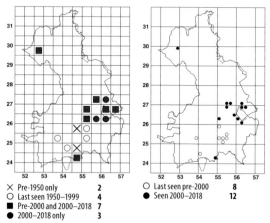

In addition to its occurrence in north-facing chalk grassland on the Devil's Dyke, TL56X, 66B, F, *Fissidens adianthoides* is also recorded on dry, chalky soil at Coploe Hill Pit, TL44W, Stow cum Quy Fen, TL56B and Fordham Church, TL67F. However, it is much more frequent in moist, calcareous wetlands, especially in open fen vegetation, fen carr and woodland at Wicken Fen, TL56P, 57K, Q and Chippenham Fen, TL66J, P. The isolated northern site is Bassenhally Pit, TL29Z, where it is found in a base-rich poolside marsh.

First record: Isle of Ely, W. Vernon, *c.* 1696 (Vernon's annotated Ray 1696: 35, as *Muscus Filicifolius seu pennatus, aquaticus maximus*). The next records were from Hinton Moor, TL45NE (Martyn 1763: 35, as *Hypnum adiantoides*), Sawston Moor,

✕ Pre-1950 only  **2**
○ Last seen 1950–1999  **4**
■ Pre-2000 and 2000–2018  **7**
● 2000–2018 only  **3**

○ Last seen pre-2000  **8**
● Seen 2000–2018  **12**

TL44NE, and Teversham Moor, TL55NW (Relhan 1820: 442, as *Dicranum adiantoides*), and these long-destroyed calcareous wetlands would presumably have provided an ideal habitat for this species. Like *Fissidens dubius*, *F. adianthoides* has also declined markedly in its chalkland sites; it has not been recorded recently from Fleam Dyke, TL54L, M, the Roman Road, TL55B and from several chalk pits.

Autoicous or dioicous. Capsules frequent (58% tetrads), recorded in both grassland and wetland habitats; swollen capsules turning brown in October, dehiscing in February.

## Fissidens fontanus

An aquatic, recorded at the side of the canalised River Nene in urban Peterborough, where it grows on concrete and wooden planks below the normal water level. It is a shade-tolerant species which grows under the large bridge which carries the A1139 over the river as well as in more open stretches. It has also been recorded in recent years in the River Nene in Northamptonshire (2007) and Huntingdonshire (2013), upstream of the Cambridgeshire sites.

First and only record: North side of River Nene, Peterborough, TL19Y, 29D, J.J. Graham and C.D. Preston, 2008, BBSUK.

Autoicous. Capsules not recorded in Britain. Small, easily detached branchlets 1.5–4 mm long found on the Cambridgeshire plants presumably act as a means of vegetative dispersal.

# DITRICHACEAE

## †*Pleuridium acuminatum*

A calcifuge, last seen in the county in the 1950s.

First record: Gamlingay, TL25SW, J.S. Henslow, 1827, CGE, unnamed, det. M.O.H. and C.D.P. (see Appendix 2). The only later native records are of plants occurring 'in small quantity only' on the turfy soil of a path across the brecks by Half Moon Plantation, Newmarket–Thetford road, TL66Z (E.W. Jones, 1934) and in a stubble field near White Wood, Gamlingay, TL25SW (M.C.F. Proctor, 1951). However, in 1955 Whitehouse found plants growing with *Ceratodon purpureus* on a pocket of earth on a Carboniferous limestone boulder imported to Cambridge Botanic Garden, TL45N, from Westmorland.

Paroicous. Capsules cleistocarpous, recorded December, January, April.

## †*Pleuridium subulatum*

A calcifuge, recorded from both the western and eastern fringe of the county but not seen since 1993.

First record: Abundant on bare clay in clearing, Little Widgham Wood, TL65S, P.W. Richards, 1946, NMW, conf. C.D.P. Never seen again at this site, but recorded from Gamlingay Wood, TL25L, on five occasions between 1957 and 1993, from Mount Pleasant Farm, Gamlingay, TL25F, in 1976 and in small quantity on sandy ground in a pit near Kennett, TL66Z, in 1966. The species is an ephemeral of open ground and it might well be refound at Gamlingay Wood after suitable soil disturbance.

Autoicous. Capsules cleistocarpous, green and immature, February.

## *Pseudephemerum nitidum*

Seen during the recent survey on disturbed soil from a newly redug ditch and pond at Great Heath Plantation, Gamlingay, TL25F, in 2002 and 2018, and on a muddy track in White Wood, Gamlingay, TL25A, in 2016.

First record: Wet slope in rough meadow, Mill Hill, Gamlingay, TL25F, P. Adam, J.C. Gardiner and M. Milnes-Smith, 1977, BBSUK. This site had been drained and ploughed by 1983, but *P. nitidum* was first found at Great Heath Plantation in 1988, growing with *Pohlia lescuriana* on the side of a newly-cut ditch.

Synoicous. Capsules cleistocarpous, seen at all sites, in October, December and March; in October they were immature, mature and breaking up.

## *Trichodon cylindricus*

Small plants are found in arable fields (wheat and barley stubbles, direct-drilled rape and game cover) on Oxford and Ampthill Clay, sandy Boulder Clay and peaty, gravelly, sandy and silty soils. It is markedly calcifuge. We found it in 15 of the 76 SBAL fields we surveyed, usually with a soil pH of 5.8–6.8 (10 sites) with outlying pH values of 5.3 (one site), 7.2–7.4 (three sites) and, surprisingly, 8.1 (a site on Fenland silt; this field presumably had patches of more acidic soil). Characteristic associates include *Bryum klinggraeffii*, *B. rubens*, *B. violaceum*, *Dicranella schreberiana*, *D. staphylina*, *Phascum cuspidatum* and *Tortula truncata*. The outlying southern site is on sandy soil at Thriplow, TL44M, perhaps the site of the former Thriplow Heath. *T. cylindricus* is rarely

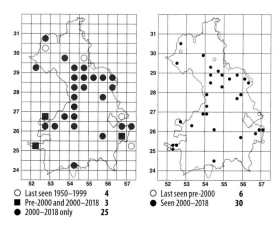

| | |
|---|---|
| ○ Last seen 1950–1999 | 4 |
| ■ Pre-2000 and 2000–2018 | 3 |
| ● 2000–2018 only | 25 |

| | |
|---|---|
| ○ Last seen pre-2000 | 6 |
| ● Seen 2000–2018 | 30 |

recorded on disturbed soil in other habitats, including sandy soil on the rootplate of a fallen tree in Gamlingay Heath Plantation, TL25F, the edge of a farm reservoir at Whittlesey, TL29M, and bare soil (perhaps an old molehill) on a track at Chatteris, TL48H.

First record: Stubble field near Bedlam farms, by March–Upwell road, TL49N, P.F. Lumley, 1960 (*Whitehouse species file*; see Appendix 2). Known to Crompton and Whitehouse (1983) from only five 10-km squares, but the recent survey has shown that it is much more frequent in Fenland than has hitherto been supposed.

Dioicous. Capsules not recorded and very rare nationally. Tubers always present, developing very early in the life-cycle and sometimes seen on plants which consist of a protonemal carpet with only a few small leafy shoots.

## Ditrichum gracile

An extremely rare plant of chalk grassland which is kept short by trampling, recorded alongside the paths on the top of Fleam Dyke, TL55M, and Devil's Dyke, TL66A.

First record: Short turf on chalk, Devil's Dyke, P.W. Richards, 1929, BBSUK. It has decreased in abundance at both its extant sites. It was described as frequent on the Devil's Dyke by E.W. Jones in 1933 and present in fair quantity by M.O.H. in 1966. Similarly P.W. Richards said that it was abundant on the northern part of Fleam Dyke in 1932 and M.O.H. found it 'locally in rather large quantity on bare patches … just to the Balsham side of the railway cutting' in 1966. It has apparently been lost from Eversden chalk pit, TL35R (rare in 1933), the Roman Road, Gog Magog Hills, TL55G (in several places according to Proctor 1956), and the banks of the old railway near Worsted Lodge, TL55G (abundant in 1932). *D. gracile* can be a frequent plant on open limestone substrates (e.g. in disused quarries) and it even colonises limestone chippings on forest tracks in western Britain and Ireland. Its decline in Cambridgeshire doubtless reflects its inability to persist in closed grassland swards. Cambridgeshire material is small and difficult to identify, but the modern material and available older specimens are *D. gracile* rather than *D. flexicaule* (Preston & Hill 2006), and we have assumed that all records refer to this segregate.

Dioicous. Capsules not recorded and not seen recently in Britain (see Blockeel *et al.* 2014).

## Ceratodon purpureus

*Ceratodon purpureus* is not as abundant in Cambridgeshire as it is in many areas where the geology is less calcareous. Nevertheless, it can normally be found without undue difficulty, especially in built-up areas, on dry, acidic substrates such as asphalt paths, rotting wood, old railway sleepers and telegraph poles, concrete, brickwork, metalwork, clinker, cinder tracks, sandstone tombstones and granite chippings on graves, disturbed sandy and gravelly ground and asbestos, felt, slate, thatch and tile roofs. It was locally abundant over a large area of the disused railway sidings at March, TL49E. Elsewhere we have seen only moderate quantities, except on thatched roofs where it may flourish in the toxic environment created by galvanised wire netting. It is sometimes found on soil or in pavement cracks subjected to repeated applications of herbicide. It colonises the rubber surrounding the windows of cars whose owners have better things to do than clean them, and discarded rubbish such as old mats and carpets and polypropylene rope. In the arable landscape it also grows in stubble fields, on the wooden planks of old farm trailers and on the occasional 'bog oak'. In stubble fields it is recorded on Ampthill and Gault Clay, Boulder Clay, peat and sandy loam, usually at pH 5.3–6.4 (eight sites) but, surprisingly, sometimes on more calcareous soils (pH 7.4–8.0, three sites). It was present in an open, moist, waterside community on the Corallian limestone (pH 8.0) at Kingfishers Bridge, TL57L, in 2001. It is an infrequent epiphyte, recorded from apple (33% of tetrad records), willow (22%), pear (17%), elder (11%) and once or twice on several other hosts (Appendix 3). In orchards Robin Stevenson recorded it on 107 (11%) of the 951 apple trees he examined and 52 (30%) of the 173 pears.

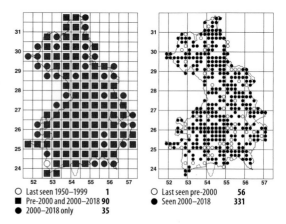

| | | |
|---|---|---|
| ○ Last seen 1950–1999 | 1 | |
| ■ Pre-2000 and 2000–2018 | 90 | |
| ● 2000–2018 only | 35 | |

| | | |
|---|---|---|
| ○ Last seen pre-2000 | 56 | |
| ● Seen 2000–2018 | 331 | |

First record: Relhan (1785: 399, as *Mnium purpureum*). Henslow collected fruiting plants at Gamlingay in 1838 (CGE), the first localised record. It is less abundant now in Cambridge than it was in the 1960s when Hill (1967) described it as 'especially abundant in urban habitats' and noted that it would even colonise calcareous substrates such as 'smoke-covered limestone' in towns.

Dioicous. Capsules frequent (35% tetrads); young setae may be visible from October onwards and can usually be seen from December to March; capsules swell from February onwards and approach maturity in April; recorded once as dehisced in June.

# RHABDOWEISIACEAE

## Dicranoweisia cirrata

*Dicranoweisia cirrata* grows as an epiphyte, on rotting wood and, much less frequently, on brickwork and acidic stonework. As an epiphyte it is recorded, often as small tufts, on apple (15% of tetrad records), willow

(14%), hawthorn (13%), ash (9%), *Prunus* (7%), pear (7%), birch (7%) and oak (5%). It is notably rare on elder (3%) and field maple (1%) but it occurs on a wide range of other hosts, many of them exotics (Appendix 3). It is more frequent in open habitats than in sheltered and shaded woodland sites. It is common in orchards, recorded from 407 (43%) of the 951 apple trees surveyed by Robin Stevenson and 120 (69%) of the 173 pear trees. On rotting wood it is very much commoner on artefacts in the open than on decaying stumps and logs in woodland, growing on fence rails, gate posts and old notice boards and crosses in churchyards, as well as on old railway sleepers, stacked telegraph poles and the planks of abandoned farm trailers. On horizontal wooden surfaces its large clumps may

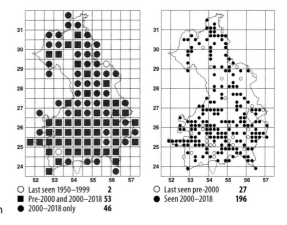

| | |
|---|---|
| ○ Last seen 1950–1999 | 2 |
| ■ Pre-2000 and 2000–2018 | 53 |
| ● 2000–2018 only | 46 |

| | |
|---|---|
| ○ Last seen pre-2000 | 27 |
| ● Seen 2000–2018 | 196 |

grow together into extensive patches. It is rare on sandstone stonework and tombstones and on brick walls.

First record: Gamlingay, TL25SW, J.S. Henslow, no date, CGE, unnamed by Henslow. It was unknown to Rhodes (1911) but Paul Richards found it on a walnut tree at Trinity College in 1929 and it was recorded frequently thereafter. In the 1960s and 1970s, when the epiphyte flora of the county was very poor, this was the commonest specialist epiphyte, described by Whitehouse (1964) as 'abundant on tree-trunks and wooden palings'. *D. cirrata* was favoured by high levels of SO$_2$ pollution which give it a physiological advantage over other species (Adams & Preston 1992). It has decreased since the 1970s and other epiphytes have increased, so that it is certainly less common now than *Orthotrichum affine*. Before 1900 most British records were from rocks, walls or thatch (Hill *et al.* 1992) and it appears to have spread later as an epiphyte in response to acidification. In very recent years we have increasingly found it only on rotting wood, suggesting that it may be retreating to its original habitat. Excluding orchard occurrences, 64% of records (and 64% of tetrad occurrences) with habitat details were of epiphytic plants in 2001–2005; the figures were similar in 2006–2010 (61% records, 58% tetrads) but fell to 30% of records (32% tetrads) in 2011–2015. A population still persists on the sandstone porch of Gamlingay church, TL25L, where it was first recorded in 1960.

Monoicous. Capsules usually present (91% tetrads), immature October–March, dehiscing January–April. Gemmae usually present, often frequent, arising in a band near the base of the abaxial sides of the leaves.

## DICRANACEAE

### *Dicranella schreberiana*

Most records of *Dicranella schreberiana* are from stubble fields or other arable habitats (such as rape direct-drilled into stubble or game strips alongside cereal fields). However, it also grows on disturbed soil in woodland, grassland and churchyards, sand and gravel pits, on mud by ponds, ditch sides, stream dredgings and by flooded chalk and clay pits, around rabbit burrows and on paths and disused railway sidings. It tolerates some winter-flooding (e.g. in *Lythrum hyssopifolia* hollows). We found it in 22 of the 76 SBAL fields we surveyed, growing on a range of soils, including Ampthill, Gault, Oxford and Boulder Clays, chalk, sandy loam, sand and silt, at pH 5.3–8.1 but usually 6.8–8.1 (16 sites). It is rare on peat, although we have seen tiny plants on damp peat by the lake at Kingfisher's Bridge, TL57L.

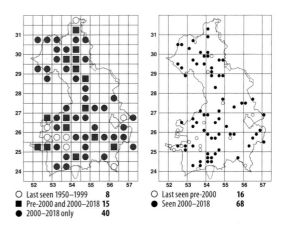

| | |
|---|---|
| ○ Last seen 1950–1999 | 8 |
| ■ Pre-2000 and 2000–2018 | 15 |
| ● 2000–2018 only | 40 |

| | |
|---|---|
| ○ Last seen pre-2000 | 16 |
| ● Seen 2000–2018 | 68 |

First record: Edge of drain, Burrow Moor, March, TL39X, BBSUK, and side of dyke, Chainbridge–March road, TL49J, B. Reeve, 1959 (see Appendix 2). This is an exceptionally late first record for a species which is widespread in the county and has long been known to British bryologists (Preston 2006). Whitehouse (1964) described it as rare in the county but it was almost certainly overlooked along with other small, tuber-bearing species.

Dioicous. Capsules rare (4% tetrads). Tubers are always present on the rhizoids and occasionally also in the lower leaf axils.

## Dicranella varia

Dicranella varia is most characteristically found on moist, calcareous soils, particularly chalk and clay, as on the sides of lakes, ponds, rivers, streams, springs and ditches, on waterside dredgings, in ruts on woodland rides, and in brick pits and flooded gravel pits. It sometimes grows in abundance on the wet floors of active chalk pits. However, it also grows on drier calcareous soil in a range of other habitats, including stubble and set-aside fields and strips of game cover, anthills, molehills and other disturbed sites in grassland, around badger setts and rabbit burrows, on sparsely vegetated soil in chalk pits, chalk rubble and limestone chippings, newly dug graves in churchyards and on paths and tracks. There is one record from shaded brickwork.

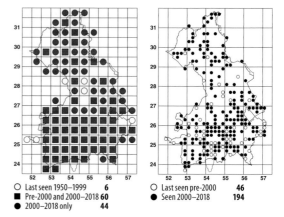

| | |
|---|---|
| ○ Last seen 1950–1999 | 6 |
| ■ Pre-2000 and 2000–2018 | 60 |
| ● 2000–2018 only | 44 |
| ○ Last seen pre-2000 | 46 |
| ● Seen 2000–2018 | 194 |

Its preference for calcareous soils is shown by its occurrence at pH 7.0–8.1(–8.6) in 23 SBAL sites, with three records at pH 5.8–6.3 on less basic clays. *Pohlia melanodon* is a frequent associate.

First record: Relhan (1785: 407, as *Bryum simplex*); he later (1820: 440, as *Dicranum varium*) specified the localities Gog Magog Hills, TL45SE, and Newmarket Heath, TL66SW. There are fruiting specimens from Henslow's herbarium collected from chalk at the source of Quy Water (1826) and from [Cherry] Hinton, TL45NE (1827). Rhodes (1911) recognised it as frequent in the chalk district, and Proctor (1956) as frequent on both chalky and clayey soils.

Dioicous. Capsules occasional (20% tetrads), with young setae January, February, capsules green October, brown but undehisced October–January, dehiscing and recently dehisced March, April. They are less frequent in arable fields (found in only one of the 24 SBAL fields) than in less disturbed places such as waterside habitats or in chalk or clay pits. Tubers sometimes present on mature plants, although they are not always found and are never abundant.

## Dicranella staphylina

This is predominantly a species of cultivated ground, including stubble fields, rape fields (including rape direct-drilled into stubble), game-cover and bird-seed mixes, vegetable crops (asparagus, cabbages, onions), set-aside fields and flower beds in domestic gardens. It also grows on disturbed soil in other situations, such as woodland rides, tracks and roadsides, disturbed areas in grassland, sandy ground in gravel pits, molehills and recently dug graves in churchyards and soil around rabbit burrows. It is most frequent on acidic soils but it grows in cultivated ground on all the soils in the county, including chalk and peat. It was present in 45 of the 76 SBAL fields we surveyed, including 96% of those on peat, sand and silt, 46% of those on

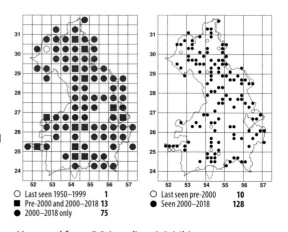

| | |
|---|---|
| ○ Last seen 1950–1999 | 1 |
| ■ Pre-2000 and 2000–2018 | 13 |
| ● 2000–2018 only | 75 |
| ○ Last seen pre-2000 | 10 |
| ● Seen 2000–2018 | 128 |

clay and loam but none of the five fields on chalk. The pH ranged from 5.3 (sand) to 8.2 (silt).

First record: Arable field, Thorney, TF20Q, P.J. Bourne, 1960 (NMW; see Appendix 2). The early records were published as *Dicranella rufescens* by Whitehouse (1964) and Hill (1967) recorded it under the pet-name *Dicranella 'pusilla'*. It was described as a new species, *Dicranella staphylina*, by Whitehouse (1969). Until the recent survey it was regarded as an uncommon calcifuge in the county, with the exception of its occurrence in the winter-flooded *Lythrum hyssopifolia* hollows in arable fields on chalk (Preston 1989, Crompton & Whitehouse 1983). The wider distribution revealed by the recent survey was a surprise. Whitehouse may not have begun to recognise it until most of the fieldwork for the 1964 flora had been completed, but Hill (1967) also regarded it as uncommon in Cambridgeshire and confined to lime-free soils. Its rapid production of numerous small tubers may have given it a competitive advantage in modern, intensively farmed arable fields.

Dioicous. Female inflorescences are sometimes seen on mature plants but male plants and sporophytes have not been seen in the county (male plants are rare nationally and sporophytes unknown in the wild). Tubers usually frequent or abundant on the rhizoids, and sometimes also found on robust, branched protonemata and on short rhizoids in the lower leaf axils; older plants (e.g. in set-aside fields) become straggly and often have only sparse tubers.

### †*Dicranella cerviculata*

A calcifuge, known only as an apparently short-lived colony at one site in the county where it was last seen in 1968.

First record: Under *Phragmites* by edge of path, Manea Pit, TL48Z, G. Crompton and F.H. Perring (vegetative) and J.H. Dickson (c. fr.), 1965, CGE, conf. M.O.H. It grew here with *Polytrichum commune, P. juniperinum* and *Pohlia nutans* (Whitehouse 1966b). Dickson's specimen is a large one, suggesting that the plant was locally abundant. It was refound in 1966 (BBSUK) and 1968 but has not been seen since.

Dioicous. Capsules recorded November.

### *Dicranella heteromalla*

In Cambridgeshire's woodlands *Dicranella heteromalla* is usually a very local plant, restricted to small areas of acidic ground, especially slightly raised areas at the base of beech and oak trees and on the rootplates and disturbed ground around fallen trees and rotting stumps. It is frequent on the ground and on banks only in those few woods on acidic soil, such as White Wood, Gamlingay, TL25A, B, and Gamlingay Heath Plantation, TL25F. It colonises plantations and shelter belts such as Six Acre Plantation, TL68E, a Fenland sycamore plantation over peat (pH 4.1). It even grows, like other calcifuges, at the base of beeches in the 19th-century beechwood on the chalk of the Gog Magog Hills, TL45X. Its non-woodland sites include ditch banks and banks of clay and sandy soil in disused brick pits.

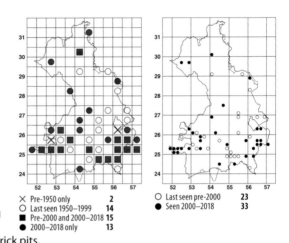

| | |
|---|---|
| ✕ Pre-1950 only | 2 |
| ○ Last seen 1950–1999 | 14 |
| ■ Pre-2000 and 2000–2018 | 15 |
| ● 2000–2018 only | 13 |

| | |
|---|---|
| ○ Last seen pre-2000 | 23 |
| ● Seen 2000–2018 | 33 |

First record: Gog Magog Hills, TL45SE, Relhan (1785: 404, as *Bryum heteromallum*). The populations in some western and eastern boulder-clay woods are clearly persistent, and it was refound in the recent survey in some sites where it was first seen before 1950, including Hardwick Wood, TL35N (1945), Over Wood, TL64J (1932) and Little Widgham Wood, TL65S (1938). It was first recorded at Wicken Fen in 1960, and Lock (1964) described it as the commonest calcifuge bryophyte there, growing on old *Molinia* tussocks, stumps, exposed tree roots and dead sedge, and fruiting regularly and abundantly. It was last seen at Wicken in 1989. The Frescalo analysis shows that *D. heteromalla*, like several other widespread calcifuges, has declined since the 1980s in the county as a whole.

Dioicous. Capsules occasional (27% tetrads); swollen, green capsules December, young setae and brown capsules February. The species produces dense mats of perennial protonemata bearing filamentous gemmae (Duckett & Matcham 1995).

### *Dicranum scoparium*

We have recorded *Dicranum scoparium* with equal frequency as an epiphyte and in other habitats. As an epiphyte, it is found on a range of trees in woodland and scrub, including ash, birch, field maple, hawthorn, larch, sycamore and willow, and on apple and pear in orchards. It usually grows on only a few trees and in small quantity but it is somewhat unpredictable in its occurrence and it was abundant (> 200 tufts) on a single ash on the Devil's Dyke, TL65P, in 2003, a surprising occurrence on this calcareous earthwork. Its rarity in orchards is shown by the fact that Robin Stevenson did not find it on any of the 951 apples he examined in detail, though he did find it on two of the 173 pears. Its terrestrial habitats are more obviously acidic, and include decorticated and rotting logs, branches and stumps of both coniferous and hardwood trees, sandy soil, old ballast in disused railway sidings, brick rubble in clay pits and stone chippings on graves. There is a large stand on the chalky but probably acidified floor of the Beechwood reserve on the Gog Magog Hills, TL45X.

First record: Gog Magog Hills, TL45SE, Newmarket Heath, TL66SW, etc., Relhan (1785: 404, as *Bryum scoparium*). It persists on sandy ground at Hildersham Furze Hills, TL54P, where it was first collected by F.Y. Brocas in 1874 (SWN). There is clearly a turnover in its localities, but the Frescalo analysis suggests an overall decline from a peak in the 1980s. Many of the sites in which it has not been refound were small thickets, plantations or woodlands. It was first recorded at Wicken Fen in 1963 and was widespread in the mid 1970s; unlike many calcifuges, it was still present there (on St Edmund's Fen, TL57Q) in 2008. Most of the records in the north of the county are from sites which were not surveyed before 2000.

Dioicous. Capsules not recorded.

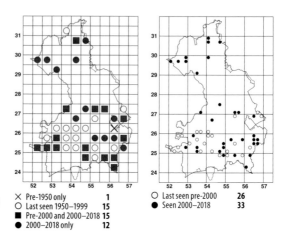

× Pre-1950 only      1
○ Last seen 1950–1999    15
■ Pre-2000 and 2000–2018   15
● 2000–2018 only      12

○ Last seen pre-2000    26
● Seen 2000–2018      33

## Dicranum tauricum

*Dicranum tauricum* is found on decaying hardwood and softwood, including fallen and often decorticated logs and branches but also decaying stumps; it grows with *Nowellia curvifolia* on the remarkably durable fallen oaks in Hayley Wood, TL25W, and associates elsewhere include *Lophocolea heterophylla*, *Aulacomnium androgynum* and *Orthodontium lineare*. It often grows on oak wood and is also recorded on birch and yew, although we have not always been able to identify its decaying substrates to genus. Like *Platygyrium repens*, it is apparently a recent colonist which nevertheless favours ancient woodland, fen woodland and parkland rather than sites in the wider countryside

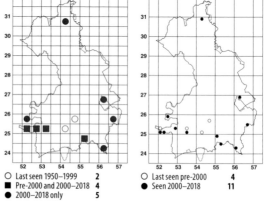

○ Last seen 1950–1999    2
■ Pre-2000 and 2000–2018   4
● 2000–2018 only      5

○ Last seen pre-2000    4
● Seen 2000–2018      11

(Preston & Hill 2016). There are single records from the living bark of ash, beech and willow in woodland, and one record from an orchard, at Wisbech St Mary, TF40J, where it grew with *Dicranoweisia cirrata* on pear.

First record: Bark of willow, Hauxton gravel pits, TL45F, H.J.B. Birks, 1977, BBSUK (the voucher is labelled 'bark of old ash tree' but on a follow-up visit two months later this identification was apparently corrected). This occurrence in a disused gravel pit, and a later record from an old apple tree in a garden at Luard Road, Cambridge, TL45T, are slightly different habitats to those in which it has been recorded in the present survey. Like *Campylopus introflexus*, but unlike most other widespread calcifuges, it has increased in frequency in the county in recent decades. However, it is much less frequent in Cambridgeshire than in some midland counties (e.g. Staffordshire).

Dioicous. Capsules not recorded. The tips of the extremely finely pointed leaves break off very easily and may act as vegetative propagules.

## Dicranum montanum

This species is frequent in parts of White Wood, Gamlingay, TL25A, B, growing (sometimes in abundance) on the lowest 0.5 m of the trunks of some sweet chestnuts and oaks, and also occurring on beech. Elsewhere it appears to be a very uncommon species, although its small, compact tufts are easily overlooked as *Dicranoweisia cirrata*. We found it in the recent survey on a birch trunk (with *Lophocolea heterophylla*) and a very rotten stump in Gamlingay Wood, TL25L, on a tree trunk in an abandoned garden at Jeavons, Cambourne, TL35J, and on the base of an ash tree and rotting birch bark at Chippenham Fen, TL66P.

First record: On both living and dead oaks, White Wood, Gamlingay, TL25A, C.C. Townsend, 1955, BBSUK. It was described as frequent in White Wood in 1988, especially on rotten stumps, and there is also a record here from lime bark. The other records before 2000 were from a tree in Hauxton gravel pit, TL45F, in 1977 and a dead oak log, with *Tetraphis pellucida*, in Hayley Wood, TL25W, in 1990.

Dioicous. Capsules not known in Britain. The leaves are deciduous and almost certainly act as vegetative propagules.

## LEUCOBRYACEAE

### †*Campylopus fragilis*
First and only record: On fallen and partly decayed log, Chippenham Fen, TL66P, P. Adam, 1977, BBSUK. A specimen collected by Whitehouse on this occasion (CGE) has been confirmed by M.O.H. as excellent material of this species, which is very rare in eastern England. It usually grows on acidic humus or mineral soil (Blockeel *et al.* 2014).

Dioicous. Capsules not recorded. The species reproduces vegetatively by deciduous leaves.

### *Campylopus pyriformis*
There are only six records from the recent survey. At Gamlingay it has been found on stumps at White Wood, Gamlingay, TL25A, B, at Gamlingay Cinques, TL25G, and in Gamlingay Wood, TL25L. It was abundant in a glade on the 'sand lens' at Gamlingay Wood in 2016, with frequent small patches of *C. introflexus* and large patches of *Polytrichastrum formosum*; the glade had been extended by clearing nearby trees about four years previously. It was found in smaller quantity on a piece of rotten bark on the ground in pony-grazed fen carr at Wicken Fen, TL56P; on a rotten stump, with *Lophocolea heterophylla* and *Hypnum cupressiforme*, at Little Widgham Wood, TL65S; and on a birch stump at Chippenham Fen, TL66P.

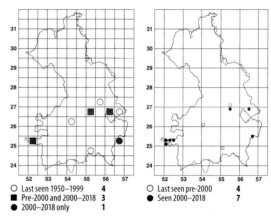

| | |
|---|---|
| ○ Last seen 1950–1999 | 4 |
| ■ Pre-2000 and 2000–2018 | 3 |
| ● 2000–2018 only | 1 |

| | |
|---|---|
| ○ Last seen pre-2000 | 4 |
| ● Seen 2000–2018 | 7 |

First record: Rotten tree stump, Great Heath Plantation, Gamlingay, TL25F, P.W. Richards, 1930, NMW; still present in 1988. *C. pyriformis* was subsequently recorded on sandy soil and rotten wood at several other sites in Gamlingay. It was first found at Chippenham Fen in 1951 and Wicken Fen in 1963. At Wicken it became the commonest *Campylopus* species, growing on old *Molinia* tussocks and on ridges between peat diggings, but it had declined by 1989 (Lock 1990). There are also records from rotten wood at Ladybush Close, Girton, TL46A (1962) and from Pampisford Hall, TL54E (1959, 1978).

Dioicous. Capsules seen once recently (17% tetrads), fairly recently dehisced in Gamlingay Wood in late April. Deciduous leaves are usually present.

### *Campylopus flexuosus*
*Campylopus flexuosus* has been recorded on the base of birch trees and on fallen and rotting branches, logs and stumps (including oak stumps and conifer logs). It occurs over Woburn Sands at Gamlingay in White Wood, TL25B, and Great Heath Plantation, TL25F, over Boulder Clay at Hayley Wood, TL25W, Kingston Wood, TL35G, and Little Widgham Wood, TL65S, and in the wooded parts of Chippenham Fen, TL66P.

First record: On stumps, etc., Great Heath Plantation, Gamlingay, TL25F, P.W. Richards, 1930, NMW; still present here in 2002. It was also recorded between 1950 and 1999 at Gamlingay Wood, TL25L, Madingley Wood, TL45E, Byron's Pool, TL45H, Fulbourn Fen, TL55I, Wicken Fen, where it was found in the open and in fen carr, TL56P, 57K

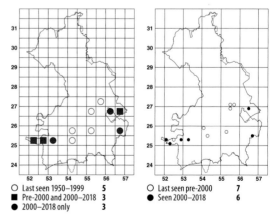

| | |
|---|---|
| ○ Last seen 1950–1999 | 5 |
| ■ Pre-2000 and 2000–2018 | 3 |
| ● 2000–2018 only | 3 |

| | |
|---|---|
| ○ Last seen pre-2000 | 7 |
| ● Seen 2000–2018 | 6 |

and 57Q, between 1963 and 1978, and on the base of a beech trunk near Newmarket, TL66. Like all the *Campylopus* species except *C. introflexus*, it appears to have decreased in frequency in the county.

Dioicous. Capsules not recorded. Deciduous branchlets usually present.

### Campylopus introflexus

The frequency of this drought-tolerant, calcifuge species in the county is an indication of its impressive ability to colonise small areas of acidic substrate in an overwhelmingly calcareous landscape. Unlike *Dicranum tauricum*, it is very much a species which has spread into the wider countryside. It is most typically found on rotting wood (including decaying stumps and logs, worked wood such as fence posts, discarded telegraph poles and the planks of abandoned farm trailers, and even the prehistoric wood of 'bog oaks' where these are displayed in the open) and acidic roofing materials (such as slates, wooden slats and the metal bars on greenhouse roofs, where it may form tall cushions with characteristically vertical sides). It also

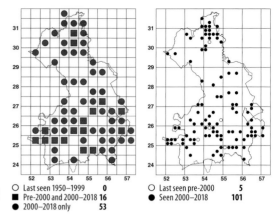

grows on sandy ground, disused railway sidings, and as an epiphyte. Most epiphytic records are from fruit trees in orchards: Robin Stevenson found it on 14 (1%) of the 951 apple trees and 25 (14%) of the 173 pears he surveyed in Cambridgeshire orchards. There are also 1–2 records of occurrences on alder, beech, birch, box, elder, oak, sweet chestnut and willow. Although it may be abundant on a roof or an abandoned farm trailer, it is never found in quantity over large areas.

First record: On an old *Molinia* tussock in carr, Verrall's Fen, Wicken Fen, TL57K, J.M. Lock, 1965, BBSUK (see Appendix 2). It was described by Lock (1990) as not uncommon at Wicken by 1975; it was rarer by 1989 but still present in 2008. This alien moss was first collected in Britain in 1941 but not recognised as distinct from the native *C. pilifer* until 1963. Despite the discovery at Wicken in 1965, its initial colonisation of the county appears to have been rather slow. It was not seen in a second site until 1975, when it was found on railway ballast near Hayley Wood, TL25W. It was then noted on sandy ground at Gamlingay, TL25F, in 1976 and on a log in woodland at Hildersham Hall, TL54P, in 1980, these being the only four sites known to Crompton & Whitehouse (1983). It was recorded at a steadily increasing number of sites from the mid 1980s, and especially from the start of the recent survey in 2000.

Dioicous. Capsules occasional (11% tetrads). Deciduous branchlets frequently present.

### Leucobryum glaucum

The sole recent record is from wet woodland in Compartment 9, Chippenham Fen, TL66P, where it was seen by N.G. Hodgetts and K. Warrington in 2001. As it has not been seen on group excursions to Chippenham, before or since, it is presumably present in only small quantity.

First record: In old coppiced stump, Little Widgham Wood, TL65S, H.L.K. Whitehouse, 1941, CGE (see Appendix 2). The only other records before the recent survey were from Wicken Fen, TL57K, where it was first found in carr near the brickpits in 1965 (CGE). A few plants were subsequently found in other parts of the fen; it was last seen at Wicken in 1979 (Lock 1990). The cited specimens are both *L. glaucum* rather than the segregate *L. juniperoideum*.

Dioicous. Capsules not recorded.

## POTTIACEAE

### Eucladium verticillatum

Most frequently found on the sides of watercourses such as moats, chalk streams and weirs in rivers, growing in small quantity above the water level on brickwork or, more rarely, concrete. It is also found near the foot of north-facing church walls, as in its only site in the north of the county, Tydd St Giles church, TF41I, and on north-facing brickwork of gutters around the base of churches. However, much the largest known population in the county is in a cave in the face of a disused chalk quarry at Balsham, TL55Q, where there are dense patches many square metres in area on the chalk walls 5 m from the entrance; by 15 m inside the cave the patches of dense shoots are confined to those parts of the cave walls which face the entrance and 25 m from the entrance, on the back wall of the cave, *Eucladium* shoots are very thinly scattered. Its shade-tolerance is also shown by its presence at the base of the clunch walls near the choir stalls *inside* the church at Orwell, TL35Q, where it was first found by M.O.H. in 1966 and still present in 2015.

First record: With the cyanobacterium *Oscillatoria* sp. on wet brickwork, King's Mill Weir, Cambridge, TL45P, E.W. Jones, 1932, NMW; a few vigorous clumps still present here (Mill Pit), 2008. The older records are from similar habitats to those in the recent survey, although it was also reported from the rootplate of an upturned tree by a stream at Thriplow Meadows, TL44I, in 1997 and from crumbling chalk soil on the sides of the parish boundary ditch at Little Wilbraham Fen, TL55E, in 1994.

Dioicous. Both male and female inflorescences have been found (in different sites) but not capsules. Protonemal gemmae are recorded from the shaded populations at Balsham and Orwell.

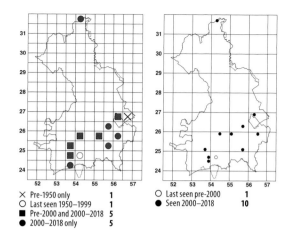

| | |
|---|---|
| ✕ Pre-1950 only | 1 |
| ○ Last seen 1950–1999 | 1 |
| ■ Pre-2000 and 2000–2018 | 5 |
| ● 2000–2018 only | 5 |

| | |
|---|---|
| ○ Last seen pre-2000 | 1 |
| ● Seen 2000–2018 | 10 |

### *Weissia controversa* var. *controversa*

*Weissia controversa* grows in open chalk grassland, or on disturbed sites in coarser grassland (e.g. by a fox's earth), on the Fleam Dyke, TL55L, M, and the Devil's Dyke, TL56, 66. It has also been found in dry, nutrient-poor but more acidic soils in a few other sites on sandy banks, ditch sides, recently planted hedges and on railway sidings. It persists as an introduction on Carboniferous limestone and sandstone rocks in Cambridge Botanic Garden, TL45N.

First record: Relhan (1785: 405, as *Bryum viridulum*); see Appendix 2. It was collected by J.S. Henslow at Gamlingay, TL25SW, in 1838 (CGE, det. H.L.K. Whitehouse). The next records were from Quy Fen, TL56SW, where it was recorded by A.W. Graveson in 1914 (as *Weissia viridula*), seen with

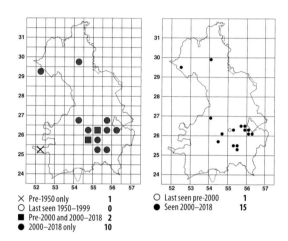

| | |
|---|---|
| ✕ Pre-1950 only | 1 |
| ○ Last seen 1950–1999 | 0 |
| ■ Pre-2000 and 2000–2018 | 2 |
| ● 2000–2018 only | 10 |

| | |
|---|---|
| ○ Last seen pre-2000 | 1 |
| ● Seen 2000–2018 | 15 |

*Fissidens dubius* on north-east side of coprolite pit by D.E. Coombe in 1957 and finally found by H.L.K.W. in 1961. It was present on recently imported limestone in the Botanic Garden in 1957 (Preston & Whitehouse 1992b) but not recorded again until 2011, perhaps because of the difficulty of finding fruiting plants. It was not recorded on the Devil's Dyke until 2001, and was presumably overlooked earlier as *W. brachycarpa*.

Autoicous. Only identifiable with capsules; brown but undehisced January–April, dehisced May.

The population of *W. controversa* on the Devil's Dyke includes plants in which the peristome is short but clearly visible under the microscope, and others in which it is only visible under high-power magnification. *W. brachycarpa*, which also grows here, differs in having broader capsules on shorter setae and, more reliably, by the presence of a membrane which partially covers the mouth of the dehisced capsule and by its larger spores. On the Devil's Dyke the spores of *W. controversa* are 13–15 µm, those of *W. brachycarpa* (16–)17–21 µm. These agree with the values given by Dixon (1924) but not those stated by Smith (1978a, 2004) who gives 16–20 µm for *W. controversa* and 20–28 µm for *W. brachycarpa* var. *obliqua*. Our problems in recording these two species have been exacerbated by the fact that we normally visit the chalk earthworks in February, when their capsules are usually immature; by the time they dehisce, the conditions tend to be too dry for optimum bryology. *W. controversa* was first recorded from the Devil's Dyke when we happened to visit the site in May 2001 on a non-bryological excursion to celebrate the retirement of Professor P.J. Grubb.

### *Weissia brachycarpa* var. *obliqua*

This is frequent in open patches in chalk grassland and on disturbed chalk soil in scrub on the Fleam Dyke, TL55L, M and the Devil's Dyke, TL56, 66. Elsewhere, it has been recorded recently only on the crumbling, sandy soil at the top of the bank of Millbridge Brook, Gamlingay, TL25F, open chalky soil of the A505 road cutting at Hyde Hill, TL34Q, at Cherry Hinton chalk pit, TL45X, and on sandy soil in Six Mile Bottom churchyard, TL55Y.

First record: Wood on the Gog Magog Hills, TL45SE, H.E. Lowe, 1834, WARMS, as *Phascum curvicollum*, det. H.L.K. Whitehouse. The species was found between 1950 and 1966 at several sites in the Gogs area (Wormwood Hill, TL45W; Golf Links, TL45X; Roman Road, TL45X, TL55B) and from both the Roman Road and the railway embankment at Worsted Lodge,TL55F, G but there are no later records from these sites. Its other pre-2000 sites included sandy soil at Hildersham Furze Hills, TL54P, a railway cutting at Shudy Camps, TL64I, and gravel pits at Thriplow, TL44M, and near Kennett, TL66Z.

Autoicous. Only identifiable with capsules; immature November, January; brown but undehisced, February, April; dehisced April.

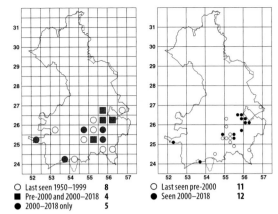

| | |
|---|---|
| ○ Last seen 1950–1999 | 8 |
| ■ Pre-2000 and 2000–2018 | 4 |
| ● 2000–2018 only | 5 |

| | |
|---|---|
| ○ Last seen pre-2000 | 11 |
| ● Seen 2000–2018 | 12 |

### Weissia squarrosa

A persistent population in a grassy, set-aside field on Ampthill Clay, pH 6.9, by the A14 Boxworth interchange, TL36M, was originally seen in 1991–92 and refound in 2001 and 2004. The field had been ploughed between 1992 and 2001 but was in set-aside for much of this period. In 2004 one large and a few smaller clumps of *W. squarrosa* grew with *W. longifolia*. A single tuft was also found at the edge of a stubble field direct-drilled with rape on Ampthill Clay at Conington, TL36I, in 2001.

First record: Among *W. longifolia* in arable field between Boxworth and Fen Drayton, TL36N, M.O. Hill, 1991, herb. M.O.H., det. S.D.S. Bosanquet. This field, like that at the Boxworth interchange discovered later in 1991, is on Ampthill Clay. These records were initially reported as *W. rostellata* (see Preston & Hill 2004).

Autoicous. Only identifiable with capsules, which have been seen in November, April and June; they are often variable in size and do not develop synchronously. The lid of the capsules is dehiscent but a membrane across the mouth of the capsule prevents the release of spores until the walls of the capsule disintegrate, leaving the bare setae still in place (Bosanquet & Preston 2005).

### †Weissia rostellata

Last seen in the county in 1965.

First record: Side of ditch, Gamlingay Wood, TL25L, H.L.K. Whitehouse, 1957, BBBUK, conf. D.T. Holyoak. It was refound for some years in Gamlingay Wood, initially on what was presumably the same ditch side by C.C. Townsend and H.L.K.W. in 1958 (OXF). A single capsule was collected by E.F. Warburg in a rut on a ride in the wood in 1960 (OXF) and finally David Coombe found a single plant on the ride in 1965. It has never been seen again despite repeated searches. The stretch of ride on which it was reported is still particularly wet. The only other record, from a stubble field on Boulder Clay at Hatley St George, TL25R, made by H.L.K.W. in 1960, is best treated as dubious as the only voucher is difficult material grown by Whitehouse on sterile soil from a single spore (OXF); it may have been a misidentification of *W. squarrosa*.

Autoicous. Only identifiable with capsules; recorded October, November, February. The capsules differ from those of *W. squarrosa* in having indehiscent lids; seta and capsule are shed as a single unit.

### Weissia sterilis

In open chalk grassland on the Devil's Dyke north of the A1304 road, TL66A, where it was seen most recently by J.G. Duckett in 2003 and by M.O.H. and C.D.P. in 2017.

First record: In small quantity, Fleam Dyke, TL55, H.L.K. Whitehouse, 1940 (*Whitehouse species file*). This was Harold Whitehouse's first significant bryophyte record, though it was initially recorded as *Trichostomum brachydontium*. It has never been refound on Fleam Dyke but it was discovered on Devil's Dyke by M.C.F. Proctor in 1952. It has been refound there at intervals in TL66A, with one record from further north in TL66B (R.D. Porley, 1994).

Autoicous. Capsules cleistocarpous, recorded October, February–March, May. Frustratingly, we (M.O.H. and C.D.P.) have been able to find only vegetative material.

### Weissia longifolia var. longifolia

We have found *W. longifolia* var. *longifolia* in stubble fields, set-aside and arable fields which are uncultivated pending development, on recently dug graves, hedges, roadside verges and ditch banks, disturbed soil in orchards, and in recently planted woodland and paths in ancient woods. It grows on a range of soils including dry, sandy soil and both heavy, calcareous and slightly acidic (Ampthill) clays.

First record: Entrance to rabbit burrow in meadow, Knapwell, TL36G, H.L.K. Whitehouse, 1952, BBSUK. Harold Whitehouse and his colleagues recorded var. *longifolia* in 10 stubble fields and grass leys between 1959 and 1961, especially on the western clays, but we found it in only twelve arable or set-aside sites between 2001 and 2016, suggesting that it might have decreased in these habitats.

Autoicous. Only identifiable when fruiting. Capsules cleistocarpous; green, immature October, December, March, April; brown, mature March, April.

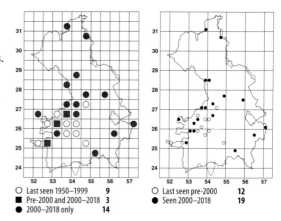

| | |
|---|---|
| ○ Last seen 1950–1999 | **9** |
| ■ Pre-2000 and 2000–2018 | **3** |
| ● 2000–2018 only | **14** |

| | |
|---|---|
| ○ Last seen pre-2000 | **12** |
| ● Seen 2000–2018 | **19** |

Old, disintegrating capsules survive on plants into the following winter when they can be found with the new season's immature capsules, sometimes on the same plants, demonstrating that plants are perennial.

During the recent survey we followed the taxonomic treatment of *Weissia* subgenus *Astomum* set out by Crundwell & Nyholm (1972). We did not always find that the two varieties of *W. longifolia* were easy to separate and a few sites with plants which we were unable to allocate to one taxon or the other are omitted from the maps. In a new treatment of the group which was completed as we were finalising this flora, Des Callaghan, Neil Bell and Laura Forrest have proposed treating the two varieties as species. Des Callaghan has identified a specimen collected by M.O.H. from a path in Hayley Wood, TL25W, in 2003 as the plant hitherto known as *W. multicapsularis*, previously regarded as an extremely rare species in Britain. Our material of var. *longifolia* will obviously require revision in the light of this new treatment.

### *Weissia longifolia* var. *angustifolia*

Var. *angustifolia* is virtually confined to chalky soil, growing in open chalk grassland, on the faces of chalk pits, road and railway cuttings and trackside banks and in disturbed sites in secondary woodland (e.g. around rabbit burrows or at the base of wind-blown trees). There are no recent records (and only one old record) from arable fields on chalk.

First record: [Cherry] Hinton, TL45W, J.S. Henslow, 1827, CGE. Plants of var. *angustifolia* on the chalk can be identified even if the capsules are very immature, so it is much easier to record than *W. brachycarpa* and *W. controversa*. This may be the reason why it does not appear to have suffered the same decline in chalkland sites as *W. brachycarpa*.

Autoicous. Only identifiable when fruiting.

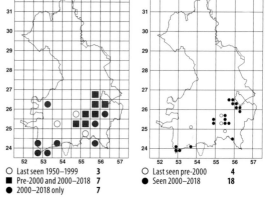

| | |
|---|---|
| ○ Last seen 1950–1999 | **3** |
| ■ Pre-2000 and 2000–2018 | **7** |
| ● 2000–2018 only | **7** |

| | |
|---|---|
| ○ Last seen pre-2000 | **4** |
| ● Seen 2000–2018 | **18** |

Capsules cleistocarpous; green, immature November–February; brown, maturing December–February; mature April.

Hybrids between var. *angustifolia* and one of the species with an elongated seta, *W. brachycarpa* or *W. controversa*, have been found in chalk grassland on the Devil's Dyke, TL66B, F. They have short, sometimes more or less arcuate setae and a mixture of capsules, some pale and sporeless and others brown.

### *Tortella tortuosa*

*Tortella tortuosa* is apparently extinct as a native species. However, it is still known as an introduction on Carboniferous limestone imported from Westmorland to the Cambridge Botanic Garden, TL45N, where it was first recorded in 1955, soon after the limestone arrived. In 2008 and 2011 it grew on partially shaded rocks in several places, and in the open in a hollow on the upper rock surface.

First record: Gravel Hill, TL45NW, Gog Magog Hills, TL45SE and Newmarket Heath, TL66SW, Relhan (1786: 18, as *Bryum tortuosum*). Skrimshire's collection (WBCH) includes a specimen from Newmarket, TL66, collected by J. Hemsted in 1796. It was first recorded from the Devil's Dyke by E.W. Jones in 1934; Jones found 'several large tufts close together on top of the dyke near the Grandstand' (NMW, as *Trichostomum tortuosum*) and 'several tufts in a small area of a few square yards' (CGE). M.C.F. Proctor described it as locally frequent in 1951 at TL6062 and TL6161. It was last seen by M.O.H. in 1966, when it grew with *T. inclinata* by the path along the top of the earthwork. M.O.H. also recorded it on imported limestone in a garden at 11, Chaucer Road, Cambridge, in 1965, but it has not survived there. It is frequent on calcareous substrates in northern and western Britain but it fades out rapidly eastwards and it is absent (except on introduced stone) from Norfolk and Suffolk.

Dioicous. Capsules not recorded and rare nationally.

### Tortella inflexa

*Tortella inflexa* grows as small but dense patches on chalk stones. It occurs in short grassland and under trees on the ancient chalk earthworks of the Fleam Dyke, TL55L, M, and on both the north- and south-facing sides of the Devil's Dyke, TL66A, F, and in sycamore scrub on old spoil by a chalk pit at Morden Grange, Steeple Morden, TL23Z.

First record: On lumps of chalk, Devil's Dyke, TL66A, E.F. Warburg, 1961, BBSUK, NMW, OXF. It was first found on Fleam Dyke in 1980. When it was first discovered in Cambridgeshire this species was thought to be spreading rapidly in Britain (Whitehouse 1962), but it is an inconspicuous plant and in retrospect it seems likely that it had previously been overlooked.

Dioicous. Capsules not recorded and very rare nationally.

### Tortella inclinata

A rare species of chalk grassland, only seen once during our survey, in open chalk grassland on the Devil's Dyke, TL66B, in 2017.

First record: Devil's Dyke, Rhodes (1911, misidentified as *Trichostomum flavovirens*). It was formerly widespread; Proctor (1956) knew it 'scattered .… from just south of the Cambridge–Newmarket road for about a mile or so to the north', TL66A, B, F. There are only two records from the Dyke since 1981, both from TL66B. The only other record is from Fleam Dyke, TL55, where it was recorded once, in 1980.

Capsules not recorded and very rare nationally.

### Trichostomum brachydontium

Unlike *Tortella tortuosa*, *Trichostomum brachydontium* is known to survive in open chalk grassland on the Devil's Dyke, TL66A, B, where it occasionally forms largish patches. Plants seen here in 2005 were an acute-leaved variant of this very variable species.

First record: Devil's Dyke, TL66, E.F. Warburg, 1944, OXF. It was recorded once, in 1973, in chalk grassland on Fleam Dyke, TL55S.

Dioicous. Capsules not recorded and very rare nationally; female plants known from the Devil's Dyke.

### Trichostomum crispulum

This species still persists at the Devil's Dyke, TL66A, B, F, where it grows in chalk grassland and more frequently on bare chalky soil on the heavily trampled edge of the path along the top of the earthwork. In 2017 the population included frequent patches along one 20 m length of path in TL66A. It is also known from chalky soil in East Pit, Cherry Hinton, TL45X.

First record: Devil's Dyke, TL66, M.C.F. Proctor, 1950, BBSUK. In 1952 Proctor described it as abundant over a limited area south of the main Cambridge–Newmarket road [now A1304], a locality which corresponds with our record from TL66F. J.G. Duckett and E.R.B. Little collected it in Cherry Hinton chalk pit in 1966 (NMW), the only record there before the recent survey. There is a single record from imported Carboniferous limestone in Cambridge Botanic Garden, TL45N, in 1980.

Dioicous. Capsules not recorded.

### Pottiopsis caespitosa

This nationally scarce species, which is characteristically unpredictable in its occurrence, was found on chalky soil at Orwell Clunch Pit, TL35Q, in 2015. There had been very extensive scrub clearance at the site since our previous visit, in 2000.

First record: Bare ground in chalk grassland, top of Devil's Dyke, TL66SW, E.F. Warburg, 1962, BBSUK. The only other record is from chalk grassland on Fleam Dyke, TL55M, where it was discovered by R.A. Finch in 1980.

Autoicous. Only likely to be recorded with capsules; immature capsules seen February, April.

The material at Orwell differed from the usual British plant in having immature fruits with longer setae (*c*. 8 mm rather than *c*. 3 mm) and strongly corkscrew-twisted cells in the capsule lid; it may be the variant formerly known in Europe as *Trichostomum triumphans* but now regarded as conspecific with this species.

### *Gyroweisia tenuis*

This tiny plant grows on brickwork, mortar or stonework in sites which are both moist and shaded, as on the north walls of churches, or moist but unshaded, as on bridges and walls by village ponds. It is also recorded from chalk stones in nettle beds and elder scrub in a disused quarry at Balsham, TL55Q, and on shaded oolite rock (with *Tortula marginata*) and only slightly shaded sandstone rock (with *Leptobarbula berica*) in Cambridge Botanic Garden, TL45N.

First record: On sandstone rocks in Water Garden, Cambridge Botanic Garden, TL45N, C.C. Townsend, 1956, E, det. H.L.K. Whitehouse. Early records from Madingley Hall and the Botanic Garden were much confused with *Leptobarbula berica* until they were sorted out by Harold Whitehouse (Preston & Whitehouse 1986a); all material at Madingley is *Leptobarbula* but both species grow in the Botanic Garden, sometimes intermixed. The lack of correspondence between the pre- and post-2000 records presumably reflects the tendency of the plant to grow in sites which are not regularly visited and the low probability that will be found on any one visit. Two earlier records, from crumbling chalk soil on a ditch side at Little Wilbraham Fen, TL55E, and concrete 'sandbags' by Little Wilbraham River, TL55J, are from habitats in which it has not been seen since 2000.

Dioicous. Female inflorescences are known from five sites but neither male plants nor capsules are recorded. Nationally, female plants are much more frequent than males (Whitehouse in Hill *et al*. 1992). Protonemal gemmae are recorded.

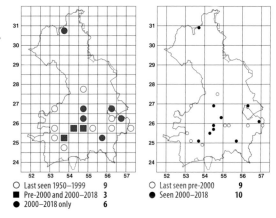

| | | |
|---|---|---|
| ○ Last seen 1950–1999 | **9** | |
| ■ Pre-2000 and 2000–2018 | **3** | |
| ● 2000–2018 only | **6** | |

| | | |
|---|---|---|
| ○ Last seen pre-2000 | **9** | |
| ● Seen 2000–2018 | **10** | |

### *Leptobarbula berica*

This is apparently rarer in the county than the similar *Gyroweisia tenuis*. It was refound during the recent survey in both its known sites, on the oolitic limestone of an ornamental, semi-circular pool adjoining the north wall of Madingley Hall, TL36V, and on shaded oolite and slightly to densely shaded sandstone in Cambridge Botanic Garden, TL45N. On the sandstone it may grow in dense swards covering several square centimetres, sometimes mixed with *Gyroweisia tenuis* and *Tortula marginata*. We also discovered five new sites, at least four on brickwork, at the base of a wall by Clare Bridge, Cambridge, TL45P, and on the north walls of Madingley church (with *Tortula marginata*), TL36V, Histon church, TL46G, Kirtling church, TL65Y, and Elm church, TF40T.

First record: Wet stonework by pool, Madingley Hall, TL36V, M.C.F. Proctor, 1951, herb. M.C.F.P., det. H.L.K. Whitehouse. It was frequently refound here but until 1986 it was thought to be *Gyroweisia tenuis*. It was still present in 2005 but not refound in 2016, when the stonework had apparently been cleaned. It was also discovered in the Botanic Garden by M.C.F.P. in 1951.

Dioicous. Female plants are known from all seven sites; male plants and capsules have not been found in Cambridgeshire. Male plants are much rarer than females nationally (Whitehouse in Hill *et al*. 1992).

### *Ephemerum recurvifolium*

A minute ephemeral of chalk or calcareous clay soils, found in stubble and set-aside fields (pH 7.4–8.6, 8 sites), open or trampled chalk grassland and disused chalk pits, disturbed soil in churchyards (sometimes in places which appear to have been treated with herbicide), vehicle tracks and lightly trampled paths, areas of bare ground under scrub and in newly planted woodland. Although it is so small, it does not seem to require recent disturbance and it has been found on the disturbed soil around the base of saplings in two 'millennium woods' six years after they were planted. It is often present in small quantity but at Childerley Hall, TL36K, it was so frequent on a bank in January 2009 that its mature capsules coloured the area reddish brown. Associates include *Barbula unguiculata*, *Bryum rubens*, *Dicranella schreberiana*, *D. staphylina*, *D. varia*, *Fissidens incurvus*, *Microbryum davallianum* and *Pohlia melanodon*.

First record: Sainfoin field near Comberton, TL35Y, E.W. Jones and P.W. Richards, 1934, OXF, NMW. Jones clearly had his eye in for this plant, as he found it in six sites in the first three months of 1934 and on another specimen, from a fallow clover field near Comberton (NMW), he described it as 'frequent in the district'. However, it was only seen on five further occasions in the county in the next 50 years. It was not found on the Devil's Dyke until 1989, although it is apparently widespread and sometimes locally frequent there (TL56S, W, X, 66B).

Pseudodioicous. Usually recorded with capsules (89% tetrads). Plants vegetative or with archegonia August, November–December; capsules cleistocarpous, immature, green September–February; mature, brown January–February, old and decaying in February, March. The terminal parts of the protonema are extremely fragile and presumably act as vegetative propagules. Plants also produce tubers just below the soil surface and these, unlike most moss tubers, are starch-filled and regenerate rapidly (Pressel et al. 2005).

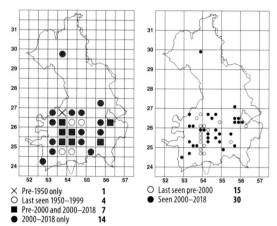

| × Pre-1950 only | 1 |
| ○ Last seen 1950–1999 | 4 |
| ■ Pre-2000 and 2000–2018 | 7 |
| ● 2000–2018 only | 14 |

| ○ Last seen pre-2000 | 15 |
| ● Seen 2000–2018 | 30 |

## Ephemerum cohaerens

Liz Kungu found this rare species on a BBS meeting in October 2017, growing with *Bryum klinggraeffii* and *Dicranella varia* on disturbed peat on Baxter West Ride, Chippenham Fen.

First record: Chippenham Fen, TL66P, E.M. Kungu, 2017, BBSUK, det. C.D.P. This is only the fifth recent site for the species in Britain. Since 2000 it has been found in the draw-down zone of three reservoirs, two in Northamptonshire and one in Worcestershire, and the soil bank of the River Camlad in Montgomeryshire. In Europe most records are from artificial water bodies, including gravel pits and reservoirs, though there is a single record from a *Schoenus nigricans* mire in France (Hugonnot et al. 2012).

Pseudodioicous. The Chippenham plants had both green capsules and lipid-filled tubers.

## Ephemerum minutissimum

*Ephemerum minutissimum* is found in similar habitats to *E. recurvifolium* but it is a calcifuge, recorded from acidic clays and silt in stubble fields, direct-drilled rape and set-aside (pH 6.0–6.9 at four sites), and on bare patches on grassy woodland rides and old molehills in woodland. Associates include *Bryum rubens*, *Dicranella schreberiana*, *D. staphylina*, *Fissidens taxifolius*, *Phascum cuspidatum* and *Weissia* sp.

First record: Cambridgeshire, J. Hemsted, 1797, Smith (1798); vouchers in BM (*Sowerby drawings*) and LINN, former confirmed as *E. serratum sens. lat.* by C.D.P. and F.J. Rumsey. The first collection which has been identified as *E. minutissimum* was collected with *Fissidens exilis* and *Pleuridium subulatum* from

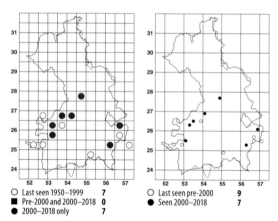

| ○ Last seen 1950–1999 | 7 |
| ■ Pre-2000 and 2000–2018 | 0 |
| ● 2000–2018 only | 7 |

| ○ Last seen pre-2000 | 9 |
| ● Seen 2000–2018 | 7 |

bare clay in a clearing at Little Widgham Wood, TL65S, by P.W. Richards, 1946, NMW, det. C.D.P. Richards did not notice that he had collected this tiny plant in his specimens of the two associates, and it was added to the county list by G. Halliday in 1957 from bare sandy ground in a recently cleared area at Gamlingay Wood, TL25L (BBSUK). It was last seen in Gamlingay Wood in 1999 and it has not been found in several other woods in which it was recorded on rides or in recently coppiced plots before 2000, namely Hayley Wood, TL25W, Ten Wood, TL65S, Ditton Park Wood, TL65T, and Great Wood, TL75C. The striking mismatch between the old and recent records reflects our failure to refind it in these sites and the low probability of rediscovering such a rare and ephemeral species in arable habitats.

Pseudodioicous. Usually recorded with capsules (all tetrads); capsules cleistocarpous, green October, January; brown October, January, spores mature October, February. The species lacks the fragile protonemal tips and the tubers found in *E. recurvifolium*.

## Dialytrichia mucronata

Only seen recently at the base of two sycamore trees in secondary woodland by the River Granta, one at 'Aconite Wood', Great Abington, TL54J, where only a few stems were found, and the other at Sluice Wood, TL54J, where a patch of *c.* 125 cm² grew with *Rhynchostegium confertum* just above the water level.

First record: Trees by R. Kennett near Red Lodge, TL66Z, P.W. Richards, 1941 (*Richards file*); never seen in this area again. It has been recorded at intervals on the base of trees (including a willow) along a 4-km stretch of the Granta valley at Little Linton, TL54N (1953), Hildersham Hall, TL54 (1978), Hildersham, TL54P (1953) and in 'Aconite Wood' (1957 onwards). C.C. Townsend described it as common on tree roots by the Granta at Great Abington in 1959 (E). Blockeel *et al.* (2014) note a significant increase in British records since 2000, in part because of its increasing tendency to grow on tarmac, but this is not yet apparent in Cambridgeshire.

Dioicous. Capsules not recorded.

## Pseudocrossidium hornschuchianum

Does any other Cambridgeshire moss grow in more unprepossessing habitats? It is most frequent on trampled or lightly driven-over ground, including stony, gravel and tarmac paths and tracks, on concrete tracks (especially where the concrete is covered by a shallow soil layer), the cracks between paving slabs and courtyard cobbles, the edge of roadside verges and unsurfaced car parks. It may be locally abundant on disturbed soil in sand and gravel pits, and is also recorded from the floors of chalk pits or piles of chalk rubble, railway clinker, brick hardcore, at the edge of arable or set-aside fields and (rarely) on the wooden planks of foot bridges or farm trailers. It is sometimes found in places which have been treated with glyphosate

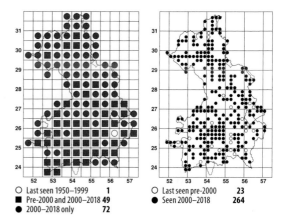

○ Last seen 1950–1999    1
■ Pre-2000 and 2000–2018   49
● 2000–2018 only     72

○ Last seen pre-2000    23
● Seen 2000–2018    264

herbicides. Plants growing on highly trampled ground between paving slabs can be very small.

First record: Abundant on sandy ground around Half Moon Plantation by Newmarket–Thetford road, Kennett, TL66Z, E.W. Jones, 1934, NMW. Despite the relatively late first record, Proctor (1956) recognised that it was frequent in the county.

Dioicous. Capsules rare (10% tetrads) and not seen in the most highly trampled sites; young setae October–January, March, April; expanded capsules January, March, April; mature but undehisced and dehisced capsules June.

## Pseudocrossidium revolutum

The habitats of this species are much less mundane than those of *P. hornschuchianum*. Most records are from churchyards, where it grows on coping stones and mortar of old boundary walls, on oolitic limestone monuments (vertical tombstones, horizontal slabs at ground level and the raised, flat tops of table tombs) and on the north walls of the church itself. It is unusual to find it on a monument less than 150 years old and the best way of finding it in a churchyard is to examine the oldest limestone monuments in sight. Secular sites include old brick walls and, rarely, the paths below them, old bridges, oolite monuments in the gardens of country houses (including the pool with *Leptobarbula berica* at Madingley Hall, TL36V, and an ornamental

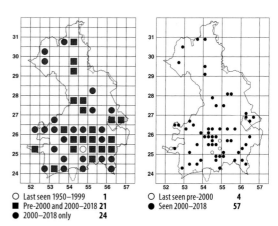

○ Last seen 1950–1999    1
■ Pre-2000 and 2000–2018   21
● 2000–2018 only     24

○ Last seen pre-2000    4
● Seen 2000–2018    57

pineapple at Chippenham Park, TL66U) and oolite and sandstone rockery stones in college and domestic gardens. It grows on a low wall in front of Sir Giles Gilbert Scott's University Library building, Cambridge, TL45P, which was opened in 1934, the youngest substrate we are able to date.

First record: Flat top of chalk wall, Great Wilbraham, TL55N, E.W. Jones, 1932, NMW. Jones recorded it in a total of five sites in 1932–33 and there were several further records available to Proctor (1956).

Dioicous. Capsules occasional (13% tetrads); young setae October, December, January; capsules expanded, green, January, swollen, brown April. Gemmae on the leaves frequent according to Whitehouse (1964) but not seen recently.

## Bryoerythrophyllum recurvirostrum

This species grows on a wide range of substrates, although they are normally stable rather than disturbed, shaded and well-drained. They include sandstone and oolitic limestone walls and churchyard monuments, sandstone and Carboniferous limestone in rock gardens, old brickwork, concrete and breeze blocks, roof tiles and roofs of corrugated asbestos, asphalt paths and drives, soil on roadside cuttings and at the cut edge of lawns, in chalk pits and under beech trees, and on living and fallen tree trunks and rotting stumps. As an epiphyte it is recorded from ash, beech, elder, elm, hawthorn and willow, often on silty bark by streams and ditches but also in scrub away from water. Although many records are from the chalk, it sometimes grows on non-calcareous substrates such as rotting beech stumps and granite hoggin. Despite this wide habitat range, *B. recurvirostrum* is not a frequent species and it tends to crop up rather unpredictably, as the maps suggest.

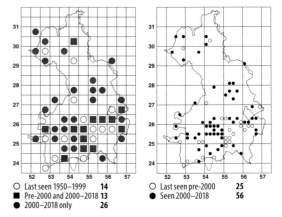

○ Last seen 1950–1999    14
■ Pre-2000 and 2000–2018   13
● 2000–2018 only    26

○ Last seen pre-2000    25
● Seen 2000–2018    56

First record: Coton, TL45NW, G.D. Haviland and J.J. Lister, 1880, CGE; the next record was made by E.W. Jones in 1932. The records in the 1950s and 1960s were mainly from the chalklands, and the large number of squares in the south of the county where the species has not been refound since 2000 may reflect a more intensive concentration in earlier years on sites within a short distance of Cambridge. By contrast, we have discovered more sites in Fenland.

Synoicous or paroicous. Capsules very frequent (75% tetrads); their phenology is uncertain as we have recorded young setae in May and October, immature capsules in November–February, colonies with a mixture of mature and dehiscing capsules in October, January and February and with more or less freshly dehisced capsules in March. Colonies have been found with only old setae in April, suggesting that they do not fruit every year. Bosanquet's (2010) more numerous fruiting observations from Pembrokeshire suggest that there is no regular seasonal pattern of fruiting.

## Barbula convoluta

Most records of *Barbula convoluta* are of plants growing on the ground, in well-drained, disturbed or trampled places. Typical sites include paths and tracks, including those made up with gravel, limestone rubble or crushed bricks, the cracks between paving stones or courtyard cobbles, roadside verges, flower beds, trampled areas in lawns, ditch banks, chalk soil in beech woods and chalk grassland, disused chalk, sand and gravel pits, and disused railway tracks and sidings. It is frequent in stubble fields and other arable crops (including asparagus and marginal game mixes). We found it in 31 of the 76 SBAL fields surveyed, especially on chalk, peat, sand and silt, less frequently on loam and rarely on clay, usually in basic sites with pH

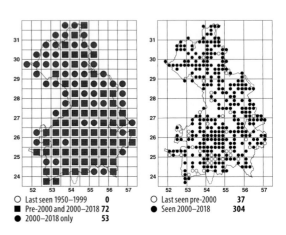

○ Last seen 1950–1999    0
■ Pre-2000 and 2000–2018   72
● 2000–2018 only    53

○ Last seen pre-2000    37
● Seen 2000–2018    304

7.2–8.2 (26 sites) but occasionally on more acidic soils of pH 5.3–6.5 (five sites) including a sandy loam of pH 5.3 at Gamlingay, TL25L. It is also found on brick walls, oolitic limestone monuments, shaded concrete and tarmac, on chippings on graves, granite hoggin and (rarely) on rotting logs. There are a few records from damper ground, including peaty mud at the edge of The Mere, Wicken Fen, TL56P, and horse-grazed upper saltmarsh at Foul Anchor, TF41T. It tolerates herbicide applications, growing on treated pavements, under wire fences and in stubble fields where all vascular plants have been killed.

First record: Hill of Health, TL45NW, Gog Magog Hills, TL45SE, etc., Relhan (1793: 9, as *Bryum convolutum*; see Appendix 2). There were no further localised records until P.G.M. Rhodes found it at Cherry Hinton in 1907, and it was not until E.W. Jones (1933–34) and E.F. Warburg (1941–44) were bryologising in the county that it was recorded with any frequency.

Dioicous. Capsules rare (9% tetrads); young setae January, March; capsules swollen, green, March, April, freshly dehisced February, June. Tubers frequent.

We have recorded var. *convoluta* and var. *sardoa* rather half-heartedly, assigning small, neat plants with plane leaf margins to var. *convoluta* and larger plants with wavy margins to var. *sardoa*. The discontinuity in leaf length suggested by Frahm & Ahmed (2004) is not present in our material, much of which is intermediate. There is also a broad overlap in their habitat requirements in Cambridgeshire. In 2007, when walking along the Roman Road, TL45X, C.D.P. found frequent plants of var. *convoluta* along the stony path until he reached a bonfire site with a vigorous population of var. *sardoa*, suggesting that the differences can sometimes be phenotypic. Plants are usually fairly uniform within stands and we do not recall seeing the two varieties growing intermixed, although Frahm & Ahmed (2004) cite a report of a mixed tuft.

## Barbula unguiculata

This is the most frequent acrocarpous moss in the county. It grows on unsurfaced paths, tracks and car parks and those made up with gravel, limestone rubble or crushed bricks, on trampled soil, roadsides, stream and ditch banks, dredgings from lakes, streams and ditches, on disused railway lines, on chalky banks, in both active and disused chalk pits and in open chalk grassland, in disused clay, gravel and sand pits, and indeed on disturbed soil almost anywhere. It is very frequent in stubble fields, fields of other crops and set-aside, found in 63 of the 76 SBAL fields surveyed. It grows over a wide range of soils including chalk, clay, loam, peat, sand and silt, usually on basic soils (pH 6.8–8.6, 54 sites), more rarely acidic (pH 5.3–6.3, six sites). It also grows on the horse-grazed upper saltmarsh at

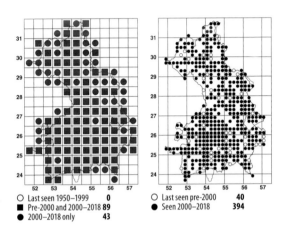

O Last seen 1950–1999    0
■ Pre-2000 and 2000–2018 89
● 2000–2018 only    43

O Last seen pre-2000    40
● Seen 2000–2018    394

Foul Anchor, TF41T. More solid substrates include concrete, Carboniferous limestone rockery stones, oolite monuments in churchyards and chippings on graves and it was recorded once on a polypropylene rope. It is a rare epiphyte, sometimes found on the bases of ash and willow by streams and ditches and recorded once as an epiphyte on elder. It is similar in its ecology to *B. convoluta* and the two often grow together, but unlike that species it is a particularly frequent plant on calcareous clay, and it may become the dominant bryophyte on such soils in sites such as arable land abandoned pending development.

First record: Relhan (1793: 10, as *Bryum unguiculatum*). John Hemsted sent Skrimshire a fruiting specimen collected at Newmarket, TL66, in 1796 (WBCH, as *Tortula unguiculata*). Jenyns recorded it on banks near the Swan Inn (now the White Swan), Bottisham, TL56F, in his annotated Relhan (1820) and it was collected (but not named) by Henslow at Coton, TL45NW, in 1833 and by H.E. Lowe at Teversham, TL45NE, in 1834 (both CGE). In the early years of the 20th century L.J. Sedgwick described it as very common on chalky and clayey banks everywhere, often with fruit (*Richards file*).

Dioicous. Capsules frequent (41% tetrads); young setae seen September–December, swollen, green capsules September–January, brown, undehisced capsules October–February and recently dehisced capsules January–March. The species does not have rhizoid tubers and capsules are not usually present in stubble fields unless these have reverted to set-aside or been abandoned, so the large populations which are so frequent in this habitat presumably arise from vegetative fragments of plants which survive ploughing.

## Didymodon acutus

The olive-green tufts of this species have recently been rediscovered in the county on open chalky soil and on an old railway track. Since 2012 it has been seen at the base of a chalk cliff, East Pit, Cherry Hinton, TL45X, growing in a tuft mixed with *Barbula unguiculata*, *Calliergonella cuspidata*, *Didymodon fallax* and *Homalothecium lutescens*; on bare chalk soil on a little-used road verge in Great Wilbraham, TL55M, with *Aloina ambigua*, *Barbula unguiculata*, *Bryum argenteum*, *B. ruderale*, *Pseudocrossidium hornschuchianum*,

*Microbryum rectum* and *Tortula lanceola*; in small quantity in chalk grassland on Fleam Dyke, TL55M; and in fair quantity along the middle of the old railway crossing the Devil's Dyke, Swaffham Prior, TL56S.

First record: A few shoots, with *Barbula convoluta*, *Bryum 'caespiticium'*, *B. dichotomum* and *Didymodon fallax*, clunch-pit south of Great Wilbraham, TL55M, H.L.K. Whitehouse, 1956, CGE, conf. M.O.H. It was found at seven further sites between 1957 and 1960, growing on chalky soil in four: chalk pits at Cherry Hinton, TL45Y, and Little Trees Hill, TL45W, a fallow field at Worsted Lodge, TL55SW, and on disturbed ground of an old rifle range on the Devil's Dyke, TL66F. The others were old concrete hut foundations at Shepreth,

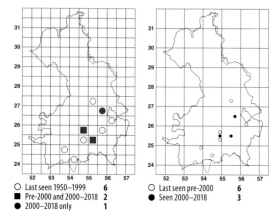

○ Last seen 1950–1999    6
■ Pre-2000 and 2000–2018    2
● 2000–2018 only    1

○ Last seen pre-2000    6
● Seen 2000–2018    3

TL34Z, a gravel pit south of Thriplow, TL44M, and a Jurassic limestone quarry, Upware North Pit, TL57L. The only later records were from Cherry Hinton, where there were one or two records per decade until 1985.

Dioicous. Female plants known from Cherry Hinton, Great Wilbraham and Thriplow; male plants and capsules not recorded. Gemmae were reported by Whitehouse (1964) but have not been found by other Cambridgeshire bryologists. According to Kučera (1999), *D. acutus* lacks gemmae and reports of their presence may result from the admixture of some *D. rigidulus* in samples of *D. acutus*.

## Didymodon rigidulus

*Didymodon rigidulus* is almost confined to hard substrates, found on sandstone and limestone masonry, concrete, bricks and mortar, oolitic limestone monuments and ornaments, stone paving slabs and tarmac. It grows more rarely on breeze blocks, granite walls, roof tiles, Carboniferous limestone rockery stones and the Wimpole Stone, a glacial erratic. Most records are from churchyards, perhaps because that is normally where we sample such habitats, but it is also found in cemeteries, farmyards, old-established parks and gardens and on old walls in towns and villages. There are single records from exposed beech roots and a gravel path. It is sometimes found in the open but it is much less often encountered in open

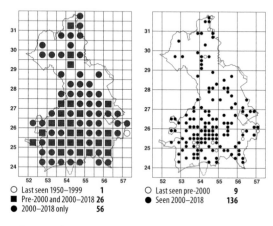

○ Last seen 1950–1999    1
■ Pre-2000 and 2000–2018    26
● 2000–2018 only    56

○ Last seen pre-2000    9
● Seen 2000–2018    136

habitats than it is in Ireland and western Britain. It is much more frequent and luxuriant here in shaded sites, such as on the north side of churches, and may be found in deep shade, as under churchyard yews.

First record: Impington, TL46SW, L.J. Sedgwick (Rhodes 1911). It was described by Proctor (1956) as 'apparently rare, but perhaps overlooked'. In retrospect the second suggestion was clearly the correct one and Hill (1967) recorded it from numerous sites in Cambridge.

Dioicous. Capsules rare (7% tetrads), unexpanded, swollen brown and nearly mature in different sites, October. Gemmae almost always present and sometimes abundant in the leaf axils.

## Didymodon nicholsonii

Usually found on asphalt (65% of tetrad records) and occasionally on concrete or thin soil over concrete (14%), particularly on paths and drives and less frequently in car parks and old tennis courts. It is usually found in at least light shade and in places where trampling or traffic is not too heavy, including old asphalt which is beginning to break up. There are a few records from compacted gravelly tracks, flat stonework (flagstones on a terrace and hard standing by a garage), cobbled areas, brickwork (including the brickwork of a bridge) and soil at the edge of a lawn alongside a tarmac path.

First record: Top of brick wall, Gamlingay, TL25SW, P.W. Richards and E.F. Warburg, 1945, BBSUK, OXF. It was refound in this habitat at the Baptist Chapel, Gamlingay, TL25G, by H.L.K. Whitehouse in 1960 (CGE) but not seen again in the county until the recent survey. We first found it in 2001 at Hinxton, TL44X, and Sawston Hall, TL44Z, and regularly thereafter in the south of the county. The first records further north were at the Ouse Washes, TL37X, in 2006 and Little Downham, TL58G, in 2009. The species, once an uncommon plant of riverside habitats, has spread markedly in Britain and in mainland Europe in recent decades.

Dioicous. Female plants are known from Gamlingay and Cambridge; plants with numerous male inflorescences were present on a compact gravelly track at Anglesey Abbey, TL56G, in 2008, only the second record of male plants in Britain. Capsules not recorded and very rare nationally.

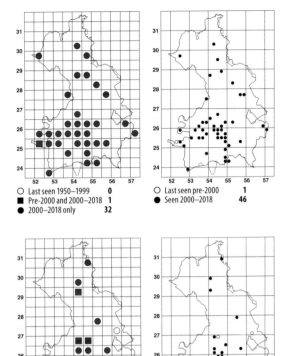

○ Last seen 1950–1999    0
■ Pre-2000 and 2000–2018    1
● 2000–2018 only    32

○ Last seen pre-2000    1
● Seen 2000–2018    46

### Didymodon umbrosus

The usual habitat of this species is as an associate of *Tortula muralis* on the shaded brickwork, stonework or (less frequently) concrete of walls or churchyard tombs. Typical sites include the north walls of churches and the steps below ground level which lead down to church crypts, and the damp lowest course of bricks at the base of walls in urban streets. It occasionally grows on more open stonework by ponds and ornamental pools. Less usually, it was found with *Ephemerum recurvifolium* on lightly trampled chalky soil on a garden path at Pampisford Hall, TL54E, on compacted soil with *Bryum radiculosum* and *B. ruderale* in Waterbeach churchyard, TL46X, and on small stones or clinker in railway sidings at Chesterton, TL46Q, and March,

○ Last seen 1950–1999    3
■ Pre-2000 and 2000–2018    7
● 2000–2018 only    10

○ Last seen pre-2000    6
● Seen 2000–2018    21

TL49E. Plants at Chesterton were short-leaved and looked very different from the normal variant with long, narrow leaf apices; at Waterbeach the lower leaves were broad with a triangular apex but the upper leaves were more typical.

First record: By Newnham mill pond, Cambridge, TL45N, M.O. Hill, 1965 (Crompton & Whitehouse 1983); still present there in quantity, 2010. This species was first collected in Britain in 1958 and it was discovered by M.O.H., R.A. Finch and H.L.K. Whitehouse at several sites in Cambridge before its identity was recognised and the species added to the British flora by Crundwell & Whitehouse (1978). Most later records were from the typical habitats but plants were discovered on earth banks within 2 m of the chalk springs at Nine Wells, Great Shelford, TL45S, in 1984 (see Preston & Whitehouse 1985); when C.D.P. revisited this site in 2006 the soil was much disturbed by recent scrub clearance and he could not refind the plant. It was also recorded away from the immediate vicinity of water on shaded chalk banks at Bassingbourn, TL34G, in 1985 and on open calcareous ground at Cambridge Airport, TL45Y, in 1999.

Dioicous. Female plants known from Newnham and Chesterton; male plants and capsules not recorded in Britain. Tubers are recorded.

### Didymodon vinealis

*Didymodon vinealis* is frequent on brickwork, concrete and oolitic limestone, growing on walls and bridges, and on the tops and sides of monuments in churchyards and cemeteries. It also occurs on other hard substrates such as the sides of chalk pits, breeze blocks, tarmac, Cotswold stone roofing tiles, Carboniferous limestone and sandstone rockery stones and the Wimpole Stone, a glacial erratic. It also occurs occasionally on soil, especially chalky and sandy soils, and on consolidated gravel drives, consolidated railway clinker and gravelly waste ground. There are a few records as an epiphyte on apple, elder, hawthorn, sycamore and willow, usually where they are thinly covered by chalk dust or soil, and a single record from dumped tyres covered in a thin film of chalky soil.

First record: Brick wall, Jesus Lock, Cambridge, TL45P, H.N. Dixon, 1883, BM, det. R. Braithwaite (see

Appendix 2). It was not recorded again until E.F. Warburg found it in Cambridge Botanic Garden, TL45N, in 1941 (OXF). He subsequently listed it from three further sites, and by the time that Proctor (1956) compiled his flora it was recognised as the common species it is.

Dioicous. Capsules rare (7% tetrads), green and starting to swell and swollen October, January, unexpanded March, brown but intact May, and both immature and recently dehisced in the same colony, October. These five observations are consistent with the accepted view that capsules mature in spring and summer (Hill *et al.* 1992).

The habitats of the county's predominantly saxicolous *Didymodon* species are not very distinct, and two or more can often be found growing

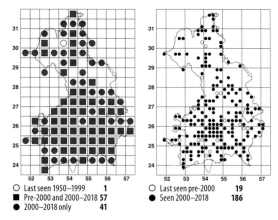

| O Last seen 1950–1999 | 1 |
| ■ Pre-2000 and 2000–2018 | 57 |
| ● 2000–2018 only | 41 |

| O Last seen pre-2000 | 19 |
| ● Seen 2000–2018 | 186 |

together. *D. vinealis* is the one most likely to be found on exposed and dry substrates. *D. luridus* and *D. rigidulus* grow in more shaded sites, and *D. luridus* is perhaps a more exacting calcicole. *D. insulanus* is also found in more shaded or humid habitats but otherwise its habitats are rather varied. *D. umbrosus* is typically found in places which are too shaded even for these species. Interestingly, the rank order of four of these species in Cambridgeshire (*D. vinealis* commonest, followed by *D. luridus*, *D. rigidulus* and *D. insulanus*) is precisely reversed in the wetter and more geologically varied environment of Pembrokeshire (Bosanquet 2010).

## Didymodon insulanus

*Didymodon insulanus* grows on a variety of habitats, including brickwork, concrete, worked sandstone and oolitic limestone, Carboniferous limestone in rock gardens, gravel and tarmac paths, fine gravel on graves, railway clinker, granite hoggin, the faces and floors of chalk pits and chalky ground in scrub and beech woodland, sandy soil in gravel pits, clay banks and ditch sides, on the base of ash and poplar trees, including street trees, and on exposed tree roots. There is a single record from rotting wood and another from a whale vertebra by a garden pond. It is usually found in sites which are humid or shaded and rather mossy, although it may grow in the open, as on a disused railway siding at Stanground Wash, TL29D, with *Brachythecium*

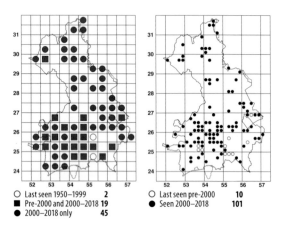

| O Last seen 1950–1999 | 2 |
| ■ Pre-2000 and 2000–2018 | 19 |
| ● 2000–2018 only | 45 |

| O Last seen pre-2000 | 10 |
| ● Seen 2000–2018 | 101 |

*albicans* and *Polytrichum juniperinum*. None of the wide range of habitats in which it grows can be described as particularly characteristic, except perhaps chalk soil in beech woodland, and it seems to occur in most at rather low frequency.

First record: Chalk district, R.S. Adamson (Evans 1913); the first localised record was from Pampisford Hall Wood, TL54E, H.L.K. Whitehouse, 1949. There were enough records in the 1950s for Proctor (1956) to be able to summarise its habitat and he described it, correctly, as 'rather uncommon compared to several of the other species' then placed in the genus *Barbula*.

Dioicous. Neither capsules nor tubers have been found in the county, although we have rarely searched for the latter.

The similarity between *D. insulanus* and *D. vinealis* is well known; its superficial similarity to variants of *D. fallax* with long, curly leaves is more likely to take recorders unawares.

## Didymodon luridus

Like other common *Didymodon* species, *D. luridus* grows in a range of habitats but it is perhaps most frequent on shaded calcareous stonework and chalky soil. Typical habitats include oolitic limestone stonework in churchyards, brickwork, shaded concrete and thin soil over concrete, silty substrates (including wood) by streams, the crumbling faces of chalk pits and open chalky banks, and chalk soil and stones in beech woods, grassland and, very rarely, stubble fields. It is also recorded from trees and shrubs, including ash, beech, blackthorn, buddleia and willow, usually growing close to ground level in places where the bark receives a fine covering of chalk dust or waterside silt, and on shaded gravel and tarmac paths, gravelly soil and railway clinker.

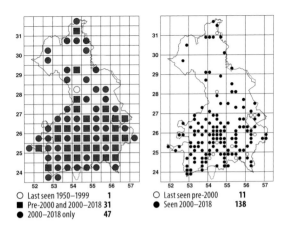

○ Last seen 1950–1999      1
■ Pre-2000 and 2000–2018   31
● 2000–2018 only          47

○ Last seen pre-2000      11
● Seen 2000–2018     138

First record: On stones in Crassulaceae bed, Cambridge Botanic Garden, TL45N, E.F. Warburg, 1941, OXF; refound here by M.C.F. Proctor in 1952. Strangely, Proctor (1956) knew this rather distinctive species from only four localities but Whitehouse and his contemporaries soon corrected this under-recording.

Dioicous. Capsules rare (1% tetrads); ripe and dehiscing in December.

## Didymodon sinuosus

*Didymodon sinuosus* is found on sheltered calcareous substrates both by water and in the built environment, usually in heavy shade. By lakes, ponds, ditches, streams and rivers, it grows above the water level but in areas which are occasionally flooded. Its substrates include the exposed and often silty roots and bases of trees (including ash, elder, elm, field maple, hawthorn, horse chestnut, sycamore and willow) and shaded brickwork, concrete and stonework. In villages, churchyards and old-established gardens it is found mainly on shaded but otherwise dry brickwork, concrete, limestone, tarmac and soil. Less often, it occurs in intermittently damp places such as concrete by leaky downpipes and in gutters around the base of buildings. It is

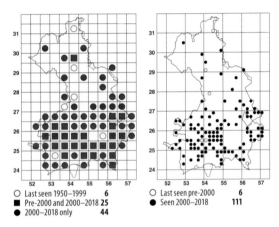

○ Last seen 1950–1999      6
■ Pre-2000 and 2000–2018   25
● 2000–2018 only          44

○ Last seen pre-2000      6
● Seen 2000–2018     111

occasional as an epiphyte away from water, at the base of ash and hawthorn on chalky slopes, on exposed roots in beech woods and on the base of ornamental trees (including birch and *Prunus*) in churchyards. In a few localities it is present in large quantity, as at Toft, TL35S, where it is very frequent on the limestone coping stones of the churchyard wall and abundant elsewhere in the churchyard.

First record: With *Leskea polycarpa* on willow trunks overhanging Bourn Brook, Grantchester, TL45H, P.W. Richards, 1929, NMW (see Appendix 2). It was frequently found thereafter by the more specialist bryologists recording in the county.

Dioicous. Only female plants are recorded in Cambridgeshire and throughout the range of the species, which may therefore represent a single clone. The leaf tips characteristically break straight across near the tip and the broken fragments perhaps act as vegetative propagules.

## Didymodon tophaceus

This is ecologically quite distinct from the preceding *Didymodon* species in its preference for wet, base-rich soils. It grows on chalk and calcareous clay on the banks of ditches, moats, streams and rivers and at the edges of lakes, farmland reservoirs and ponds, in disused clay and gravel pits, on the moist floors of chalk pits and on moist brickwork. It also grows on wet peat below the electric fences at Carroll's Ground RSPB reserve alongside the Ouse Washes, TL48Y, on peat trampled by water buffalo at Chippenham Fen, TL66P, and on the horse-grazed upper saltmarsh at Foul Anchor, TF41T (elsewhere in Britain it is frequent on moist earth on sea cliffs). It is rare on apparently drier chalky banks, churchyard tombs and disused railway sidings.

As the maps suggest, it is as frequent in Fenland as it is further south, and it has no preference for the built environment.

First record: Parson Drove, TF30NE, M.J. Berkeley, 1828, CGE, as *Tortula revoluta*, det. M.O.H. and C.D.P. It was first recognised as a Cambridgeshire plant by P.W. Richards in 1928, growing on a wet limestone wall at King's College, Cambridge, TL45P (NMW). Proctor (1956) described it as frequent by water.

Dioicous. *D. tophaceus* fruits more freely than our other *Didymodon* species (29% tetrads). The capsules do not appear to be strictly seasonal in their phenology as different stages can be seen at the same time in a single colony. Young setae seen November–January, swollen green capsules October–January, brown capsules December– January and dehiscing capsules October, November, March.

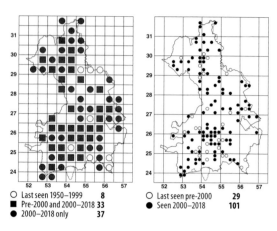

O Last seen 1950–1999    8
■ Pre-2000 and 2000–2018   33
● 2000–2018 only    37

O Last seen pre-2000    29
● Seen 2000–2018    101

## Didymodon fallax

*Didymodon fallax* grows on unshaded, disturbed soil, especially chalky soils and to a lesser extent basic clay, never on rock or stone. It is found in active and disused chalk pits, disused clay pits, on road cuttings and trampled roadside verges, tracks which are unsurfaced or made up with limestone chippings, lakeside dredgings, the banks of farm reservoirs, river banks, ditches and ponds, in chalk grassland, recently planted woods and mature beech woodland. It is rare in stubble fields (three of our 76 SBAL sites, pH 6.9–7.9). It also grows on sandy soil in gravel pits, in gravelly car parks, on disused railway lines and sidings and occasionally on tarmac.

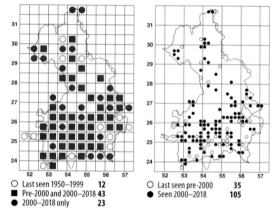

O Last seen 1950–1999    12
■ Pre-2000 and 2000–2018   43
● 2000–2018 only    23

O Last seen pre-2000    35
● Seen 2000–2018    105

First record: [Cherry] Hinton, TL45NE, 1827, J.S. Henslow, WARMS, mixed with *Dicranella varia* (see Appendix 2). It was detected in this specimen by H.L.K. Whitehouse. A specimen collected at Teversham, TL45NE, in 1834 (CGE) and labelled 'Tortula (fallax)?', apparently by H.E. Lowe, also includes a few shoots of *D. fallax* as well as much *Barbula unguiculata* (in fruit) and *Bryum rubens*. *D. fallax* was collected by both Dixon (1882, BM) and Sedgwick (1904, LSR) and Proctor (1956) described it as a common species in Cambridgeshire.

Dioicous. Capsules infrequent (11% tetrads); young setae December, January; capsules swollen, green December, January, nearly mature September, January, dehisced January, March. A colony in early January had capsules green, brown and dehisced, suggesting that like *D. tophaceus* it does not have a strictly seasonal phenology.

Although this species normally has distinctively neat, recurved leaves, it is sometimes more vigorous and such plants can be confused with *D. insulanus*.

## Pterygoneurum ovatum

This species, not seen in the county for 28 years, was unexpectedly rediscovered in a disused clay pit in 2005. A single clump with four capsules was found at Kings Dyke Nature Reserve, Whittlesey, TL29N, growing with *Lophocolea bidentata*, *Dipsacus fullonum* and *Epilobium* spp. on an open slope of Oxford Clay in a pit which had been abandoned in the 1950s but was still only partially colonised by vascular plants. Since then it has been seen in four more sites: on bare but shaded chalk soil at the edge of scrub at the top of Ruddery Pit, Guilden Morden, TL24V; on dumped clay overburden, with *Aloina* sp., *Barbula unguiculata*, *Dicranella varia* and *Didymodon fallax*, and on chalky spoil heaps at Barrington Cement Works, TL35V; c. 100 plants with *Aloina aloides* and *A. ambigua* in three patches on newly cleared chalky soil on the floor of East Pit, Cherry Hinton, TL45X; and as small patches in several places on chalky soil at the edge of the path and on the south-facing slope of the Devil's Dyke, TL56W.

First record: 'On the mud Walls of the first cottage in Trumpington, next to Cambridge, etc.', TL45M (Relhan 1793: 9, as *Bryum ovatum*). It was collected from Gog Magog Hills, TL45SE, by Henslow in 1821 (CGE) and from a mud wall in Parker's-piece Lane, Cambridge, TL45NE, by H.E. Lowe in 1837 (WARMS). Mud walls or mud-capped walls, a habitat which has now been lost, once supported a famously rich suite of calcicolous bryophytes. The species was described by Proctor (1956) as frequent on bare chalky soil and by Whitehouse (1964) as occasional on chalk banks in chalk pits or at the margins of arable fields. It was found in at least 14 sites between 1950 and 1977, mainly in chalk pits and on bare patches in chalk grassland but also in 1951 on sandy soil in a sand pit on the Gog Magog Golf Course, TL45W.

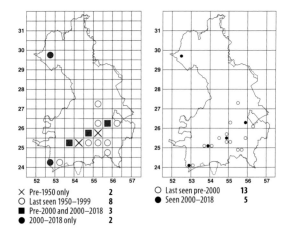

| | |
|---|---|
| ✕ Pre-1950 only | 2 |
| ○ Last seen 1950–1999 | 8 |
| ■ Pre-2000 and 2000–2018 | 3 |
| ● 2000–2018 only | 2 |

| | |
|---|---|
| ○ Last seen pre-2000 | 13 |
| ● Seen 2000–2018 | 5 |

These sites included three of the five recent localities, Barrington (1960), Cherry Hinton (numerous records, the last in 1974) and Devil's Dyke (first found 1933, refound once, at TL66F in 1951). The last record before the recent survey was made at Fleam Dyke, TL55SW, in 1977. The rediscovery of this species in the county in 2005 merited an article in Peterborough's *Evening Telegraph* on 16 December 2005. The decline in Cambridgeshire is reflected in a similar decline throughout its British range.

Autoicous. Capsules usually present (all tetrads); swollen, green November; green to brown December; brown January–March; some still with lids, most dehisced February.

### †*Pterygoneurum lamellatum*

This is the one Cambridgeshire bryophyte which is extinct not only in the county but in Britain as a whole; the last Cambridgeshire record (1970) is also the last British record. It was formerly recorded from four sites around the Gog Magog Hills.

First record: Very chalky 'soil', chalk pit behind 'The Hill Trees', TL45S, M.C.F. Proctor, 1951, BBSUK, conf. T.L. Blockeel; refound here on chalk rubble in 1953 (see Appendix 2). It was later found on a chalk bank facing south-east at Little Trees Hill, TL45W, in 1956, in the parish sand pit at the top of Wort's Causeway, TL45X, in 1957 and finally in East Pit, Cherry Hinton, TL45Y, in 1970. *P. lamellatum* was always rarer in Britain than *P. ovatum* and it declined to extinction in the 20th century.

Autoicous. Capsules abundant (Whitehouse 1964); Proctor's specimen, collected in December, has a mixture of capsules which are unexpanded, expanded but intact and dehisced.

### †*Aloina brevirostris*

First record: Floor of chalk pit, East Pit, Cherry Hinton, TL45X, H.J.B. Birks and J.G. Duckett, 1966, E. Refound here in 1975, 1982, 1985 and 1989 but not seen since; the pit ceased to be worked in the 1980s. This Boreo-arctic Montane species is the rarest of the four British *Aloina* species, all of which were recorded in this chalk pit in the 1980s.

This is the only synoicous *Aloina* in Britain; the other species are dioicous. Capsules abundant (Crompton & Whitehouse 1983).

### *Aloina rigida*

This small *Aloina* has perhaps always been rare in Cambridgeshire. In the recent survey we found it on the east side of Barrington Cement Works, TL35V, in 2006, where it grew with *A. ambigua* and *Barbula unguiculata* on disturbed chalk soil in what was then an actively worked chalk quarry.

First record: Cherry Hinton chalk pit, TL45X, P.G.M. Rhodes, 1908, BM, det. M.O.H. Refound on chalky soil here by H.L.K. Whitehouse in 1950 (BBSUK) and subsequently at intervals until 1989. It was also recorded on bare chalk soil on the Roman Road near Copley Hill, TL55B, in 1953, on bare chalk soil on the track across the old railway cutting near Worsted Lodge, TL55G, in 1951 and from a chalk pit near West Wickham, TL64E, in 1960; specimens from all these sites have been confirmed by M.O.H.

Dioicous. Only likely to be identified with capsules (100% tetrads); capsules green, brown and one dehisced, December; dehiscing October–February.

## Aloina aloides

This is most frequent on disturbed chalk soils (11 tetrads in our survey), growing in both active and disused chalk pits, on road cuttings and pathsides, around the base of wind-thrown trees on a railway embankment and in a set-aside field. It is also recorded from calcareous clay (five tetrads), sand or gravel (three), chalky sand or gravel (two) and brick rubble (one) in clay, sand and gravel pits, and on the banks of farm reservoirs, tracks and paths. It has been found with the closely related *A. ambigua* in a little-used path made of chalky gravel at Pampisford Hall, TL54E, and both may occur in the same clay, chalk, sand and gravel pits. The absence of both species from the open, chalky soil on the well-recorded Fleam Dyke and Devil's Dyke reflects their preference for sites with recent major disturbance.

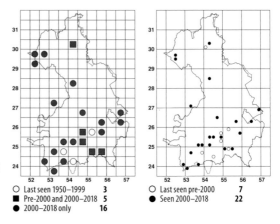

○ Last seen 1950–1999    3
■ Pre-2000 and 2000–2018   5
● 2000–2018 only    16

○ Last seen pre-2000    7
● Seen 2000–2018    22

First record: On chalk, floor of eastern chalk pit, Cherry Hinton, TL45X, H.L.K. Whitehouse, 1950, CGE; still present here in 2012. For comments on the historical records, see *A. ambigua*. Proctor (1956) and Whitehouse (1964) regarded *A. aloides* (three hectads in 1964) as much rarer than *A. ambigua* in the county (12 hectads) but the current records suggest a more equal balance between them. Even this is unusual nationally, as *A. aloides* is much more frequent in most of Britain and Ireland than *A. ambigua*.

Dioicous. Only identifiable with ripe capsules; small non-fruiting *Aloina* populations are sometimes found and cannot be identified to species. Immature, mature and dehisced capsules are often found in the same stand; freshly dehisced capsules seen November–February. All stages of the plant are tolerant of desiccation (Goode *et al.* 1994). The leafy shoots of herbarium specimens can regenerate for up to four years after collection. 'Brood cells' with thick, multistratose walls and lipid-rich contents develop on the protonemata, especially in response to drought, and are believed to act as vegetative propagules. The same is true of the thick-walled cells of the leaf laminae, which tend to fall away when leafy shoots dry up in the summer and their lamellae become very brittle.

## Aloina ambigua

As the maps show, this species is less closely tied to the chalk than the closely related *A. aloides*. The records from chalk soils (six tetrads in our survey) are outnumbered by those from other substrates, which include sand or gravel (six), calcareous clay (three), chalky clinker or gravel (two), Corallian limestone (one) and brick rubble (one). Its sites include active and disused chalk pits, sand, gravel and brick pits, railway sidings, roadside verges and ditches and little-used paths. On bare chalk soil of a roadside verge at Great Wilbraham, TL55M, it grew with *Barbula unguiculata*, *Bryum argenteum*, *B. ruderale*, *Didymodon acutus*, *Microbryum rectum*, *Pseudocrossidium hornschuchianum* and *Tortula lanceola*.

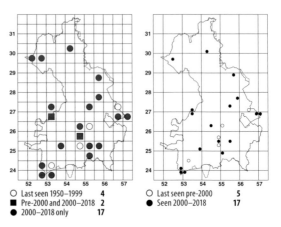

○ Last seen 1950–1999    4
■ Pre-2000 and 2000–2018   2
● 2000–2018 only    17

○ Last seen pre-2000    5
● Seen 2000–2018    17

First record: In small quantity, 'Hill Trees' Pit, Gog Magog Hills, TL45W, C.C. Townsend, 1955, E. The characters given for the separation of *Aloina aloides* and *A. ambigua* by Dixon (1924) were unreliable and misled British bryologists until the publication of Smith's *Moss Flora* (1978a) and the revision of the distribution of *A. ambigua* by Corley & Hill (1981). There is an *Aloina* specimen from Newmarket, TL66, in Skrimshire's herbarium (WBCH) but it has few capsules and we have not attempted to examine them microscopically. It is unfortunate that there are few voucher specimens for the records in the 1964 flora, when '*Aloina ambigua*' was recorded from several small chalk and gravel pits from which we have no recent records.

Dioicous. Only identifiable with ripe capsules. Immature, mature and dehisced capsules are often found in the same stand. Freshly dehisced capsules seen November–December, February–March; even in mid March stands have been seen with a majority of the capsules green and immature.

### Tortula subulata

Found on tree bases and at the foot of trees on well-drained soils. In the recent survey it was found under beeches in woods or shelter belts on chalk at Morden Grange, TL24V, Royston, TL34Q, and Stetchworth, TL66A, on soil in a rabbit-infested shelter belt at Arrington, TL35G, at the base of a large sycamore on chalk grassland on the Devil's Dyke, TL66A, and at the base of a tree on sandy Boulder Clay in Great Wood, Kirtling, TL75C, an ancient wood.

First record: Gamlingay, TL25SW, W. Vernon, c. 1696 (Vernon's annotated Ray 1696: 29, as *Muscus capillaris, corniculis longissimis incurvis*). J. Martyn also recorded it (1729b: 13, as *Bryum erectis, longis* and *acutis, falcatis capitulis, calyptra subfusca, foliis serpylli pellucidis*), without a locality, and Henslow collected it at Gamlingay in 1827 (CGE). All records are mapped here except those determined as *T. schimperi* (see below); the confirmed specimens of *T. subulata* are listed by Charman & Preston (2012). In Cambridgeshire it has not been refound during the recent survey in several sites, including Wandlebury, TL45W (last recorded 1975), the Beechwood reserve on the Gog Magog Hills, TL45X (1984), Cherry Hinton chalk pit, TL45Y (1977), Fleam Dyke, TL55 (1984) and Chippenham Fen, TL66P (1961). It would be rash to suggest that it is extinct at all of these sites, but it is a fairly conspicuous species which has certainly decreased in frequency since 1950. There is strong evidence for a decline in Britain as a whole in the same period (Hill & Preston 2014), but the reasons for this are obscure.

Autoicous. Capsules frequent (80% tetrads), recorded at several stages of immaturity from young and unexpanded to brown but undehisced January–March. Nationally capsules mature in spring and summer (Blockeel *et al.* 2014).

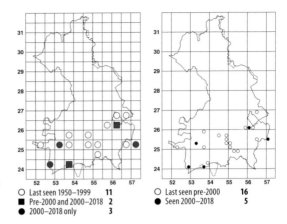

○ Last seen 1950–1999    11
■ Pre-2000 and 2000–2018    2
● 2000–2018 only    3

○ Last seen pre-2000    16
● Seen 2000–2018    5

### Tortula schimperi

The only recent record is of fruiting plants growing on chalky soil below trees on a stream bank in the small valley south of Over Wood, TL64J, in 2002.

First record: Disused gravel pits near Gray's Moor, TF40A, E.A. George, 1960, CGE, det. C.D.P. This taxon was included within the variable *T. subulata* until Cano *et al.* (2005) showed that the bistratose border of *T. schimperi* provides a clear distinction between them. A subsequent revision of Cambridgeshire specimens revealed that most are *T. subulata* but the two cited here are *T. schimperi* (Charman & Preston 2012). *T. subulata* is much more frequent nationally but in Suffolk *T. schimperi* appears to be the commoner plant.

Autoicous. Both specimens are fruiting; capsules unexpanded and expanded but intact April, intact and dehisced May.

### Tortula marginata

*Tortula marginata* is usually found on highly shaded brickwork low down on walls, including the brick gutters around the base of churches. It also grows with *Pseudocrossidium revolutum* on oolite stonework on the north wall of Elsworth church, TL36B, with *Gyroweisia tenuis* and *Leptobarbula berica* on oolite and sandstone rocks near water in the Cambridge Botanic Garden, TL45N, on a small rockery stone in a Cambridge garden, TL45T, and on shaded chalk stones on the wooded stretch of the Devil's Dyke, TL65J, P. Most records are from churchyards, but perhaps that simply reflects our intensive scrutiny of churchyard habitats. *T. marginata* is certainly uncommon in the county, but it usually grows with the superficially similar, morphologically variable and very much more abundant *T. muralis*, so it is doubtless often overlooked. This may be the reason for the limited correspondence between 20th- and 21st-century records.

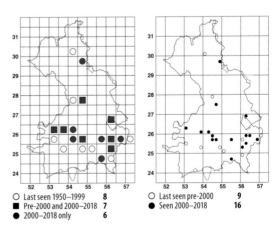

○ Last seen 1950–1999    8
■ Pre-2000 and 2000–2018    7
● 2000–2018 only    6

○ Last seen pre-2000    9
● Seen 2000–2018    16

First record: Base of stonework by fountain, Madingley Hall, TL36V, P.W. Richards, 1949, BBSUK. It was then found in the Botanic Garden (1950), at Babraham, TL55A (1957) and at further sites from 1960 onwards.

Dioicous. Capsules very frequent (88% tetrads); very immature November–March, some very immature and others swollen, green, some turning brown, April.

### Tortula vahliana

On partially or heavily shaded dry chalk soil below woodland and scrub, and occasionally as a few stems on chalky soil on tree bases, in disused chalk pits or old earthworks. In these places there is very limited competition from other bryophytes, largely because of shading but in some sites the chalky ground on which it grows has also been kept open by a limited degree of trampling, unofficial motor cycle scrambling, or by the activities of badgers. Its associates include *Aloina aloides*, *Barbula convoluta*, *B. unguiculata*, *Bryum dichotomum*, *Dicranella varia*, *Fissidens viridulus*, *Oxyrrhynchium hians*, *Pohlia melanodon*, *Pseudocrossidium hornschuchianum* and *Tortula muralis*. Since 2000 it has been recorded from Wellhead Spring, Bassingbourn, TL34G, Hill

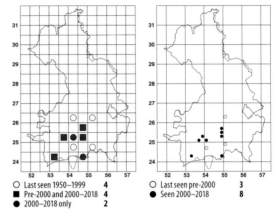

| | |
|---|---|
| ○ Last seen 1950–1999 | 4 |
| ■ Pre-2000 and 2000–2018 | 4 |
| ● 2000–2018 only | 2 |

| | |
|---|---|
| ○ Last seen pre-2000 | 3 |
| ● Seen 2000–2018 | 8 |

Plantation, Barrington, TL35Q, Harlton Clunch Pit, TL35W, Coploe Hill Pit, TL44W, Haslingfield Pit, TL45A, Wandlebury Ring, TL45W, and West Pit, East Pit and Lime Kiln Close, Cherry Hinton, TL45X, Y.

First record: Hedgerow by road from Cambridge just going into Cherry Hinton, TL45NE, H.N. Dixon, 1882, BM, CGE (cf. Dixon 1884). This was the first correctly identified British record of this nationally rare moss, which is more frequent in Cambridgeshire than elsewhere. Rhodes (1911) found it in abundance in several spots, growing on calcareous road scrapings thrown under the hedge. In 1961 Whitehouse reported that it was threatened by the spread of ivy on the sides of Lime Kiln Road, Cherry Hinton, and since 1970 all the records at Cherry Hinton have been made inside the chalk pits. The next colony was discovered by M.C.F. Proctor on chalky soil in a hawthorn hedge along the track from Horningsea to Quy Fen, TL56B, in 1953. It was later found in smaller quantity on chalk banks (spoil from coprolite pits) in dense elder and hawthorn scrub on Quy Fen itself and last seen in this area in 1966. There are 17 packets of this population in E and NMW alone, including eight collected on a BBS meeting in 1961, an illustration of the rather rapacious habits of earlier generations of bryologists. Further sites for *T. vahliana* were found in the county from 1973 onwards. Our populations are small and a detailed survey of all its known sites in the county would be worthwhile.

Autoicous. Capsules often present (63% tetrads); young setae January–March, young green capsules February. According to Proctor (1956), 'capsules ripen in late spring and early summer and are not easy to gather in good condition' and we have never seen mature fruit. Birks (1974) says that the capsules are adversely affected by late spring frosts.

### Tortula muralis

This aptly-named plant is our most frequent colonist of building materials. It is almost ubiquitous on the stonework, old brickwork, concrete and mortar of boundary walls, churches and ruined buildings, and commonly found even on detached bricks, breeze blocks and concrete fragments in the countryside. It is frequent in exposed places (asbestos roofs are another typical habitat) but often even more abundant on shaded substrates. It is, however, uncommon on the walls of inhabited buildings, except sometimes at the very base. It commonly occurs on chalk rock exposures and sometimes on shaded chalk lumps and compacted calcareous soil. It is not uncommon as an epiphyte, growing (almost always in small quantity) on isolated trees and shrubs, including street trees, as well as in orchards,

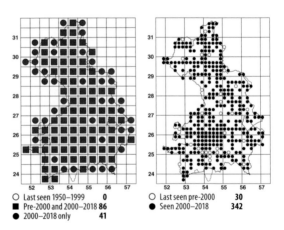

| | |
|---|---|
| ○ Last seen 1950–1999 | 0 |
| ■ Pre-2000 and 2000–2018 | 86 |
| ● 2000–2018 only | 41 |

| | |
|---|---|
| ○ Last seen pre-2000 | 30 |
| ● Seen 2000–2018 | 342 |

scrub and small plantations, and at the edges of woods or in clearings. Almost half the epiphytic records are from elder (46% of tetrad records) followed by apple (18%), willow (12%), hawthorn (4%) and pear (4%), with a few other hosts (Appendix 3). In orchards Robin Stevenson found it on 35 (4%) of the 951 apple trees he surveyed and on 11 (6%) of the 173 pears. It is rare on decaying woodwork and old railway sleepers and on miscellaneous substrates such as rubberised matting and polypropylene rope; it is extremely rare on asphalt (only three recent records), especially in view of the frequency with which this habitat adjoins walls on which it is abundant. We have found it on walls 5.5 and seven years after their construction and it is one of the first species to reach new housing estates and isolated buildings.

First record: J. Martyn (1729b: 14, as *Bryum minus, erectis, minus falcatis capitulis, foliis latiusculis, congestis in pilum canescentem desinentibus*); published by T. Martyn (1763: 24, as *Bryum murale*). Skrimshire collected it in Wisbech, TF40NE, in 1794 (WBCH), noting that it was common on old walls and the roofs of houses. Later it was described as 'abundant everywhere' by L.J. Sedgwick [c. 1905] (*Richards file*), 'common on stone or brick walls throughout the county' by P.W. Richards in 1929, 'abundant everywhere on stone and brick walls' by Proctor (1956) and 'Abundant throughout the county on the mortar of walls. Very common on brick, stone and concrete.' by Hill (1967). Gilbert's (1968, 1970) studies of the Tyne valley showed that it grew on mortar in the suburbs of Newcastle upon Tyne and on asbestos roofs in the city centre at the height of $SO_2$ pollution, only being eliminated from the latter substrate by 'really heavy pollution'. There is no indication that it was seriously limited by the lower levels of $SO_2$ pollution which prevailed in Cambridgeshire. However, although it was seen on elders on the Fleam Dyke in 1943 and on elms at Barrington in 1961, it was largely absent from bark during the period of the highest $SO_2$ pollution, 1955–80. Harold Whitehouse collected it on elder at Devil's Dyke in 1990 but named the specimen *T. laevipila* (CGE).

Autoicous. Capsules usually present in abundance (92% tetrads); immature, unexpanded or green, September, November–March; brown, December, January, March–May; freshly dehisced January, March, July. Miles *et al.* (1989) found that in a Berkshire population archegonia, antheridia and young sporophytes developed throughout the year but the later stages of fruiting were more seasonal. In the London area fertilisation is more restricted temporally but the later stages of fruiting are similar to those in Berkshire, with capsules darkening from mid February, dehiscing from mid July and most spores shed by early autumn (Duckett & Pressel 2017). These detailed results suggest a more strictly seasonal pattern than our casual observations.

## Tortula lanceola

On open chalky soil on a roadside verge, a walled vegetable garden, in chalk pits and on the sides of Fleam Dyke, TL55L, and Devil's Dyke, TL56S, 56W, 66F. It is also recorded from a calcareous clay slope, and from a mixture of soil and brick rubble, in the Whittlesey brick pits, TL29N, and from a concrete 'sandbag' in a culvert at Thorney, TF20Y. Associates on chalk include *Aloina ambigua*, *Barbula unguiculata*, *Bryum argenteum*, *B. dichotomum*, *B. ruderale*, *Didymodon acutus*, *Microbryum rectum*, *Phascum cuspidatum*, *Pseudocrossidium hornschuchianum* and *Tortula protobryoides*.

First record: On banks, Wisbech, TF40NE, W. Skrimshire, [c. 1796], WBCH (as *Grimmia lanceolata*). Relhan (1802: 423, as *Bryum lanceolatum*) knew it from mole hills between Cherry Hinton and

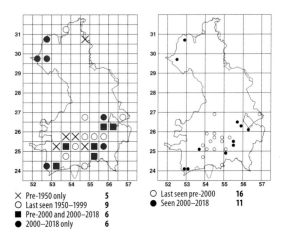

| | |
|---|---|
| ✕ Pre-1950 only | 5 |
| ◯ Last seen 1950–1999 | 9 |
| ◼ Pre-2000 and 2000–2018 | 6 |
| ⬤ 2000–2018 only | 6 |

| | |
|---|---|
| ◯ Last seen pre-2000 | 16 |
| ⬤ Seen 2000–2018 | 11 |

Teversham, TL45NE, and it was recorded in seven further sites in the 19th century, suggesting that it could be found much more easily then than now. One of the early specimens was collected by Haviland and Lister from a wall at Grantchester, TL45H, in 1878 (CGE). Rhodes (1911) described it as common on the chalk. Whitehouse (1964) also regarded it as 'frequent in chalk-pits and occasional in grassland and arable fields on the chalk', although there is in fact only one record from arable land in his dataset, from a stubble field near Coploe Hill Pit, TL44W. Since 1964 it has been lost from many small chalk and gravel pits as these have become scrubbed over or been filled in, and from sites such as the Roman Road where the open chalk verges have become overgrown. There have been no further records from arable fields.

Autoicous. Only likely to be identified when fruiting (all tetrads). Capsules green and brown, November, January; brown but not dehisced February; dehiscing February.

## Tortula modica

A plant of disturbed, well-drained soil, recorded since 2000 from roadside verges and in the gardens of large houses on the chalk in the south (at one site with *T. lanceola*), on gravel drives and paths or the edges of tracks in Fenland, from a ploughed but uncultivated field at Wisbech St Mary, TF40H, and from soil in a pear orchard at Fitton End, TF41G.

First record: Chalk district, R.S. Adamson (Evans 1913); the first localised record was from a sandy field, Furze Hill, Hildersham, TL54P, M.C.F. Proctor, 1951, BBSUK (see Appendix 2). Other 20th-century records were from chalk and gravel pits, gravelly roadside verges and drives, stubble fields, a chalky railway cutting, a cemetery and a college lawn. The species was described as 'scattered and infrequent'

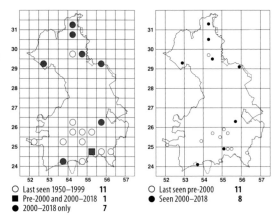

○ Last seen 1950–1999    **11**
■ Pre-2000 and 2000–2018    **1**
● 2000–2018 only    **7**

○ Last seen pre-2000    **11**
● Seen 2000–2018    **8**

by Proctor (1956) and so it remains. The only site where it has been recorded more than once is Coploe Hill Pit, TL44W (1960, 1982). In part this may reflect problems in identifying this species, which intergrades with *T. truncata*. In the field it can be distinguished by its larger size and narrower capsules; in the recent survey we only accepted records of plants which conformed to *T. modica* in most characters, including the presence of thickened rows of cells below the capsule mouth.

Autoicous. Only identifiable with capsules; swollen, green, November, December; brown, December; dehisced in January.

## Tortula truncata

Although this is a very common weed of disturbed soil in much of lowland Britain, it is a calcifuge and this limits its distribution in Cambridgeshire. Many of our records are from stubble fields, direct-drilled rape or set-aside land on Ampthill Clay, Oxford Clay or silt, more rarely on Boulder Clay, sandy clay or peat. Its characteristic associates on such sites are *Barbula unguiculata, Bryum dichotomum, B. rubens, B. violaceum, Dicranella schreberiana, D. staphylina, Phascum cuspidatum* and *Trichodon cylindricus*. Of 14 SBAL fields for which pH values are available, 12 had pH values 5.8–7.2 (mean 6.6) but the remaining two on fen silt had pH 8.0–8.1 (in these fields it may have grown on patches of more acidic soil). Only one of the 14 fields (pH 6.9) supported both *T. truncata* and

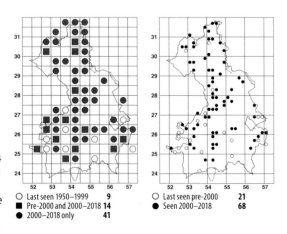

○ Last seen 1950–1999    **9**
■ Pre-2000 and 2000–2018    **14**
● 2000–2018 only    **41**

○ Last seen pre-2000    **21**
● Seen 2000–2018    **68**

*Microbryum davallianum*. In addition to arable sites, *T. truncata* grows on disturbed, non-calcareous ground in places such as churchyards, orchards, gravel pits, gravel tracks, roadsides, recently planted hedgerows and plantations, river dredgings, newly cut ditch banks, woodland rides and banks and thin soil over concrete and tarmac.

First record: Gamlingay, TL25SW, W. Vernon, *c.* 1696 (Vernon's annotated Ray 1696: 30, as *Muscus capillaris minimus, capitulis subrotundis erectis, in pediculis brevissimis*). Records by J. Martyn and T. Martyn are doubtful (see Appendix 2) and the species was not recorded again until found in fallow fields at Lolworth, TL36SE, and Long Stanton, TL36NE, by E.W. Jones in 1934 (*Richards file*). The concentration on the Woburn Sands and Jurassic clays of the west and the Breckland fringe of the east was noted by Whitehouse but recent fieldwork has provided many new records from the Fens.

Autoicous. Only likely to be identified when fruiting (all tetrads). Plants in a population can show surprising variation in size, as very small plants or unusually large ones can be mixed with those of typical size. In autumn plants growing together may have capsules at different stages of development, from green through brown to freshly dehisced; capsules dehisce October–March.

### Tortula protobryoides

Most characteristically found on lightly trampled ground on well-drained soil, especially gravel paths but also gritty tracksides, disturbed roadside verges, in cracks between paving slabs and (rarely) on tarmac paths. It is also found on disturbed soil in gardens, orchards and set-aside fields. It grows on open chalky soil at Wandlebury, TL45W, and East Pit, Cherry Hinton, TL45X, and in places where scrub has been cleared on the Devil's Dyke, TL66F. It is much less gregarious than *Microbryum davallianum*, *Phascum cuspidatum* or *Tortula truncata*, usually occurring as rather few individuals scattered amongst other bryophytes such as *Bryum argenteum*, *B. dichotomum* and *Pseudocrossidium hornschuchianum*.

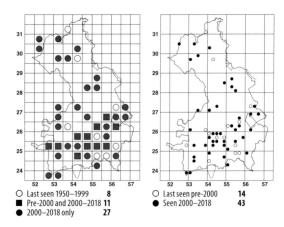

○ Last seen 1950–1999   8
■ Pre-2000 and 2000–2018   11
● 2000–2018 only   27

○ Last seen pre-2000   14
● Seen 2000–2018   43

First record: In a close near Moor Barns, TL45E, Relhan (1820: 434, as *Phascum bryoides*). There is an unlocalised specimen sent by Relhan to Skrimshire in WBCH, and it was collected from 'St Neots Road near Madingley Turnpike', TL45E, by W.L.P. Garnons in 1825 (SWN). The numerous 20th-century records in south Cambridgeshire might suggest that this inconspicuous species has declined, but they are more likely to reflect the more concentrated attention given then to sites around Cambridge. The habitats of *T. protobryoides* in Suffolk are similar to those in Cambridgeshire (Sanford & Fisk 2010) but outside East Anglia it is a scarce plant of chalk and limestone soils, not the rather undistinguished ruderal known to us.

Autoicous. Only likely to be identified when fruiting (all tetrads); the capsules are usually indehiscent but are brown and thus presumably mature November–March; one dehisced capsule seen in December.

### Phascum cuspidatum

A common and often abundant ephemeral, found on disturbed ground in almost any unshaded or lightly shaded habitat. It was recorded in 70 of the 76 arable fields recorded in the county for the BBS SBAL project, spanning the full range of soil types (chalk, clay, loam, peat, sand, silt) and pH values (5.8–8.6). Other characteristic habitats include flower beds, soil around badger setts and rabbit burrows, anthills and molehills in grassland, gravel paths, recently cut ditch sides and lake and river dredgings. It is not infrequent on recently dug graves but it was unusual to find it growing on a bone fragment in a flower bed in Grantchester churchyard, TL45H, in 2002. E.W. Jones noted a 'small brown form' growing with the type at Comberton,

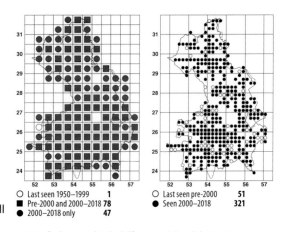

○ Last seen 1950–1999   1
■ Pre-2000 and 2000–2018   78
● 2000–2018 only   47

○ Last seen pre-2000   51
● Seen 2000–2018   321

TL35X, in 1934 (Proctor 1956) and populations often consist of plants which differ considerably in size.

First record: Shady places and on banks, J. Martyn (1729b: 13, as *Sphagnum acaulon foliis in bulbi formam congestis majus*); published without the habitat detail by T. Martyn (1763: 31, as *Phascum acaulon*) from Madingley Wood and Moor Barns Thicket. W.L.P. Garnons collected it at Moor Barns Plantation, Madingley Turnpike, in 1825 (SWN). It was refound in a recently coppiced plot in Madingley Wood, TL45E, in 1986 (Preston & Whitehouse 1987), and at Moor Barns Farm, TL45E, in 2002. Skrimshire collected it at Wisbech, TF40NE, in 1796 (WBCH), describing it as common there. The SBAL survey confirms that P.W. Richards description of the species as 'common on ploughed fields on all soils throughout the county' in 1929 still applies.

Autoicous. Capsules usually present (90% tetrads; also recorded in 68 of the 70 SBAL fields mentioned above), cleistocarpous. Sporophytes must begin to develop very early in the life of the gametophyte as immature capsules can almost always be found if apparently vegetative plants are dissected under the microscope. In winter populations usually include plants at different stages of capsule development; mature capsules noted August–October, March, April.

Most plants are var. *cuspidatum*. Var. *piliferum* has been recorded only once, growing in the 'Cambridgeshire saltmarsh' at the foot of the embankment of the R. Nene south of Foul Anchor, TF41D, by Paul Adam in 1977 (BBSUK). R.A. Finch found var. *papillosum* with var. *cuspidatum* in a 'wild flower margin' on chalky soil at Hill Farm, Whittlesford, TL44N, in 2004 but the material (CGE), though convincing, was too scanty to provide a voucher specimen for BBSUK. Since Dr Finch's death no-one has been as diligent in checking their material for this variety. Plants referable to var. *schreberianum* occur very occasionally but Cambridge bryologists trained by Dr Whitehouse have generally treated this variety with contempt and it is rarely recorded. Whitehouse (1964) reported, as var. *bivalens*, plants which had presumably regenerated from immature sporophytes and which developed apogamous capsules at the tips of the midribs. These were first detected by J.G. Hughes in material collected by Geoffrey Halliday in an arable field on the Gog Magog Hills, TL45SE, in 1954 (Hughes 1969) and later found by Whitehouse himself in a stubble field near Papworth St Agnes, TL26S, in 1960. There are no later records of this phenomenon.

## Microbryum davallianum var. davallianum

A plant of disturbed soil, growing in similar habitats to *Phascum cuspidatum* but more restricted to calcareous soils, especially chalk and calcareous clay. In the SBAL project it was recorded in stubble fields, wild-bird cover, direct-drilled rape and recent set-aside, with *Barbula unguiculata, Bryum argenteum, B. dichotomum, B. klinggraeffii, B. rubens, B violaceum, Dicranella varia* and *Phascum cuspidatum* as frequent associates. The recorded pH range was 6.1–8.6 but 20 of the 22 SBAL fields in which it was recorded had a pH of 7.4 or more and the mean pH was 7.8. Its other habitats include active and disused chalk pits, gravel pits, roadside banks and verges, newly cut ditch sides, flower beds, open chalk grassland and disturbed patches (including anthills and molehills)

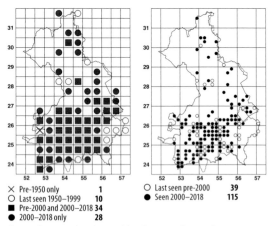

| | |
|---|---|
| ✕ Pre-1950 only | 1 |
| ○ Last seen 1950–1999 | 10 |
| ■ Pre-2000 and 2000–2018 | 34 |
| ● 2000–2018 only | 28 |

| | |
|---|---|
| ○ Last seen pre-2000 | 39 |
| ● Seen 2000–2018 | 115 |

in other grasslands, stream dredgings, muddy river banks and recently planted hedges and woods.

First record: Madingley, TL35/45, J.S. Henslow, 1821, CGE, as *Gymnostomum conicum*. There are also specimens in CGE collected at Shelford, TL45SE, by Henslow in 1828 (unnamed) and at Histon, TL46SW, by C.E. Broome in 1835 (as *G. conicum*). Proctor (1956) described it as common on calcareous soils.

Autoicous. Only likely to be identified when fruiting (all tetrads). Fruits from August to April; from August until February green, mature and dehisced capsules can often be found within the same population, but in March and April we have seen only mature and dehisced capsules.

## Microbryum rectum

A tiny gem. It is more conspicuous than most ephemerals of similar size because plants are typically grouped in small but dense colonies with shiny red capsules which are easily spotted against the open chalky soil on which they grow. It is recorded from open patches in chalk grassland, open ground in chalk pits and on chalky banks, paths and roadside verges. We have one record of plants in scrub. It is most frequent on the Devil's Dyke but it is not confined to ancient grassland; it was recorded in 2004 in the chalk grassland sown at Magog Down, Wandlebury, in 1991. There were two records from arable land during the recent survey, one from wheat stubble (pH 7.9) on the Gogs, TL45X, and the other from a ploughed but uncultivated marginal strip (pH 8.0) by Morden Grange Plantation, TL33E.

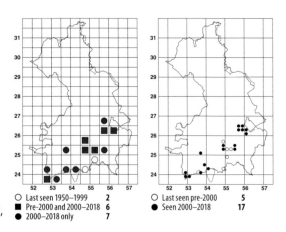

| | |
|---|---|
| ○ Last seen 1950–1999 | 2 |
| ■ Pre-2000 and 2000–2018 | 6 |
| ● 2000–2018 only | 7 |

| | |
|---|---|
| ○ Last seen pre-2000 | 5 |
| ● Seen 2000–2018 | 17 |

First record: Newmarket, TL66, W. Skrimshire, 1796, WBCH, as *Phascum curvicollum* (*P. rectum* was not described until that year). It is possible that this specimen came from John Hemsted, as material of *M. rectum* sent from Newmarket by Hemsted (BM, LINN) was illustrated in *English Botany* as *P. curvicollum* and the name only later corrected (Smith 1796a, 1801). Relhan (1802: 414) included the species (as *Phascum rectum*) on the basis of Hemsted's record and later (1820: 433) added the Gog Magog Hills. Proctor (1956) described it as 'locally common in stubble fields on the Gogs between Cherry Hinton and Worsted Lodge', suggesting that it might be less common in this habitat now than it once was.

Autoicous. Only likely to be identified when fruiting (all tetrads). Capsules cleistocarpous, green December–January, brown or red, December–March.

## Microbryum curvicollum

This grows in similar habitats to *M. rectum* and is sometimes mixed with it. A modicum of care is needed to distinguish the occasional plants of *M. rectum* with a curved seta from *M. curvicollum*, which has narrower leaves than *M. rectum* and ovoid rather than globose capsules. Like *M. rectum*, this species is most frequent in open turf on the Devil's Dyke, but it is also recorded from calcareous grassland elsewhere, and in chalk pits and railway cuttings, by paths and in a cemetery.

First record: In the small plantation on Gog Magog Hills, by the road to Babraham, TL45SE, Relhan (1793: 8, as *Phascum curvicollum*). It was first recorded from the Devil's Dyke in 1824 (BTH, CGE) and from the Roman Road on the Gogs in 1879 (CGE). Like many calcicoles it has declined in the

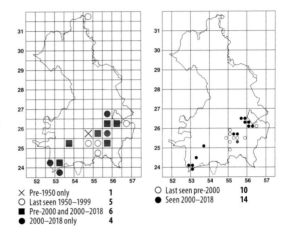

| | |
|---|---|
| ✕ Pre-1950 only | 1 |
| ◯ Last seen 1950–1999 | 5 |
| ■ Pre-2000 and 2000–2018 | 6 |
| ● 2000–2018 only | 4 |

| | |
|---|---|
| ◯ Last seen pre-2000 | 10 |
| ● Seen 2000–2018 | 14 |

Gogs area. It was described by P.W. Richards as 'abundant here and there' on 'bare soil (mostly where turf has been cut) by the Roman Road from the Gog Magog Golf-links southward for about 1 mile' in February 1932. Although less abundant there in 1933 and 1934, it was present 'in some quantity' in 1941 and it persisted on the Roman Road, TL45X, until 1968. The only record from arable land in Cambridgeshire is H.N. Dixon's specimen from a chalky fallow field by the Roman Road, collected in 1882 (BM).

Autoicous. Only likely to be identified when fruiting (all tetrads). Capsules cleistocarpous, both green and mature in November, mature February, April.

## Microbryum floerkeanum

This tiny ephemeral resembles a diminutive, reddish *Phascum cuspidatum*. It may occur as scattered individuals but in one colony where plants were more numerous we counted 30 on one square centimetre of soil and even at this density they did not appear crowded. It is an arable specialist; most records are from stubble fields, unsown strips alongside arable fields and fallow or early set-aside land; it has also been found on ground with recently planted saplings. We found it in 14 SBAL fields, six on chalk, six on fen silt and one each on Gault Clay and chalky peat (pH 7.2–8.1, mean 7.8). *Barbula unguiculata* and *Phascum cuspidatum* grew in all these fields and *Barbula convoluta*, *Bryum argenteum*, *B. dichotomum*, *B. klinggraeffii*,

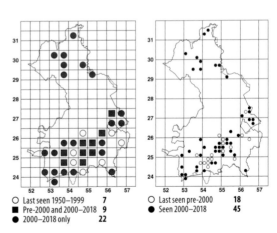

| | |
|---|---|
| ◯ Last seen 1950–1999 | 7 |
| ■ Pre-2000 and 2000–2018 | 9 |
| ● 2000–2018 only | 22 |

| | |
|---|---|
| ◯ Last seen pre-2000 | 18 |
| ● Seen 2000–2018 | 45 |

*B. violaceum*, *Dicranella varia*, *D. staphylina* and *Microbryum davallianum* in more than half. There are a few records from open chalk grassland, chalky tracksides, chalk pits (once on soil in a wooded chalk pit), and it still occurred in open patches on Magog Down, TL45W, in 2004, 13 years after the site had been converted from arable to chalk grassland. Unusually, it grew on a cattle-trampled bank of a dried-up pond at Castle Camps, TL64G, and in an area of herbaceous fen vegetation disturbed by water buffalo at Chippenham Fen, TL66P.

First record: Seven Springs [presumably Nine Wells], Shelford, TL45SE, H.N. Dixon, 1882, BM. Unlike *M. rectum* it is still frequent in chalky arable fields in the Gogs area, no doubt able to persist because of its capacity to complete its life-cycle so rapidly. It was not recorded from Fenland until the recent survey.

Autoicous. Only likely to be identified when fruiting (all tetrads). Capsules cleistocarpous, green and brown August, December, nearly mature October–November, mature December. We have few records in January and very few in February; the latest was made on 20 February. It must be under-recorded on account of its small size and short season; the short season may be the explanation for the very few records from Fleam Dyke and Devil's Dyke, as we usually visit these sites in February or March.

### Hennediella stanfordensis

Only seen in three sites in the recent survey. We found it on compact soil, including one patch on very chalky soil, in riverside woodland by the River Cam south-east of Whittlesford Mill, TL44U, in 2001, on trampled chalky ground at Nine Wells, Trumpington, TL45S, in 2006 and on shaded paths in the grounds of Girton College, TL46F, in 2017.

First record: Grounds of Hamilton Kerr Institute, Whittlesford Mill, TL44U, H.L.K. Whitehouse, 1977, BBSUK; still present in 1982. We have not visited this rather private site since, but the plants by the Cam are presumably derived from the same original source.

Dioicous. Capsules not seen and very rare in Britain. Rhizoid tubers frequent.

This alien species is particularly associated with Harold Whitehouse, who (with D.E. Coombe) discovered it new to Britain in Cornwall in 1958 and who did much to investigate its distribution and ecology. Twenty years later he began to suspect that there were two species in Britain and his paper establishing this was published after a further 10 years of detailed study (Whitehouse & Newton 1988). The Whittlesford Mill population was one of those shown to have a chromosome number of n=13, as distinct to n=52 in the polyploid *H. macrophylla*.

### Hennediella macrophylla

On disturbed soil around rabbit holes and badger setts and on woodland rides and river banks, and on trampled ground on roadside verges and by paths. It often occurs under trees, where in urban areas it is characteristically found alongside exposed roots which provide some protection from trampling. None of the populations we have seen is very large, but it grows in several places in Cambridge.

First record: Trampled soil of path by castle, Cherry Hill, Ely, TL57P, C.D. Preston, 2003, BBSUK. The distribution in the county is clearly scattered but the sites at Little Abington, TL54J, Byron's Pool, TL45H and Cambridge, TL45P, are close to the Rivers Granta and Cam. This suggests the possibility of spread down the river. Alternatively plants in Cambridge,

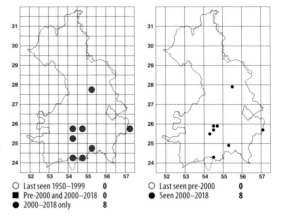

| | |
|---|---|
| ○ Last seen 1950–1999 | 0 |
| ■ Pre-2000 and 2000–2018 | 0 |
| ● 2000–2018 only | 8 |

| | |
|---|---|
| ○ Last seen pre-2000 | 0 |
| ● Seen 2000–2018 | 8 |

where it was first found on The Backs in Queen's Road, TL45P, in 2005, may have been introduced on the feet of tourists, as the species is well established in the London area (e.g. at Hampton Court, Runnymede and Windsor).

Monoicous. Capsules not seen. Rhizoid tubers occur, as in *H. stanfordensis*, though we have not seen them in Cambridgeshire material.

### Hennediella heimii

Unlike the vascular plants, there are few British bryophytes which are largely confined to saline habitats but this is one. In Cambridgeshire it is known from horse-grazed upper saltmarsh by the River Nene at Foul Anchor, TF41T, the famous 'Cambridgeshire saltmarsh'. Its only other locality is on damp ground by a gravel pit near the A14 road at Impington, TL46K, where it was discovered in 2011.

First record: Foot of the embankment, R. Nene south of Foul Anchor, TF41T, P. Adam, 1977, BBSUK (cf. Adam & Akeroyd 1978). Like vascular plants such as *Cochlearia danica* and *Puccinellia distans*, *H. heimii* has spread along roadsides inland, but it is not found in such abundance. Chris Tipper (2007) cycled along 40 miles of heavily salted roadside verges in Bedfordshire, Buckinghamshire and Hertfordshire in 2006 and found just three colonies.

Autoicous, rarely synoicous. Capsules seen at both sites; dehisced but with lids still attached to the columella in June.

### †*Acaulon muticum*

A calcifuge ephemeral, not seen since 1965.

First record: Rare, with *Riccia glauca, R. sorocarpa, Ephemerum minutissimum* and *Trichodon cylindricus*, in stubble field on Oxford Clay near Papworth St Agnes, TL26S, P.J. Bourne, 1960, BBSUK. It was later seen on Ampthill Clay near Doddington, TL49A, in 1962, in a gravel pit at Bourn Bridge, Pampisford, TL54E, in 1962 and on a disused gravel pit at Great Abington, TL54J, in 1965. The species appears to be in long-term decline in south-east England (Blockeel *et al.* 2014).

Rhizautoicous. Only likely to be identified when fruiting. Capsules cleistocarpous, immature, November.

### *Syntrichia*

Whitehouse's (1964) account of the *Syntrichia* species agrees with all except the most recent national texts in describing an apparently simple situation. He described *S. ruralis* var. *ruralis* as most characteristically found on roofs but with a wide habitat range, including tree bases. *S. ruralis* var. *ruraliformis* was a plant of sandy soils found on the coast or in Breckland, but it had also been found in a bunker on the Gog Magog golf course. *S. laevipila* was the epiphytic species, and *S. montana* a plant of brick and limestone walls. It was not until we started the current recording project in 2000 that we realised how much things had changed. *S. ruralis* var. *ruraliformis* is now widespread in a range of habitats. *S. montana* has increased in habitat range so that it is now more frequent on many roofs than *S. ruralis* var. *ruralis*. Both *S. montana* and *S. ruralis* var. *ruralis* are more frequent as epiphytes than *S. laevipila*, although the latter remains an almost exclusively epiphytic species, and *S. virescens* – first recorded in the county in 1965 – is now the most frequent epiphytic *Syntrichia* of all. We have noted *S. virescens* as an epiphyte in 117 tetrads, followed by *S. montana* (102), *S. ruralis* var. *ruralis* (82), *S. laevipila* (57), *S. papillosa* (36), *S. latifolia* (35) and *S. ruralis* var. *ruraliformis* (3). As the accounts below demonstrate, epiphytic populations of these species are similar in their host preferences.

### *Syntrichia ruralis* var. *ruralis*

A plant of a wide range of well-drained, stable, calcareous or acidic habitats, in open or lightly shaded sites. They include concrete and brick walls, flat concrete hard-standings, oolite gravestones, slate, tile and corrugated asbestos roofs, sandy and chalky soil, gravel paths, tarmac pavements, granite chippings on graves, railway clinker, decaying bales of straw, old, slightly decaying worked wood, tree stumps and iron drain covers. It has also been found on other substrates such as discarded metal drums, the foam spilling out of a disintegrating sofa, an old carpet roll, old tyres covered by a film of chalk dust and an old fibreglass boat. It is a fairly frequent epiphyte, although it is usually present on trees and shrubs in small quantity. More than half the

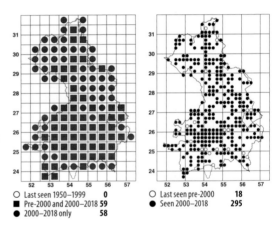

○ Last seen 1950–1999    0       ○ Last seen pre-2000    18
■ Pre-2000 and 2000–2018   59      ● Seen 2000–2018    295
● 2000–2018 only    58

epiphytic records are from elder (58% of tetrad records) with apple the only other frequent host (14%); there are a few records from the exposed roots, bases or trunks of other species (Appendix 3).

First record: Thatch roof, Linton, TL54NE, F.Y. Brocas, 1874, SWN (see Appendix 2); Brocas noted that he had also seen non-fruiting material at Hildersham Furze Hills, TL54P. It was traditionally regarded as a species of roofs; Richards described it in 1929 as 'common on roofs of slate, tiles or thatch throughout the county'. Proctor (1956) repeated this phrase, adding 'less frequent on the ground, and then chiefly on the chalk', and Whitehouse (1964) also regarded it as 'most characteristic of thatched or tiled roofs, where it may form huge cushions'. Although still found on roofs, it is no longer such a characteristic species in this habitat. It is often absent from thatch roofs, perhaps excluded by the run-off from the chicken-wire which usually protects them; *S. montana* is now more frequent on tile roofs and both var. *ruraliformis* and *S. montana* can accompany var. *ruralis* on corrugated asbestos. Whitehouse (1964) acknowledged that it was also 'frequent in a wide range of habitats' and his notes confirm its occurrence on concrete, chalky ground, gravel paths, tarmac pavements, rotten wood and tree bases. However, its presence as an epiphyte at higher levels on trees and shrubs seems to be a recent phenomenon. Nationally, it has increased in frequency in recent decades (Hill & Preston 2014).

Dioicous. Capsules occasional (21% tetrads). Young setae seen December–February, April; capsules expanded, green and brown January.

### Syntrichia ruralis var. ruraliformis

This variety occurs sporadically in similar habitats to var. *ruralis*, but especially on flat concrete hardstandings where it may form large stands. It is also found on tile and corrugated asbestos roofs, sandy and gravelly ground, railway clinker, tarmac, logs and wooden planks. It is very rare as an epiphyte, recorded once from apple, ash and elder. In mixed colonies with var. *ruralis*, which are often found on concrete hard-standings and roofs, it has appreciably taller shoots as well as at least some leaves tapering gradually to the apex. Leaf apex shape can, however, be variable and plants are sometimes found with some leaves with a rather intermediate shape. As in the national *Atlas* (Blockeel *et al.* 2014), all such plants are mapped as var. *ruraliformis*.

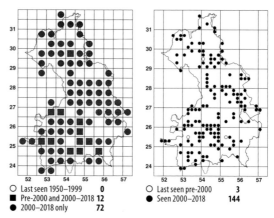

○ Last seen 1950–1999    0
■ Pre-2000 and 2000–2018    12
● 2000–2018 only    72

○ Last seen pre-2000    3
● Seen 2000–2018    144

First record: On sandy ground, Furze Hills, Hildersham, TL54P, C.C. Townsend, 1955, E; still present here in 2002 (see Appendix 2). This is classically a species of coastal sands, though it also occurs in abundance on the inland sands of Breckland. The Furze Hills population is presumably an outlier of these native sites but the next record, from a bunker on the Gogs golf course, TL45X, made by D.F. Chamberlain in 1960 (E), was clearly an introduction with sand. The next locality was a track near Buff Wood, East Hatley, TL25V, where it was found in 1969 and still present in 2000. It was recorded in two further tetrads in the 1980s and it was only in the late 1990s that we began to record it frequently. Nationally, the spread inland has been most marked in East Anglia (Hill & Preston 2014).

Dioicous. Capsules found twice (1% tetrads); in February 2016 a large population on flat concrete near Burwell, TL66B, was fruiting freely in places with expanded but not yet mature capsules.

### Syntrichia montana

Primarily a species of base-rich substrates, often frequent on stonework, mortar and to a lesser extent brickwork of walls and churchyard monuments, on tile and asbestos roofs and on concrete; recorded also on breeze blocks. It is often abundant in exposed or even sun-baked sites, such as south-facing roofs, although it may also grow in shaded places. At Stuntney, TL57P, it had colonised the mortar of a brick garden wall within 5.5 years of its construction. It is also found on gravel paths and on tarmac. It is fairly frequent as an epiphyte, but like *S. ruralis* var. *ruralis* it usually found as a single tuft or a few tufts. It also resembles *S. ruralis* in being most frequent as an epiphyte on elder (38% of tetrad records), followed by apple (16%, mostly apples in orchards but with one

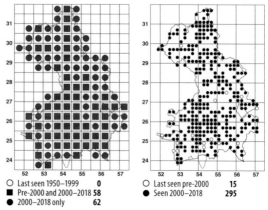

○ Last seen 1950–1999    0
■ Pre-2000 and 2000–2018    58
● 2000–2018 only    62

○ Last seen pre-2000    15
● Seen 2000–2018    295

record from an ornamental crab apple), willow (14%), ash (8%) and pear (6%). Robin Stevenson's results suggest that it is the most frequent *Syntrichia* in orchards, being recorded on 225 (24%) of the 951 apple trees he examined and 15 (9%) of the 173 pears. However, some of these records may have been based on *S. ruralis*, which was recorded on just one tree in this study (Stevenson, pers. comm.). We also have records from many other species, both native and exotic (Appendix 3). It is rare on worked and rotting wood and we once found it on old rubberised matting.

First record: Impington, TL46SW, L.J. Sedgwick, 1905 (*Richards file*); presumably included with *S. ruralis* by earlier authors. It was described by Whitehouse (1964) as frequent on brick and limestone walls. Of the 44 records he compiled for the flora, covering the period 1927–1961, 36 (82%) were from walls, bridges or unspecified habitats in churchyards and only three (7%) from roofs, the latter all of outbuildings in or near country villages, not in Cambridge. There were no records of epiphytic plants. It was recorded slightly later on old tarmac at Baitsbite, TL46W (1965) and the corrugated asbestos roof of a Cambridge boatyard, TL45U (1966) but since 1980 it has increased greatly on roofs and as an epiphyte. Like *Orthotrichum anomalum* and *Schistidium crassipilum* it has no doubt responded to the reduction in SO$_2$ pollution – all three were absent from the centre of London and the inner suburbs during the most polluted period (Adams & Preston 1992). *S. montana* has increased in frequency nationally in recent decades (Hill & Preston 2014).

Dioicous. Capsules frequent (37% tetrads); populations on roofs sometimes fruit copiously. Capsules unexpanded September, October, December, January, March, just swelling January, swollen, green January, February, turning brown February, brown but undehisced March, May.

## Syntrichia virescens

*S. virescens* is most frequently recorded as an epiphyte. It is sometimes abundant on the bases of isolated trees in urban areas, in parks or by streams and rivers in the countryside, and it grows in smaller quantity on the higher trunks and branches of a range of trees and shrubs. Elder is a favoured host (30% of tetrad records), followed by willow (16%), ash (14%) and apple (11%). It was recorded by Robin Stevenson on 30 (3%) of the 951 apple trees and four (2%) of the 173 pears he examined in the county's orchards. Other hosts on which it occurs infrequently are listed in Appendix 3. Asphalt paths are another typical habitat and it is also recorded on concrete, especially by riversides, on corrugated asbestos and, much more rarely, on tile roofs, churchyard

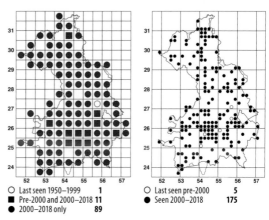

○ Last seen 1950–1999   **1**
■ Pre-2000 and 2000–2018   **11**
● 2000–2018 only   **89**

○ Last seen pre-2000   **5**
● Seen 2000–2018   **175**

monuments and worked, decaying wood. There are single records from a decaying straw bale, the lagging of an old metal pipe, an old tarpaulin and the rotting fabric of a dumped armchair. Plants can sometimes be identified fairly confidently in the field because of their small size, less conspicuous midribs and the tendency of the greyish green leaves to bend inwards when dry, but we find other colonies impossible to distinguish in the field from stunted *S. montana* or *S. ruralis* var. *ruralis*; in any event we have adopted a cautious approach and checked almost all our material microscopically.

First record: Horizontal shaded concrete by a ditch, Garrett Hostel Lane, Cambridge, TL45P, M.O. Hill, 1965, BBSUK. It was not recorded again until it was refound in Garrett Hostel Lane in 1985; thereafter it was seen with increasing frequency, especially from 2001 onwards. The species was added to the British flora as recently as 1959 and, although well described by Warburg & Crundwell (1959), it was not well known to bryologists for some time afterwards. Nevertheless, like some more distinctive species of *Syntrichia*, it seems likely that it is now much more frequent than it was in Cambridgeshire rather than just better recorded.

Dioicous. Capsules rare (9% tetrads), young setae and swollen, very immature capsules seen in December and green capsules in January. Male plants are recorded almost three times as frequently as female plants in non-fruiting colonies but perhaps this is because the male inflorescences are more conspicuous. Plants with irregular, few-celled 'gemmae' on the midrib seen three times; the 'gemmae' arise on both the dorsal and the ventral side of the midrib and do not appear to have a means of dehiscence. A few 'juvenile plants' just like those illustrated by Gallego (2005), grew on the leaves of such plants at Odsey, TL23Y.

## Syntrichia laevipila

An epiphyte of less acidic bark, growing on the exposed roots, bases, trunks or branches of isolated or well-spaced trees in gardens, parks, orchards, cemeteries and hedgerows, and on streamsides and the edges of woods. Rarely found in woodland interiors but a recently fallen ash in Hardwick Wood had a colony 10 m above the base, so it may be more frequent in the canopy than we suppose. It has been recorded most frequently on elder (23% of tetrad records), apple (18%), ash (17%), hawthorn (12%) and willow (6%), with a few records from a large number of other hosts (Appendix 3). In orchards Robin Stevenson found it on 46 (5%) of the 951 apple trees he examined but on only one of the 173 pears. It is not only much less common on trees in the county

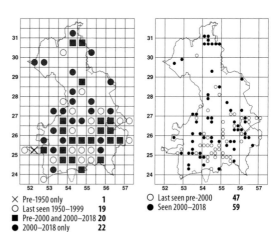

✕ Pre-1950 only   **1**
○ Last seen 1950–1999   **19**
■ Pre-2000 and 2000–2018   **20**
● 2000–2018 only   **22**

○ Last seen pre-2000   **47**
● Seen 2000–2018   **59**

than some other *Syntrichia* species but it also occurs as an epiphyte in fewer tetrads than *Grimmia pulvinata* or *Tortula muralis*, something one would never guess by reading the standard accounts of the habitat of these species.

First record: On trunks of trees about Wisbech, TF40NE, W. Skrimshire, 1795, WBCH, as *Tortula ruralis*. In addition to the epiphytic records, there is one record from a wall near Biggen Cottage, Fordham, TL66J, in 1960 (CGE) and another from an old wooden bridge at Earith, TL37X, in 1961. Interpretation of the history of this species is complicated by the possibility that some 20th-century records may have been misidentifications of *S. virescens*, but most of the vouchers in CGE are correctly identified. It therefore seems likely that the species has declined in frequency in the county. The Frescalo analysis suggests a decline between the 1960s and the 1980s and then little change, a contrast to the increase shown by *S. montana*, both varieties of *S. ruralis* and *S. virescens* since the 1980s. Nationally the evidence suggests a slight and unspectacular increase in areas of formerly high $SO_2$ pollution (Hill & Preston 2014). It is puzzling that this freely fruiting epiphyte with a Submediterranean-Subatlantic distribution has not responded more positively to the recent reduction in $SO_2$ pollution.

Typically synoicous. Capsules very frequent (69% tetrads); swollen, green capsules seen November–March and capsules mature but undehisced February, almost dehisced March, dehisced April. In the recent survey we recorded plants with leafy gemmae in just seven tetrads; according to Blockeel *et al.* (2014) such plants are usually dioicous.

## Syntrichia papillosa

Almost all records are of epiphytic plants, which characteristically grow on the bases or trunks of well-illuminated trees in streets, parks, gardens and orchards and by rivers and disused gravel pits, and in apparently more shaded and humid sites in elder and hawthorn scrub. Apple accounts for 32% of the host tetrad records followed by elder (20%), ash (10%), willow (10%), *Prunus* spp. (7%, including plums and ornamental cherries) and pear (5%). We have 1–2 records each from cedar of Lebanon, false acacia, hawthorn, lilac, Norway maple, oak and poplar. Apple orchards are a favourite habitat, and Robin Stevenson recorded it from 77 (8%) of the 951 apples he examined in the county, but on only one of the 173 pears. The concentration of records in orchards

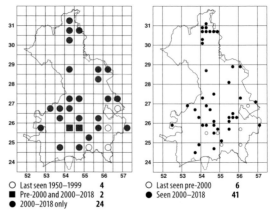

○ Last seen 1950–1999   4
■ Pre-2000 and 2000–2018   2
● 2000–2018 only   24

○ Last seen pre-2000   6
● Seen 2000–2018   41

near Wisbech is apparent from the maps but elsewhere in the county the species is unpredictable in its appearance and this is reflected in the sporadic distribution. It is unmistakeable when moist, but small clumps are easily overlooked when they are dry. The only non-epiphytic records since 2000 are from a wooden stile at Meldreth, TL34S, the wooden roof of a decaying hen house at Littleport, TL58U, and the relatively new brickwork of a railway bridge at Barnwell Road, Cambridge, TL45U.

First record: Trunk of young ash tree at fen margin, Chippenham Fen, TL66P, R.E. Parker, 1952, BBSUK. It was discovered in only five further sites between 1952 and 1999, but much more frequently on our survey. Some colonies may be short-lived: it was first found on a memorial in Grantchester churchyard, TL45H, in 1984 and spread slightly on the memorial until 1992, but dwindled and disappeared in the late 1990s. As a species of the wider countryside it is more likely to be recorded by our surveys than on the 20th-century excursions to special sites but it nevertheless seems to have undergone a real increase in Cambridgeshire, as it has nationally (Hill & Preston 2014).

Dioicous. Inflorescences and capsules unknown in Britain. Gemmae always present.

## Syntrichia latifolia

*Syntrichia latifolia* is most frequent in its traditional habitat of silty waterside substrates. It grows in the flood zone of rivers, large streams and major Fenland drains on trees, concrete, brickwork, the wooden planking of bridges and on rotting wooden posts. The diagonal line across the tetrad map illustrates its frequent occurrence in the Ouse Washes. It appears to be less flood-tolerant than *Leskea polycarpa*, as shown in a willow holt on the Washes near Jolly Banker's Bridge, TL47D, where a mass of *Leskea* covered the lower 1.2 m of the *Salix viminalis* trunks and branches, and *Syntrichia latifolia* grew above this zone where it was mixed with *Orthotrichum affine* and *O. diaphanum*. *S. latifolia* also occurs occasionally away from water, on shrubs, trees, asphalt paths, worked wood and (very rarely) shaded soil in gardens, by streets, in churchyards and in the precincts of Ely Cathedral, TL58K. Willows are, not surprisingly, the most frequent hosts (42%), followed by elder (17%), ash (8%) and hawthorn (6%), with 1–2 records each from several other species (Appendix 3).

First record: Henslow (1829: 30, as *Tortula muralis* β *mutica*). The first localised record was from a hawthorn by the R. Cam at Grantchester Meadows, TL45NW, P.G.M. Rhodes, 1909, CGE, as *Tortula mutica* (cf. Rhodes 1911). Unlike the other *Syntrichia* species, there is no evidence for change in the habitats or frequency of *S. latifolia* in the county.

Dioicous. Capsules rare (8% tetrads); unexpanded in December, swollen and green in March, on point of dehiscence in early April. Gemmae always present.

### *Cinclidotus fontinaloides*

Locally frequent just below, at or above the water level by major waterways, growing on almost any available substrate including brickwork, concrete, iron pilings, timber (including floating wooden platforms) and the base of willows. It is sometimes found with *Fontinalis antipyretica* and sometimes above the *Fontinalis* zone; by the Ouse Washes it grows below the *Leskea polycarpa* zone. It is known from three catchments. The most extensive population grows by the River Great Ouse at Over, TL37Q, R, at the south end of the Ouse Washes at Earith, TL37X, then northwards by the New Bedford River at Sutton Gault, TL47J, and by both Old and New Bedford Rivers at Mepal, TL48F. It is also found by the canalised River Nene in urban Peterborough, TF19NE,

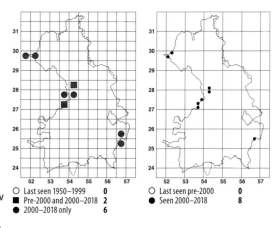

| | |
|---|---|
| ✕ Pre-1950 only | 2 |
| ○ Last seen 1950–1999 | 4 |
| ■ Pre-2000 and 2000–2018 | 21 |
| ● 2000–2018 only | 19 |

| | |
|---|---|
| ○ Last seen pre-2000 | 14 |
| ● Seen 2000–2018 | 52 |

| | |
|---|---|
| ○ Last seen 1950–1999 | 0 |
| ■ Pre-2000 and 2000–2018 | 2 |
| ● 2000–2018 only | 6 |

| | |
|---|---|
| ○ Last seen pre-2000 | 0 |
| ● Seen 2000–2018 | 8 |

29D, J, and by a tributary of the River Stour near Kirtling, TL65S. Its absence from the Cam was attributed by Whitehouse (1964) to insufficient seasonal variation in the water level of that river.

First record: Wood and stone of lock, Brownshill Staunch, Over, TL37R, H.L.K. Whitehouse, 1957, BBSUK; still present in 2009. The colonies in the other catchments were not discovered until the recent survey.

Dioicous. Capsules not seen in the county, though not infrequent nationally. Female plants seen at Sutton Gault, TL47J, in August 2008 with archegonia maturing asynchronously within the inflorescence (some old, some green and immature) and appearing unfertilised.

## SPLACHNACEAE

### †*Splachnum ampullaceum*

*Splachnum ampullaceum* grows on slowly decaying animal dung, especially cattle dung, in wetlands. It has not been seen in the county since 1841.

First record: Cherry Hinton, TL45NE, Teversham, TL55NW, and Gamlingay, TL25SW, W. Vernon (Ray 1696: 30, as *Adianthum aureum minus palustre, capitulis erectis coronatis*, with the localities added in Vernon's annotated copy). Vernon noted that it fruited in summer. J. Martyn (1729b: 13 and 1732 vol. 1: 117, as *Bryum erectis gigartinis capitulis, foliis Serpylli pellucidis, acutis*) recorded it on Hinton Moor in April and May. Relhan (1785: 396) repeated Hinton Moor as the only locality but he later added Sawston Moor, TL44NE, Teversham Moor, TL55NW (1802: 414) and Gamlingay Bogs, TL25SW (1820: 436). The final record was from Gamlingay Bogs, where a fine fruiting specimen was collected by I. Brown in June 1841 (E), shortly before the site was drained. *S. ampullaceum* has undergone a catastrophic decline in south-east England, initially caused by habitat destruction and later by a reduction in the grazing of the remaining wetlands. It was last seen in East Anglia at Gooderstone Fen, Norfolk, in 1975 (NMW). Now that it is the fashion to graze conservation wetlands it could perhaps return, although its main vectors, coprophilous flies, might not manage the necessary long-distance dispersal.

# MEESIACEAE

## *Leptobryum pyriforme*

This fine-leaved acrocarp grows in three main habitats in the county. We have found it on damp, seasonally flooded soil in 24 tetrads, growing on river and ditch sides, by lakes, ponds and scrapes dug for birds, in flooded gravel pits, on the floor of a drained moat and on ground trampled by water buffalo. In such places it may grow on a range of soils (including clay, chalk, peat, sand and gravel), very frequently associated with *Bryum klinggraeffii* and sometimes with *Aphanorrhegma patens*. Secondly, it is found on peat and, less frequently, silt soils (pH 5.8–8.1) in Fenland arable fields (13 tetrads). By the River Lark, TL67M, N, it grows on the river banks, on bankside dredgings and in adjacent arable fields, suggesting how it might

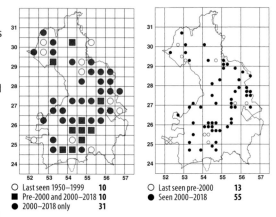

○ Last seen 1950–1999    **10**
■ Pre-2000 and 2000–2018   **10**
● 2000–2018 only      **31**

○ Last seen pre-2000    **13**
● Seen 2000–2018    **55**

have spread from one habitat to the other. The winter-flooded hollows in chalky fields south of Cambridge combine these two habitats, and provide our only records of *Leptobryum pyriforme* on arable land south of the Fens. Finally it is sometimes a frequent garden weed, especially in plant pots. We have such records from only 11 tetrads, but it must be under-recorded in the county's gardens and greenhouses. We found it three times on soil on the north side of churches or farm buildings and once on damp mortar by a drainpipe, peaty rotten wood, coarse chippings in a cemetery and trampled soil.

First record: Although it was first reported by Relhan (1802: 421, as *Bryum aureum*) from the hothouse of the old Botanic Garden, TL45P, it was not seen in the wild until P.W. Richards found it at Wicken Sedge Fen, TL56/57, in 1930, where it was very abundant, and fruiting, after a fire in the preceding summer (NMW). It was refound in a burnt area at Wicken in 1953. Both Proctor (1956) and Whitehouse (1964) knew it as a waterside plant and a garden weed but neither reported it from arable land, though the first such record was made by P.J. Bourne near Thorney, TF20Q, in 1960. Hill (1967) found it on damp walls in five Cambridge streets, TL45, in 1965–66, but it cannot be refound in any of these streets now, suggesting that it has decreased in this habitat. Gilbert (1971) also found it on damp walls in Newcastle upon Tyne, often on derelict property; he considered even then that its sites were vulnerable to redevelopment.

Capsules occasional (16% tetrads), but frequent and often abundant in plant pots (55% garden tetrads) and seen mature in our survey only in gardens and on damp mortar, rare in waterside populations (8% tetrads, young setae) and not found in arable fields. The species has a fashionably non-binary sexuality. Dixon (1924) describes it as synoicous or imperfectly dioicous and Smith (2004) as usually synoicous. Plants on imported sand by a lake at Bassingbourn Barracks, TL34I, had young setae arising from synoicous inflorescences but all the inflorescences we examined in non-fruiting populations on dried mud at Fen Drayton Gravel Pits, TL37K, and in a *Lythrum* hollow at Whittlesford, TL44P, were male and all those from plants on chippings at the American Cemetery, Madingley, TL45E, and in wheat stubble at Wimblington, TL49G, were female. A population on river dredgings at East Fen, Isleham, TL67M, had both female and synoicous inflorescences and the synoicous ones seemed to be on larger plants. In cultivation antheridia appear in synoicous inflorescences 15–20 days before archegonia (Chopra & Rawat 1977), so male (but not female) inflorescences might conceivably become synoicous. The distinctive, relatively large tubers are always present and may occur on protonemata, rhizoids and in the leaf axils. Very young plants with tiny shoots may have tubers on the protonemata and we have seen a more mature plant with tubers in 11 successive leaf axils. One inflorescence we dissected from the East Fen population had two tubers rather than sex organs inside the perichaetial leaves.

# ORTHOTRICHACEAE

On excursions in the 1970s Harold Whitehouse, when he saw an undergraduate eagerly scanning tree trunks for bryophytes, would often comment rather ruefully, 'I'm afraid that Cambridgeshire isn't the place to study epiphytes'. No family better illustrates the expansion of these species in response to reduced $SO_2$ levels since then than the Orthotrichaceae. Whereas only five species were seen in the 1960s and 1970s – *Orthotrichum affine*, *O. anomalum*, *O. diaphanum*, *O. lyellii* (a single, casual occurrence) and *Zygodon viridissimus* – we recorded 18 in the recent survey.

## Zygodon

With the exception of a few populations on stonework, which we have been prepared to name as *Zygodon viridissimus* in the field, all records of *Zygodon* in the recent survey were based on microscopic examination of the gemmae, which are borne on the stems.

### Zygodon viridissimus var. viridissimus

*Zygodon viridissimus* is most frequent as an epiphyte (108 tetrads) but it is also widespread as an epilith (43 tetrads). As an epiphyte it grows in ancient and secondary woodland, plantations, orchards, scrub on the Fleam and Devil's Dykes and in disused chalk, clay and gravel pits, on trees by rivers, streams and ditches and in gardens. Though it is often found in sheltered sites, it is very infrequent in the closed interiors of ancient woods, although more likely to be found in shrubby clearings, by ponds or on the woodland edge. Elder is much the most frequent host (42% tetrad records) and the species reaches maximum abundance on over-mature and moribund elders where it can grow in dense masses. Its other common hosts are ash (13%), apple (10%), willow (7%) and hawthorn

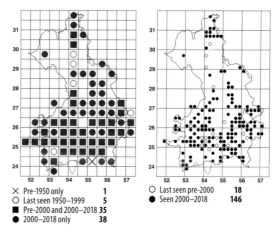

| | | |
|---|---|---|
| ✕ Pre-1950 only | 1 | |
| ○ Last seen 1950–1999 | 5 | |
| ■ Pre-2000 and 2000–2018 | 35 | |
| ● 2000–2018 only | 38 | |
| ○ Last seen pre-2000 | 18 | |
| ● Seen 2000–2018 | 146 | |

(5%). In orchards Robin Stevenson recorded it on 29 (3%) of the 951 apple trees he surveyed but on none of the 173 pears. There are a few records from a large number of other native and exotic species, listed in Appendix 3. Epilithic plants grow on base-rich masonry, brickwork and mortar of old walls, including those of churches and churchyards, on gravestones and ornamental stone ornaments, on concrete and on the Wimpole Stone, TL35F, a glacial erratic. They are most frequent in shaded sites, such as the north walls of churches and the footings of concrete bridges. There are single records from worked wood, rotting wood and a fibreglass boat stored under trees.

First record: On shrubs on edge of road, copse near Madingley [perhaps Whitepits Plantation, TL35U], P.W. Richards, 1928, NMW, conf. C.D.P. (see Appendix 2). The species remained frequent in the county during the period of maximum SO$_2$ pollution. Proctor (1956) and Whitehouse (1964) knew of no epilithic records but recorders presumably overlooked it in these habitats as shortly afterwards Hill (1967) found it on shaded concrete in two Cambridge sites, TL45N, P, and on the limestone of Orwell church, TL35Q.

Dioicous. Capsules rare (1% tetrads), only recorded once in the recent survey, in a large population on elders, green and swollen in December. Gemmae always present.

### Zygodon rupestris

With one exception (detailed below), all our recent records come from Robin Stevenson's orchard survey. He has recorded it on 39 (4%) of the 951 apples he surveyed individually, and one (1%) of the 173 pears. The only orchard in which it was at all frequent was Franklin's Old Orchard, Cottenham, TL46N, where it grew on 11 of the 29 trees of an unidentified apple cultivar examined but on only one of the 20 Bramley apples studied.

First record: Covering almost all the trunk of an elm from about 18 to 40 inches above the ground (with *Hypnum cupressiforme* below), Fleam Dyke near Dungate Farm, TL55R, E.W. Jones, 1932, NMW (as *Z. viridissimus*), det. M.O.H. and C.D.P. This specimen was only redetermined in 2017, and the first published record was made by C.D.P. from near

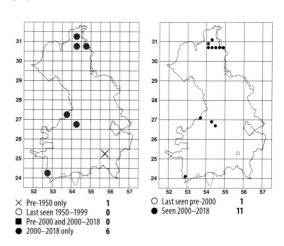

| | | |
|---|---|---|
| ✕ Pre-1950 only | 1 | |
| ○ Last seen 1950–1999 | 0 | |
| ■ Pre-2000 and 2000–2018 | 0 | |
| ● 2000–2018 only | 6 | |
| ○ Last seen pre-2000 | 1 | |
| ● Seen 2000–2018 | 11 | |

the base of an ash tree in secondary woodland on the north side of Morden Grange chalk pit, TL24V, in 2005 (BBSUK). *Z. rupestris* was first found in orchards in 2007.

Dioicous. Capsules not recorded. Gemmae always present.

### Zygodon conoideus var. conoideus

An epiphyte which in recent years has colonised sheltered trees and shrubs in ancient and secondary woods and plantations, scrub in disused chalk and gravel pits and on chalk earthworks, fen carr, riversides and gardens. Elder (42% of tetrad records) and willow (13%) are the most frequent hosts, followed by apple (13%), pear (13%) and hawthorn (6%). In orchards Robin Stevenson recorded it on 24 (3%) of the 951 apples he surveyed and two (1%) of the 173 pears. There are two records from ash and single records from elm, rose and sycamore, and on the wooden roof of a decaying hen house.

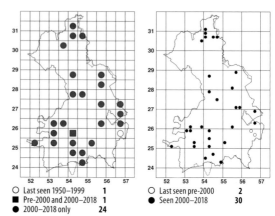

○ Last seen 1950–1999　　1
■ Pre-2000 and 2000–2018　1
● 2000–2018 only　　24

○ Last seen pre-2000　　2
● Seen 2000–2018　　30

First record: Frequent on branch of one elder at edge of ride, Ditton Park Wood, TL65T, C.D. Preston, 1991, BBSUK. It was found on the Devil's Dyke, TL65P, in 1992, at the Bird Sanctuary, Adams Road, Cambridge, TL45J, in 1994 and then more frequently from 2000 onwards. Before these records no *Zygodon* had been recorded at Ditton Park Wood or the Bird Sanctuary, demonstrating that this species had not previously been misidentified there as *Z. viridissimus*. Its history here reflects its dramatic spread since 1990 in central and eastern England and in the Netherlands (Blockeel *et al.* 2014).

Dioicous. Capsules rare (3% tetrads), recorded only once in the county, on elder. Fruits are frequent in western Britain and Ireland, where the species fruits much more freely than *Z. viridissimus*. Gemmae always present.

### Orthotrichum lyellii

The most distinctive and the most frequent of the recent *Orthotrichum* colonists, both in Cambridgeshire and in the south of England as a whole. In orchards, a habitat which it probably favours (it can be found in olive groves in the Mediterranean region), it has been recorded on 70 (7%) of the 951 apple trees and 12 (7%) of the 173 pears surveyed by Robin Stevenson, whereas none of the other recent colonists have been recorded on more than 1% of either host. Elsewhere it is known from many ancient woods and from secondary woods, especially wet woodland, scrub, and on trees by streams, in gardens and even on roadsides; there are two records from Cambridge street trees. Many colonies are found on tree trunks 1.5–4 m

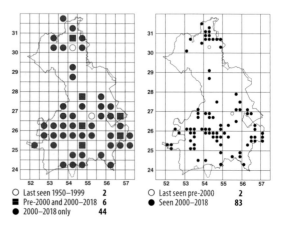

○ Last seen 1950–1999　　2
■ Pre-2000 and 2000–2018　6
● 2000–2018 only　　44

○ Last seen pre-2000　　2
● Seen 2000–2018　　83

above ground level, and in dry weather the higher plants can be detected by the characteristic outline of the tall, gently curved stems. Colonies sometimes consist of a single small tuft or one large vigorous patch but in some sites several plants may be found on one tree or plants may grow on several trees. The main hosts are ash (25% of tetrad records), apple (17%), willow (16%), pear (9%), hawthorn (6%), oak (5%) and field maple (4%) and there are 1–3 records from several other native and exotic species (Appendix 3). We also have one record from a dead log and one from a shaded wooden seat.

First record: Madingley, TL36V, P.G.M. Rhodes (Rhodes 1911). Not seen again until H.J.B. Birks found it on a beech at Wandlebury, TL45W, in 1973, a casual occurrence (it was often searched for in the exact place in subsequent years but never refound). Its discovery on an elder at Chippenham Fen, TL66P, in 1990 (CGE) was the first sign of its recent spread; this was followed by six further sites in the 1990s (three from orchards, preceding Stevenson's special survey) and many more in the 21st century.

Dioicous. Capsules not recorded. Gemmae always present, sometimes sparse, sometimes abundant.

### Orthotrichum striatum

The records in the Wisbech area, TF30, 40, come from apple and pear trees in orchards. Although Robin Stevenson has found it on general surveys of several orchards, it was only present on four of the 951 apples he surveyed systematically, and on none of the 173 pears. Elsewhere the species has been found on a planted sycamore at Welney, TL59H, poplar at Wimpole Park, TL35F, white willow in riverside woodland, Paradise LNR, Cambridge, TL45N, a sloping ash trunk in Balsham Wood, TL54Z, ash and field maple in Basefield Wood, TL65N, two willow bushes at Chippenham Fen, TL66P and a hawthorn in secondary woodland at Newmarket, TL66Q.

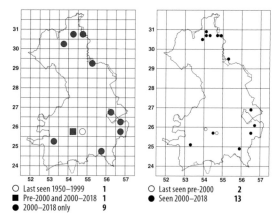

| | |
|---|---|
| ○ Last seen 1950–1999 | **1** |
| ■ Pre-2000 and 2000–2018 | **1** |
| ● 2000–2018 only | **9** |

| | |
|---|---|
| ○ Last seen pre-2000 | **2** |
| ● Seen 2000–2018 | **13** |

First record: Madingley, TL45E, J.S. Henslow, 1821, CGE. Early unlocalised records of *Orthotrichum striatum* (T. Martyn 1763 and Relhan 1785, as *Polytrichum striatum β*; Henslow 1829) have hitherto been assumed to be errors for *O. affine*, which none of these authors reported (Proctor 1956), but Henslow's recently rediscovered specimen is correctly identified. An unlocalised and undated specimen from Cambridgeshire in the herbarium of the Suffolk bryologist F.K. Eagle (1785–1856) is also *O. striatum*, as labelled (CGE). The next record, from an apple tree in a garden in Luard Road, Cambridge, TL45T, R.A. Finch, 1995 (BBSUK), was a rather early precursor of the current wave of colonisation. Further records were not made until 2006.

Autoicous. Only identifiable with capsules; nearly ripe November, freshly dehisced March, April, old and empty May. Although the leaves of this species taper to a finer point than those of *O. affine*, confident identification requires the presence of mature capsules. Such capsules are rarely present in autumn and early winter and most of our records were made between February and May, suggesting that the species might be under-recorded.

### Orthotrichum speciosum

First recorded in the county during the recent survey, growing on an ash tree at Balsham Wood in 2008 (see below) and on the branches of an old Bramley and a Discovery apple tree at Garner's Orchard, North Brink, Wisbech, TF40D, in 2009.

First record: Several tufts growing with *Amblystegium serpens* and *Orthotrichum affine* on sloping trunk of ash in moist area of Balsham Wood, TL54Z, M.O. Hill & C.D. Preston, 2008, BBSUK. There were a few 19th-century records of this species from England, but by the mid 20th century it had retreated to Scotland, where it was largely confined to the eastern Highlands. It was rediscovered in Co. Durham in 1999 and since 2008 it has been found in several scattered sites further south in central and eastern England.

Autoicous. Only identifiable with capsules; immature and dehisced February, March.

### Orthotrichum affine

This is the most frequent specialist epiphyte in the county, found on the trunks, branches and twigs of trees and shrubs in a wide range of habitats including ancient woodland, secondary woodland and plantations, orchards, scrub, fen carr, churchyards, cemeteries and gardens and by running and still waters, roads and tracks. Although rarely found on urban street trees, it grows epiphytically in the centre of Cambridge in Great St Mary's churchyard, TL45P. In orchards Robin Stevenson recorded it on 610 (64%) of the 951 apple trees he surveyed and 106 (61%) of the 173 pears. Although its ecological range has a broad overlap with that of the even more frequent generalist *Orthotrichum diaphanum*, which often grows with it, *O. affine* is

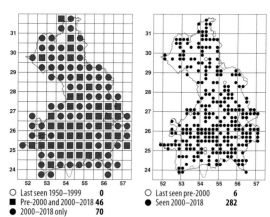

| | |
|---|---|
| ○ Last seen 1950–1999 | **0** |
| ■ Pre-2000 and 2000–2018 | **46** |
| ● 2000–2018 only | **70** |

| | |
|---|---|
| ○ Last seen pre-2000 | **6** |
| ● Seen 2000–2018 | **282** |

much less common on the more exposed trees and shrubs (often with very nutrient-enriched bark) which may support abundant *O. diaphanum*, whereas *O. affine* is more frequent on trees in more shaded, sheltered and humid sites such as wet woodland interiors. It almost always accompanies the rarer epiphytic *Orthotrichum* species, and doubtless they are sometimes overlooked amongst this common and variable plant. Elder (21% of tetrad records), ash (16%) and willow (15%) are the most frequent hosts, as they are in the very different environment of Mid-west Wales (Bates 2015) although in Pembrokeshire sycamore edges elder out of the top three (Bosanquet 2010). Other hosts recorded in at least 10 tetrads are apple (6%), hawthorn (6%), field maple (4%), elm (3%), oak (3%), pear (3%), sycamore (3%) and poplar (2%); the long list of uncommon hosts is given in Appendix 3. It is rare on concrete, gravestones, wall tops and mortar (10 tetrads), usually in shaded sites, and on decaying woodwork, such as old fences, seats, planks of farm trailers, telegraph poles and railway sleepers (14 tetrads). There are single records from a caravan, a fibreglass boat, a rotting armchair and some plastic matting, all under trees, and from railway clinker and asphalt on a little-used road.

First record: Trunk of ash tree, Hardwick Wood, TL35N, G.D. Haviland, 1881, CGE (see Appendix 2); still present here in 2014. It may previously have been confused with *O. striatum* (q.v.). It was frequent during the period of maximum SO$_2$ pollution, approaching the centre of Cambridge as closely as Adams Road Bird Sanctuary, TL45J, where one occurrence (1964) was on a wet wall, and Banham's Boatyard, TL45U, on the corrugated asbestos roof of a shed. By contrast, it was absent from trees for 10 miles (16 km) upwind of the centre of the industrial city of Newcastle upon Tyne in the same period (Gilbert 1970). It appears to have had a narrower habitat range in Cambridgeshire in earlier decades. Proctor (1956) described it as 'usually found on isolated trees, often in damp places, or in small thickets, rather than in extensive woods'. Of the 28 records available to Whitehouse (1964), seven were from chalk pits and only one from an ancient wood; it was not recorded from Hayley Wood until 1975, for example, Gamlingay Wood until 1993 and Buff Wood until 2000. The Frescalo analysis indicates a marked increase since the 1980s.

Autoicous. Capsules very frequent (83% tetrads) although it does not fruit as freely as *O. diaphanum* and vegetative tufts are often encountered. Capsules very young December, February, March; swollen, green April, May; freshly dehisced August–December. The old capsules are persistent, and often accompany the young capsules of the next generation.

## Orthotrichum obtusifolium

Only known from one site in the county, a commercial orchard, where it was first discovered on the branch of a Bramley apple tree in 2007 (see below). This colony consisted of 75–100 shoots spread over 25 cm of the branch, growing with *Orthotrichum diaphanum*. It was still present on this tree in 2010, when Robin Stevenson found a second small colony on the branch of a Bramley in an adjacent row. This stand of Bramleys is about 70 years old.

First record: W. Norman's orchard, Begdale Road, Elm, TF40T, C.R. Stevenson, 2007, BBSUK. *O. obtusifolium* was known from central England in the 19th century but, like *O. speciosum*, it retreated to north-east Scotland in the period of maximum SO$_2$ pollution. There have been a few recent records from England and Wales in recent years, including one from Warboys Wood, Hunts.

Dioicous. Capsules not recorded and unknown in Britain. Gemmae always present.

## Orthotrichum anomalum

This is a specialist epilith, more or less confined to hard, flat or sloping (but not vertical), base-rich, exposed or moderately (but not heavily) shaded stone or similar substrates. Almost half our tetrad records (46%) are from churchyards and cemeteries, and we have found it in 55% of the churchyards we have visited. Here it grows on stonework ledges, window sills and buttresses of the church walls, on the flat tops of table tombs, on other monuments and gravestones, on the coping stones of boundary walls and sometimes on concrete steps and paths. Oolitic limestone is a favoured substrate. In the wider countryside concrete is the main substrate (56% of tetrad records), followed by corrugated asbestos roofs (11%), trees (8%) and stonework (6%). It colonises isolated structures in rural areas, such as

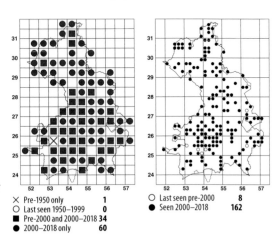

| | |
|---|---|
| ✕ Pre-1950 only | 1 |
| ○ Last seen 1950–1999 | 0 |
| ■ Pre-2000 and 2000–2018 | 34 |
| ● 2000–2018 only | 60 |

| | |
|---|---|
| ○ Last seen pre-2000 | 8 |
| ● Seen 2000–2018 | 162 |

World War II pill boxes and the concrete blocks used as barriers across farm tracks, as well as concrete in built-up areas. There are three records from asphalt and 1–2 from brickwork, fibreglass, mortar, railway clinker, roof slates and tiles, rusty iron and worked wood, as well as imported Carboniferous limestone in gardens. As an epiphyte there are three records from elder and one from ash, elm, horse chestnut and walnut.

First record: Walls of Grantchester churchyard, TL45H, and Trumpington churchyard, TL45M, Relhan (1820: 446). It was collected from Bottisham, TL56, by Jenyns in 1824 (BTH) and from Coton churchyard, TL45E, by Henslow in 1830 (CGE). Rhodes (1911) noted that it was still present in both Grantchester and Trumpington churchyards and this is still the case. In the 1950s and 1960s these were the closest known populations to Cambridge, except for records on the imported limestone in the Botanic Garden and Chaucer Road, TL45N, and one record from the Grange Road Rifle Range, TL45J. Stonework and limestone are the only substrates mentioned for the mid 20th-century records, although the precise habitats of plants in churchyards or on walls are not always specified. In the recent survey it was found at numerous sites in the built-up parts of the city and on the wider range of substrates listed above. The species is sensitive to air pollution (Gilbert 1968) and it has increased in frequency not only in Cambridgeshire but in the country as a whole (Hill & Preston 2014). Its history in the county parallels that of *Schistidium crassipilum* and the Frescalo plots are very similar.

Autoicous. Only identifiable with capsules, but it fruits freely and we have only rarely found small vegetative populations which could not be positively identified. Capsules very young September–November, immature November–March, May; mature but undehisced March, April; dehiscing or freshly dehisced March–May; old and empty September–November.

## Orthotrichum cupulatum

A morphologically and ecologically similar species to the more frequent *Orthotrichum anomalum*, which often grows with it. A higher proportion of tetrad records is from churchyards and cemeteries (73%), although we have found it in only 18% of the sites visited. It shows a distinct preference for ancient rather than modern churchyards, and within the churchyard it occurs on flat or sloping stonework or, more rarely, concrete in the same microhabitats as those listed for *O. anomalum*. Other typical associates are *Grimmia pulvinata*, *Syntrichia montana* and *Tortula muralis*. In the wider countryside most records are from concrete (57% of these tetrad records) and stonework (21%) with single occurrences on imported Carboniferous limestone,

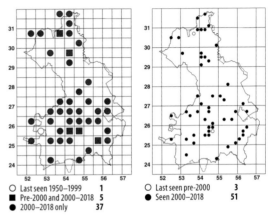

O Last seen 1950–1999    1
■ Pre-2000 and 2000–2018    5
● 2000–2018 only    37

O Last seen pre-2000    3
● Seen 2000–2018    51

roof tiles and on the base of a beech tree on a garden lawn (where a single tuft grew, surprisingly, with much *Dicranoweisia cirrata*). There is no clear ecological distinction between it and *O. anomalum*, but in some sites it shows a preference for shade, which is not usually the case with *O. anomalum*, and several of the records of *O. cupulatum* in the wider countryside are on stonework and concrete near water.

First record: Bridge, Murrow, TF30T, A.O. Chater, 1955 (*Whitehouse species file*; see Appendix 2). No longer present in 2002, when the brick bridge, built in 1833, was in a state of disrepair and the coping stones had gone, some fallen into the ditch below. *O. cupulatum* was not recorded again in the county until found in churchyards at Croxton, TL25P, in 1985 and Grantchester, TL45H, in 1986. Although *O. anomalum* was present on Carboniferous limestone when it arrived in the Botanic Garden in 1955, *O. cupulatum* was not seen on these rocks until 1986 (Preston & Whitehouse 1992b). It is not clear whether it was overlooked for 30 years or whether it colonised the limestone after arrival. As in Cambridgeshire, the species has shown a dramatic increase nationally since 1990 (Hill & Preston 2014).

Autoicous. Only identifiable with capsules, but it fruits freely. Capsules immature December–April, losing calyptrae but lids still in place March–May; dehiscing and freshly dehisced April–May; old and empty October, December–January.

Plants vary in the hairiness of the calyptrae; in 2002 most plants on the wall of Gamlingay churchyard, TL25L, had naked calyptrae but some had frequent stiff hairs.

## Orthotrichum stramineum

The scattered records of this epiphyte come from a range of hosts and habitats: apples (21% of tetrad records) and pears (5%) in orchards, ash (26%) in ancient woods, field maple (16%) in ancient and secondary woods, sycamore (11%), elder (5%) and traveller's joy (5%) in secondary woodland and plantations and willow (11%) in fen carr. In his orchard surveys Robin Stevenson found it on three of the 951 apple trees he surveyed and on one of the 173 pears; all the trees were in different orchards. Populations elsewhere were similarly small; sometimes only a single tuft was seen although numerous tufts were found on a single willow at Wicken Poor's Fen, TL57Q, in 2002.

First record: On trunk of sloping elder in sheltered ditch, Devil's Dyke, TL56S, C.D. Preston, 1994, BBSUK. Not seen again in the county until 2002 and then found almost annually until 2010. Like several of its congeners, *O. stramineum* has spread dramatically in eastern England in recent decades (Hill & Preston 2014).

Autoicous. Only identifiable with capsules. With the exception of one record, made in early January, all our records were made between 26 January and 5 April. This is the time when the small, neat tufts of this species are covered by numerous immature fruits with characteristically dark-tipped calyptrae and are thus at their least inconspicuous.

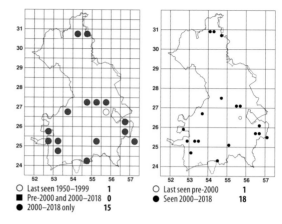

| | |
|---|---|
| ○ Last seen 1950–1999 | 1 |
| ■ Pre-2000 and 2000–2018 | 0 |
| ● 2000–2018 only | 15 |

| | |
|---|---|
| ○ Last seen pre-2000 | 1 |
| ● Seen 2000–2018 | 18 |

### Orthotrichum tenellum

Although the records of *Orthotrichum tenellum* are as scattered as those of *O. stramineum*, and also cover a range of hosts and habitats, they come on the whole from more open sites. They include records from apple trees (29% of tetrad records) and pears (6%) in orchards, where the species is as rare as *O. stramineum* judging by Robin Stevenson's records of plants on five of the 951 apple trees surveyed and on one of the 173 pears, with only 1–2 trees of those surveyed in any one orchard. It has also been found on elders (29%) by rivers, streams and ditches, in a Fenland sycamore plantation and in scrub on the Devil's Dyke, and on willows (18%) by rivers and in holts on the Ouse Washes. There are single records (6%) from birch in fen carr, ginkgo in a college garden and ash and oak in ancient woodland.

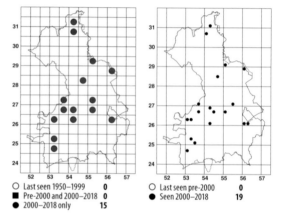

| | |
|---|---|
| ○ Last seen 1950–1999 | 0 |
| ■ Pre-2000 and 2000–2018 | 0 |
| ● 2000–2018 only | 15 |

| | |
|---|---|
| ○ Last seen pre-2000 | 0 |
| ● Seen 2000–2018 | 19 |

First record: On elder by stream, Grange Farm, Knapwell, TL36G, M.O. Hill, 2000, BBSUK. Its discovery in Cambridgeshire is symptomatic of its spread into eastern England between the two national bryophyte atlases (Hill *et al.* 1994, Blockeel *et al.* 2014).

Autoicous. Only likely to be recognised when fruiting. Capsules immature December, February, March; freshly dehisced September; dehisced August, November; old capsules can be found alongside the immature fruits in spring. It has been recorded throughout the winter, as both the tall, rocket-shaped calyptrae and the rich brown colour of the old capsules are recognisable once their appearance is known. Gemmae are occasionally numerous or even abundant on the lower leaves.

### Orthotrichum pumilum

A tuft of this tiny species was discovered towards the end of our recent fieldwork, growing on hawthorn in a thin strip of woodland along the south side of the railway line across Coldham's Common, Cambridge.

First record: Coldham's Common, Cambridge, TL45U, C.D. Preston, 2017, BBSUK. This is one of the rarer of the recolonising *Orthotrichum* species. It has always been rare in Britain, and recent plants are presumably derived from spores blown in from continental Europe (Blockeel *et al.* 2014). In the Netherlands, where it was rare until 1990, it is now much more frequent but it nevertheless often occurs as only a single tuft. Our plant belongs to the segregate species *O. schimperi* (fide T.L. Blockeel).

Autoicous. Only identifiable with capsules, which are frequent; expanded, green March.

### Orthotrichum diaphanum

*Orthotrichum diaphanum* differs from the other British *Orthotrichum* species in its capacity to grow with equal facility as an epiphyte or an epilith. Its frequency in the county can be attributed to its tolerance of dry and nutrient-enriched substrates, and in favourable habitats its low, crowded stems may form a continuous sward and completely cover the underlying substrate. As an epilith it is found on stonework, concrete (very commonly) and corrugated asbestos in built-up areas, in churchyards and farmyards and on isolated structures in the arable landscape such as bridges and culverts. It also grows, perhaps less frequently, on asphalt, brickwork and roof tiles; it is rarely found on worked and rotting wood and there are single records from metal bridges, plastic matting, railway clinker and rubber tyres. Plants grow epiphytically in orchards and plantations, hedges, willow holts, scrub, parks and gardens, by roads and tracks and by rivers, streams and ditches. They are found

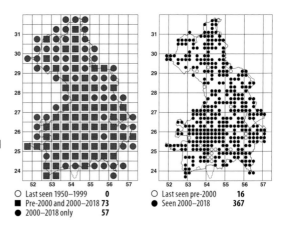

around the edges of woods but are uncommonly seen in woodland interiors, except in clearings. However, *O. diaphanum* was present on the upper branches of a 150-year old oak felled during coppicing at Hardwick Wood, TL35N, suggesting that we might unwittingly pass below plants in the canopy. It was present in 69% of churchyards we visited and on 701 (74%) of the 951 apple trees in orchards and 96 (55%) of the 173 pears surveyed by Robin Stevenson. It is tolerant of occasional but not prolonged flooding; it often occurs on silty streamside willows (perhaps one of its ancestral habitats) and in the Ouse Washes it grows on trees above the *Leskea polycarpa* zone. Extreme habitats in which it is much more frequent than other epiphytes include isolated or hedgerow elders in arable landscapes, on which it may be abundant, and urban street trees, where it is sometimes confined to rain tracks where the trunk forks into branches. The most frequent host is elder (25% of tetrad records), as elsewhere (Bosanquet 2010, Bates 2015), followed by willow (15%), ash (13%), hawthorn (7%), apple (6%), sycamore (5%) and over 30 other species (Appendix 3).

First record: Madingley, TL45E, J.S. Henslow, 1821, CGE. Described as abundant by Whitehouse (1964) in similar habitats to those in which it grows today.

Autoicous. Capsules almost always present in abundance (95% tetrads). Their development is not strictly seasonal, as dehiscing capsules can be found throughout the bryological season (September–April) and in autumn young, swollen green, freshly dehisced and old fruit can be found in the same population. However, our records suggest a general tendency for immature capsules in September–December and peak dehiscence in March–April. Whitehouse (1964) was probably correct in regarding gemmae are abundant; we have only rarely noted their presence (twice in abundance) but we have rarely examined this immediately identifiable species at all closely.

### Orthotrichum pulchellum

By 2003 this attractive moss, a recent colonist, was frequent at Wicken Fen, TL56P, 57K, before much of the fen carr in which it grew was cleared away to restore open vegetation. Most other records are also from moist scrub or woodland, including ancient and secondary woods and trees in disused, seasonally flooded pits and by streams and ponds; there is one record from a hedgerow. In these sites the species was less frequent than at Wicken and sometimes only a single tuft was found. It is also rare in orchards, where Robin Stevenson recorded it on seven (1%) of the 951 apple trees and one (1%) of the 173 pears he surveyed, all in TF40. Willow is the most frequent host (26% of tetrad records) followed by ash (15%), field maple (13%), apple (8%) and elm (8%); there are 1–2 records from several other species (Appendix 3). With the exception of the fruit trees, all its hosts are native taxa, reflecting its

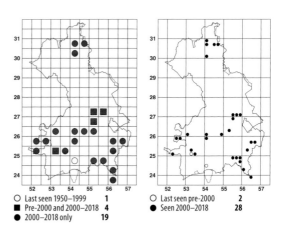

restriction to relatively closed, semi-natural vegetation and contrasting with other *Orthotrichum* species such as *O. lyellii*.

First record: Bark of elder, north-west end of Malcarse Dyke, Wicken Fen, TL57K, J.M. Lock, 1990, CGE. By 2000 it had been recorded elsewhere at Wicken and at Fowlmere RSPB reserve, TL44C (1993) and Wimpole Park, TL35F (1999). We encountered it with increasing frequency from 2002 onwards, a local symptom of its very marked increase in frequency nationally (Hill & Preston 2014).

Autoicous. Only identifiable with capsules. Capsules immature December–April, dehiscing or freshly dehisced March, April. Some populations seen in April had capsules at a range of stages of development from immature to freshly dehisced.

### Ulota crispa sens. lat.

Relhan (1802: 425) first reported *Ulota crispa* (as *Bryum crispum*) from Madingley Plantations, TL36V, and Wood Ditton Park, TL65NE, but no specimens survive and we cannot therefore attribute these records to either of the segregates currently recognised in the county, *U. bruchii* and *U. crispa sens. str.* The only historic specimen, collected in 1881, is *U. bruchii* and plants that have reinvaded the county since 1984 are predominantly this species, which has less crisped leaves than *U. crispa* but can only be identified with confidence if mature capsules are present. Our identifications have been based on the characters provided by Rosman-Hartog & Touw (1987) and Smith (2004). We often find tufts with lightly crisped leaves but without or with only immature capsules. Although these cannot be critically identified we have included the records with the confirmed records of *U. bruchii*, the taxon to which we believe they belong. Two further species related to *U. crispa* have recently been recognised by Capparós *et al.* (2016) and Blockeel (2017). *U. crispula* has recently been recorded in Huntingdonshire and will doubtless be found in Cambridgeshire too; the range of the third taxon, *U. intermedia*, is as yet poorly documented in Britain but it may be infrequent in the south and east.

### Ulota crispa

The recent survey produced a few records of *Ulota crispa sens. str.*: from willows in Cobb's Wood, Wimpole Park, TL35K, and in a stagnant pool at Fowlmere RSPB reserve, TL44C; *Cotinus coggygria* in Holbrook Road, Cambridge, TL45S; oaks in Great Chitlings Wood, TL65N, where it grew on several trees in a wood converted into an oak plantation, and in Ten Wood, TL65S; and hawthorn in Sixteen Acre Plantation, TL66R.

First record: On shaded willow branch in swampy woodland, Fordham Wood, TL66J, C.D. Preston, 1990, BBSUK. This was the only record before the recent survey.

Autoicous. Only identifiable with capsules, immature and dehisced March.

### Ulota bruchii

On the trunks and branches of sheltered trees and shrubs in a range of habitats including ancient and secondary woodland and plantations, orchards, woodland and scrub in disused clay and gravel pits, fen carr, thin belts of woodland and isolated trees by rivers and streams and, rarely, in churchyards and large gardens. It is sometimes found in woodland and scrub on dry ground but is more frequent over moist or seasonally flooded soils. Unlike many epiphytes it does not seem to have colonised the scrub on the Fleam and Devil's Dykes, although it is found in several woods just south of the latter. The main hosts are ash (18% of tetrad records) and willow (18%), followed by apple (12%), pear (8%), hawthorn (7%), oak (7%), elm (5%), field maple (5%) and other

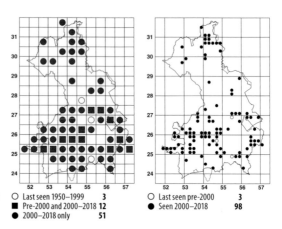

| | |
|---|---|
| ○ Last seen 1950–1999 | 3 |
| ■ Pre-2000 and 2000–2018 | 12 |
| ● 2000–2018 only | 51 |

| | |
|---|---|
| ○ Last seen pre-2000 | 3 |
| ● Seen 2000–2018 | 98 |

species listed in Appendix 3. It is one of the more frequent orchard epiphytes, recorded by Robin Stevenson on 76 (8%) of the 951 apple trees he has surveyed in detail and 29 (17%) of the 173 pears. The frequency on pear and oak suggests that it tolerates acidic substrates.

First record: Hardwick Wood, TL35N, D.G. Haviland and J.J. Lister, 1881, CGE, OXF (as *U. crispa*), det. M.O.H. It was not seen again until found on a willow branch near ground level in a wooded area west of the brickpits, Wicken Fen, TL57Q, by C.D.P., in 1984 (BBSUK). The appearance of tufts of *Ulota crispa sens. lat.*, initially low on willows in a flooded gravel pit just over the county boundary at Red Lodge, Suffolk, in 1983 and then at Wicken, was the first local sign of the return of the epiphytes. The next Cambridgeshire record was from Great Widgham Wood, TL65S, in 1988, then new sites were found more or less annually in the 1990s and more frequently thereafter.

Autoicous. Capsules very frequent (86% tetrads). Young calyptrae can be seen throughout the bryological season (September–April), often in tufts in which old capsules survive, but we have recorded green, swelling capsules only in November and April, recently dehisced capsules in October and November and dehisced but not very old capsules in December. This is not dissimilar to Bosanquet's observations (2010) that in Pembrokeshire unexpanded capsules occurred throughout the year but brown or recently dehisced capsules from July to October and December. The lack of seasonality in the young capsules but the apparently more restricted season of dehiscence is puzzling.

### Ulota phyllantha

This species is quite distinct from those in the *Ulota crispa* aggregate, and immediately recognisable by the small balls of chocolate-coloured gemmae on the tips of the young leaves. It has been found on the trunks and branches of trees and shrubs in ancient and secondary woodland, orchards, wooded chalk and gravel pits, willow holts, fen carr, wet woodland and isolated trees by rivers and streams and, rarely, churchyards and gardens. These are similar habitats to those in which we find *U. bruchii*, and indeed that species has been recorded from 38 (76%) of the 50 sites in which we have recorded *U. phyllantha* since 2000. Its hosts are also similar, mainly willow (24% of tetrad records), apple (17%) and ash (17%) followed by oak (11%) and pear (7%) and the species listed in Appendix 3. It is, however,

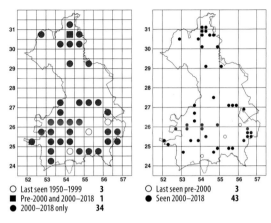

○ Last seen 1950–1999    3
■ Pre-2000 and 2000–2018    1
● 2000–2018 only    34

○ Last seen pre-2000    3
● Seen 2000–2018    43

much less frequent than *U. bruchii* in orchards, recorded from only 14 (1%) of the 951 apple trees scrutinised by Robin Stevenson and 5 (3%) of the 173 pears.

First record: Bark of old elder in ditch, Devil's Dyke north-west of Newmarket Road, TL66A, P.W. Richards, 1986, BBSUK. The next locality was on hawthorn on the Fleam Dyke, TL55H (1988), but we have not refound the species since on either earthwork, despite our detailed surveys of both. There were two records in the 1990s, at Fowlmere RSPB reserve, TL44C (1993) and Rummers Lane Orchard, Wisbech St Mary, TF40D (1999), and many more from 2001 onwards. Until 1980 this species had a western range in Britain, and it is especially abundant in exposed coastal sites, so it was one of the more surprising epiphytic colonists.

Dioicous. Capsules not recorded and very rare nationally. Gemmae almost always present, just occasionally missing when washed away by recent rain.

## HEDWIGIACEAE

Both the *Hedwigia* species recorded below are primarily rupestral plants of the north and west. *H. stellata* is much the commoner species, and is usually found on exposed rocks; *H. ciliata* has its stronghold in the Welsh borders where many records are from old roof tiles. Both occur, albeit rarely, as casual epiphytes outside their main range (Blockeel *et al.* 2014).

### Hedwigia ciliata var. *ciliata*

One small tuft was found during the recent survey, growing with *Amblystegium serpens*, *Orthotrichum affine* and *O. diaphanum* on the upper trunk of an elder in eutrophic scrub.

First record: Scrub on north side of Swaffham Lock, Swaffham Bulbeck, TL56I, C.D. Preston, 2006, BBSUK. Autoicous. Capsules not recorded.

### Hedwigia stellata

This species was found as a single tiny plant, growing with *Orthotrichum affine* and *O. diaphanum*, on a wooden seat in a lakeside clearing in secondary woodland.

First record: Adams Road Bird Sanctuary, Cambridge, TL45J, C.D. Preston, 2002. The specimen was checked by C.D.P. and sent to the BBS Recorder for Mosses but lost in the post.

Autoicous. Capsules not recorded.

## BARTRAMIACEAE

### †*Bartramia pomiformis*
Formerly recorded in the Lower Greensand area at Gamlingay.

First record: Gamlingay, TL25SW, W. Vernon, *c.* 1696 (Vernon's annotated Ray 1696: 30, as *Muscus trichoides medius, capitulis sphaericis*). Vernon noted that it fruited in winter. It was later reported from White Wood, Gamlingay, by Relhan (1793: 10, as *Bryum pomiforme*) and finally collected at Gamlingay by Henslow in 1838 (CGE). In central and eastern England *Bartramia pomiformis* is a plant of shaded earth banks and road cuttings on strongly acidic sandstones and gravels (Blockeel *et al.* 2014). It has declined markedly since the 19th century.

Autoicous or synoicous. Henslow's material, collected in May, was fruiting.

### †*Philonotis fontana*
A common and conspicuous species of both acidic and base-rich springs and flushes in upland Britain, last recorded in Cambridgeshire in 1838.

First record: Gamlingay, TL25SW, W. Vernon (Ray 1696: 33, as *Muscus stellaris ramosus palustris, pediculo aureo erecto, capitulo magno sphaerico*, with the locality added in Vernon's annotated copy). Vernon also noted that Ray's *Muscus palustris cinereo-viridis, scapis longis tenuibus, foliolis brevissimis* (1696: 32) grew at Gamlingay and fruited in summer; he cross-referenced the two species, presumably implying that they were the same. It was recorded from Gamlingay Bogs by T. Martyn (1763: 40, as *Bryum fontanum*) and fine fruiting plants were collected by Henslow 'On the Bogs' at Gamlingay in 1838 (CGE, conf. M.O.H.). It was also known from the more calcareous wetlands of Hinton Moor, TL45NE (Relhan 1785: 398, as *Mnium fontanum*) and Sawston Moor, TL44NE (Relhan 1820: 448, as *Bartramia fontana*). Rhodes (1911) regarded it as extinct at all its known localities. It has declined markedly in lowland southern and eastern England.

Dioicous. Henslow's fruiting plants were collected in May.

## BRYACEAE

### *Bryum*
This is the largest of the British moss genera, although there have been initial attempts to subdivide it using molecular data (Holyoak & Pedersen 2007). Two groups of species in the county were under-recorded by Whitehouse (1964), for different reasons. The taxonomy of a range of species that reproduce primarily by vegetative propagules was not worked out until the 1960s and 1970s. Harold Whitehouse was closely involved in the revision of tuberous species in the '*Bryum erythrocarpum* aggregate' (Crundwell & Nyholm 1964) and consequently he was able to include records of *B. klinggraeffii*, *B. rubens*, *B. ruderale*, *B. subapiculatum* and *B. violaceum* in the flora, missing only the rare *B. bornholmense* and *B. tenuisetum*. Taxonomic revisions of the bulbiferous species in the *B. dichotomum* aggregate in Britain, including *B. gemmiferum* and *B. gemmilucens* (Smith & Whitehouse 1978), and the *B. capillare* aggregate, including *B. moravicum* with its characteristic axillary gemmae (Syed 1973), were not published until after the 1964 flora.

The second group of under-recorded species comprises perennial plants that reproduce sexually. As the taxonomy of *Bryum* was traditionally based on sporophyte characters these species were well known by 1964, but they fruit in the summer, the off-season for Cambridgeshire bryologists, and they were under-recorded for this reason. The vegetative plants encountered in winter tended to be named *B.* cf. *caespiticium* or, less excusably, *B. caespiticium*, so that our records of that species have required revision. In the early years of the recent survey we held '*Bryum* days' in June to search specifically for the summer-fruiting species, which also include *B. algovicum*, *B. archangelicum*, *B. creberrimum*, *B. intermedium* and *B. pallescens*.

### *Bryum pallens*
Found in 2008 on peaty mud, on wet, rotting wood and on the exposed roots on the stump of a cut birch tree in compartments 2 and 5, Wicken Fen, TL57K, in areas in which scrub had been cleared about three years previously. It was frequent in 2009 as scattered stems or dense patches on mud in an area of fen trampled by water buffalo in compartment 9, Chippenham Fen, TL66P.

First record: Damp floor of gravel pit near Hauxton, TL45SW, M.C.F. Proctor, 1953 (*Whitehouse species file*). Subsequently found by the pond in the water garden, Botanic Garden, Cambridge, TL45N, by Harold Whitehouse, on the margin of a flooded gravel pit at Milton, TL46SE, by Mike Lock in 1963 and 1965 (CGE) and on moist ground near a ditch at Great Wilbraham Common SSSI, TL55I, in 1977. As there are no earlier records from Chippenham or Wicken, it has presumably colonised the newly disturbed habitats there recently.

Nationally, *B. pallens* appears to have declined in both upland and lowland areas in recent decades (Blockeel *et al.* 2014), for unknown reasons, and Richard Fisk has failed to refind it in Suffolk (Sanford & Fisk 2010). Care sometimes needs to be taken to prevent confusion with highly pigmented plants of *B. klinggraeffii*.

Dioicous. Green and swollen capsules present at Chippenham Fen in April 2009.

### Bryum algovicum

On well-drained, disturbed sandy, gravelly or gritty ground, or railway clinker, usually in areas such as slight depressions which are damp during the winter. We have found it in disused gravel pits, on disused railway lines and railway sidings, on a gravel drive and the base of the parapet of a motorway bridge; it may be frequent in limited areas or even abundant, as in gravel workings near Halfmoon Plantation, Kennett, TL66Z. There are single records from a low oolite tomb in Grantchester churchyard, TL45H, crushed granite hoggin in a Cambridge car park, TL45J, and the concrete of a works building in a gravel pit at Wimblington Common, TL49F.

First record: Shelford Common near Cambridge, TL45SE, 1829, CGE (as *Bryum caespiticium*), det. M.O.H. This specimen, from Henslow's herbarium,

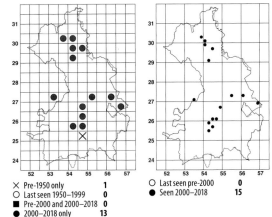

| | |
|---|---|
| × Pre-1950 only | 1 |
| ○ Last seen 1950–1999 | 0 |
| ■ Pre-2000 and 2000–2018 | 0 |
| ● 2000–2018 only | 13 |

| | |
|---|---|
| ○ Last seen pre-2000 | 0 |
| ● Seen 2000–2018 | 15 |

is labelled in a distinctive but as yet unidentified hand. It was overlooked until 2017, and the first published record was from wet, sandy ground between Halfmoon Plantation and B1085, Kennett, TL66Z, made by C.D.P. in 2001 (BBSUK). Blockeel *et al.* (2014) suggest that the scattered and often impersistent inland records of this species in Britain are derived by colonisation from the larger and more permanent coastal populations. However, *B. algovicum* has been present on sandy ground on the Cambridgeshire/Suffolk border since the 1950s (see Appendix 2), suggesting that like other coastal species it might be well established in Breckland.

Synoicous. Only identifiable with mature capsules; young setae March; capsules just beginning to dehisce May; most recently dehisced, some still intact June. Old capsules may persist through the winter and sometimes into spring and the characteristic peristome teeth mean that even rather decrepit material of this species can be identified. The concentration of records around Cambridge suggests that it is under-recorded elsewhere.

### Bryum archangelicum

A weedy species which is recorded spasmodically and unpredictably in the county. There are recent records from a flower pot at Sawston Hall, TL44Z, where it grew with *Funaria hygrometrica*, bare ground in East Pit, Cherry Hinton, TL45X, damp gravelly ground by a pit at Impington, TL46K, soil at the base of a planted tree in a recent plantation on former arable land west of Balsham, TL55Q, and on disturbed sand in gravel workings west of Halfmoon Plantation, Kennett, TL66Z.

First record: Garden soil in tub, Barton Road, Cambridge, TL45I, M.O. Hill, 1976, BBSUK (see Appendix 2). There were no further records before the recent survey. As in Cambridgeshire, many national records are of impermanent populations.

Synoicous. Only identifiable with mature capsules; capsules immature April (grown on for identification), dehisced June, July, dehisced 'some time ago' September.

### Bryum intermedium

Another weedy *Bryum*, usually found on open, damp substrates. Our recent records are from open, damp sandy ground at Block Fen, Chatteris, TL48G, and by a puddle on clinkery ground in disused railway sidings at March, TL49E.

First record: Sandy soil, Wimblington gravel pit, TL49F, B. Reeve, 1959, BBSUK (see Appendix 2). There were no further correct records until the recent survey (but see *B. pallescens*). The March railway sidings in which we recorded the species in 2001 have already been built on.

Synoicous. Only identifiable with mature capsules. Very young and mature capsules were present in the March population in April, and the capsules were just about to dehisce at Block Fen in April.

## Bryum donianum

Only known from a single site, on the steep sandy bank of a stream where it grew with *Oxyrrhynchium pumilum*.

First record: R. Granta west of Shudy Camps, TL64C, J.J. Graham and M.O. Hill, 2004, BBSUK. The Mediterranean-Atlantic *B. donianum* was scarcely known in East Anglia when mapped by Hill *et al.* (1994), but there is now a good scattering of records, especially in Suffolk where Richard Fisk finds it on light soil on roadside banks.

Dioicous. Capsules not recorded and rare nationally.

## Bryum capillare

A very common species on a wide range of stable surfaces, found (for example) in 98% of the churchyards we visited. It is especially frequent on artificial substrates, commonly seen on asphalt paths, concrete, corrugated asbestos and tile roofs, masonry, brickwork, worked wood (especially when it has begun to decay) and rotting wood. It turns up on all sorts of objects – we have found it on discarded tyres, plastic matting, a decaying foam sofa, a decaying carpet roll, a fibreglass boat, a polypropylene rope and a whale vertebra. It is also found on chalk cliffs and boulders in chalk pits and on limestone and sandstone in rock gardens. It colonises acidic substrates such as granite chippings on graves and the wood of bog oaks. As an epiphyte it grows in woodland, scrub and on isolated trees;

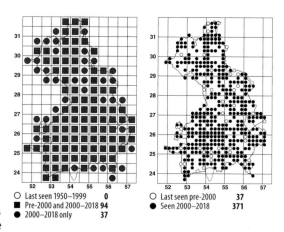

| ○ Last seen 1950–1999 | 0 |
| ■ Pre-2000 and 2000–2018 | 94 |
| ● 2000–2018 only | 37 |

| ○ Last seen pre-2000 | 37 |
| ● Seen 2000–2018 | 371 |

it is sometimes confined to exposed roots and tree bases but it extends onto trunks and branches in more sheltered sites. Elder (27% of tetrad records) and willow (16%) are the most frequent hosts, followed by apple (11%), ash (9%), hawthorn (5%), pear (5%) and many other species (Appendix 3). It is certainly frequent in orchards, recorded by Robin Stevenson on 488 (51%) of the 951 apple trees he examined and 49 (28%) of the 173 pears, but the fruit trees are perhaps over-estimated as hosts as host data are always available from orchard surveys but have not always been recorded elsewhere. *Bryum capillare* is uncommon on soil, although it is frequent on chalky soil in beech woods and also occurs on the ground in disused chalk and clay pits and is even recorded on disturbed peat. It was found in only two of the 76 arable fields recorded for the BBS SBAL project, in one as a single tussock in a set-aside field and in the other as plants which were 'rooted' but had probably blown in from nearby farm buildings.

First record: Relhan (1785: 399, as *Mnium capillare*). Fruiting plants were collected by W. Skrimshire from walls at Wisbech, TF40NE, in 1797 (WBCH, as *Dicranum purpureum* var.), by M.J. Berkeley at Parson Drove, TF30NE, in 1828 (CGE) and by Henslow in Cambridge, TL45, in 1833 (CGE). It was apparently just as common when Proctor (1956) wrote his flora as it is today.

Dioicous. Capsules frequent (63% tetrads); young setae December–February, capsules swollen, green December–May, dehiscing June. The old capsules persist into the following winter. Our observations are consistent with more detailed studies in the London area (Duckett & Pressel 2017), where most archegonia are fertilised in March and April but remain dormant until the autumn, when the capsules begin to develop. It is fortunate that this summer-fruiting species is easily identifiable vegetatively. Rhizoid tubers are frequent.

## Bryum moravicum

'Armpit-hair moss', as it is colloquially known, resembles *Bryum capillare* but differs in having thread-like axillary gemmae, the eponymous hairs. It often grows with *B. capillare* but has a much more restricted habitat, being primarily an epiphyte (80% of tetrad records) with a minority of records from rotting wood (16%) and the ground (4%). As an epiphyte it tends to grow in sheltered and rather humid sites in ancient and secondary woodland and plantations, wet willow woodland on washland and in disused gravel pits, fen carr, scrub in chalk pits and on the Fleam and Devil's Dykes, orchards and hedgerows. Several records are from trees by rivers, lakes, ponds and ditches, or along the north side of woods, but we have also found it growing on hedgerow trees where conditions are not especially humid. Its main hosts are similar to those of *B. capillare*: elder (27% of tetrad records), ash (17%), hawthorn (13%), apple (11%), willow (9%) and field maple (7%), with some additional species listed in Appendix 3. It is uncommon in orchards, seen on 74 (8%)

of the 951 apple trees surveyed by Robin Stevenson and one (1%) of the 173 pears. It is sometimes found on rotting hardwood or softwood stumps and logs in woodland and scrub or, rarely, by ditches. The records of plants on the ground are also from woodland and scrub, with the exception of those growing on thin soil over rocks on the railway embankment over the Ouse Washes, TL58E.

First record: Hayley Wood, TL25SW, E.F. Warburg, 1941, OXF (as *B. capillare*), det. H. Syed. Cambridgeshire bryologists knew this plant for some years before it was formally recognised as a British species by Syed (1973), most notably as a population on decaying logs in Madingley Wood, TL45E. Harold Whitehouse first collected it there as '*Bryum capillare* with axillary filamentous gemmae'

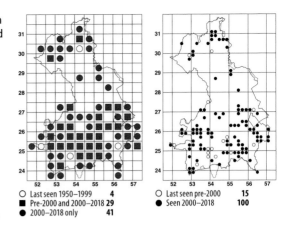

O Last seen 1950–1999    4
■ Pre-2000 and 2000–2018    29
● 2000–2018 only    41

O Last seen pre-2000    15
● Seen 2000–2018    100

in 1955 and gathered it again in 1957, growing the latter plant in a pot for three years (Whitehouse 1974; CGE). He was therefore well placed to start recording it systematically immediately after it was recognised in Syed's (1973) revision of the *B. capillare* aggregate. There is some evidence that it has decreased in the county since the 1990s (see Chapter 15).

Dioicous. Capsules not recorded and unknown in Britain. Gemmae always present, sometimes abundant.

### *Bryum torquescens*

An elusive species in Cambridgeshire, seen on only one of our numerous visits to the Devil's Dyke during the recent survey, in 2014. It grew on south-facing chalk grassland south-east of the disused railway, TL56S.

First record: Devil's Dyke near Reach, TL56S, H.L.K. Whitehouse, 1958, CGE. It was only reported once more on the Dyke during the 20th century, a tentative record made by H.L.K.W. in 1976 south of the Burwell Road, probably in TL56X. Like *Bryum moravicum*, the taxonomy of this member of the *B. capillare* aggregate was clarified by Syed's (1973) revision. It has a Mediterranean-Atlantic distribution and is a nationally scarce species with a scattered distribution in calcareous sites in southern Britain.

Usually synoicous. Capsules not present in 1958, but the recent collection was fruiting. Tubers also occur.

### †*Bryum creberrimum*

First and only record: Damp sandy soil, Gray's Moor Pits, TF40A, B. Reeve, 1959, BBSUK. *Bryum creberrimum* is closely related to *B. pallescens*, but is much rarer in Britain and most if not all of its populations appear to be transient (Blockeel *et al.* 2014). J.G. Duckett and E.R.B. Little attempted to refind the species at Gray's Moor in April 1967, without success.

Synoicous. Reeve's specimen, collected in October, had capsules with ripe spores.

### *Bryum pallescens*

Most of the Cambridgeshire populations of *Bryum pallescens* grow in moist places that receive water draining from metal surfaces. These include north-facing thatched roofs under wire netting, or concrete at ground level below them; ground on the north sides of churches moistened by water from a lead roof; gutters, clay tiles, concrete and rotting wood below galvanised metal roofs (e.g. of farm buildings or bike sheds); and ground below chicken-wire fences. Plants in such places are perennial and may form an extensive, deep turf. The population discovered under a fence at Orwell Clunch Pit in 2000 (see below) was still present in 2015, with clumps of moss which were admittedly looking rather moribund by then but nevertheless had young setae. *B. pallescens* has also been found

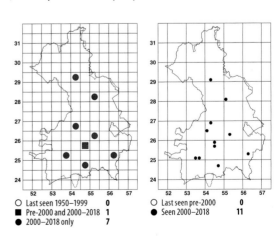

O Last seen 1950–1999    0
■ Pre-2000 and 2000–2018    1
● 2000–2018 only    7

O Last seen pre-2000    0
● Seen 2000–2018    11

as a weed in plant pots in Cambridge, TL45N, P, and on a bonfire site at Wimblington Common gravel pit, TL49F, although the slow colonisation of the latter suggested that something noxious had been burnt there.

First record: With *Bryum argenteum*, *Funaria hygrometrica* and *Leptobryum pyriforme* on a vertical brick wall under a dripping drainpipe in Coronation Street, Cambridge, TL45N, M.O. Hill, 1965, BBSUK, det. E.V. Watson. The buildings with damp brickwork in Coronation Street have succumbed to redevelopment. Although determined as *B. pallescens*, this specimen was reported as *B. intermedium* by Hill (1967) and Crompton & Whitehouse (1983) and the first published record of *B. pallescens* was from a thatched roof under galvanised netting at Orwell village, and on zinc-contaminated ground under a wire netting fence at the nearby Clunch Pit, TL35Q, where it was found by M.O.H. in 2000 (BBSUK). Smith (1978a) does not mention the tolerance of *B. pallescens* to high metal concentrations, and its occurrence in such sites has only become widely known since it was described by Hill (1988) in North Wales. Armed with this knowledge, recorders have recorded it much more frequently than in the past, although it is perhaps more frequent in the moister climates of western Britain and Ireland than in our area.

Synoicous. Capsules usually present (90% tetrads), young inflorescences November, young setae December–February, most capsules dehisced May, all dehisced July; the old capsules survive into the following winter. The Coronation Street population had all stages from inflorescences to mature capsules in October. In July 2003 sporophytes in a Cambridge population had been damaged by the drought of February–May that year.

### Bryum pseudotriquetrum

Widespread on damp peaty soil at Wicken Fen, TL56P, 57K, and Chippenham Fen, TL66P. It can be found in traditionally managed communities dominated by *Cladium mariscus* or *Phragmites australis*, or with a mixture of *Juncus subnodulosus*, *Molinia caerulea* and fenland herbs, and also in places where the management is more innovative, as on peat disturbed by water buffalo at Chippenham and on pony-grazed areas at Wicken from which scrub has been cleared. It colonised the latter within about three years of the scrub clearance. We have not seen it in closed fen carr. It is also known from East Fen Meadow, a wet peaty meadow at Fulbourn, TL55I. The other records from the county are of small, and perhaps more transient,

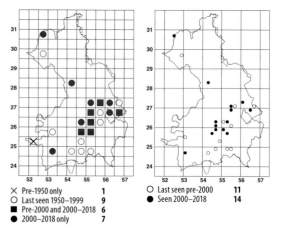

| | |
|---|---|
| ✕ Pre-1950 only | 1 |
| ○ Last seen 1950–1999 | 9 |
| ■ Pre-2000 and 2000–2018 | 6 |
| ● 2000–2018 only | 7 |

| | |
|---|---|
| ○ Last seen pre-2000 | 11 |
| ● Seen 2000–2018 | 14 |

populations on damp concrete and brickwork by lakes, streams and ditches, on open muddy or sandy ground by lakes, ponds and gravel pits and on a rotting log in wet woodland.

First record: Hinton Moor, TL45NE, and Teversham Moor, TL55NW, W. Vernon (Ray 1696: 34, as *Muscus capillaris major* and *elatior* etc.). It was also recorded from these sites by Relhan (1785: 401, as *Mnium triquetrum*), and later from Shelford Moor, TL45SE (1820: 451, as *B. bimum* and *B. ventricosum*). He sent a fruiting specimen of what he thought was *B. ventricosum* from Hinton Moor for illustration in *English Botany* (BM, *Sowerby drawings*) and Sowerby drew it, but Smith considered that it was 'rather *bimum*' and the drawing was not published. Our Fulbourn plants might conceivably be the last relics of these populations on the calcareous 'moors'. Henslow collected fine specimens with stems to over 5 cm long at Gamlingay, TL25SW, in 1827 and (fruiting) in 1838 (CGE). Thereafter it was not seen until found at Wicken in 1883 and 1929, at Quy Fen, TL56B, in 1955 and at Chippenham Fen in 1955. Some of the later 20th-century records were from woods and gravel pits. Thus the records on the distribution map are built up from a variety of populations, some well-established (at least until eliminated by habitat destruction) and others more or less transient.

Capsules occasional (25% tetrads); setae young in January, April, capsules green and swollen in April, still not dehisced in May, dehisced July. Filamentous gemmae sometimes present or even abundant in the leaf axils.

Although Relhan recorded both var. *pseudotriquetrum* (as *Mnium triquetrum* and *Bryum ventricosum*) and var. *bimum* (as *B. bimum*), they were not separated by the current criterion (var. *pseudotriquetrum* is dioicous, the polyploid var. *bimum* is synoicous). Identification of the Hinton Moor specimen, and an unlocalised specimen sent by Relhan to Skrimshire (WBCH), would be unnecessarily destructive. The only confirmed record of var. *pseudotriquetrum* is Henslow's fruiting specimen of 1838. All the later specimens which have been examined critically are var. *bimum*, including recent material from Rouses Wood, Croydon, TL34D, Chippenham and Wicken.

### Bryum caespiticium

We have found this weedy *Bryum* most frequently on brick walls, including their coping stones (six tetrads); it grew on a particularly dirty wall at Whittlesey, TL29I. There are also records from a brick path and a limestone garden ornament. Its other major habitat is clinker on disused railway lines or sidings where we have records from four tetrads, including one site at March, TL49E, where it grew with *B. algovicum* and *Ceratodon purpureus*. In a further tetrad it grew on gravelly waste ground.

First confirmed record: Wisbech, TF40NE, 1796, W. Skrimshire, WBCH. It was collected at Coe Fen, Cambridge, TL45NW, by J.S. Henslow in 1826 and at Gamlingay, TL25SW, the following year (both CGE). Although *B. caespiticium* was listed by Relhan (1785), the name has often been applied too broadly

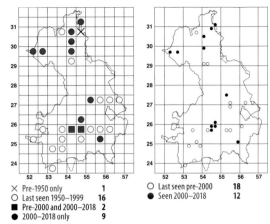

| | |
|---|---|
| ✕ Pre-1950 only | 1 |
| ○ Last seen 1950–1999 | 16 |
| ■ Pre-2000 and 2000–2018 | 2 |
| ● 2000–2018 only | 9 |

| | |
|---|---|
| ○ Last seen pre-2000 | 18 |
| ● Seen 2000–2018 | 12 |

(as explained in the introduction to *Bryum*). In particular, until 1959 Cambridgeshire bryologists treated as *B. caespiticium* plants on walls which we now call *B. radiculosum*. Only records based on fertile plants are accepted here, following a purge of the records by Preston & Hill (2008). The mapped records almost certainly greatly under-estimate the former distribution of the species, but they nevertheless suggest that it was known from a wider range of habitats between 1950 and 1999 than it is today. The 20th-century records not only come from roadside walls, railway bridges and dumped ash and clinker, but also from rotting logs and tree stumps in several places, the wooden planks of a bridge, sandstone rocks in the Botanic Garden, TL45N, sandy soil in gravel pits and burnt ground. It was probably favoured by the age of coal, when many walls were darkened by soot particles, levels of $SO_2$ pollution were high and ashes and cinders were readily available as a waste product suitable for surfacing paths.

Dioicous. Only identifiable with inflorescences or capsules; young setae December, capsules immature April, nearly ripe May, dehiscing and dehisced June.

A plant collected in 1985 with *Tortula vahliana* under hawthorn scrub in a disused chalk pit at Bassingbourn, TL34G by A.J. Davidson and H.L.K. Whitehouse had small, smooth red tubers and was provisionally assigned to this species (CGE), although believed to represent another taxon (Hill *et al.* 1994). It was refound in the same site in 2007. D.T. Holyoak has examined material from this site but found that the plants were too poorly developed to be identified.

### Bryum argenteum

The most extensive stands of *Bryum argenteum* are found in sites such as the edges of pavements and farm tracks where a thin layer of fine soil lies over asphalt or concrete, places where it usually grows with *B. dichotomum*. The tallest plants grow in only lightly trodden sites but both these species require only the minimum protection from trampling and small plants are frequent in cracks in urban pavements. Its silvery tufts grow on a wide range of other substrates including concrete, stonework, rotting woodwork, asbestos, felt and tile roofs and gravel or hardcore paths. It is found on disturbed soil both in the wild and as a weed in window boxes and plant pots, and in some of its sites it flourishes in places which have been heavily treated with weed-killer. It was found in 39 of the 76 arable

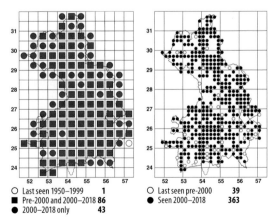

| | |
|---|---|
| ○ Last seen 1950–1999 | 1 |
| ■ Pre-2000 and 2000–2018 | 86 |
| ● 2000–2018 only | 43 |

| | |
|---|---|
| ○ Last seen pre-2000 | 39 |
| ● Seen 2000–2018 | 363 |

fields recorded for the SBAL project, although usually in small quantity ('rare' in 25, 'abundant' in only one). It grew in 80% of fields on light soils (chalk, peat and sand), 62% of those on loam and silt but only 28% of fields on clay (36% of the clay fields with five or more species). As an epiphyte it is usually confined to the base of trees. It also colonises human artefacts such as metal gratings, discarded mats and carpets and the rubber surrounding the windows of unloved cars. It is favoured by nutrient-enrichment, and it often grows where birds perch on stone ledges and churchyard monuments. At Weston Green, TL65G, it formed a broad band below the chimney stack on a wire-covered thatch roof.

First record: R. Davies in J. Martyn (1729b: 13, as *Bryum capitulis subrotundis, reflexis, cauliculis teretibus, argenteis*); published by T. Martyn (1763: 24). The first localised records were specimens collected by Skrimshire from old walls, old rails and on the ground about Wisbech, TF40NE, in 1796 (WBCH) and by Henslow 'near Madingley turnpike', TL45E, in 1829 (CGE). It was described by Proctor (1958) as 'very tolerant of smoke' and 'much commoner in and about Cambridge than in the surrounding country'. We have not noticed this contrast, but Proctor's rural records probably came from semi-natural sites such as woods and fens, rather than the arable landscapes we have also covered.

Dioicous. Capsules frequent (24% tetrads), characteristically found on well-grown plants on flat surfaces such as concrete tracks, including sites where water pools briefly after rain. None of the plants seen in the SBAL fields were fruiting. The capsules often show some variation in maturity within a stand; young setae September, October; swollen green capsules September–January; brown capsules September, October, December–February; capsules dehiscing October. Whitehouse (1964) noted that capsules were frequent in some years, rare in others. We noted that 2004/05 and 2009/10 were good fruiting seasons and both these winters had been preceded by a wet July and August, but systematic observations are lacking. Bulbils are also frequent in the leaf axils (recorded in 46% of the SBAL populations but perhaps less frequent in drier sites).

## Bryum gemmiferum

This small moss is primarily a plant of very open, base-rich soils. It is often found in wet places, as on clay or silt soils by ditches, lakes, pools and reservoirs, river banks and dredgings, moist sandy ground in gravel pits, damp peaty ground in fens and open areas in seasonally flooded grassland. There are single records from the horse-grazed upper saltmarsh at Foul Anchor, TF41T, wooden planking in washland, the base of a riverside willow and tarmac which was frequently water-splashed. It is also found on dry as well as wet soils in active and disused chalk and Coralline limestone pits and on chalk earthworks, with single records from the chalky rootplate of a fallen tree and earth on a step in a little-used doorway. It was 'rare' in all seven of the 78 SBAL fields in which we found it, growing at pH 5.8–8.0 in cereal stubble on clay, chalk and peat soils.

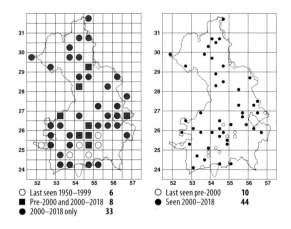

| | |
|---|---|
| ○ Last seen 1950–1999 | 6 |
| ■ Pre-2000 and 2000–2018 | 8 |
| ● 2000–2018 only | 33 |

| | |
|---|---|
| ○ Last seen pre-2000 | 10 |
| ● Seen 2000–2018 | 44 |

First record: Wimpey's gravel pit, Chippenham, TL66Z, C.C. Townsend, 1956, NMW (cf. Smith & Whitehouse 1978). *B. gemmiferum* is a distinctive member of the *B. dichotomum* aggregate. British bryologists knew it for many years by the pet name of *B. cassingtonense* (after a 1948 specimen from Cassington, Oxfordshire) and were taken by surprise when Wilczek & Demaret (1976) described it as *B. gemmiferum* from Belgium. Its occurrence in Britain was then documented by Smith & Whitehouse (1978). Whitehouse's early records are not documented in his Cambridgeshire papers but there are specimens in NMW, and Hill (1967) recorded it in several sites.

Dioicous. Capsules recorded once in the recent survey (2% tetrads), on disturbed clay in a flooded gravel pit, green in March. Townsend's material, collected in January, has some intact capsules but most have dehisced. Only identifiable by the numerous tiny bulbils in the leaf axils.

## †Bryum gemmilucens

A nationally rare species of disturbed soil, recorded in the county only once.

First and only record: Stubble field, Papworth St Agnes, TL26S, H.L.K. Whitehouse, 1960 (Smith & Whitehouse 1978). Harold Whitehouse cultivated material from this gathering on soil (CGE) and agar (NMW). It was the first time that this species had been recognised as a distinct entity, although older specimens were later discovered in herbaria. As with *B. gemmiferum*, it was described by Wilczek & Demaret (1976), working independently in Belgium.

Dioicous. Capsules not recorded and unknown in Britain. Only identifiable by its characteristic bulbils.

## Bryum dichotomum

*Bryum dichotomum* favours similar, nutrient-rich habitats to those of *B. argenteum*, with which it often grows. It is found on asphalt, brickwork, concrete, stonework, tile roofs, worked wood, railway clinker, gravel paths and tracks, in cracks between paving stones, on waste and trampled ground, in chalk, clay and gravel pits, on chalk earthworks, on the bases of trees, soil and dredgings by still and running waters and as a weed of arable land, flower beds and plant pots. Like *B. argenteum*, it is tolerant of herbicides. It is more tolerant of moist habitats than that species, and it is sometimes abundant on wet brickwork by eutrophic water, where it may grow in pure stands and where it usually has gemmiferous protonemata in addition to leafy shoots (Pressel *et al.* 2007). It is

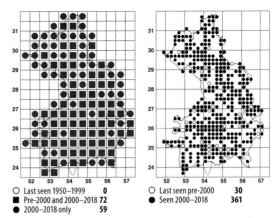

○ Last seen 1950–1999   **0**
■ Pre-2000 and 2000–2018 **72**
● 2000–2018 only   **59**

○ Last seen pre-2000   **30**
● Seen 2000–2018   **361**

also more frequent on disturbed soil. In the SBAL survey we found it in 54 of the 76 arable fields we studied, and in 18 of these it was 'frequent' or 'abundant'. It was present in 87% of the fields on light soils (chalk, peat and sand), 83% of those on loam and silt and 53% of fields on clay (but 68% of the clay fields with five or more species). It will also colonise artefacts such as dumped carpets, metal gratings and polypropylene rope.

First record: Near Newmarket, TL66SW, G.D. Haviland and J.J. Lister, 1878, CGE, OXF, as *B. atropurpureum*. H.N. Dixon collected a fine fruiting clump on the Roman Road, Gog Magog Hills, TL45X, in 1883 (BM). It is surprising that Rhodes (1911) square-bracketed the species as of doubtful occurrence in the county and that Proctor (1956), knowing only six 20th-century records, described it as 'probably rather common, but not often recorded'. Whitehouse recorded it frequently from 1957 onwards and by 1961 had records from all the 10-km squares he recognised in the county.

Dioicous. Capsules frequent (35% tetrads), found in some arable populations as well as in other habitats. They often show some variation in maturity within a stand; young setae October–February; swollen, green November–April; brown November, January, April; dehisced January, March, April, June. Bulbils are almost always present although sometimes not produced by fruiting plants; tubers are frequent.

*B. dichotomum* is very much more frequent than the related *B. gemmiferum* and *B. gemmilucens*. A further, predominantly coastal, segregate, *B. dunense*, was described by Smith & Whitehouse (1978) as a plant with an excurrent nerve and large bulbils; it remained distinct in cultivation. Harold Whitehouse considered that he was pressed into publishing the account of *B. dunense* prematurely, and although he would readily examine specimens of most of his 'pet' species, he would always grimace when asked to check potential *B. dunense*. Holyoak (2003) reduced it to a synonym of *B. dichotomum*, as he found frequent intermediates between them, although in a later study there was a molecular separation between the two taxa (Holyoak & Pedersen 2007). The first Cambridgeshire record of *B. dunense* was from wood in a chalk pit on Rowley's Hill, Harston, TL44J, H.L.K. Whitehouse, 1956 (CGE), but our recent records of this morphotype have been from chalk soil, in Orwell Clunch Pit, TL35Q, and on Devil's Dyke, TL56W, X.

## Bryum radiculosum

The tightly packed, slightly glossy stems of *Bryum radiculosum*, held together by densely matted rhizoids, are frequent on the mortar of brickwork, on calcareous masonry and (less frequently) on concrete, growing on the sides and coping stones of walls and bridges, on churchyard monuments and on ornamental stonework around country houses. We have also seen this species on Carboniferous and oolitic limestone and sandstone in garden rockeries and on the top of wooden pilings by water. It occurs in both exposed sites and in shade (e.g. at the base of the north wall of churches). It is most frequent in built-up areas (we recorded it in 54% of the churchyards we surveyed) and there is evidence for fairly rapid colonisation of new substrates over short distances –

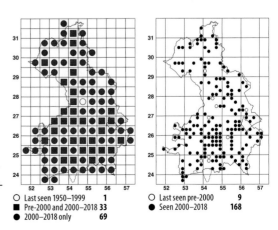

○ Last seen 1950–1999   **1**
■ Pre-2000 and 2000–2018 **33**
● 2000–2018 only   **69**

○ Last seen pre-2000   **9**
● Seen 2000–2018   **168**

we found it on a brick wall built 5.5 years previously at Stuntney, TL57P, and on the stonework of a seven-year old pond at Chippenham Park, TL66U. However, it is much less frequent than *Grimmia pulvinata*, *Orthotrichum anomalum*, *Schistidium crassipilum* or *Tortula muralis* on isolated concrete structures in the arable landscape. Plants with a looser habit also grow on chalk rubble and on disturbed chalky soil, including soil in open chalk grassland and in stubble fields.

First record: In small quantity in grass on dry chalky bank, Devil's Dyke, TL56, R.E. Parker, 1952, BBSUK. Recent surveys have shown that it is widespread in chalk grassland on the Dyke. In the 1950s plants on walls were often recorded as *B. caespiticium* (q.v.) and Parker's record was the only one known until 1965. Hill (1967) realised that it was widespread on walls and also present on flagstones in Cambridge, TL45N, P. Nevertheless it was not recorded at all frequently in the county until the start of the Bryophyte Group's systematic surveys of churchyards in 1987.

Dioicous. Capsules occasional (20% tetrads), green and swollen December–April so presumably dehiscing in summer. In the London area archegonia are fertilised between February and April but remain dormant until the seta begins to elongate in the autumn, with the capsules eventually dehiscing in July and August (Duckett & Pressel 2017). Duckett & Pressel note that the old capsules are less persistent than those of *B. capillare*. Tubers usually present, occasionally frequent but often sparse. *B. radiculosum* is unusual in producing highly branched, gemmiferous protonemata from rhizoids in the lower leaf axils (Pressel *et al.* 2007).

Although the tuberous *Bryum* species are usually well defined, we have had real problems in separating *B. radiculosum* (which usually has papillose brown rhizoids and brown or reddish brown tubers) and *B. ruderale* (papillose violet rhizoids, red tubers), a difficulty noted by Holyoak & Pedersen (2007). In arable fields we find plants which appear to be *B. ruderale* with brown rhizoids, and D.T. Holyoak (who kindly examined several problematic specimens) tentatively identified as *B. ruderale* those with bright red tubers and as *B. radiculosum* those in which the tubers were dull brownish red.

## Bryum ruderale

This is one of the more characteristic species of lightly trampled places in the county, although one of the more easily overlooked. It grows on roadsides, the edges of gravel drives, around buildings in farmyards and industrial estates, on disused railways, on paths and tracks of asphalt, concrete, limestone rubble, sand and soil, and in cracks between paving stones. It is also found on soil which has been disturbed once, or only intermittently, as on graves and bonfire sites, in vegetable gardens and flower beds, in gravel pits, in open patches and on ant hills in chalk grassland, around badger diggings and on rabbit-infested ground. We recorded it in 11 of the 76 fields surveyed for the SBAL survey but it was 'rare' in

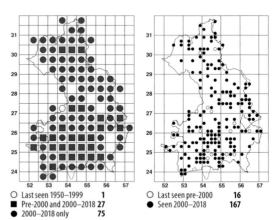

O Last seen 1950–1999   1
■ Pre-2000 and 2000–2018   27
● 2000–2018 only   75

O Last seen pre-2000   16
● Seen 2000–2018   167

seven fields and 'frequent' or 'abundant' in only two. It grew on a range of soils (chalk, clay, loam, peat, sand and silt), usually at high pH (7.9–8.1 in eight fields) but once on acidic sandy soil (pH 5.3) at Gamlingay, TL25L. Unusual habitats include the trunk of an elder covered by dust in a chalk pit and a discarded carpet.

First record: Gravel paths, Pampisford Hall, TL54E, H.L.K. Whitehouse, 1957 (*Whitehouse diary* 2: 41). A few specimens in CGE and NMW bear the name *Bryum muelleri* which was briefly used for this species *c.* 1962; once they realised that this name was misapplied, Crundwell & Nyholm (1963) described it as *B. ruderale*. Whitehouse (1964) described it as 'abundant on roadsides and paths'.

Dioicous. Harold Whitehouse's cultivation experiments showed that both male and female plants occur in the county. Sporophytes have been recorded in recent years from Coploe Hill Pit, TL44W, and the edge of an arable field near Carlton Wood, TL65L, but neither record has detailed notes and there are no confirmed records of fruits from Britain or Ireland (Blockeel *et al.* 2014). Tubers are usually present and are often frequent but are sometimes difficult to find in summer and early autumn; we have sometimes identified plants solely by their papillose, intensely violet rhizoids. The stems of this species appear to persist for at least two years; they are perhaps less long-lived than those of *B. radiculosum* but certainly more so than those of the small-tubered species *B. violaceum* and *B. klinggraeffii*.

The above figures for SBAL fields are based on morphologically typical plants with purple rhizoids. The plants with brown rhizoids discussed under *B. radiculosum* occurred with them in two of these fields and in at least four other SBAL fields.

## Bryum violaceum

The vast majority of the records of this neat little plant are from arable habitats. Most are from cereal stubble, but it also grows in crops of asparagus, cabbages, potatoes and rape as well as in marginal strips left unsown or sown with grasses or with plant mixes for game birds, wild birds or insect pollinators. It was found in 44 of the 76 SBAL fields, where it spanned a wide range of pH values (5.8–8.5). The fields comprised 73% of those on light soils (chalk, peat and sand) and 79% of those on loam and silt but only 31% of fields on clay (40% of the clay fields with five or more species). *Barbula unguiculata*, *Bryum dichotomum*, *B. klinggraeffii*, *B. rubens*, *Dicranella staphylina* and *Phascum cuspidatum* were present in more than 30 of the 44

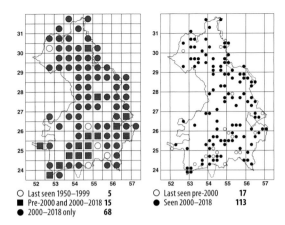

○ Last seen 1950–1999   **5**
■ Pre-2000 and 2000–2018 **15**
● 2000–2018 only   **68**

○ Last seen pre-2000   **17**
● Seen 2000–2018   **113**

fields. There are records of *B. violaceum* from non-arable habitats in 16 tetrads, mainly disturbed chalky soil by paths, on roadsides and in chalk pits and on chalk earthworks, including soil around rabbit burrows, but also on gritty and silt soils on roadsides and the horse-grazed upper saltmarsh at Foul Anchor, TF41T.

First record: Mixed with *B. klinggraeffii*, stubble field near Thorney, TF20Q, P.J. Bourne, 1960, CGE (see Appendix 2). This species was recognised at a late stage of Crundwell and Nyholm's investigation of the *Bryum erythrocarpum* aggregate, which was carried out in close collaboration with Harold Whitehouse (Crundwell & Nyholm 1963). Several specimens in CGE collected in 1961 are labelled *Bryum jonesii*, clearly then a 'pet name' for the species. Whitehouse (1964) described it as 'frequent in arable fields' but Hill (1967) disputed this, pointing out that he had often found *B. klinggraeffii* in arable fields in the county but never *B. violaceum*. There is a possibility that the increasingly intensive cultivation of arable land in recent decades has favoured it because of its ability to produce numerous, small tubers rapidly, but the evidence is inadequate (see *Dicranella staphylina* for a similar case).

Dioicous. Harold Whitehouse's field observations and cultivation experiments showed that female plants occur in the county but male plants are much rarer nationally and have not been recorded here. Capsules unknown in Britain. Tubers are always present and usually frequent.

The characteristic violet colour of the rhizoids is now scarcely discernible in specimens collected in the early 1960s.

## Bryum klinggraeffii

The two key features of the ecology of *Bryum klinggraeffii* are its ability to reproduce rapidly by tubers, which it shares with *B. violaceum*, and its tolerance of winter waterlogging. Like *B. violaceum*, it is frequent in a range of arable habitats, found, for example, in 52 of the 76 SBAL fields we sampled and spanning the complete range of pH values (pH 5.3–8.6). However, it is much more evenly distributed across different soil types than that species, recorded in 73% of fields on light soils (chalk, peat and sand), 62% of those on loam and silt and 72% of fields on clay (88% of the clay fields with five or more species). On drier soils it grows with other tuberous *Bryum* species but it is usually the only such species in winter-flooded hollows and

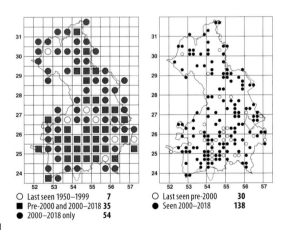

○ Last seen 1950–1999   **7**
■ Pre-2000 and 2000–2018 **35**
● 2000–2018 only   **54**

○ Last seen pre-2000   **30**
● Seen 2000–2018   **138**

streamside margins in arable fields, including the deeper parts of the *Lythrum hyssopifolia* hollows south of Cambridge. Away from arable, it grows on rides and soil in recently coppiced plots in woodland, on disturbed chalky soil and ant hills in chalk pits and chalk grassland, disturbed peat in fens, muddy areas in washland, winter-flooded ground in gravel pits, and on rutted tracks, the sides of lakes, ponds, streams and ditches and waterside dredgings.

First record: Arable field, Trumpington Hall, TL45H, H.L.K. Whitehouse, 1956 (*Whitehouse species file*). Harold Whitehouse first recognised the species in December 1960 (Whitehouse 1961) and systematically recorded it from then onwards, initially as *B. erythrocarpum* var. *hegelmaieri* Podp. (which turned out to be a synonym of *B. subapiculatum*). By 1962 he had found it in 'numerous localities' (Crundwell 1962) and Hill (1967) described it as 'fairly common in arable fields on all soils'.

Dioicous. Male and female inflorescences are sometimes seen in the wild. Sporophytes only seen twice (1% tetrads): setae just emerging, chalky ditch side, Little Wilbraham, TL55J, 2005, only the second recorded occurrence of sporophytes in Britain (Hill 2006) and one patch with tall setae but unexpanded capsules in a stubble field, Kingston, TL35G, 2007. Tubers on the rhizoids are usually frequent and sometimes extremely abundant; they are very rarely also present in the lowest leaf axils where they sometimes appear sessile and are sometimes clearly borne on short rhizoids. We have also seen small tubers on the brownish protonemata of young plants in a stubble field.

### Bryum tenuisetum

Found only once, on moist, very humified acidic peat (pH 6.0) at the edge of a recently re-excavated water body in rather open willow woodland, growing with frequent *B. klinggraeffii* and with *Aphanorrhegma patens*, *Bryum subapiculatum* and *Leptobryum pyriforme*.

First and only record: Decoy Wood, Nene Washes, TF30A, M.O. Hill, 2003, BBSUK. This is a nationally scarce calcifuge, most frequently found in moist or seasonally inundated sites.

Dioicous or occasionally synoicous. Capsules not recorded. Tubers present.

### Bryum subapiculatum

An uncommon species of non-calcareous soils, usually recorded in the recent survey in stubble fields. In the SBAL survey we found it in three fields, on sand (pH 5.3), loam (pH 6.3) and silt (pH 7.2). The only recent non-arable record was from very humified acidic peat (pH 6.0) in the Nene Washes, TF30A, where it grew with *B. tenuisetum* (q.v.).

First record: Gravel pit near Kennett, TL66Z, D.F. Chamberlain, 1960, CGE, E (cf. Crundwell & Nyholm 1964). The only other site known to Whitehouse (1964) was a hedge at Woodbury Low Farm, TL15W, on Jurassic clay, where it was collected by P.J. Bourne in 1961. The name *B. zuluense* and the pet name *B. scanicum* appear in Whitehouse's notes on these collections, or on the CGE specimens;

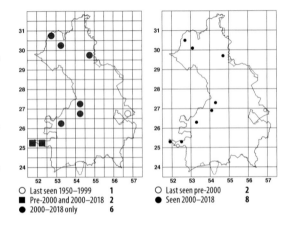

| Last seen 1950–1999 | ○ | 1 |
| Pre-2000 and 2000–2018 | ■ | 2 |
| 2000–2018 only | ● | 6 |

| Last seen pre-2000 | ○ | 2 |
| Seen 2000–2018 | ● | 8 |

for a brief period in the 1960s the former was regarded as perhaps the correct name of the species. After publication of the 1964 flora it was found on the Woburn Sands in sandy pasture at Mill Hill, Gamlingay, TL25F, in 1977 and in Gamlingay Meadow, TL25F, in 1978, and in the east at Chippenham Pit, TL66Z, in 1965. Although it has not been recorded on the Breckland fringe of the county since, it may well persist on sandy soils in that area. It is easily overlooked as it is characterised by the absence of the distinctive features of *B. rubens*, our other species with large red tubers.

Dioicous. Young setae are present on Chamberlain's specimen, collected in December. Only identifiable with tubers, which are usually frequent.

### Bryum bornholmense

This was the last species added to the county list before we went to press, found in large quantity in an area of disturbed sandy soil at Gamlingay (see below). *B. bornholmense* is similar morphologically to *B. rubens* but a marked calcifuge. The classic British locality is at Rowney Warren in Bedfordshire, TL14F, which is also on the Woburn Sands.

First record: Gamlingay Heath Plantation, TL25F, M.O. Hill, 2018, BBSUK.

Dioicous or sometimes synoicous, rarely autoicous. Capsules not recorded. Tubers present.

### Bryum rubens

Found on disturbed soil in all manner of sites including woods (e.g. on rides, in coppice plots and by badger setts), orchards, grassland (on molehills, anthills, by rabbit burrows and on other disturbed ground), ditch banks, chalk and gravel pits, chalk earthworks, churchyards (e.g. on graves 1–3 years after the interment), gardens, on lightly trampled soil by roads, paths and tracks, on old bonfire sites and as a weed of flower pots. In arable fields it occurs in association with many crops including cereals, rape, vegetables (including asparagus, cabbages, beans, onions, potatoes), mixes for wild and game birds and set-aside. We found it in 51 (67%) of the 76 fields sampled for SBAL, where it was 'rare' in 14, 'occasional' in 16, 'frequent' in 16 and 'abundant' in only five. It grew over a range of soils and at pH values of 5.3 to 8.2. Like many bryophytes, it is tolerant of herbicide application and thus found on ground treated with 'Roundup' under fences or in preparation for tree-planting. It is rarely found on substrates other than soil, but we have seen it on discarded felt and on the cut surface of a tree stump.

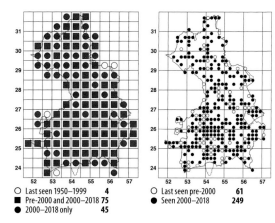

First record: Teversham, TL45NE, H.E. Lowe, 1834, CGE, det. H.L.K. Whitehouse. The specimen, in Henslow's herbarium, has a label written by Lowe. R.S. Adamson was the first to record 'Bryum erythrocarpum' (Evans 1913) but his plant was from Gamlingay and might have been B. subapiculatum. Two records made in 1943, near Kingston Wood, TL35G, and from broken turf in Cambridge, TL45N, were doubtless B. rubens. Whitehouse began to record 'B. erythrocarpum' frequently in 1957 and when reviewing his records for the 1964 flora he accepted most as B. rubens. Hill (1967) regarded B. rubens as ubiquitous in arable fields, amongst other habitats, although often in small quantity, but (as noted above) he failed to find B. violaceum in this habitat. The relative frequency of the two species has clearly changed since then, presumably because B. violaceum is more successful in intensively farmed arable land. In Pembrokeshire B. rubens is still much more frequent than B. violaceum in arable fields (Bosanquet 2010).

Dioicous. Sporophytes seen only three times in the recent survey (1% tetrads), as young setae with unexpanded capsules (December, March) and as swollen, green capsules (March). B. rubens is scarcely identifiable without its characteristic tubers, which often occur in the lower leaf axils and are usually frequent on the rhizoids.

### †*Rhodobryum roseum*

A conspicuous and attractive moss of well-drained turf or (more rarely) open woodland on infertile soils, not seen in the county since 1955.

First record: Gog Magog Hills, TL45SE, Relhan (1820: 452, as *Bryum roseum*). It was reported from Hildersham Furze Hills, TL54P, by L.J. Sedgwick (Rhodes 1911) and refound by A.W. Graveson in 1914 ('in fair quantity'), M.C.F. Proctor in 1951 ('amongst grass') and C.C. Townsend in 1955 ('on sand overlying chalk', E), the last county record. The Furze Hills have suffered since the 1950s from sand extraction and scrub invasion following myxomatosis (Trist 1988). The only other site was a heathy field with *Cytisus scoparius* at Gamlingay, TL25SW, where P.W. Richards found it in 1929 and collected two small stems (NMW). As his specimens usually contain a more than adequate quantity of material, this presumably indicates that *R. roseum* was very rare at the site and it has never been seen there again. It has undergone a long-term and continuing decline in Britain.

Dioicous. Capsules not recorded and rare nationally.

## MIELICHHOFERIACEAE

### *Pohlia nutans*

We have found this calcifuge moss in acidic sites in woodland at White Wood, Gamlingay, TL25B, Great Heath Plantation, Gamlingay, TL25F, and Balsham Wood, TL54Z. In White Wood and Balsham Wood it grew with *Dicranella heteromalla* at the base of beech tree, and it was also seen at the base of a beech in a shelter belt near Thriplow, TL44M. The other recent records are from a decaying sleeper at the edge of secondary birch woodland on disused railway sidings at March, TL49E, and as large, deep but non-fruiting tufts on wire-covered thatched roofs at Shepreth, TL34Y, Duxford, TL44T, and Weston Green, TL65G.

First record: Gamlingay area, TL25SW, P.G.M. Rhodes, det. W. Ingham (Rhodes 1911 as *Webera nutans*). Proctor (1956) noted that *P. nutans* was common only at Gamlingay Heath Plantation, where it fruited freely. However, although never present in any great quantity elsewhere, it was clearly much more frequent in the

1950s and 1960s than it is today. It grew at the base of trees, on rotting stumps and more rarely on soil in woods, plantations and hedges. Several records were from the base of beech trees on chalky soils. It colonised acidic fen carr at Wicken, TL56P, 57K, where it was first found in 1963 and became quite frequent (Lock 1990) but was seen only once after 1979 (in 1994). It was also frequent on clinker at the Madingley sewage works, TL36V, and found with *Dicranella cerviculata* in Manea clay pit, TL48Z. The marked decline of this species in Cambridgeshire is matched nationally, especially in areas of formerly high SO$_2$ pollution (Blockeel *et al.* 2014).

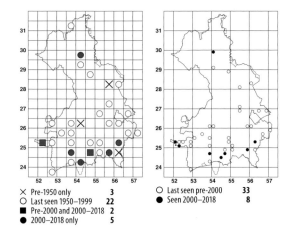

| | |
|---|---|
| ✕ Pre-1950 only | 3 |
| ○ Last seen 1950–1999 | 22 |
| ■ Pre-2000 and 2000–2018 | 2 |
| ● 2000–2018 only | 5 |

| | |
|---|---|
| ○ Last seen pre-2000 | 33 |
| ● Seen 2000–2018 | 8 |

Paroicous. Capsules occasional (25% tetrads).

### †*Pohlia annotina*

Only known from the county as a single, casual occurrence.

First and only record: With *Ceratodon purpureus* and *Polytrichastrum 'longisetum'* [but voucher is *P. formosum*] on aluminium glazing bars on outside of glasshouse, Cambridge Botanic Garden, TL45N, M.C.F. Proctor and H.L.K. Whitehouse, 1982, BBSUK. In neighbouring counties this is a rare species, most frequently found on disturbed sandy soil on woodland rides.

Dioicous. Capsules not recorded and very rare nationally; axillary bulbils present in abundance.

### *Pohlia lutescens*

A species of disturbed sandy soil, seen during the recent survey only on the rootplate of a fallen tree at Gamlingay Heath Plantation, TL25F, in 2002.

First record: With *Ceratodon purpureus* and *Dicranella heteromalla* in entrance to rabbit burrow on Lower Greensand, Mill Hill, Gamlingay, TL25F, M.E. Smith, 1977, BBSUK. This site had been drained and ploughed by 1983, but *P. lutescens* was refound at Gamlingay, in Great Heath Plantation, in 1988. It was also detected by H.L.K. Whitehouse (who had a particular fondness for the species) at Great Wood, Kirtling, TL75C, in 1991, growing with *Bryum klinggraeffii*, *B. rubens*, *Ephemerum minutissimum*, *Tortula truncata* and *Trichodon cylindricus* in a limited area of non-calcareous soil dominated by *Dicranella heteromalla* and *Kindbergia praelonga*.

Dioicous. Capsules unknown; the characteristic tubers are always present.

### *Pohlia lescuriana*

Refound in 2018 at Great Heath Plantation, its only site in the county, growing on the recently recut edge of a woodland pond.

First record: On side of newly-cut ditch near Old Plantation Cottage, Great Heath Plantation, Gamlingay, TL25F, M.O. Hill, P.W. Richards, C.R. Stevenson and H.L.K. Whitehouse, 1988, BBSUK.

Dioicous. Capsules not recorded; the characteristic tubers are always present.

### *Pohlia melanodon*

Unlike all the preceding *Pohlia* species, *P. melanodon* is a calcicole, although not a particularly exacting one. It is frequent on wet, base-rich soils (especially on chalk or clay) by water, including sites above the usual water level on the banks of lakes, reservoirs, ponds, rivers, streams and ditches. It grows in both open and shaded sites, associated with species such as *Dicranella varia* and *Didymodon tophaceus*. It is also found, much more rarely, on waterside tree roots and brickwork. Other habitats include damp sandy soil in flooded gravel pits, rides in boulder-clay woods, disturbed peat in fens and disturbed calcareous soils in chalk pits and other sites. It is occasional in arable fields, although often as small plants, sometimes tinged with a copper colour, which are easily overlooked as a species of *Bryum*. We found it in 11 of the 76 SBAL fields we studied, on clay, loam, peat and silt, usually (eight sites) at pH 7.8–8.1. *Barbula unguiculata*, *Bryum klinggraeffii*, *B. rubens*, *Dicranella staphylina*, *D. varia* and *Phascum cuspidatum* grew in eight or more of these fields. It is also, unsurprisingly, found with *Lythrum hyssopifolia* in the winter-flooded hollows in chalky fields south of Cambridge.

First record: In and about the Moors, Cherry Hinton, TL45NE, and Teversham, TL55NW, T. Martyn (1763: 35, 37, as *Bryum carneum*). Specimens from Cambridgeshire collected by Hemsted were illustrated in

English Botany by Smith (1796b) and an unlocalised specimen of this species, sent by Hemsted to Skrimshire, is in the latter's herbarium (WBCH). Relhan (1820: 449) reported it from Sawston Moor, TL44NE, but there were no further localised records until H.N. Dixon collected it in Cambridge, TL45, in 1883 (BM) and A.W. Graveson found it on streamside mud at Little Linton, TL54N, in 1914. There is little evidence for any change in frequency or in its habitat preferences since the 1950s. It was recorded in the *Lythrum* hollows from 1958 onwards, although it was not until the recent survey that it was found more widely in arable fields.

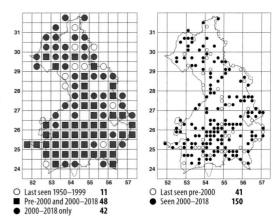

○ Last seen 1950–1999    11
■ Pre-2000 and 2000–2018 **48**
● 2000–2018 only    **42**

○ Last seen pre-2000    **41**
● Seen 2000–2018    **150**

Dioicous. Capsules occasional (10% tetrads), antheridia shed November, young setae December–January, capsules green, swollen December–January, starting to dehisce March. It is much less difficult to see the moniliform 'tubers' on the rhizoids than Smith (2004), following Arts (1986), suggests; they seem to be usually but not invariably present and they vary in maturity (perhaps because they develop rather slowly) as well as in abundance. Pressel *et al.* (2007) interpret them as chains of brood cells rather than tubers.

### *Pohlia wahlenbergii* var. *wahlenbergii*

This distinctive, bluish green moss has been found in two ancient woods since 2000. In Ditton Park Wood, TL65T, in 2001, we saw it on one track near the entrance which had been made-up 10 years previously, and in ruts on another unsurfaced ride. The unsurfaced ride was one on which we had seen the species in 1991 but which in 1992 was reduced to a deep clay slurry by vehicles undertaking timber extraction. It was still present on rutted rides in at least three places in Ditton Park Wood in 2017, growing with *Pellia endiviifolia*. In 2016 a few small patches, perhaps 20 stems in total, were seen with *Pellia* sp. on a muddy ride in Gamlingay Wood, TL25L. There were two surprising records in 2017, from a disturbed ride at Chippenham Fen, TL66P, and in a plant pot in an urban garden in Cambridge, TL45Q.

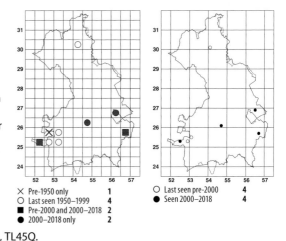

✕ Pre-1950 only    1
○ Last seen 1950–1999    4
■ Pre-2000 and 2000–2018    2
● 2000–2018 only    2

○ Last seen pre-2000    4
● Seen 2000–2018    4

First record: Moist Boulder Clay in ride, Kingston Wood, TL35SW, P.W. Richards, 1938, NMW. Almost all subsequent records are from rides in ancient boulder-clay woodland. It was first found in Gamlingay Wood in 1945. There are no recent records from Eltisley Wood, TL25U (last recorded 1945), Hayley Wood, TL25W (1982), Kingston Wood, TL35SW (1985) and Longstowe Hall, TL35C (1983). The only other record is from Gray's Moor Pits, TF40A, where it was seen by J.G. Duckett and E.R.B. Little in 1967. This is a much commoner species in northern and western Britain, where it is 'ready colonist' of tracks and waste ground (Blockeel *et al.* 2014) and also occurs in a wide range of other moist and wet habitats.

Dioicous. Capsules not recorded. We cannot explain how this species persists in its Cambridgeshire sites through periods when its woodland rides are unsuitable because of too much or too little disturbance. Similarly capsules are rare even in those parts of Britain where it is a frequent colonist. Slender branchlets, its only known vegetative propagules, are rarely seen and have not been found in Cambridgeshire.

## MNIACEAE

### *Mnium hornum*

A robust calcifuge, usually seen in ancient woodland or plantations on Woburn Sands or Boulder Clay. There are also populations in woodland or fen carr on peat, notably at Wicken Fen, TL56P, 57K, and Chippenham Fen, TL66J, P, and in wet alder woodland. In all its sites it is characteristically found on slightly raised ground at the base of trees or on decaying logs and tree stumps, or sometimes on shaded banks; in wet woodland or fen carr it is clearly confined to areas above the ground which is usually flooded. On the Gog Magog Hills, TL45X, it grows at the foot of a beech tree on acidified ground over chalk. It is also found on imported sandstone rocks in Cambridge Botanic Garden, TL45N. North of Wicken, the isolated records are from Lattersey LNR, TL29Y, a wooded brick pit, and Six Acre Plantation, TL68E, an isolated plantation in the arable landscape where it was abundant on acidified peaty ground (pH 4.1). The pH of the soil or rotting wood on which it grew in seven other sites ranged from 4.0 to 5.8, with a higher value of 6.8 on ground at Wicken Fen.

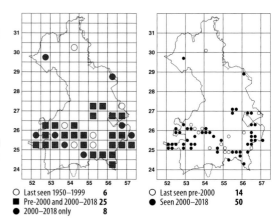

First record: Gamlingay, TL25SW, W. Vernon (Ray 1696: 35, listed as 'Musci stellaris speciem nobis exhibuit *D. Vernon*', with the locality added in Vernon's annotated copy). Vernon also noted that it fruited in spring. Relhan (1786: 17, as *Bryum hornum*) initially knew it from Hinton Moor, TL45NE, but later (1802: 420) added Gamlingay and it is still present there at White Wood, TL25A, B, Gamlingay Heath Plantation, TL25F, and Gamlingay Cinques, TL25G. It was first noted in the beechwood on the Gog Magog Hills as a few stunted plants in 1914; by 1940 large patches were present but in 2017 we could find only one small patch. It was also known from Wandlebury, TL45W, presumably on acidified substrates. The Frescalo analysis shows a decline since the 1970s.

Dioicous. Capsules occasional (14% tetrads), seen in both woodland and fenland populations; swollen, green February, dehisced April.

## CINCLIDIACEAE

### Rhizomnium punctatum

The most luxuriant patches of this rather luscious moss are found on wet or shallowly flooded ground in woodland and scrub (41% of tetrad records). Its sites include ancient and secondary woods on Woburn Sands and Boulder Clay, the edges of the ornamental lake in Wimpole Park, TL35F, the flooded part of Upware North Pit, TL57L, fen carr at Wicken, TL57K, Q, and (the largest population) wet woodland at Chippenham Fen, TL66J, P. However, the species is more widespread on wet rotten logs and stumps of broad-leaved and conifer trees (59% of tetrad records), usually in ancient woodland but also in secondary woodland, fen carr and the wooded part of Upware North Pit. On this substrate the dominant phase of the life-cycle is often the

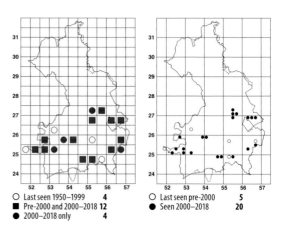

densely felted, persistent brown protonemata, and leafy shoots may be very small and scattered. We have found colonies on individual logs which lack leafy shoots but so far we have not found a site in which all colonies consist only of protonemata.

First record: Wood at Chippenham Fen, TL66P, R.A. Lewin and P.M. Priestley, 1941 (*Richards file*; see Appendix 2). There is no evidence for a significant change in its distribution since 1964.

Dioicous. Capsules rare (10% tetrads), recorded only from Gamlingay Heath Plantation and Chippenham Fen, unexpanded and swollen, green October, green and buff-brown March. Gemmae are usually present on the protonemata; they are well described by Duckett & Ligrone (1994).

## PLAGIOMNIACEAE

### Plagiomnium cuspidatum

This distinctive *Plagiomnium* species was seen during the recent survey only on chalky soil under beeches in the Beechwood reserve on Wort's Causeway, TL45X, where it grew with *Ctenidium molluscum*.

First record: Amongst grass, Old Court, Queens' College, Cambridge, TL45P, M.C.F. Proctor, 1950 (*Richards file*; see Appendix 2); searched for here but not refound in the recent survey. It was also recorded on a shaded lawn at King's College, TL45P, in 1953. There are also 20th-century records of it growing under beech trees at Wandlebury, TL45W, and Hildersham Hall, TL54P, and on rotten wood at Wandlebury and in the 'Aconite Wood' near Great Abington, TL54J. Nationally, as in Cambridgeshire, this is an uncommon species which often grows in short, base-rich turf or on decaying wood over base-rich soils, two apparently dissimilar habitats. Blockeel *et al.* (2014) refer rather sceptically to the possibility that it has declined in southern and eastern England, pointing out that it has always

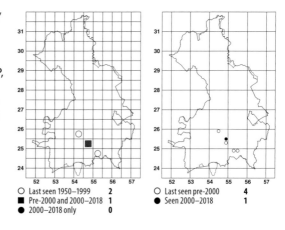

○ Last seen 1950–1999    2
■ Pre-2000 and 2000–2018   1
● 2000–2018 only    0

○ Last seen pre-2000    4
● Seen 2000–2018    1

been rare in these areas, but rarities are particularly liable to decline and there are obvious reasons why the species might have been lost from its grassland sites. Its rarity on decaying wood, and its decline in these sites, is less explicable.

Synoicous. Capsules seen recently in the Wort's Causeway beechwood (green, turning brown, April) and an older specimen, from a decayed log in a hollow in 'Aconite Wood', collected in January 1957 (CGE), has numerous young setae.

## Plagiomnium affine

An uncommon species of well-drained, sandy, gravelly or chalky soils. We recorded it during the recent survey from thin or disturbed turf (including anthills and old graves) in pastures, lawns, churchyards and on banks, and in the dry shade under specimen trees on lawns, isolated shrubs in chalk grassland or under beeches on the chalk.

First confirmed record: White Wood, Gamlingay, TL25SW, H.L.K. Whitehouse, 1955, CGE (see Appendix 2). The taxonomy of *Plagiomnium affine* and related species was clarified by Timo Koponen (1968, 1971, 1980). Before Koponen's work the distinctions between the species were not well understood and more recently there has still been a tendency to over-record *P. affine*, which is often

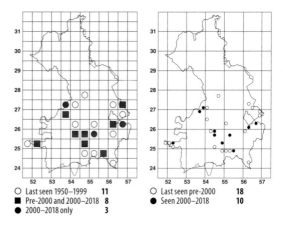

○ Last seen 1950–1999    11
■ Pre-2000 and 2000–2018   8
● 2000–2018 only    3

○ Last seen pre-2000    18
● Seen 2000–2018    10

regarded (quite erroneously) as the 'default' species. All the other *Plagiomnium* species in the county except *P. cuspidatum* have on occasion been named *P. affine*, including *P. elatum*, *P. rostratum* and juvenile forms of *P. undulatum*. The older records mapped here are based on a revision of herbarium material by M.O.H. which showed that 10 of the 22 specimens in CGE were misidentified. Records have been accepted if confirmed by specimens or if consistent with the confirmed ecology and distribution.

Dioicous. Capsules not recorded and very rare nationally.

## Plagiomnium elatum

This is a conspicuous feature of the bryophyte flora of Wicken Fen, TL56P, 57K, Q and Chippenham Fen, TL66P. It is found on trampled droves, mown rides and fen communities maintained by mowing or by the grazing of ponies or water buffalo. It is less frequent in taller fen vegetation but it grows luxuriantly in wet fen carr and fen woodland. In wet carr at St Edmund's Fen, Wicken, TL57Q, for example, it grows on slightly raised ground with *Brachythecium rivulare*, *Eurhynchium striatum* and *Kindbergia praelonga*, a zone just overlapping with that of *Mnium hornum* which is restricted to higher ground or the bases of shrubs. *P. elatum* is also found in wet woodland at Commissioners' Pit, TL57F, Fordham Abbey, TL66J, and Fordham Hall Yard Wood, TL67F.

First record: Wicken Fen, abundant, P.G.M. Rhodes, 1908, CGE (as *Mnium affine* var. *elatum*). It was first found at Chippenham Fen in 1941. P.D. Sell collected it at Mill Homes, Bassingbourn, TL34SW, in 1952. Until the early 1950s this area was regularly flooded and supported a large *Dactylorhiza* population. By 2002 the species-rich community had been replaced by a thick grass cover, there appeared to be no suitable area for *P. elatum* and Peter Sell said that he had been unable to find any *Dactylorhiza* there the preceding summer (2001). The other 20th-century site was at Thriplow, TL44N, where it was collected near Great Nine Wells by G. Crompton in 1958, growing with *Samolus valerandi*, and from Fen Wood by G. Crompton in 1958 and S.M. Walters in 1959 (CGE), growing with *Cladium mariscus*.

Dioicous. Neither sex organs nor capsules recorded and the latter are unknown in Britain.

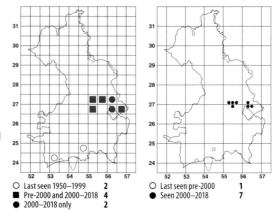

| | |
|---|---|
| ○ Last seen 1950–1999 | 2 |
| ■ Pre-2000 and 2000–2018 | 4 |
| ● 2000–2018 only | 2 |

| | |
|---|---|
| ○ Last seen pre-2000 | 1 |
| ● Seen 2000–2018 | 7 |

## Plagiomnium ellipticum

Only found twice during the recent survey. At Upware North Pit, TL57L, in 2015 it formed an almost pure carpet below a mixed community containing *Berula erecta*, *Eupatorium cannabinum*, *Galium palustre*, *Iris pseudacorus*, *Lythrum salicaria*, *Phragmites australis*, *Rumex hydrolapathum*, *Solanum dulcamara*, *Teucrium scordium* and *Typha latifolia* (BBSUK). On a BBS meeting in October 2017, R.H. Carter found it on the side of a tussock in a wet, grazed fenland community at Chippenham Fen, TL66P.

First record: Amongst *Carex acutiformis* in ditch, north margin of Wicken Fen, TL57SE, R.E. Parker, 1953, CGE, as *Mnium affine*. The specimen, which is mixed with *P. elatum*, was redetermined by T. Koponen in 1967 and his re-identification has been recently confirmed by MOH. The species is similar in its ecology to *P. elatum* but tends to grow in less base-rich habitats.

Dioicous. Male plants seen at Upware; capsules not recorded and very rare in Britain.

## Plagiomnium undulatum

Despite its frequency, this large and distinctive species has a rather narrow habitat range, usually growing on mesic ground in habitats which are at least lightly shaded. It is found in primary and secondary woodland and plantations, including woods on obvious ridge and furrow such as South Lodge Plantation, TL25NE, fen carr and wooded, disused chalk, clay and gravel pits. It also grows in well-established grassland and sometimes on stream and ditch sides outside woodland, disused railways and in old gardens. We have found it in 51% of the churchyards we have surveyed, where it is most frequently found in the thin grassy sward on the north side of the church, often with *Lophocolea bidentata*. It becomes increasingly restricted to

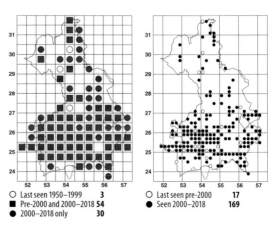

| | |
|---|---|
| ○ Last seen 1950–1999 | 3 |
| ■ Pre-2000 and 2000–2018 | 54 |
| ● 2000–2018 only | 30 |

| | |
|---|---|
| ○ Last seen pre-2000 | 17 |
| ● Seen 2000–2018 | 169 |

churchyards towards the north of the county, and 18 of the 23 sites north of northing 28 are churchyards or cemeteries. The species is mildly calcicole, and thus tolerant of most of the soils in the county. Established populations sometimes spread from the ground to other substrates such as rotting logs, gravestones and other masonry, brickwork and, at one site, a fibreglass boat.

First record: Trumpington, TL45, and Teversham, TL45/55, W. Vernon, *c*. 1696 (Vernon's annotated Ray 1696: 36, as *Muscus ad Polytrichoidem ascendens, arbusculam referens, foliis longis*). It was next found by Thomas Martyn in 1760–61 (*Martyn letters*, as *Mnium serpillif[olium] undulatum*). Relhan knew it from Eversden Wood, TL35L, and Madingley Wood, TL45E (Relhan 1820: 453, as *Bryum ligulatum*), W.L.P. Garnons collected it in Madingley Wood in 1827 (SWN) and it still grows in both sites. Skrimshire found it at Bushy Place, Wisbech, TF41K (1824, WBCH), growing on the ground by the side of a ditch. The species appears to have rather limiting colonising powers, but there is little evidence for significant change in its distribution in recent decades.

Dioicous. Capsules rare (4% tetrads), seen seven times in the recent survey, young setae November, swollen green capsules February. All the plants we have noted with sex organs and fruits have been in woodland, except for female plants on the disused railway line which runs alongside Hayley Wood, TL25W. In some woods we saw only a single clump of fruiting plants, but they were more frequent in swampy woodland at Fordham Hall Yard Wood, TL67F, in February 2003 (after a wet winter) when they had up to nine capsules per inflorescence and three inflorescences (13 capsules) per stem.

### Plagiomnium rostratum

This species has much in common with *P. undulatum* in its requirement for mesic or damp soil in shaded sites, but it is apparently less able to cope with competition from grasses in turf or from pleurocarpous mosses on the ground in woodland. Its prostrate or low, arching stems are therefore usually found on otherwise rather bare soil, especially silty streamsides, the banks of shaded streams and ponds, and rides, paths and tracks in woodland. Although normally found on the ground, it also grows on tree roots and rotting wood. At its best, on lightly trampled, moist shaded tracks, it may be abundant over many square metres. It does sometimes grow in trampled grassland, including lawns, and on mown fen rides at Chippenham Fen,

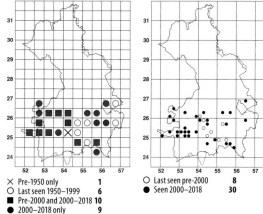

| | |
|---|---|
| ✕ Pre-1950 only | 1 |
| ○ Last seen 1950–1999 | 6 |
| ■ Pre-2000 and 2000–2018 | 10 |
| ● 2000–2018 only | 9 |

| | |
|---|---|
| ○ Last seen pre-2000 | 8 |
| ● Seen 2000–2018 | 30 |

TL66P. Like *P. undulatum* it grows in primary and well-established secondary woodland and plantations, as well as parks, old gardens and a wooded clunch pit, but we have only three recent records from churchyards.

First record: Near Madingley Bath, TL45E, Relhan (1820: 452, as *Bryum rostratum*). Fruiting material was collected here by W.L.P. Garnons in 1827 (SWN), H.E. Lowe in 1834, 'from the side of the Bath', and Henslow in 1838 (both CGE). The species is easily overlooked unless it is fruiting and this perhaps explains the lack of concordance between old and recent records.

Synoicous. Unlike *P. undulatum*, *P. rostratum* is synoicous and capsules occur occasionally (33% tetrads), young setae November, January, February; capsules green, swollen February, March, dehiscing April.

## AULACOMNIACEAE

### Aulacomnium palustre

This common plant in a range of moist, more or less acidic habitats in northern and western Britain was seen only twice in Cambridgeshire during the recent survey. It was found on clinker at the edge of a depression in disused railway sidings at March, TL49E, in 2001 and with *Thuidium tamariscinum* on acidic ground (pH 5.8) in birch scrub in compartment 2, Wicken Fen, TL56P, in 2003. The March site has now been redeveloped and we have no evidence that *A. palustre* has survived the recent, extensive scrub clearance at Wicken.

First record: Gamlingay, TL25SW, W. Vernon, *c.* 1696 (Vernon's annotated Ray 1696: 338, as *Muscus trichoides major palustris citrini coloris*). T. Martyn found it in 1760–61 (*Martyn letters*, as *Mnium palustre*) but did not cite any localities in his flora (1763: 24). Relhan's first record (1785: 399) was from Hinton Moor, TL45NE; he later added Gamlingay Bogs, TL25SW, and Shelford Moor, TL45SE (1820: 449). It was collected at Gamlingay by Henslow in 1827 and G.D. Haviland and J.J. Lister in 1881 (both CGE). Henslow's specimen has robust, tall (10 cm), straight stems whereas the later specimen is of shorter and much more straggling growth, an almost certain indication of the deterioration of the bog vegetation in the intervening decades. The only 20th-century records were from Wicken Fen, where it was discovered in 1965 by J.M. Lock and was subsequently found scattered throughout the Fen on peat beneath fen carr (Lock 1990). There were several records from compartment 2 between 1974 and the recent survey.

Dioicous. Capsules not recorded.

### Aulacomnium androgynum

*Aulacomnium androgynum* is a calcifuge which is slightly less frequent as an epiphyte on living trees (42% of tetrad records) than as a colonist of decaying wood (50%), although the distinction is not clear-cut as it can be found on the dry, rotten heartwood of living willows and on the base and bark of recently fallen trees and shrubs. The other records (8%) are from soil at the base of a tree and on a rootplate, and the worked wood of a rotting fence rail and an old railway sleeper. It can be found in ancient and more recent woodlands, plantations, scrub, orchards, hedges and on isolated streamside trees. Willow is the most frequent host (27% of tetrad records), followed by hawthorn (19%) and oak (11%) with 1–2 records from several other species (see Appendix 3). In orchards Robin Stevenson found it on 11 (6%) of the 173 individual pear trees he surveyed but did not find it on any of the 951 apples.

First record: Chippenham/Kennett area, R.S. Adamson (Evans 1913; see Appendix 2). The first precisely localised records were from Gamlingay, TL25SW, where it was found at Gamlingay Wood by T.G. Tutin in 1929 (*Richards file*) and at Great Heath Plantation by P.W. Richards in 1930 (NMW). Whitehouse (1964) described it as frequent on stumps and rotten wood. Hill (1967) pointed out that it favoured lighter and drier places than *Orthotrichum lineare* and that the two seldom occurred together.

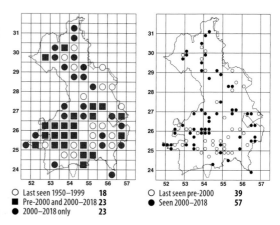

○ Last seen 1950–1999    18
■ Pre-2000 and 2000–2018   23
● 2000–2018 only    23

○ Last seen pre-2000    39
● Seen 2000–2018    57

However, at Wicken Fen, TL56P, 57K, Q, it formerly grew on old *Molinia* tussocks in fen carr as well as on the bases of old birches (Lock 1990). Both Whitehouse (1964) and Hill (1967) considered that it 'appears to have increased in frequency in recent years, as, until 1940, it was known only from the neighbourhood of Gamlingay and from the Breck fringe'. This increase proved to be rather short-lived. It is certainly rarer now than it was in the 1960s and 1970s, when it was frequently found on excursions and, as a completely unmistakeable species, provided a much-needed source of encouragement to beginners. The Frescalo analysis shows a marked decline since its peak in the 1980s. Nationally its frequency has followed a similar trajectory to that in Cambridgeshire, increasing until 1980 and then falling rapidly (Hill & Preston 2014).

Dioicous. Capsules not recorded and very rare nationally; gemmae on 'drumsticks' almost always present.

## ORTHODONTIACEAE

### *Orthodontium lineare*
This introduced calcifuge has a rather narrow niche. It is usually found on rotting logs and tree stumps in ancient woodland and mature secondary woodland and plantations (78% of tetrad records), especially on the remains of conifers (acidic) or oaks (acidic and very long-lasting). One rotten log on which it grew in Marmer's Wood, TL65N, had a pH of 3.1. It is sometimes restricted to shaded and relatively dry microsites under overhangs, where it escapes competition from the more vigorous bryophytes but is often accompanied by the lichen *Cladonia*. In such sites it is easily overlooked unless specifically searched for. It also occurs as an epiphyte on the base of trees or rarely on the lower bole or on the rotting interiors of living trees (16%), most frequently on oak but also on alder, ash, birch and Douglas fir. The remaining records are from worked

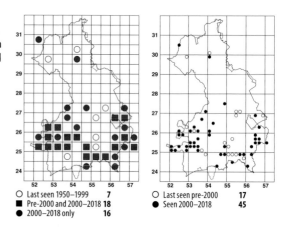

○ Last seen 1950–1999    7
■ Pre-2000 and 2000–2018   18
● 2000–2018 only    16

○ Last seen pre-2000    17
● Seen 2000–2018    45

wood (6%), including decaying fence timbers and a decaying railway sleeper in March sidings, TL49E.

First record: Pine stump, South Lodge Plantation, Croxton, TL25P, P.W. Richards, 1947, BBSUK. This is a Southern Hemisphere species, first collected in Europe in Cheshire in 1910. By 1940 it was widespread in northern England and it spread into much of central and eastern England and southern Scotland in the next two decades (Smith 1978b). By the time of Proctor's (1956) flora it was rare and local in Cambridgeshire but abundant near Cockayne Hatley, Bedfordshire, TL25Q, on the other side of the county boundary. It might have spread into the county from this area as several early records are from the acidic woods in the south-west including Great Heath Plantation, TL25F (1951), White Wood, Gamlingay, TL25SW (1955) and Gamlingay Wood, TL25L (1957). Whatever the source of the propagules, it had reached Overall Grove, TL36G, by 1954, Copley Hill on the Gogs, TL55B, by 1956 and Chippenham Fen, TL66P, by 1961. At Wicken Fen, TL56P, 57K, Q it was first found on old *Molinia* tussocks in 1963 and subsequently spread extensively but by 1989 it had become restricted to the base of old birch trees (Lock 1990) and it has not been seen there since. It was never as abundant in Cambridgeshire as it became in areas of more acidic soils and large conifer plantations elsewhere in East Anglia, and it is probably less frequent here now than it was in the decades of heavy $SO_2$ pollution, when it grew even in woods on chalk soils. The Frescalo chart shows a very similar trend to that of *Aulacomnium androgynum*, an increase until the 1980s then a sharp decline. This parallels the national trend (Hill & Preston 2014).

Autoicous. Capsules very frequent (87% tetrads); young setae December–February, capsules expanded, green November, February–April. Protonemal gemmae abundant.

## HOOKERIACEAE

### †*Hookeria lucens*

This large-celled, instantly recognisable species, the sole European representative of a tropical family, was formerly a short-lived colonist at Wicken Fen.

First record: A few shoots on old *Molinia* tussocks in fen carr near the brickpits, Wicken Fen, TL57Q, J.M. Lock, 1963, CGE. It was refound near the brickpits as a patch about 1 m across in 1972 (Anon. 1973) and then seen in two further sites on the Fen, one patch in the Godwin Plots in 1974 (CGE) and near Barnes Mere, TL57K, in February 1975 (Lock 1990). These were the last records, and the colonies may have succumbed to drought in the summers of 1975 and 1976.

Autoicous. Capsules not recorded.

## FONTINALACEAE

### *Fontinalis antipyretica* var. *antipyretica*

*Fontinalis antipyretica* grows in water or in frequently inundated sites at the water's edge. It occurs by flowing water in the county's major rivers and in streams, large Fenland drains and smaller ditches, and by standing water in lakes (including flooded gravel pits), ponds and (exceptionally) in periodically flooded hollows in willow scrub in a disused brick pit. In the very sluggish River Cam near Cambridge the best populations are found in the more rapidly moving and well-aerated water by sluices and weirs, as at Jesus Lock, TL45P. The strong populations along the River Kennett, TL66Z, 67Q, V, 76E, persist even though the river dries up completely in droughts. Many plants in the Kennett are attached to small chalk stones on the river bed, and some of

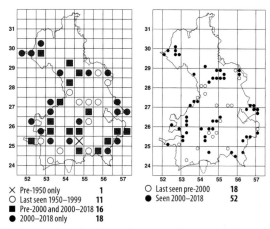

| | | |
|---|---|---|
| × Pre-1950 only | 1 | |
| ○ Last seen 1950–1999 | 11 | |
| ■ Pre-2000 and 2000–2018 | 16 | |
| ● 2000–2018 only | 18 | |

| | |
|---|---|
| ○ Last seen pre-2000 | 18 |
| ● Seen 2000–2018 | 52 |

these stones are washed onto the bank when the river is in spate. In other sites plants may be attached to woodwork or stonework edging canalised rivers, the brickwork walls of locks or the exposed roots or bases of waterside trees (including ash, sycamore and willow). In some Fenland drains the species is found in large, loose masses which are apparently unattached to the substrate. Like many aquatics it is variable in habit; it has long training stems in favourable conditions but some colonies consist of a few small and stunted plants.

First record: In the river [Great Ouse] beyond Stretham ferry, TL57SW, Ray (1663, as *Muscus triangularis aquaticus*). Ray's comment that the leaves 'be so disposed all along the stalk as to make it appear triangular' confirms the identity of his plant. Vernon noted in his annotated copy of Ray (1696: 37) that he had often found it at 'Chesterton *et aliis locis*'. J. Martyn (1729b: 12 and 1732 vol. 1: 263, as *Fontinalis major foliis triangularibus, complicatis, capitulis in foliorum alis sessilibus*) was the first to record the plant 'in the well at Coton', TL45E, and fine fruiting plants were gathered there several times by Henslow and his contemporaries (e.g. 1825, CGE). T. Martyn (1763: 31–32) also knew the plant from 'the well by the road side' at Madingley, i.e. Moor Barns (Swale & Belcher 1993). There is little doubt that the species has disappeared from many of the springs, wells and ponds, including woodland ponds, in which it was formerly known. It has also been lost from some sites by larger waters; it was last seen at Wicken Fen, TL57K, in 1963 and it is no longer 'common in the Cam' as it was described in 1929 by the undergraduate Paul Richards. On the other hand it has colonised the gravel pits in Milton Country Park, TL46W, which support healthy populations.

Dioicous. Capsules rare (2% tetrads), recorded January, March–May, August. Capsules apparently develop only after the stems are exposed above the water surface and so tend to be found by the smaller water bodies. There are old Cambridgeshire records of fruiting plants from Coton (see above), a pond at East Hatley, TL25V (1934) and one in Buff Wood, TL25V, perhaps the same site (1985). There is one recent record of plants submerged in a dyke at Chippenham Fen, TL66P, with frequent fruits on the older stems (2002).

## CLIMACIACEAE

### Climacium dendroides

This robust plant spreads by short underground stems to form clones which, once established, are apparently long-lived. In the recent survey one clonal patch was seen in a mown fen community at Wicken Fen, TL57K, and a few stems found on the edge of a mown ride at Chippenham Fen, TL66P. The Wicken site was flooded when the species was found (in 2008) and only the tops of the 'trees' were emerging above the water. The other apparently native site is at Hauxton Gravel Pits, TL45F, where a narrow band (20 × 1 m) grew in a goose-grazed sward at the edge of one of the lakes in 2003. Climacium also turned up in 2007 by the edge of the pond in Jonathan Graham's garden in Cross Road, Whittlesey, TL29T, where it may have been

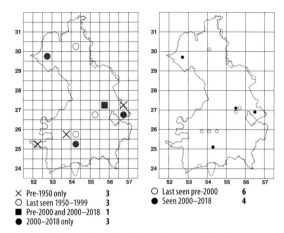

| | | |
|---|---|---|
| × Pre-1950 only | 3 | |
| ○ Last seen 1950–1999 | 3 | |
| ■ Pre-2000 and 2000–2018 | 1 | |
| ● 2000–2018 only | 3 | |

| | |
|---|---|
| ○ Last seen pre-2000 | 6 |
| ● Seen 2000–2018 | 4 |

unintentionally introduced with tiny, wild-collected plugs of *Hydrocotyle vulgaris* or other marsh plants, perhaps from Woodwalton Fen. The two small groups of c. 3 and 15 stems seen originally had increased to a 60 × 60 cm patch by 2016, but the species (unlike the *Hydrocotyle*) had failed to spread to other sites around the pond.

First record: Gamlingay, TL25SW, W. Vernon (Ray 1696: 32, as *Muscus dendroides elatior, ramulis crebris minus surculosis, capitulis pediculis brevibus insidentibus*); the last Gamlingay record is a specimen in Henslow's herbarium, collected in 1827 (CGE, *fide Richards file*). J. Martyn (1729b: 15, as *Hypnum erectum, arbusculam referens, ramulis subrotundis confertim nascentibus*) listed the species from Madingley Wood and Moor Barns Grove, TL45E. His records might be thought doubtful as he did not record *Thamnobryum alopecurum* in the county but T. Martyn underlined Madingley Wood in his annotated copy, indicating that he also saw the species there. It was refound at the eastern end of Madingley Wood nearly two centuries later, in 1956 (CGE) and 1957. It was also known from a moist hollow in Whitepits Plantation, Hardwick, TL35U, between 1927 and 1945; Richards' substantial collection (1928, NMW) shows that the plants were vigorous specimens 8 cm high. Like the records from Madingley, those from Wicken Fen are remarkably discontinuous for such a conspicuous species. P.W. Richards recorded it in a field near the brick pits, TL57Q, in 1930 and it was refound on ground under carr there in 1967, then in fen carr on Verrall's Fen in 1979 (TL57K) and again in young birch carr in 1994 (TL56P), and in the Godwin Plots on the Sedge Fen, TL57K, in 1980 (CGE). The other records are from the Hill of Health, Cambridge, TL45P (Relhan 1820: 454, as *Hypnum dendroides*), Isleham Plantation, TL67SE (in 1930) and Gray's Moor Pits, TF40A (in 1967).

Dioicous. Capsules not recorded.

## AMBLYSTEGIACEAE

### †Palustriella commutata

This attractive pleurocarp, which is particularly associated with calcareous springs, was always rare and is now apparently extinct in the county.

First record: Thriplow Peat Holes, TL44N, undated but c. 1928 (*Richards file*; see Appendix 2). There is no specimen, but a 19th-century description of the crystal-clear spring at Thriplow is quoted by Crompton (1959), who also details the extraordinary rich vascular plant flora formerly found in this area. The spring habitat suggests that the plant was *P. commutata* rather than the segregate *P. falcata*, not then treated as a separate species. *P. commutata* was discovered at Chippenham Fen, TL66P, by F.H. Perring in 1951 and refound there, by a 'spring in the central area', by D. Welch in 1960 (CGE). Two springs are mapped by Kassas (1950) in what is now Compartment 8. The plants collected by Welch are very small, so the habitat was presumably suboptimal even in 1960; the species has not been seen there again. *P. commutata* has declined in Norfolk and Suffolk (Beckett *et al.* 1999, Sanford & Fisk 2010) and has not been seen in Bedfordshire since the 19th century (Boon & Outen 2011).

Dioicous. Capsules not recorded.

### †*Palustriella falcata*
Known from only two collections

First record: Bog, Senior Wrangler's Walk, Cambridge, H.N. Dixon, 1883, BM (as *Hypnum falcatum*). The Walk ran alongside Hobson's Brook towards Trumpington, and Dixon's site was presumably Empty Common, TL45N. This site had a rich vascular plant flora but it was dug for coprolites between 1869 and 1872 and the holes were being filled with rubbish by 1875. However, *Blysmus compressus, Sagina nodosa* and *Triglochin palustris* were amongst the vascular plants noted here by Dixon in his annotated Babington (1860) and *Blysmus* survived until 1886, although it had gone by 1898 (Crompton 2001). The other collection of *P. falcata* is a luxuriant specimen from 'mixed sedge' at Wicken Poors' Fen, TL57Q, P.W. Richards, 1929, NMW (as *Hypnum commutatum*), det. M.O.H. and C.D.P. Richards (1932) noted that there were two patches on Poors' Fen. *P. falcata* is less closely associated with calcareous springs than *P. commutata*, but like that species it has declined in south-east England.

Dioicous. Capsules not recorded.

### *Cratoneuron filicinum*
This is a frequent species of lightly disturbed ground or hard substrates which are seasonally or more or less permanently moist. Typical habitats include stonework, brickwork or concrete just above the normal water level of rivers and streams and in the spray zone of weirs (where it may be particularly abundant), roots, tree bases or rotting wood by water, soil on stream and ditch banks, at the edge of lakes and pools, on woodland rides and in thin turf in moist pastures. It is also recorded on limestone and sandstone by ornamental lakes, tufa in gardens, the moist floors of chalk pits, shaded concrete and on tarmac and gravel tracks. It is a rare and casual colonist of stubble fields, recorded on clay and loam soil in only three of the 76 sites surveyed for the SBAL project. On soft substrates

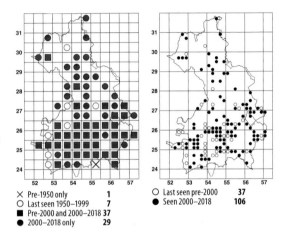

| | | |
|---|---|---|
| × Pre-1950 only | 1 | |
| ○ Last seen 1950–1999 | 7 | |
| ■ Pre-2000 and 2000–2018 | 37 | |
| ● 2000–2018 only | 29 | |

| | |
|---|---|
| ○ Last seen pre-2000 | 37 |
| ● Seen 2000–2018 | 106 |

where the water level is high or where there is little disturbance, such as moist turf, swampy lakesides and droves in the undrained fens, *C. filicinum* loses out to competing species, and is often replaced by dense carpets of *Calliergonella cuspidata*.

First record: T. Martyn, 1760–61 (*Martyn letters*, as *Hypnum filicinum*) and Martyn (1763: 25). Relhan (1785: 410) reported it from 'Hinton Moor, &c.', TL45NE, and later (1820: 463) from Shelford Moor, TL45SE, and Sawston Moor, TL44NE, and Henslow collected fruiting specimens near Cambridge, TL45, in 1821 (BTH) and 1822 (CGE). Six localised records between 1874 and 1906 perhaps hint that it was more conspicuous in the landscape then than now. In recent years we have not recorded it in dry chalk grassland on Fleam Dyke, TL55H, or on the top of the Devil's Dyke, TL66SW, where it was found in the 1950s; our only record at the latter is from the winter-wet base of the ditch, TL65P.

Dioicous. Capsules rare (4% tetrads); green, expanded April, dehiscing May, green, expanded, recently dehisced and old September.

### *Campylium stellatum*
A plant of the undrained Fenland remnants, recorded from a pony-grazed fen community at Verrall's Fen, Wicken, TL57K, and rather more widely at Chippenham Fen, TL66P, where we have found it in open, grazed fen communities, including on a tussock in a buffalo-trampled area of *Schoenus nigricans* where it grew with *Campyliadelphus elodes*, and in a small area of low, spring-fed fen which is cut and gathered in early September.

First record: Hinton Moor, TL45NE, and Chippenham Moor, TL66P, Relhan (1786: 19, as *Hypnum stellatum*). No material survives from Hinton Moor, or from Shelford Moor, TL45SE (Relhan 1820: 461). When M.O.H. revised the available specimens, only two fine fruiting specimens from Gamlingay, collected by

Henslow in 1827 and 1838 (CGE), were unequivocally attributable to this species (Preston & Hill 2005); most of the remainder were *C. protensum*. Fieldwork since 2005 has established that *C. stellatum* is found at Chippenham and Wicken, and two earlier specimens from Wicken have come to light (1883, BM; 1955, CGE), though the distinction between the two species is not always straightforward.

Dioicous. Plants with young setae seen in October and with green, swollen capsules in April at Chippenham Fen; the fruits on Henslow's plants, collected in April and May, are also immature.

## Campylium protensum

Although uncommon, *Campylium protensum* is found in a range of communities on base-rich soils. It grows in chalk grassland at East Pit, Cherry Hinton, TL45X, and on the Devil's Dyke, TL66F, and on moister, clay soils in a coppice plot in Gamlingay Wood, TL25L, and in an abandoned brick pit at Kings Dyke, Whittlesey, TL29N. It is also found in marshy vegetation by a pool in Bassenhally Pit, TL29Z, and in open fenland vegetation, including both mown and grazed communities, at Wicken Fen, TL57K, and Chippenham Fen, TL66J, P.

First record: Bottisham, TL56, L. Jenyns, 1824, CGE, det. M.O.H. and C.D.P. Several extant sites have long-established populations, including Gamlingay Wood (first recorded 1945), Whittlesey brick works (1960), Wicken Fen (1930) and Chippenham Fen

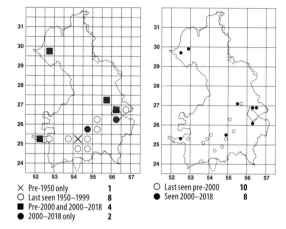

| | |
|---|---|
| ✕ Pre-1950 only | 1 |
| ○ Last seen 1950–1999 | 8 |
| ■ Pre-2000 and 2000–2018 | 4 |
| ● 2000–2018 only | 2 |

| | |
|---|---|
| ○ Last seen pre-2000 | 10 |
| ● Seen 2000–2018 | 8 |

(1902). Places where the species has not been recorded recently include Thriplow Meadows, TL44I (last seen 1958), Wandlebury, TL45W (1965) and Quy Fen, TL56B (1984). In addition, records of *C. stellatum sens. lat.* from a further four sites between 1965 and 1984 were probably based on *C. protensum* but there are no vouchers.

Dioicous. Not seen fruiting recently but Jenyns' material, collected in February, and specimens from Wicken Fen collected in May 1951 and July 1957 have immature fruits (CGE) and those collected by J. Lister and G.D. Haviland in October 1880 at Wilbraham Fen, TL55NW, have dehisced capsules (CGE, OXF).

## Campyliadelphus chrysophyllus

One of the characteristic bryophytes of rather open, long-established, species-rich chalk grassland. It is frequent in areas of older turf on the Devil's Dyke, TL56, 66, but rare or absent from those areas where scrub has only recently been cleared to re-establish herbaceous communities. It is rarer on the trampled top of the Fleam Dyke, TL55L, where in one site it grows with *Abietinella abietina*, *Homalothecium lutescens* and *Pseudoscleropodium purum*. The other recent sites are active and disused chalk pits, where it may be found with a crust of *Leiocolea turbinata* on chalky soil as well as in turf, chalky road cuttings and a bank on Gault Clay at Hauxton Gravel Pits, TL45F.

First record: Roman Road, Gog Magog Hills,

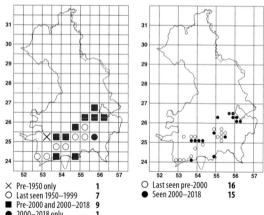

| | |
|---|---|
| ✕ Pre-1950 only | 1 |
| ○ Last seen 1950–1999 | 7 |
| ■ Pre-2000 and 2000–2018 | 9 |
| ● 2000–2018 only | 1 |

| | |
|---|---|
| ○ Last seen pre-2000 | 16 |
| ● Seen 2000–2018 | 15 |

TL45X, H.N. Dixon, 1883, BM (as *Hypnum chrysophyllum*). Rhodes also collected it there, noting on the specimen (1908, CGE) that it was 'common among grass on old chalk turf' in the county. It was last seen on the Roman Road in 1971. The species is clearly declining; there are 20th-century records from nine chalk pits in which it has not been seen recently, as well as the railway cutting at Worsted Lodge, TL55G, and chalk grassland at Great Wilbraham Common, TL55I. It is known to benefit from a degree of disturbance when it grows in calcareous grasslands, and it is frequent in military training areas such as Salisbury Plain (Preston *et al.* 2009) and Castlemartin Range (Bosanquet 2010). The steep side of the Devil's Dyke, grazed by rabbits and with sheep-grazing recently reinstated in places, clearly provides more suitable conditions that any of the other relict chalk grasslands in the county.

Dioicous. Capsules not recorded and rare nationally.

## Campyliadelphus elodes

An inconspicuous species of calcareous fenland, recorded recently in both the National Nature Reserves. It grew amongst *Drepanocladus polygamus* at the edge of the ditch alongside Gardiner's Drove, Wicken Fen, TL57K, and with *Campylium stellatum* in a tussocky area of *Schoenus nigricans* fen grazed and trampled by water buffalo at Chippenham Fen, TL66P.

First record: Fulbourn, TL55NW, L.J. Sedgwick, det. W. Ingham (Rhodes 1911, as *Hypnum elodes*). First found at Wicken Fen in 1929 by P.W. Richards, growing in old fen carr and by the edge of Wicken Lode (NMW). It was well known at Wicken, TL57K, Q, in the early 1950s; Proctor (1956) described it as growing in 'damp peaty places, perhaps most characteristically about the bases of grasses and sedges in short fen vegetation ... in some quantity at Wicken, where it occurs in the droves as well as in such diverse habitats as old fen carr and the peaty detritus in an old boat on the lode' (maybe the same old boat in which *Eleocharis acicularis* was found fruiting on mud later that year?). There are vouchers in CGE of plants collected from the base of *Cladium mariscus* (1951) – these were growing in water and mixed with *Campylium protensum* and *Drepanocladus polygamus* – and at the bases of old *Phragmites australis* stems (1953) but the species seems to have been neglected after Proctor left the county and there were no further records from Wicken until the recent survey. The only earlier record from Chippenham Fen was in 1956. The other known site was Quy Fen, TL56B, where it was first found at the edge of a pond in 1945 and refound in 1955 (CGE) and 1957 (the latter as 'a few shoots only').

Dioicous. Capsules not recorded and rare nationally.

## *Amblystegium serpens* var. *serpens*

This is the smallest of the county's common pleurocarpous mosses. It is found on a wider range of substrates than most of the others, though it is normally confined to moist or at least lightly shaded sites. It is frequent on brickwork, concrete and stonework, and also found on tarmac, worked and rotting wood, and stable soil, including chalk, clay, sand and gravel soils on ditch sides, shaded lawns, gravel paths, set-aside fields, neglected flower beds and slow-selling plant pots in garden centres. We have found it in 80% of the churchyards we have recorded, an indication of its frequency on masonry. It also grows on a wide range of artificial substrates including asbestos piling, ironwork, decaying foam furniture, plastic matting and old motor tyres. It is

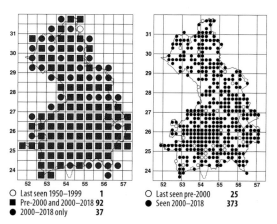

| | |
|---|---|
| O Last seen 1950–1999 | **1** |
| ■ Pre-2000 and 2000–2018 | **92** |
| ● 2000–2018 only | **37** |

| | |
|---|---|
| O Last seen pre-2000 | **25** |
| ● Seen 2000–2018 | **373** |

frequently found by water, often on moist lakeside soil bound together by a dense mass of fine willow roots. It is a frequent epiphyte, found on the bases, trunks and branches of trees and shrubs in hedges, scrub and woodland. It is especially common on elder (29% of tetrad records) where it sometimes forms a dense carpet of stems on the upper trunk and branches. It also grows on willow (14%), ash (13%), apple (8%), hawthorn (6%) and sycamore (5%) and the wide range of native and introduced species listed in Appendix 3. Although it is perhaps over-recorded on apple relative to other hosts, it is genuinely frequent in orchards, found on 514 (54%) of the 951 apple trees surveyed individually by Robin Stevenson and 70 (40%) of the 173 pears.

First record: In and near Moor Barns Thicket, TL45E, T. Martyn (1763: 31, as *Hypnum serpens*). Skrimshire recognised it when he collected it at Wisbech, TF40NE, in 1795 (WBCH) and Jenyns gathered it at Bottisham, TL56, in 1824, mixed with *Rhynchostegium confertum* (CGE), but he did not name either species. Proctor (1956) describes *A. serpens* as growing on 'tree bases, stumps and especially on rotting wood' in woods and copses, and the other 20th-century accounts (Whitehouse 1964, Hill 1967) agree in implicitly limiting its epiphytic occurrences to tree bases. Six specimens in CGE collected between 1962 and 1972 are from tree roots or stumps but none is described as growing higher on the tree. This suggests that it was less frequent on the trunks and branches of elders and other hosts then than it is now. There is a single record between 1929 and 1960 from the trunk of a willow (*Whitehouse species file*) but most of his records have insufficient habitat detail to throw further light on the question. In Berkshire and Oxfordshire, by contrast, Jones (1953) described it as growing on 'tree trunks, especially of elder and willow (in 13/16 examples on these two species)'.

Autoicous. Capsules very frequent (71% tetrads). Capsules develop rather asynchronously, even within colonies. Both young setae and swollen, green capsules can occasionally be found between August and February, and they are very frequent in March and April. We have very few records of freshly dehisced capsules (November, December, April, May, August), and presumably most of the capsules we see maturing in late spring dehisce unseen in summer. In April 2003 green capsules in dry places at Dernford Fen, TL45Q, were shrivelling under the impact of that year's spring drought. Old capsules persist for some time, and can be seen throughout the year.

## Hygroamblystegium varium

Most of our records of *H. varium* are from rotting logs and branches in damp hollows, winter-flooded depressions or ponds in woodland, such as the eutrophic woods on the flood plain of the River Cam near Croydon, TL24Y, 34D, where we found it in several places, and in Hildersham Alder Carr, TL54P, where it also colonises the bases of alders and swampy ground. It also grows on the trunk of a small willow and on a grassy track in disused gravel pits at Fen Drayton, TL36J, P, and with *Drepanocladus aduncus* in grazed wet grassland at Soham Wet Horse Fen, TL67B. Sizeable patches are found with *Leptodictyum riparium* on vertical metal pilings alongside the River Great Ouse at Stretham, TL57G. The northernmost site is on the bank of a

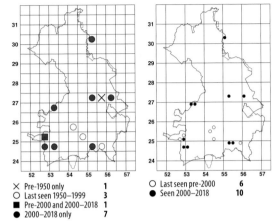

| X | Pre-1950 only | 1 |
| O | Last seen 1950–1999 | 3 |
| ■ | Pre-2000 and 2000–2018 | 1 |
| ● | 2000–2018 only | 7 |

| O | Last seen pre-2000 | 6 |
| ● | Seen 2000–2018 | 10 |

deep ditch near Outwell, TF50B. The similar although rather smaller *Amblystegium serpens* occurs much more frequently in the same sort of waterside habitats.

First record: Old tree stumps by river, Grantchester, TL45H, E.W. Jones, 1929, NMW, conf. M.O.H. (see Appendix 2). Richards collected it later in 1929 from tall carr at Wicken Sedge Fen, TL57 (NMW). It was found in similar habitats in the 20th century to those in the recent survey, but in different localities.

Autoicous. Capsules frequent (60% tetrads) but the species is particularly likely to be overlooked without them; young setae and swollen green capsules seen in March and April, dehisced capsules in April.

## Hygroamblystegium humile

Seen recently on the wooden slats of a small bridge on a path by the River Great Ouse at Fen Drayton Lakes, TL37K; close to the water level on two wooden posts by the same river at Aldreth, TL47Q; on the ground in pastures vulnerable to flooding just outside the Ouse Washes at Mepal, TL48F; and on flat peaty grazed ground within the Washes near Manea, TL58E. At the last site it grew with the flood-tolerant vascular plants *Mentha aquatica*, *Plantago major* and *Potentilla anserina*.

First records: Drying out pit pond, Ring's End near Guyhirn, TF30W, W. Jackson and B. Reeve, 1959, CGE, det. M.O.H. On decaying vegetation, Gray's Moor Pit, TF40A, B. Reeve, 1959, CGE, det. L. Hedenäs and M.O.H. These specimens, collected on the same

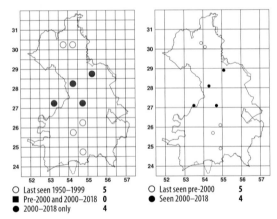

| O | Last seen 1950–1999 | 5 |
| ■ | Pre-2000 and 2000–2018 | 0 |
| ● | 2000–2018 only | 4 |

| O | Last seen pre-2000 | 5 |
| ● | Seen 2000–2018 | 4 |

day, were submitted to E.F. Warburg as new vice-county records but he was uncertain of the identity of the first ('I think this is correct') and rejected the second. Recent examination has confirmed their identity. The first published record was a specimen collected from a cement bridge over a tributary joining the River Cam, Green End, Fen Ditton, TL46V, by R.A. Finch in 1968 (BBSUK). Subsequently it was found by the Cam at Whittlesford Mill, TL44Z (1977) and on Lammas Land and Robinson Crusoe Island, Cambridge, TL45N (1985–1991). As with *H. varium*, it has not been refound at any of its earlier sites but it must surely survive somewhere by the Cam.

Autoicous. Capsules present at Mepal (25% tetrads).

## Leptodictyum riparium

*Leptodictyum* has a narrow niche in the sense that it is characteristically confined to the edge of water bodies, but it may occur by a wide range of waters from garden ponds to major rivers and it colonises many different substrates. It grows on the roots and lower trunks of living trees, rotting wood, asbestos, metal and wooden piling by streams and rivers, brickwork and concrete, limestone and sandstone rocks by ornamental lakes, stones in stream-beds, wet ground on fen droves and in reed swamps and soil on ditch banks and on the base of dried-up ponds. Although normally found above the water-line, it is sometimes seen as submerged plants and it tolerates prolonged periods of submergence. It is also a shade-tolerant species and rotting logs, branches and twigs in woodland ponds provide one of its most characteristic habitats. It occurs by free-flowing waters and by stagnant lakes and ponds over foul-smelling substrates, but it is absent or rare on substrates on which silt accumulates. Willow is,

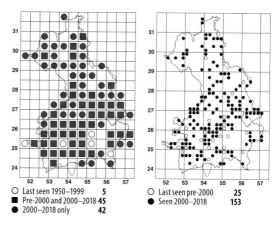

○ Last seen 1950–1999   **5**
■ Pre-2000 and 2000–2018 **45**
● 2000–2018 only   **42**

○ Last seen pre-2000   **25**
● Seen 2000–2018   **153**

not surprisingly, the most frequent host of epiphytic plants (63% of tetrad records), followed by apple (13%) and elder (8%) with 1–2 records from alder, ash, elm, pear and sycamore. *Leptodictyum* is clearly an effective colonist within the flood zone and it can be found, albeit rarely, away from water. We found it, for example, with *Bryum capillare* and *Grimmia pulvinata* on an elder in Cambridge, TL45N, and Robin Stevenson recorded it on 29 (3%) of the 951 apple trees he surveyed in orchards and one (1%) of the 173 pears, all in the Wisbech area, TF40.

First record: T. Martyn, 1760–61 (*Martyn letters*, as *Hypnum riparium*) and Martyn (1763: 25). W. Skrimshire struggled to identify the fine vegetative plants he found growing under water on some posts in a pond near Wisbech, TF40NE, in 1797 (WBCH), and Leonard Jenyns labelled his fruiting specimen, collected at Bottisham, TL56, in 1823, as '*Hypnum* (allied to *polymorphum*)' (BTH). There is no evidence for any marked change in frequency since the early 20th century and the only earlier record that does not accord with our experience is R.E. Parker's observation in 1953 (*Whitehouse species file*) that it is 'a not infrequent plant of permanent pastures on heavier soils – *not* necessarily wet!'.

Autoicous. Capsules frequent (54% tetrads). Capsules develop rather asynchronously, even within colonies, and apparently lack a well-defined phenology although there is an indication of a bimodal distribution. Young setae seen mainly in late winter and spring (August, October, January–April), green capsules mainly in autumn and spring (September–December, February–April with a peak in April), browning or brown capsules in October, December, March and recently dehisced capsules September, October, December, April. Bosanquet's (2010) observations in Pembrokeshire are not dissimilar.

## Drepanocladus polygamus

Refound in 2008 at Wicken Fen, TL57K, growing in some quantity at the edge of a ditch along Gardiner's Drove with *Campylium protensum* and *Campyliadelphus elodes*.

First record: Fenland area, Adamson (Evans 1913); the first localised record was on ground amongst *Phragmites australis* at Wicken Sedge Fen where it was found by P.J. Chamberlain in 1949 (*Richards file*). Like *Campyliadelphus elodes* it was well known at Wicken, TL57K, Q, in the 1950s but it was not seen between 1957 and the recent survey. Specimens from Wicken (CGE, NMW) were collected on a path; with *Campyliadelphus elodes* (q.v.) at the base of *Cladium mariscus*; in peat cuttings; and submerged in a ditch containing iron-rich water. The other known sites were permanent pasture at the University Farm, Cambridge, TL45NW, in 1953; an old gravel pit at Great Abington, TL54J, in 1957 (CGE); and Quy Fen, TL56B, in 1955 (CGE) and 1957.

Autoicous or synoicous. The specimen from peat cuttings at Wicken, collected in July 1957, has dehisced capsules.

## Drepanocladus aduncus

*Drepanocladus aduncus* grows in shallow water or in a band just above the water-line in Fenland ditches, by lakes, farm reservoirs, moats and ponds, and in disused clay and sand or gravel pits. It is sometimes found in swamps dominated by *Eleocharis palustris, Epilobium hirsutum, Phragmites australis* or *Typha latifolia*, and in mown fen vegetation. It also grows in damp, winter-flooded pastures, sometimes in ruts or on cattle-poached ground, as well as on wet tracks and woodland rides and in swampy alder woodland. We have seen it lining shallow water buffalo wallows in Chippenham Fen, TL66P, and colonising damp soil in plastic tubs which formerly held aquatic plants at Shepreth, TL34Y. In addition to its occurrence on the ground, it also grows on decaying wood, as in woodland ponds, and on willow branches by water.

First record: Parson Drove, TF30NE, M.J. Berkeley, 1828, CGE, as *Hypnum fluitans* (see Appendix 2). It was not recorded again until the early 20th century (Rhodes 1911). The map suggests that it has decreased in frequency in the various pits, ponds, wet meadows and other small sites in which it was recorded in the south of the county, and the Frescalo analysis indicates a decline since the 1970s.

Dioicous. Fruiting plants of *D. aduncus* are very rare nationally. Our only record, of abundant capsules on plants 'grounded' on silt by Wicken Lode, Wicken Fen, TL57SE (R.E. Parker, May 1953), is supported by an excellent specimen in CGE.

A variable species, ranging from long lax

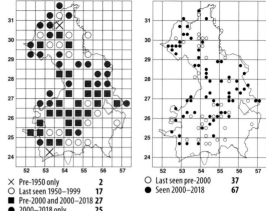

| | | |
|---|---|---|
| ✕ Pre-1950 only | **2** | |
| ○ Last seen 1950–1999 | **17** | |
| ■ Pre-2000 and 2000–2018 | **27** | |
| ● 2000–2018 only | **25** | |

| | |
|---|---|
| ○ Last seen pre-2000 | **37** |
| ● Seen 2000–2018 | **67** |

plants to more condensed states with markedly curved leaves. In the field we have often been unable to distinguish it with any confidence from vegetative *Leptodictyum riparium*. In these cases we have checked the hairs in the young leaf axils microscopically – in *L. riparium* there are 2–7 cells in the upper part of the hairs compared to 1–2(–3) in *D. aduncus* (Hedenäs 2003).

### Sanionia uncinata

Known only as a rare epiphyte on fruit trees in old orchards in the Wisbech area. It has been found on single apple trees at Rummers Lane Orchard, Wisbech St Mary, TF40D (see below), and on the south-west fringe of Wisbech, TF40N, and on a single Conference pear at Popple Drove, Leverington, TF40E.

First record: On apple, with *Amblystegium serpens*, *Brachythecium rutabulum*, *Hypnum cupressiforme* var. *resupinatum* and *Orthotrichum affine*, Rummers Lane Orchard, Wisbech St Mary, TF40D, C.R. Stevenson, 2004, BBSUK. *S. uncinata* has a Boreo-arctic range and in Britain it is rare in East Anglia although frequent in north-east England and eastern Scotland. There have been a few recent records from Norfolk and Suffolk but it has not undergone the massive recent expansion shown by some other epiphytes.

Autoicous. Capsules not recorded, although they are frequent elsewhere in Britain.

### Hygrohypnum luridum

Of the 17 recent sites for this species, 15 are in churchyards where it grows on a range of materials – brickwork, concrete, limestone and sandstone. It usually grows in shaded sites, especially on stone slabs or the sides of stone gutters at the base of the north wall of the church or on the north-facing sides of monuments, but one colony was on a grave surrounded by grass in the open churchyard. The secular sites are a flat stone ledge on the north side of Wimpole Hall, TL35F, and a shaded oolite kerb in Nevile's Court, Trinity College, TL45P. Plants vary in size (some are very small, with their largest leaves 0.8–0.9 mm long) and colonies range from the single vigorous patch 30 cm in diameter seen at Wisbech St Mary, TF40E, to that at Soham, TL57W, which

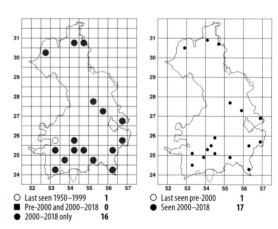

| | |
|---|---|
| ○ Last seen 1950–1999 | **1** |
| ■ Pre-2000 and 2000–2018 | **0** |
| ● 2000–2018 only | **16** |

| | |
|---|---|
| ○ Last seen pre-2000 | **1** |
| ● Seen 2000–2018 | **17** |

extended on concrete all along the north side of the church.

First record: Gravel drive through woodland, Longstowe Hall, TL35C, G. Bloom, 1978, BBSUK. This was a casual occurrence and we could not refind the plant here in 1983. The first churchyard record was from Kirtling, TL65Y, in 2001 and since then we have found it with some regularity. The classic habitat of *H. luridum* is on rocks and boulders by calcareous streams in upland landscapes; Blockeel *et al.* (2014) attribute the increase in records in lowland regions to improved recording in villages and churchyards but our evidence suggests that there may have been a genuine spread in recent years.

Autoicous. Capsules frequent (38% tetrads), young setae January–April, capsules swollen, green March, green turning brown April.

## CALLIERGONACEAE

All three species recorded from Cambridgeshire are wetland plants with Circumpolar Boreo-arctic Montane distributions. All are rare and in long-term decline in eastern England and all are extinct in Cambridgeshire.

### †*Scorpidium revolvens*
First record: Gamlingay, TL25SW, J.S. Henslow, 1827, CGE. Henslow collected at least three gatherings, of rather different appearance. It is only otherwise known from a second Henslow specimen, collected at Gamlingay on 4 April 1829, which has setae with unexpanded capsules.

### †*Scorpidium scorpioides*
First record: Hinton Moor, TL45NE, Relhan (1785: 412, as *Hypnum scorpioides*). Relhan later added Sawston Moor, TL44NE, and Fowlmere, TL44NW (1802: 435) and Shelford Moor, TL45SE (1820: 462) so it was clearly widespread on the spring-fed moors south of Cambridge. They presumably provided the fruiting material sent by Hemsted from Cambridgeshire for illustration in *English Botany* (Smith 1802; voucher in BM, *Sowerby drawings*). These were the only records until it was unexpectedly rediscovered by H.L.K. Whitehouse by the large coprolite pit at Quy Fen, TL56B, in 1955 (CGE). It was last seen there in 1957.
    Dioicous. Hemsted's specimen is fruiting though capsules are rare nationally.

### †*Calliergon giganteum*
First and only record: Damp hollow, Dernford Fen, TL45Q, T.G. Tutin, 1942, NMW, det. P.W. Richards 1943, conf. M.O.H.
    Dioicous. Capsules not recorded and very rare nationally.

## LESKEACEAE

### *Leskea polycarpa*
*Leskea* is usually found by water, growing particularly by the major rivers (Cam, Great Ouse and Nene) and in the Ouse Washes, less frequently by streams, Fenland drains, ditches, lakes, pits and ponds. It is found in the flood zone, most frequently as an epiphyte (80% of tetrad records), more rarely on worked wood (5%) and concrete (5%), with single records from asbestos piling, brickwork and rocks. It is able to cope with silt deposition, and in some small willow holts in the Ouse Washes it is much the most frequent and clearly the most flood-tolerant bryophyte, covering all the silty lower trunks and branches of the willows. Occasionally it grows well away from water, in orchards and secondary woodland or on isolated trees. Willow

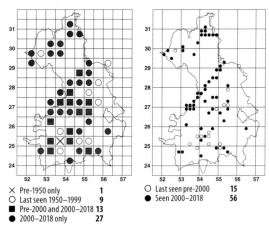

| | |
|---|---|
| × Pre-1950 only | 1 |
| ○ Last seen 1950–1999 | 9 |
| ■ Pre-2000 and 2000–2018 | 13 |
| ● 2000–2018 only | 27 |

| | |
|---|---|
| ○ Last seen pre-2000 | 15 |
| ● Seen 2000–2018 | 56 |

is the most frequent host (41% of epiphytic tetrad records), followed by apple (16%), elder (16%), ash (6%) and hawthorn (6%), with 1–2 records from other hosts listed in Appendix 3. In orchards Robin Stevenson recorded it from 20 (2%) of the 951 apples he has surveyed and one (1%) of the 173 pears. Other examples of its occurrence away from water include an elder in New Wood, Childerley, TL36F, a beech tree in the precincts of Ely Cathedral, TL58K, and a sycamore on the Devil's Dyke, TL65P. In such places care must be taken not to misidentify the prostrate pioneer shoots of *Cryphaea heteromalla* as *Leskea*; they have more neatly appressed, more finely tapering leaves with less prominent midribs.
    First record: Grantchester woods, TL45, L.J. Sedgwick, 1904, LSR; also found by P.G.M. Rhodes before 1911 (Rhodes 1911). The next (relatively) localised record was from pollard willows by the Ely Road eight miles from Cambridge, TL46, made by P.W. Richards in 1929 (NMW). There is little evidence for any change in frequency since then.
    Autoicous. Capsules frequent (57% tetrads); young setae August, January, April; brown, still intact August, October, November; freshly dehisced August–November.

# THUIDIACEAE

## *Abietinella abietina* var. *abietina*

All the populations of *Abietinella* we have seen in recent years have been from sites in which it was already known. Its stronghold is the Devil's Dyke, where we have seen four small patches on lightly trampled ground at the edge of the path along the ridge, TL66A, B, and a further small quantity along the middle of the old railway track crossing the Dyke, TL56S. We have also rediscovered a few shoots in chalk turf at Coploe Hill Pit, Ickleton, TL44W; a vigorous patch on a flat roadside verge below a chalky bank at Babraham Corner, TL55A; and thinly scattered plants in short, lightly trodden chalk turf by the footpath in one small area of Fleam Dyke, TL55L. The species is clearly dependent on disturbance, provided by trampling on the Dykes

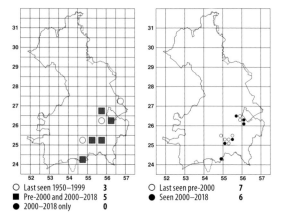

○ Last seen 1950–1999    **3**       ○ Last seen pre-2000    **7**
■ Pre-2000 and 2000–2018   **5**      ● Seen 2000–2018    **6**
● 2000–2018 only    **0**

and by vehicles running onto the roadside at Babraham. On the Dykes it grows with *Campyliadelphus chrysophyllus*, *Ctenidium molluscum*, *Homalothecium lutescens*, *Hypnum cupressiforme*, *Oxyrrhynchium hians*, *Pseudoscleropodium purum*, *Carex flacca*, *Helianthemum nummularium*, *Pilosella officinarum* and *Thymus polytrichus*. At Babraham the associates were *Brachythecium albicans*, *Didymodon vinealis*, *Homalothecium lutescens*, *Pseudocrossidium hornschuchianum* and frequent *Syntrichia ruraliformis*, a more ruderal assemblage.

First record: In the gravel pits, Gog Magog Hills, TL45SE, Relhan (1786: 19, as *Hypnum abietinum*; see Appendix 2). Leonard Jenyns collected it on the Gogs in 1825 (BTH). It was first found at Coploe Hill in 1874 and it was one of four bryophytes listed in the ecological study of the Fleam Dyke's chalk grassland reported by Tansley (1911), although it was not recorded on the Devil's Dyke until 1951. M.O.H. knew this species in 1965 at the edge of the Golf Course on the Gogs, on the adjacent Roman Road and on the Fleam Dyke, and described it as 'very local in sheltered, undisturbed chalk grassland where the turf is short ... where this species occurs, there is usually quite a lot of it'. On the top of the Fleam Dyke just north of the railway cutting, TL55M, for example, it was 'locally in fairly large quantity ... where the grass is kept short by trampling' (Hill 1967). It was also described as abundant by the path in the old railway cutting at Worsted Lodge, TL55G, further south along the Roman Road, by Whitehouse in 1952. It has clearly undergone a marked decline; it was last seen on the Roman Road in 1979 and at Worsted Lodge in 1964. The other site from which it is has been lost is Isleham Plantation, TL67SE, where it was recorded only once, in 1955. However, the apparently vulnerable population on the roadside at Babraham has survived there since it was discovered by C.C. Townsend in 1957.

Dioicous. Capsules not recorded and very rare nationally. A curious feature of the species is that it is scarcely attached to the substrate, and it can presumably be easily dislodged and dispersed over short distances as entire shoots. It may also reproduce vegetatively by deciduous branchlets, shoot apices and, more rarely, leaves (Fritz *et al.* 2010).

## *Thuidium tamariscinum*

*Thuidium tamariscinum*, the most attractive moss in the county, is usually found in woodland, growing on the ground and on stumps and logs raised above surrounding leaf litter. It is often accompanied by other robust pleurocarps such as *Cirriphyllum piliferum*, *Eurhynchium striatum*, *Kindbergia praelonga*, *Plagiomnium undulatum* and very locally by the large liverwort *Plagiochila asplenioides*. It has a strong preference for ancient woodland, growing in both the wet, calcareous boulder-clay woods in the west and in those woods in the east with sandier and rather more acidic and well-drained soils. It does sometimes occur in less ancient woodland, as at Croxton in North Lodge Plantation, TL26K, and South Lodge Plantation, TL25P, both of which overlie ridge and furrow, and in Hill Plantation, Barrington, TL35Q, a former chalk pit. It is sometimes frequent in a wood, but more often it has a patchy distribution. It grows in fen carr at Wicken Fen, TL56P, 57K, and in herbaceous fen vegetation and woodland at Chippenham Fen, TL66P. It is rarely found in well-established grassland, as in the churchyards at Papworth Everard, TL26W, Toft, TL35S, and Stetchworth, TL65P, and the road cutting at Orwell Hill, TL35Q. A single frond found on a grave in Oakington churchyard, TL46C, suggests that it may sometimes be introduced in churchyards. The northernmost record is from willow carr in a disused gravel pit at Block Fen, Chatteris, TL48G, where it must be a fairly recent colonist.

First record: Kingston and Eversden woods, and the woods about Balsham (Ray 1663, as *Muscus filicinus*). Still present in Kingston Wood, TL35G, H, Eversden Wood, TL35L, and Balsham Wood, TL54Z, 55V. It also survives in one of the sites known to T. Martyn (1763: 31, as *Hypnum proliferum*), Madingley Wood, TL35Z, 45E, although his other site, Moor Barns Thicket, TL45E, was grubbed up between 1849 and 1886 (Swale & Belcher 1993). Surprisingly, the earliest known specimen was not collected until 1880, a fruiting plant gathered in Hardwick Wood, TL35N, by G.D. Haviland and J.J. Lister (CGE).

Dioicous. Capsules very rare (2% tetrads), only seen once in the recent survey, in Eversden Wood where capsules were releasing spores in February.

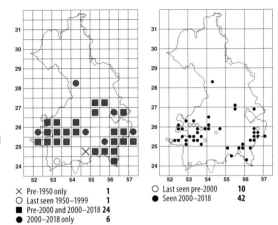

| | |
|---|---|
| ✕ Pre-1950 only | 1 |
| ○ Last seen 1950–1999 | 1 |
| ■ Pre-2000 and 2000–2018 | 24 |
| ● 2000–2018 only | 6 |

| | |
|---|---|
| ○ Last seen pre-2000 | 10 |
| ● Seen 2000–2018 | 42 |

### Thuidium assimile

This species was feared extinct in the county when we began the recent survey, but in 2001 Jonathan Graham found that it grew in the slightly calcareous, unshaded lawn at 51 Hills Avenue, Cambridge, TL45T, the rental accommodation into which he moved when he first arrived in Cambridgeshire. We later found it at the edge of a lawn at Longstowe Hall, TL35C, alongside a balcony of oolitic limestone. Jonathan discovered the plant at its third, rather different site, the marshy edge of pool at Bassenhally Pit, TL29Z, growing with *Campylium protensum*, *Drepanocladus aduncus*, *Fissidens adianthoides* and *Mentha aquatica*.

First record: Old lawn on chalk soil, Hildersham Hall, TL54P, C.D. Pigott and M.C.F. Proctor, 1951, BBSUK. It was refound here at intervals until 1980 (CGE) but not when we last visited, in 1996. Miss Rhodes, who lived in the Hall until 1978, 'forbade anyone to use artificial aids to agriculture', according to the next occupants (*Whitehouse site files*), which perhaps explains why the lawn remained suitable for the species for so long. There were no further records from the county until the recent survey, although a record of *T. tamariscinum* from Bassenhally in 1984 might well have been a misidentification of this species.

Dioicous. Capsules unknown in Britain.

## BRACHYTHECIACEAE

### Pseudoscleropodium purum

This is, with *Calliergonella cuspidata* and *Rhytidiadelphus squarrosus*, one of the three easily identified, robust pleurocarps which may occur in abundance in short, closed turf. It is not only found in lawns and other grasslands but also in chalk pits, disused gravel pits, on the clinker of disused railway lines, chippings on graves, in scrub, on woodland rides, in newly planted woods of deciduous trees or plots of Christmas trees and in stands of mature conifers in acidic woodland. It is able to persist in relatively coarse grassland and it is much more frequent in the closed turf on the north-facing side of the Devil's Dyke than on the more open, south-facing side. Similarly it grows on most of the ant-hills on Great Wilbraham Common, TL55I, but only on their

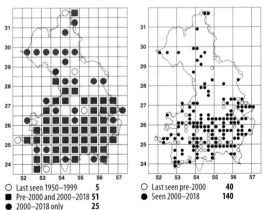

| | |
|---|---|
| ○ Last seen 1950–1999 | 5 |
| ■ Pre-2000 and 2000–2018 | 51 |
| ● 2000–2018 only | 25 |

| | |
|---|---|
| ○ Last seen pre-2000 | 40 |
| ● Seen 2000–2018 | 140 |

northern sides. It is especially characteristic of light soils, both chalk and acidic sands and gravels, and is very much less frequent on Boulder Clay. This doubtless explains its occurrence in fewer tetrads than *Calliergonella cuspidata* and *Rhytidiadelphus squarrosus* and in fewer churchyards – only 38% of churchyards visited compared with 65–67% for the other two species. It is uncommon in wet habitats but it grows on the peaty margin of the lake at Kingfishers Bridge, TL57L, and in some fenland communities on moist calcareous soils at Chippenham Fen, TL66P, including areas dominated by tall rushes and grasses (e.g. *Juncus subnodulosus*, *Molinia caerulea*) and annually mown rides. One odd occurrence was as an epiphyte on a single 28-year old Bramley apple tree in an orchard at Leverington, TF40E, even though it was not present on the ground here.

First record: T. Martyn, 1760–61 (*Martyn letters*, as *Hypnum purum*) and Martyn (1763: 25). The first localised record is a fruiting specimen dated 1824 from White Wood, Gamlingay, TL25SW, collected by Leonard Jenyns (BTH); the Gamlingay specimen in Henslow's herbarium (CGE) was collected on the same visit. The Frescalo analysis indicates a steady decline since the 1950s, though it is not a species we have hitherto regarded as being in decline. It clearly has a limited ability to spread into newly available habitats, as shown by its presence in newly planted woods over arable land and in the Kingfishers Bridge wetland. It had colonised the new grassland at Magog Down, TL45W, which was arable until 1991, by 2004.

Dioicous. Not recorded fruiting in the recent survey, but there are at least six earlier records of fruiting plants in the county. It reproduces vegetatively by deciduous stem apices and branchlets, in addition to the spread of established plants (Fritz *et al.* 2010).

### †*Scorpiurium circinatum*

This Mediterranean-Atlantic species, apparently introduced to the county, was long extinct by the start of the present survey.

First record: On limestone in rockery by pool, Hildersham Hall, TL54P, J.M. Lock, 1961, CGE. At least one of the two stones on which it was found here was imported from Killarney *c.* 1936, and the moss was assumed to have been introduced on the rock. It is known from several sites on limestone near Killarney (D.L. Kelly, *in litt.*). There are no later Cambridgeshire records.

Dioicous. Capsules are unknown in Britain and Ireland.

### *Plasteurhynchium striatulum*

This is the most surprising species added to the county list during the recent survey, its discovery significant enough to be reported in *British Wildlife* (Bosanquet 2016). Mark Hill found it on a shaded lump of concrete near shallowly flooded depressions in the wooded former gravel workings at Milton Country Park.

First record: Milton Country Park, TL46W, M.O. Hill, 2016, BBSUK. The species is primarily found in Britain on Carboniferous limestone in England and Wales, although it also occurs on the southern chalk. It does not usually colonise artificial substrates and this is the first record from East Anglia.

Dioicous. Capsules not recorded.

### *Eurhynchium striatum*

The largest populations of this species occur in woodland, where it is one of the robust pleurocarps of the forest floor, growing on the ground and sometimes on rotten wood with species such as *Cirriphyllum piliferum, Kindbergia praelonga, Plagiomnium undulatum* and *Thamnobryum alopecurum*. It is much less closely tied to ancient woodland than *Thuidium tamariscinum* (Preston & Hill 2016), as shown by its more diffuse distribution at the tetrad scale. It is also found in well-established secondary woodland (including alder woodland and fen woodland) and even in some recent plantations, in fen carr and in scrub in sheltered chalk pits and brick pits. It is also found in

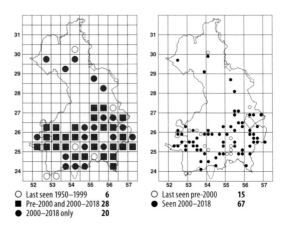

○ Last seen 1950–1999     6
■ Pre-2000 and 2000–2018 **28**
● 2000–2018 only     **20**

○ Last seen pre-2000     **15**
● Seen 2000–2018     **67**

north-facing chalk grassland and at the edge of scrub on the Fleam and Devil's Dykes and in the grass sward in one churchyard, at Quy, TL55E. The northernmost sites are from plantations at Downham, TL58I, and Doddington, TL39V, disused brick pits at Roswell Pits, TL58K, and Whittlesey, TL29N, and secondary woodland on a cindery substrate on railway sidings at March, TL49E; there is an old (1967) record from Gray's Moor Pits, TF40A.

First record: Relhan (1820: 460, as *Hypnum striatum*). Henslow marked it in his annotated Relhan (1820), presumably indicating that he knew it from the county, but the only localised 19th-century record is a specimen collected by Dixon near Madingley Wood, TL45E, in 1882 (BM). Even Rhodes (1911) knew it only from Relhan's record and concluded that it 'must be scarce', a reflection of his neglect of the county's woods, but Adamson (in Evans 1913) soon added it from the clay districts. P.W. Richards first recorded it, as abundant in Hardwick Wood, TL35N, in 1929.

Dioicous. Capsules rare (8% tetrads), lids still in place February, lids shed February, April.

### Platyhypnidium riparioides

This is an aquatic, occurring below the water level, or in frequently inundated sites, on substrates such as brickwork, concrete, stonework, stones on stream beds and tree roots. It usually grows where there is at least a moderate flow; typical sites are small streams (including chalk streams), weirs and sluices in rivers or at lake outflows and even trickles of water flowing out of pipes into streams or ditches. There are recent records from the River Cam downstream to Jesus Lock, Cambridge, TL45P. Its absence from the large rivers in the north of the county, and its rarity elsewhere in Fenland, is remarkable – who would have predicted that this aquatic, which has a very wide habitat range in Britain and is tolerant of eutrophication (Blockeel

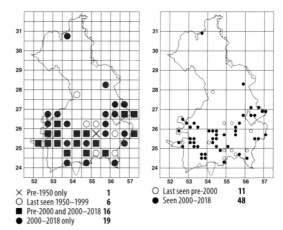

| | |
|---|---|
| ✕ Pre-1950 only | **1** |
| ○ Last seen 1950–1999 | **6** |
| ■ Pre-2000 and 2000–2018 | **16** |
| ● 2000–2018 only | **19** |

| | |
|---|---|
| ○ Last seen pre-2000 | **11** |
| ● Seen 2000–2018 | **48** |

*et al.* 2014), would be rarer in the Fens than its woodland relative *Eurhynchium striatum*? The two recent records from the north of the county are from concrete by the R. Lark at Prickwillow Bridge, TL58W, and the large and complex brick bridge (built in 1833) at the junction of major fen drains at Cloughs Cross, TF30U. Perhaps the flow of most of the Fenland waters is just too sluggish?

First record: Moor Barns Grove, TL45E, R. Davies in J. Martyn (1729b: 15, as *Hypnum repens triangularibus minoribus foliis, pediculis* and *capitulis brevioribus* and *tumidioribus majus*). It was not published by T. Martyn (1763) but Relhan (1820: 456) reported it from stones in water at Madingley Bath, the same site. The first published record was from the planks of water-mills at Newnham (Relhan 1802: 433, as *Hypnum rusciforme*) and it is still present in small quantity by Newnham Mill pit, TL45N. Fruiting plants were collected by Henslow from Baitsbite, TL46W, in 1821 (CGE) and by Leonard Jenyns from Bottisham, TL56, in 1824 (BTH). Neither the maps nor the Frescalo analysis suggest any great change in frequency but if P.W. Richards was right in describing it as 'common in the Cam' in 1929, it has apparently decreased in abundance, at least along this river. It is no longer present in the fountain in Great Court, Trinity College, TL45P, where it was recorded in 1931.

Autoicous. Capsules frequent (43% tetrads), sometimes developing asynchronously in the same population. Capsules just expanding February; swollen, green February, October; turning brown October; brown, undehisced December, February; freshly dehisced December, February.

### Rhynchostegium murale

*Rhynchostegium murale* is quite an apt name, for this is primarily a plant of shaded calcareous stonework, especially oolitic limestone but also concrete, sandstone and old brickwork. Most records are from churchyards (64%), although it is not a common churchyard plant, found in only 18% of those we have visited; it has a distinct preference for those of medieval rather than later origin. It often grows on or near the north walls of churches, at the base of chest tombs, on gravestones lying flat on the ground or on boundary walls. It grows on similar substrates by stately homes, manor houses, old farm houses and Cambridge colleges (19%). There are a few records from stonework by streams and ponds, sandstone and limestone rocks in gardens, shaded chalk stones in disused chalk pits, and as an epiphyte on ash roots, elms and poplars.

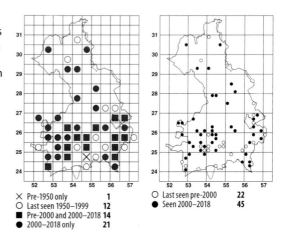

| | |
|---|---|
| ✕ Pre-1950 only | **1** |
| ○ Last seen 1950–1999 | **12** |
| ■ Pre-2000 and 2000–2018 | **14** |
| ● 2000–2018 only | **21** |

| | |
|---|---|
| ○ Last seen pre-2000 | **22** |
| ● Seen 2000–2018 | **45** |

First record: Chalk district, R.S. Adamson (Evans 1913). The first localised record is from Coton churchyard, TL45E, E.W. Jones, 1932 (NMW). Only two of the 23 records on which Whitehouse (1964) based his account were from churchyards, which were less intensively surveyed in those days, but in the 1950s it was recorded more widely by ponds, streams and ditches. As Atherton *et al.* (2010) note, glossy plants with crowded, concave leaves are very distinctive but other variants are more similar to *Rhynchostegium confertum*, which grows in similar places, and we may have overlooked such plants as that species.

Autoicous. Capsules very frequent (71% tetrads); young setae October, capsules swollen, green October; green, turning brown October, January; brown November–March; dehiscing December, February–April.

## Rhynchostegium confertum

A medium-size pleurocarp, easily recognised despite (or perhaps by) its lack of distinctive characteristics and very widely recorded as an epiphyte and on inorganic substrates. As an epiphyte it is rather uncommon in ancient woodland but more frequent in recent woodland and plantations, shelter belts, scrub and hedges, as well as on isolated trees or those growing in small groups by tracks, on ditch sides and in gardens – in fact almost anywhere except in dry urban streets. It is most commonly found on tree bases, but also extends onto trunks and lower branches, especially of shrubs. This is particularly true of the most frequent host, elder (27% of tetrad records), on which it may grow abundantly, often with *Amblystegium serpens*.

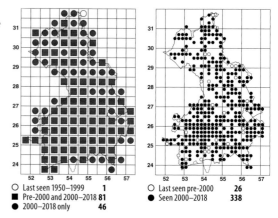

○ Last seen 1950–1999    1
■ Pre-2000 and 2000–2018   81
● 2000–2018 only    46

○ Last seen pre-2000    26
● Seen 2000–2018    338

Other hosts are willow (14%), ash (12%), apple (8%), hawthorn (7%) and the many other species listed in Appendix 3. In orchards Robin Stevenson found *R. confertum* on 383 (40%) of the 951 individual apple trees he surveyed and 50 (29%) of the 173 pears. It is occasionally found on decaying wood. It is also frequent on shaded calcareous stonework, brickwork and concrete and occasionally found on shaded soil. We have recorded it in 69% of the churchyards we have visited, often in the shade of north-facing walls or at the base of monuments. It is very common on sandstone rocks in Cambridge Botanic Garden, TL45N, also found on limestone rocks in gardens and rarely recorded from granite and tarmac.

First record: Bottisham, TL56, L. Jenyns, 1824, CGE. Jenyns did not name his material, and he collected a further specimen at Bottisham in 1825 which he called *Hypnum striatulum?* (BTH), even though there is also a specimen in his herbarium collected by M.J. Berkeley in Cambridge, TL45, in 1824 correctly named *Hypnum confertum*. It was not known to Henslow (1829, 1835) as a Cambridgeshire plant. G.D. Haviland and J.J. Lister collected it at Madingley in 1881 (CGE) and Rhodes (1911) described it as 'common in woods on Gogs'. Proctor (1956) regarded it as common and Whitehouse (1964) as abundant.

Autoicous. Capsules usually present (95% tetrads); the species fruits earlier in the winter than the other common pleurocarps. Most of our records of young setae are from September–November; swollen, green capsules September to January; brown capsules December to March; and dehiscing capsules December to February, although a few dehisce as early as September and some as late as March or, rarely, April.

## Rhynchostegium megapolitanum

The concentration of records on the chalk of south-east Cambridgeshire suggests that *Rhynchostegium megapolitanum* is a calcicole, but in fact it inhabits a range of well-drained soils. It is a primarily a plant of grassland, ranging from short, rabbit-scuffed, sheep-grazed or closely mown turf to rather coarse swards, and it grows on tracksides, roadside banks and verges, ditch sides, chalk earthworks, in churchyards and cemeteries and in disused brick, chalk and gravel pits. It had colonised the Magog Down grassland, TL45W, which was arable land until 1991, by 2004. We also have records from sandy banks, sparsely vegetated, cindery railway land, soil shaded by walls or by trees and, less usually, from a fallen laburnum trunk in a plantation, a tree stump and from the top of two churchyard walls.

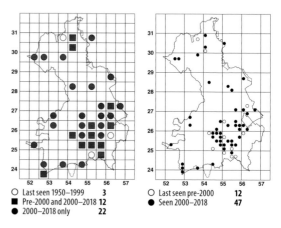

○ Last seen 1950–1999    3
■ Pre-2000 and 2000–2018   12
● 2000–2018 only    22

○ Last seen pre-2000    12
● Seen 2000–2018    47

First record: Edge of sandy field, Hildersham Furze Hill, TL54P, M.C.F. Proctor, 1951, BBSUK; still present at the Furze Hills in 2002. *R. megapolitanum* is easily overlooked as *Brachythecium rutabulum*, which often grows with it. R.E. Parker clearly knew it well, finding it in seven sites in 1952–53 and providing all but one of the records known to Proctor (1956) and half those available to Whitehouse (1964). It must still be under-recorded. Some of the records on the county boundary result from the unusually thorough searching of tetrad 'fragments' (very small areas which are the only part of the tetrad in vc 29). No doubt we would have many more records had we been able to scrutinise the entire county with such rigour.

Autoicous. Capsules occasional (29% tetrads), insufficiently frequent to justify R.E. Parker's view that it is 'one of the most commonly fruiting pleurocarpous mosses occurring in the district' (*Whitehouse species file*). Young setae November, January; capsules swollen, green October–January; swollen brown December, February; freshly dehisced December–February.

### *Rhynchostegiella tenella*

Most of the sites of this very shade-tolerant species are churchyards (82%), where it grows on brickwork and base-rich stonework (often oolitic limestone, more rarely harder limestone, sandstone or concrete) on or near the north wall of the church, on steps down to the crypt, at the base of tombs and monuments, on kerbs around graves, on gravestones lying flush with the ground and (rarely) on shaded soil. A particularly favoured habitat is the otherwise bare area at the extreme base of oolite gravestones, where it grows concealed behind grass which is not easily cut short because of its proximity to the stone. We found it on a human bone as well as on stonework at Thorney Abbey, TF20X. Outside churchyards it is found on similar habitats in the gardens of grand and

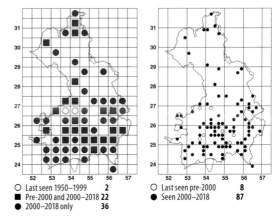

O  Last seen 1950–1999          **2**
■  Pre-2000 and 2000–2018  **22**
●  2000–2018 only                   **36**

O  Last seen pre-2000   **8**
●  Seen 2000–2018         **87**

less grand houses, as well as on shaded chalk stones in disused chalk pits or in long grass and scrub on earthworks. It manages to persist in deep shade on the back wall of a cave in the chalk quarry at Balsham, TL55Q, some 25 m from the entrance. There are single records from flints on a path, the brickwork of a disused railway bridge and the shaded bases of ash and willow trees. It still grows on the limestone of the Botanic Garden rockery, on which it was imported from Westmorland in 1955.

First record: Madingley, J.S. Henslow, 1821, CGE, as *Hypnum tenellum* (still present in 2016 at Madingley Hall and church, TL36V). It was not seen again until found on bricks in an old railway cutting at Babraham, TL55F, by D.E. Coombe and M.C.F. Proctor in 1951 (CGE). Records accumulated slowly until 1987, when we began to survey churchyards more systematically. During these excursions Robin Stevenson taught us to search for the species at the foot of oolite gravestones.

Autoicous. Capsules very frequent (70% tetrads). Young setae rarely noted (January); capsules swollen, green October–December, rarely January, February; brown November–April; freshly dehisced October–November (rare), January–April.

### *Rhynchostegiella litorea*

Unlike *Rhynchostegiella tenella*, this species is apparently confined in the county to shaded soil and the base of trees. There are recent records from the roots and lower trunks of ash trees by water at Sawston Hall, TL44Z, the steep earth bank of the Bin Brook at St John's College, Cambridge, TL45P, the root of an ash surrounded by ivy, and chalk soil nearby, in Lime Kiln Close, Cherry Hinton, TL45X, and the base of elm and nearby chalky soil in a pit at Callow Bank, Soham, TL57V.

First record: Stumps in ditch, West Wickham, TL64E, P.J. Bourne, 1960, BBSUK, CGE. Only otherwise recorded before the recent survey from tree bases in Lime Kiln Close (first found in 1985) and from the base of a stump in a ditch at Bassingbourn, TL34H (1967). This species has been neglected as until recently it was regarded as a variety of *R. tenella*. It is also likely to be under-recorded if it typically grows, as it does in Cambridgeshire, as a rare species concealed in shade in rather ordinary places. It has a Mediterranean-Atlantic range and the Cambridgeshire sites are currently the northernmost known world localities.

Autoicous. Capsules present in all tetrads, but the species is unlikely to be identifiable without them; swollen, green, December.

### Rhynchostegiella curviseta

Seen recently on shaded, flat oolitic limestone gravestones in Little St Mary's churchyard, Cambridge, TL45N, where it grows with *Didymodon luridus*; on the steep earth bank of the Bin Brook, St John's College, Cambridge, TL45P, just above the water level, growing with *Lunularia cruciata* and *Pellia endiviifolia* and only a few metres from *R. litorea*; and on silty brickwork under a bridge over the River Kennett, a clear calcareous stream, at Upend, TL75E.

First record: Base of old brick wall, with *Amblystegium serpens*, *Bryum rubens*, *Didymodon umbrosus* and *Rhynchostegium confertum*, junction of Church Rate Lane and Maltings Lane, Newnham, Cambridge, TL45N, N. Jardine, 1985, BBSUK. Professor Jardine discovered it in Little St Mary's churchyard in 1992, and it was found at Little Wilbraham Fen, TL55NW, in 1994.

Autoicous. Capsules frequent (67% tetrads); swollen but not dehisced, March.

### Rhynchostegiella teneriffae

Only seen during the recent survey on a bridge over a clear, canalised chalk stream in Melbourn village, TL34X, where it grew just above water level with *Fissidens crassipes* and *Platyhypnidium riparioides*.

First record: With *Fissidens 'bryoides'* (q.v.) on the damp, highly shaded brickwork of a tunnel carrying water beneath Newnham Mill, Cambridge, TL45N, C.D. Preston and H.L.K. Whitehouse, 1991. The identity of this plant was only recognised when it was refound here in 1995 by R.A. Finch and H.L.K.W., growing 0–10 cm above the usual water level on the plastered wall of the tunnel some 3–6 m from its north end at the mill pond (BBSUK). We have been unable to obtain access to this locality recently, and there were no other records of the species before 2000.

Autoicous. In March 1995 the Newnham population was fruiting abundantly; one green, swollen capsule and one nearly dehisced capsule were seen at Melbourn in January 2005.

### Cirriphyllum piliferum

The stems of *Cirriphyllum piliferum* usually grow amongst those of other species on the woodland floor, where their pale green colour catches the eye. They are found on the ground or, more rarely, on decaying wood or at the very base of trees, rarely ascending up the tree trunk to a height of 30 cm. *Fissidens taxifolius*, *Kindbergia praelonga*, *Plagiomnium undulatum* and *Thamnobryum alopecurum* are characteristic associates. It is a plant of primary and ancient secondary woodland, well-established recent woodland including plantations over ridge and furrow, streamside woodland, fen carr and woods and scrub in disused chalk pits and on chalk earthworks. It is also found in shaded lawns in the Botanic Garden, Cambridge, TL45N, and the Fellows Gardens of both Trinity and St John's Colleges, TL45P, in shaded turf in four churchyards, and in a nettle bed on the site of Old St Mary's Church, Ashley, TL76A.

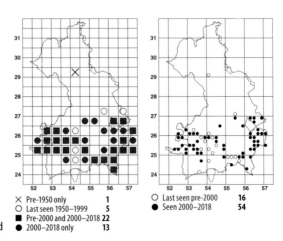

| | |
|---|---|
| ✕ Pre-1950 only | 1 |
| ○ Last seen 1950–1999 | 5 |
| ■ Pre-2000 and 2000–2018 | 22 |
| ● 2000–2018 only | 13 |

| | |
|---|---|
| ○ Last seen pre-2000 | 16 |
| ● Seen 2000–2018 | 54 |

First record: Overhall Grove, Knapwell, TL36G, P.W. Richards, 1931 (*Richards file*). There appears to be little change in its range although the northernmost site, Doddington Wood, TL49A, where it was recorded by T.G. Tutin in 1932, was grubbed up in the late 1940s. It may also have been lost from some non-woodland sites, as there were three records in the 1930s from grassy ditch banks, at Comberton, TL35Y, Great Eversden, TL35R, and Haslingfield, TL45B, but none since.

Dioicous. Capsules rare (4% tetrads), seen only twice in recent years and in small quantity; dehisced January, dehisced long ago April.

### Cirriphyllum crassinervium

*Cirriphyllum crassinervium* grows on the exposed roots, bases or horizontal trunks of trees (ash, beech, oak, sycamore), or more rarely on the ground, in a variety of wooded habitats. We have found it on the banks of rivers, streams and ditches, and away from water in the Gogs Beechwood, TL45X, in secondary woodland in estates, on the wooded south end of the Devil's Dyke, TL65P, and in disused chalk pits. There is a small concentration of records in Wimpole Park, TL35F, G, L. Only two of the sites are associated with ancient woodland, New Ditch, Kingston Wood, TL35H, and a ditch alongside Ditton Park Wood, TL65T. It is still abundant on the partially shaded sides of some of the Carboniferous limestone blocks in the Botanic Garden, TL45N, on which it was introduced from Westmorland in 1955. It is difficult to account for its sporadic distribution, but the species is much rarer in East Anglia as a whole than in some other areas of England and Wales (Blockeel *et al.* 2014).

First record: Tree stump by Fishpond, Madingley Park, TL36V, H.L.K. Whitehouse, 1951, CGE; refound in the Park in 1957 (BBSUK) and at intervals until 2016. The pre-2000 records come from a similar range of habitats to those in which we have recorded the species.

Dioicous. Capsules rare (9% tetrads), with only one fruiting patch seen in the recent survey; capsules dehisced, March.

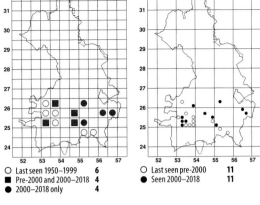

○ Last seen 1950–1999   6
■ Pre-2000 and 2000–2018   4
● 2000–2018 only   4

○ Last seen pre-2000   11
● Seen 2000–2018   11

## *Oxyrrhynchium pumilum*

As a ground-dwelling species, this small pleurocarp is confined to sites where competition from other species is reduced, especially by shade – but it cannot withstand burial by leaf litter. Most of its sites are therefore on the sloping sides of streams and ditches in woodland, including the medieval wood banks at the edge of ancient woodland, shaded banks in disued chalk pits, woodland and scrub on chalk earthworks, and, more rarely, north-facing ditch and stream banks in open country. It also grows on flat, heavily shaded and sometimes lightly trampled ground in churchyards and large gardens and there are single records from a steep railway bank, stones in a shaded culvert and the silty base of a streamside elm. It grows on chalky soils and clays or loams which are at least mildly basic. *Fissidens* species are common associates, including *F. incurvus*, *F. taxifolius*, *F. viridulus* and, more rarely, *F. bryoides*.

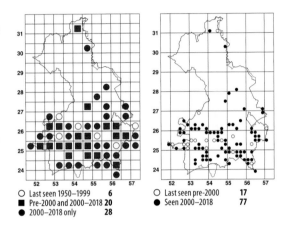

○ Last seen 1950–1999   6
■ Pre-2000 and 2000–2018   20
● 2000–2018 only   28

○ Last seen pre-2000   17
● Seen 2000–2018   77

First record: Shady clay bank and field on edge of Kingston Wood, TL35SW, D.G. Catcheside, P.W. Richards and T.G. Tutin, 1943, NMW. Records of this 'rather inconspicuous little species' (Proctor 1956) have accumulated gradually; there is no evidence for any marked change in frequency or distribution.

Dioicous. Capsules occasional (16% tetrads); young setae October, January, swollen green December–February, dehiscing February.

## *Oxyrrhynchium hians*

Like *Oxyrrhynchium pumilum*, this is a ground-dwelling species but a much more robust and competitive one which is found in a wide range of plant communities, especially in base-rich and nutrient-rich sites. It grows in woodland of all ages, scrub, orchards, churchyards, cemeteries and gardens, chalk grassland, disued chalk, clay and gravel pits, river, stream and ditch banks and stubble fields. It occasionally spreads from the ground onto tree bases, shaded oolitic limestone monuments or Carboniferous limestone rockery stones. It is most frequent in shaded, eutrophic sites such as recent plantations or elder scrub in chalk

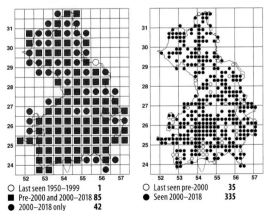

○ Last seen 1950–1999   1
■ Pre-2000 and 2000–2018   85
● 2000–2018 only   42

○ Last seen pre-2000   35
● Seen 2000–2018   335

pits, where it may be the most abundant bryophyte, growing as loose, scruffy masses and tolerating, or maybe benefiting from, a degree of disturbance. It will even flourish in nettle beds. It tends to be infrequent in undisturbed ancient woodland and it is absent from the most acidic soils. In arable fields it is uncommon and normally found in small quantity, although it may become frequent in old set-aside; it was recorded in 12 of the 76 fields we sampled for SBAL, mainly on clays or loams and at pH (6.1–)6.9–8.0.

First record: Madingley Wood, Relhan (1820: 456, as *Hypnum swartzii*); still present there, TL35Z, 45E. The earliest specimen was collected at Coton, TL45NW, in 1881 by G.D. Haviland and J.J. Lister (CGE; they named it *Eurhynchium praelongum*), and this is perhaps the earliest certain record. It was described as very common by Proctor (1956) and as one of the most abundant mosses in the county by Whitehouse (1964). This is certainly true, although how it maintains this frequency is unclear, as it lacks specialised vegetative propagules and fruits very infrequently.

Dioicous. Capsules rare (4% tetrads); capsules swollen, green turning brown October; brown November, December; most freshly dehisced February; all dehisced March.

## Oxyrrhynchium speciosum

This is a habitat specialist, confined to damp, eutrophic sites by water bodies and often found in places which are flooded when water levels are high. It grows on the open banks of rivers, streams, major Fenland drains and smaller ditches, amongst reeds by fen ditches and in grazed and mown fen communities. However, it is shade-tolerant and many sites are on wet ground in fen carr and fen woodland, in disused, wooded clay and gravel pits and in secondary woodland by lakes and ponds. It is also found on rotting wood, wooden streamside piling, and on limestone rocks by the lake in Cambridge Botanic Garden, TL45N.

First record: Very old fen carr, growing on litter of dead leaves, Wicken Fen, H. Godwin, 1929, NMW; still present at Wicken in carr and other habitats,

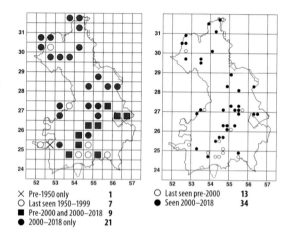

| | |
|---|---|
| ✕ Pre-1950 only | 1 |
| ○ Last seen 1950–1999 | 7 |
| ■ Pre-2000 and 2000–2018 | 9 |
| ● 2000–2018 only | 21 |

| | |
|---|---|
| ○ Last seen pre-2000 | 13 |
| ● Seen 2000–2018 | 34 |

TL56P, 57K. The species is under-recorded, both because it is easily overlooked as *Oxyrrhynchium hians* or *Brachythecium rutabulum* and because of the unpromising and sometimes rather inaccessible nature of the habitat in which it grows.

Unlike the dioicous *O. hians*, from which it almost certainly evolved by autopolyploidy, *O. speciosum* is autoicous or synoicous and capsules are frequent (44% tetrads). Fruits at different stages of development sometimes occur on the same plant. Capsules green, just beginning to swell October; swollen, green October, December; swollen, brown October, December, February; freshly dehisced February, March.

## Kindbergia praelonga

The neat fronds of *Kindbergia praelonga* are easily recognised, and grow in many different habitats. These include all types of woodland, ranging from the undisturbed floor of ancient woodland, where it is often abundant, though well-established recent woodland, plantations and newly planted stands of young trees. It extends as an epiphyte onto the bases, lower trunks and low branches of a wide range of trees and shrubs, especially in sheltered situations (Appendix 3), and it is frequent on rotting wood. In orchards Robin Stevenson found it on 92 (10%) of the 951 apples he surveyed and 41 (24%) of the 173 pears. It is common in shaded grassland, including roadside verges, lawns and churchyard turf, on stream and ditch banks, on shaded

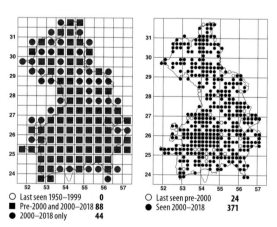

| | |
|---|---|
| ○ Last seen 1950–1999 | 0 |
| ■ Pre-2000 and 2000–2018 | 88 |
| ● 2000–2018 only | 44 |

| | |
|---|---|
| ○ Last seen pre-2000 | 24 |
| ● Seen 2000–2018 | 371 |

brickwork, concrete and masonry and on soil in neglected flower beds. Like *Oxyrrhynchium hians* it can also grow in nettle beds. Unusual substrates include a muntjac skull, a discarded motor tyre and an old tennis ball. Its frequency can be judged by its presence on 92% of our churchyard lists. It is, however, uncommon in stubble and set-aside fields, and usually present in small quantity where it occurs; it was recorded in nine of the 76 fields we sampled for SBAL, on a range of soils and at pH 6.3–8.3. It is therefore much less frequent in the most intensively arable Fenland tetrads than in more varied country but can usually be found eventually, perhaps on a roadside verge or in a garden lawn. It is most abundant in acidic places but it is frequent in calcareous sites, including some highly calcareous substrates such as shaded boulders in chalk pits, but it not a plant of exposed chalk grassland and it is sometimes replaced by *O. hians* on the more disturbed, calcareous or eutrophic ground.

First record: J. Martyn (1729b: 16, as *Hypnum repens filicinum, triangularibus, parvis foliis, praelongum*); published by T. Martyn (1763: 25, as *Hypnum praelongum*). The earliest localised record is a fruiting specimen collected by Skrimshire from willow trees in Wisbech, TF40NE, in 1797 (WBCH). As far as we can tell it is still as frequent as it was when described as common by Proctor (1956) and abundant by Whitehouse (1964) although obviously there have been changes at individual sites. Hill (1967), for example, regarded it as much the most plentiful bryophyte under old carr at Wicken Fen, TL57, but much of this carr has now been cleared.

Dioicous. Capsules occasional (18% tetrads), more frequent in wooded than in open habitats; swollen, green October, December; green turning brown or brown November–February; newly dehisced February, March.

### Sciuro-hypnum populeum

Found since 2000 at three localities – a few patches on a concrete kerb alongside the main asphalt path at Friday Bridge church, TF40S, on a dessert apple in a sheltered orchard at Cranwell Lodge, High Street, Elm, TF40T, and with *Hypnum cupressiforme* at the base of an ash coppice stool in Charcoals Wood, TL65N.

First record: Chalk grassland on south-west side of bank, Devil's Dyke about 100 yards north of A11, TL66A, J. L. Harding, 1960, BBSUK, CGE (see Appendix 2). It was found twice by M.O.H. in 1965, in a bare, shady patch of lawn on the chalk at Wandlebury, TL45W, and carpeting rather shady, limestone rocks in the garden of 11 Chaucer Road, Cambridge, TL45N, on which it had presumably been introduced. There were no further records until it was found at Friday Bridge in 2003. It is more frequent in western England and Wales than in the east; at least some of our records probably represent transient colonists.

Autoicous. Capsules had been present on the Charcoals Wood plant in March but most were missing, leaving bare setae; they were also recorded at Wandlebury in January. The species fruits freely elsewhere in Britain (Blockeel *et al.* 2014).

### Brachythecium albicans

Although we lack the large expanses of sandy soil on which this species is often abundant elsewhere in East Anglia, particularly on the coast and in Breckland, it is nevertheless frequent here, especially as small populations in artificial habitats. It grows in old sand and gravel pits, on sandy and gravelly soil on drives, paths and tracks, and on railway clinker, granite 'hoggin' and crushed brickwork. It is also found in rough acidic grassland, in lawns on light soils, newly sown grassland and on closely mown roadside verges, including the barer strips of soil at the junction of the verge with the pavement or roadside kerb. It colonises flat concrete, as on tracks, hard standings and bridges, and shaded tarmac. Although normally calcifuge, it is sometimes found in calcareous habitats such as

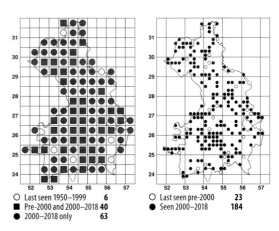

○ Last seen 1950–1999    6
■ Pre-2000 and 2000–2018   40
● 2000–2018 only    63

○ Last seen pre-2000    23
● Seen 2000–2018    184

disued chalk pits and in car parks and tracks made up with crushed oolite. Its preference for newly disturbed rather than mature habitats is shown by its presence in only 10% of the churchyards we have visited.

First record: On the east side of the River [Nene] on the bank near the Horse-shoe-hole, Wisbech, TF41SE, W. Skrimshire, 1797, WBCH, as *Hypnum myosuroides*; this specimen is fruiting and fruiting plants were refound on the bank of the Nene at Wisbech St Mary, TF40H, in 2016. Several early records were from the few areas of naturally occurring sandy soil in the county, at Gamlingay, TL25SW (1929), Hildersham Furze Hills, TL54P (1874, 1930) and the Breckland fringe at Isleham Plantation, TL67SE (1930) and it persists in all these places. Proctor (1956) described it as 'scattered about the county in dry grassland … or on sandy material dumped on roadsides, etc., but not generally common' but Whitehouse (1964) regarded it as 'frequent on roadsides and on thatch throughout the county'. This is a species one might expect to have increased since 1964, but the evidence is far from conclusive (contrast *Syntrichia ruralis* var. *ruraliformis*). One explanation may be that *Brachythecium albicans* has colonised newly imported sands and gravels but has also been lost from some of its older habitats. The first record from thatch dates from 1880, when it was found by Haviland and Lister on a barn at Coton, TL45NW (CGE, OXF) but we have not seen it on such roofs.

Dioicous. Capsules rare (2% tetrads); young setae September; swollen, brown capsules December.

### Brachythecium glareosum

Only seen in the recent survey on stone chippings over a grave in Croxton churchyard, TL25P, in 2004.

First record: Coploe Hill [as 'Corporal Hill'], Great Chesterford, TL44W, F.Y. Brocas, 1874, SWN. Recorded on chalk in five further sites before 2000, namely under hawthorn scrub on base-rich ground in Bassenhally Pit, TL29Z (1986), thin turf on chalk track by an old coprolite pit at Trumpington, TL45G (1975), sparingly on Fleam Dyke, TL55M (1928), colonising areas where turf had been removed in a clunch pit near Great Wilbraham Hall Farm, TL55M (1956) and abundant on artificial mounds of chalk at Quy Fen, TL56SW (1933). It was also found amongst grass in Cambridge Botanic Garden, TL45N (1883), on a clay bank on the edge of Over Wood, TL64J (1932) and on the ground in Basefield Wood, TL65N (1933). Nationally, the species is a colonist of disturbed, base-rich soil (Blockeel *et al.* 2014) and our records are consistent with this picture. However, the fact that it has been recorded only once from each of its 10 sites is slightly disquieting. The species is fairly distinctive and the available vouchers (BM, CGE, NMW) are correctly named, suggesting that it might be a casual colonist rather than an under- or over-recorded plant.

Dioicous. Capsules not recorded, and rare elsewhere in Britain.

### Brachythecium salebrosum

Five of our records are from fen carr or wet woodland. It grew on dead branches or logs in a swamp at Whittlesford Mill, TL44U, an alder wood at Middle Moor, Whittlesford, TL44U, and a swampy area at Hauxton Gravel Pits, TL45F, and as an epiphyte on the lower trunks of a poplar at Sawston Hall, TL44Z, and on a birch and a horizontal sallow at Wicken Fen, TL56P. The remaining three records are presumably of casual occurrences, on bare clayey ground in a bird-seed crop at Grange Farm, Knapwell, TL36G, with *Tortula truncata* in a set-aside field on Ampthill Clay at Boxworth, TL36M, and as vigorous plants on a grassy roadside at Ashley, TL76A.

First record: On fallen oak trunk, with *Brachythecium rutabulum*, grounds of Hildersham Hall, TL54P, G. Halliday, 1958, BBSUK, CGE.

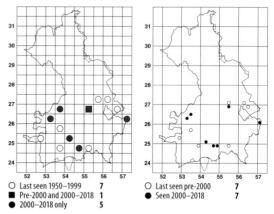

○ Last seen 1950–1999    7
■ Pre-2000 and 2000–2018    1
● 2000–2018 only    5

○ Last seen pre-2000    7
● Seen 2000–2018    7

Subsequently found on a rotting elm log in Hayley Wood, TL25W (1992), a fallen tree trunk by a stream south of Barrington, TL34Z (1960), on the ground at Hardwick Wood, TL35N (1962), in fen carr at Wicken Fen, TL56P, 57K (1979–1994), and on decayed logs in Fordham Wood, TL66F (1990) and Forty Acre Wood, Chippenham Fen, TL66P (1986). Blockeel *et al.* (2014) suggest that many of the British records of this continental species represent small and short-lived colonies.

Autoicous. Capsules frequent (43% tetrads), swollen, brown and nearly ripe but lids still in place, December.

### Brachythecium mildeanum

*Brachythecium mildeanum* is usually found in similar dry, open habitats to those of *B. albicans*. It grows in thin grassland, lawns and roadside verges; disturbed ground in sand and gravel pits; chalky, gravelly, sandy and stony tracks and waste ground; flat concrete (e.g. on roadsides and bridges); mossy tarmac; railway clinker; and stone chippings on graves. Such rather mundane places are responsible for its colloquial name 'car-park moss'. There is one record from a direct-drilled rape field. It occasionally colonises wetter places such as damp turf and woodland rides over base-rich clay and damp clay at the edge of a village pond. Robin Stevenson found it, most unusually, growing as an epiphyte on a Conference pear in a Guyhirn orchard, TF30X, and concluded that stems had been thrown up onto the tree when the grass below was being mown and had somehow managed to cling on.

First record: Wet hollow, Dernford Fen, TL45Q, P.W. Richards, 1929, BBSUK. There were only two records in the next 80 years, by pools near the R. Great Ouse, Stretham, TL57B (fruiting plants, 1957, BBSUK, CGE) and damp clay by the side of a pond at Roswell Pits, Ely, TL58K (1981). The species was confused with *B. salebrosum* until its taxonomy was clarified by Corley & Hill (1981). *B. mildeanum* was formerly regarded, and to some extent it still is regarded (Blockeel *et al.* 2014), as primarily a plant of damp, base-rich places, perhaps because it is in such sites that it tends to fruit. M.O.H. began to record *B. salebrosum* in our area as soon as he returned to Cambridge in 1986 but it was not until December 1999 that he first noted *B. mildeanum*, at Cambridge Airport, TL45Y. He, and later others taught by him, made frequent records of the plant in its ruderal habitats from 2001 onwards. It seems likely that *B. mildeanum* has increased in such places in recent decades but the species is very easily overlooked amongst *B. albicans* and *B. rutabulum*, which often grow with it, and both the fact and the timing of any such increase are unclear.

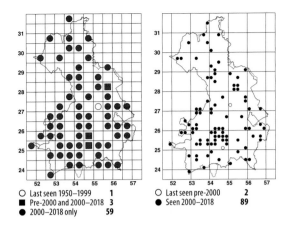

○ Last seen 1950–1999    **1**
■ Pre-2000 and 2000–2018    **3**
● 2000–2018 only    **59**

○ Last seen pre-2000    **2**
● Seen 2000–2018    **89**

Autoicous. Capsules rare (4% tetrads), found on gritty ground by a farm road at Grantchester, TL45H, in ditches at Hauxton gravel pits, TL45SW, and Croxton Park, TL25P, and in a grass ley at Chatteris, TL38Y. Capsules swollen, brown, January.

## *Brachythecium rutabulum*

This is by some margin the most frequent Cambridgeshire bryophyte, found as extensive, and sometimes more or less pure, loose mats or as more scattered shoots in most of our open or shaded habitats as long as they are neither too desiccated nor too nutrient-poor. It is conspicuous in all sorts of woodland, from ancient woodland to fen carr, recent scrub and stands of newly planted trees, and in orchards, growing on the ground and on the lower trunks and branches of trees and shrubs. Elder (24% of tetrad records), willow (19%) and ash (8%) are the most frequently recorded hosts, along with apple (12%) which is over-recorded as we have noted relatively few hosts of this abundant species outside orchards; other hosts are listed in Appendix

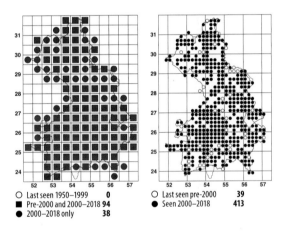

○ Last seen 1950–1999
■ Pre-2000 and 2000–2018    **94**
● 2000–2018 only    **38**

○ Last seen pre-2000    **39**
● Seen 2000–2018    **413**

3. It is one of the most frequent colonists of rotting wood, being especially abundant on soft, decaying elm logs. It also grows in stands of tall herbs, including nettle beds, in lawns (even the most manicured college lawns), churchyard turf and other grasslands, on roadside verges, stream and ditch banks, in arable and set-aside fields, on temporarily neglected land (such as arable sites awaiting development) and the edges of tracks and paths. It is frequent on shaded brickwork, concrete and masonry, grows on limestone and sandstone rocks in gardens and will colonise artificial substrates such as armchairs, carpets, towels and tyres which find their way into the countryside. The statistics confirm its frequency: it is recorded in 90% of churchyards, on well over half the orchard trees surveyed by Robin Stevenson (64% of the apples, 58% pears) and 43% of the arable fields surveyed for SBAL. In the SBAL fields it was found rather evenly across the different soil types, except on silt where its occurrence fell to 13%.

First record: J. Martyn (1729b: 15, as *Hypnum repens trichoides, arboreum, majus, capitulis* and *surculis erectis, minus ramosis*); published by T. Martyn (1763: 25, as *Hypnum rutabulum*; see Appendix 2). The first specimens were fruiting plants collected at Newmarket, TL66, by Hemsted in 1796 (WBCH), near Cambridge, TL45, by Henslow in 1821 (CGE) and at Bottisham, TL56, by Leonard Jenyns in 1825 (BTH). L.J. Sedgwick described it as 'abundant everywhere, often c. fr.' in the early 20th century and P.W. Richards as 'very common in a great variety of habitats throughout the county' in 1929 (*Richards file*). As with *Amblystegium* serpens, the later 20th-century accounts (Proctor 1956, Hill 1967) mention its occurrence on tree bases rather than as an epiphyte at higher levels.

Autoicous. Capsules frequent (44% tetrads); they are very frequent in woods but were found in only two of the 33 SBAL arable fields with the species (both set-aside). Young setae September–November(–December); capsules swollen, green (September–)October–December; swollen, brown October–March(–April); freshly dehisced January–March (–April). By April most capsules have dehisced.

Growth studies of a population of *B. rutabulum* from Sheffield (Furness & Grime 1982) have revealed some of the reasons for its ability to co-exist with competitive vascular plants. It maintained a high relative growth rate at 5°C and its maximum rate, attained at 19°C, was as high as that of the seedlings of trees and the slower growing shrubs and herbs, and nearly one-third that of nettle, *Urtica dioica*, a fast-growing species. In the field it had peak growth rate and biomass in spring and autumn, when it grew rapidly over substrates such as leaf litter.

## Brachythecium rivulare

As its name suggests, this is usually a plant of wet places, and the largest populations grow on wet or swampy ground, or occasionally on rotting wood, in secondary woodland, including fen woodland, fen carr and wooded gravel pits. It is also found on rutted rides or by ditches and ponds in ancient woodland, at the edge of reed beds or in mixed stands of *Calamagrostis epigejos* and *Phragmites australis*, in grazed fens, wet meadows or other wet grasslands, on the banks of streams and ditches (usually on the ground but sometimes on stones and on the base of ash and willow trees) and on tufa at Wimpole Hall, TL35SW. In addition, there are records from five tetrads in which it grew in drier sites: a roadside verge at Wisbech, TF40N, a chalky

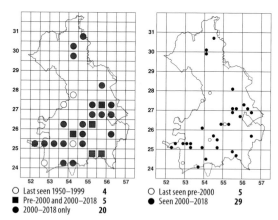

O Last seen 1950–1999    4
■ Pre-2000 and 2000–2018    5
● 2000–2018 only    20

O Last seen pre-2000    5
● Seen 2000–2018    29

roadside bank at Hyde Hill, TL34Q, estate woodland at Madingley Hall, TL36V (where a single patch was found on well-drained soil), grassy turf in Cambridge, TL45S, and a trackside at Drove Lane, Wicken, TL57Q.

First record: Chalk and Greensand districts, R.S. Adamson (Evans 1913). The first localised record was made by R.E. Parker from a calcareous spring developing into a small stream at Rivey Wood, Linton, TL54T, in 1953 (*Whitehouse list*). Parker found the species at two more sites in 1953, including Wicken Fen, TL57 (CGE), and these constituted all but one of the records known to Proctor (1956). *Brachythecium rivulare* was not discovered at Chippenham Fen, TL66P, until 2001. It is very easily overlooked as *B. rutabulum* and is itself a variable entity; we have recorded plants with both plicate and non-plicate leaves as *B. rivulare* as long as they have large auricles, but a few plants intermediate between the two species have not been recorded, or have been assigned to *B. rutabulum*. One of these is a specimen (NMW) collected in 1930 by Tutin and Warburg in a wood near Caxton Gibbet [presumably Swansley Wood, TL36SW] and named by Richards as *B. rivulare*.

Dioicous. Capsules occasional (21% tetrads), dehisced by April.

## Scleropodium cespitans

This is a member of the small group of epiphytes characteristically found on waterside trees, growing at levels which are flooded at least occasionally. Its requirements are most clearly satisfied by the county's washlands. It is abundant on the bases of alders and willows in Lord's Holt, Nene Washes, TL39E, and also present on willow in Decoy Wood, TF30A. It is also found on the bases of hawthorns and willows, and on stumps, along the railway embankment across the Ouse Washes, TL48Z, TL58E, and in winter-flooded fields just outside these Washes at Mepal, TL48F. Although it may be under-recorded, its apparent restriction to higher sites in the Ouse Washes suggests that it is much

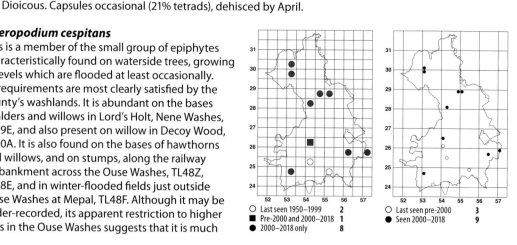

O Last seen 1950–1999    2
■ Pre-2000 and 2000–2018    1
● 2000–2018 only    8

O Last seen pre-2000    3
● Seen 2000–2018    9

less able than *Leskea polycarpa* to withstand prolonged flooding. It is also recorded on an elder by the R. Cam at Croydon, TL34D, and a pondside tree at Stetchworth, TL65N. There are two records from tarmac, with *Hypnum cupressiforme* and *Pseudocrossidium hornschuchianum* on the edges of a path at Oakington church, TL46C, and with *Didymodon nicholsonii* and *Syntrichia latifolia* on the centre and edge of an old drive at Moat Farm, Upend, TL75E.

First record: On root buttresses of large tree, Byron's Pool, Grantchester, TL45H, R.E. Parker, 1953 (*Whitehouse species file*). It was seen in three more sites in the 1950s but there were no further records until the recent survey. We might have expected more records from tarmac, judging by the accounts of its ecology elsewhere (Bates 1995, 2015, Bosanquet 2010, Stern 2010), though it is certainly not as common on tarmac nationally as *Didymodon nicholsonii*. It appears to have spread onto this substrate relatively recently (Blockeel *et al.* 2014).

Dioicous. Capsules seen once, at the Ouse Washes site (11% tetrads), young in October.

### †*Scleropodium touretii*
First and only record: Ground in beech wood, Hildersham Hall, TL54NW, a student (via M.C.F. Proctor), 1953, BBSUK. *Scleropodium touretii* is a Mediterranean-Atlantic species which is most frequent in southern England and Wales in dry coastal habitats. It is rare and declining inland, where there are several records from dry woodland (Blockeel *et al.* 2014).

Dioicous. Capsules not recorded, and rare nationally.

### *Brachytheciastrum velutinum*
It is always a slight surprise to encounter *Brachytheciastrum velutinum*, as it grows unpredictably and sporadically in the county, often in rather ordinary places. Most of its occurrences are as an epiphyte (67% of tetrad records) or from rotting stumps, logs and branches (22%), with the epiphytic sites almost equally divided between orchards (31%) and others (36%). It can be found in ancient and recent woodland, plantations and scrub, commercial and disused orchards, wooded chalk pits, chalk earthworks and railway embankments and on isolated trees on streamsides and tracksides. The most frequent host is apple (41% of host-tetrad records), followed by pear (14%), elder (11%), ash (8%) and willow (8%); there are 1–2 records from elm, field maple, hawthorn, hazel and poplar.

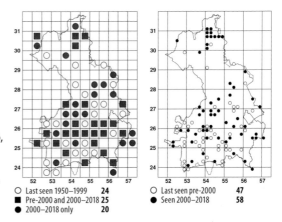

○ Last seen 1950–1999   24
■ Pre-2000 and 2000–2018   25
● 2000–2018 only   20

○ Last seen pre-2000   47
● Seen 2000–2018   58

The concentration of records in the fruit-growing area around Wisbech is apparent on the map; Robin Stevenson recorded it on 69 (7%) of the 951 apples he surveyed in orchards and 15 (9%) of the 173 pears. There are a few records from the silty posts of a bridge, shaded ground (including ground under beeches) and thatch. The species is normally found in fairly small quantity, although the two thatched roofs on which we have seen it, on a house in Shepreth, TL34Y, and an outbuilding (now demolished) in Cambridge, TL45S, had dense, pure, non-fruiting swards under the chicken-wire protecting the thatch. It is doubtless favoured in this habitat by its tolerance of heavy metals; it grows on lead and zinc mine spoil in Wales (Blockeel *et al.* 2014).

First record: On the trunks of old willow trees, Wisbech, TF40NE, W. Skrimshire, 1796, WBCH, as *Hypnum velutinum* (see Appendix 2). It was also collected by L. Jenyns at Bottisham, TL56, in 1824 (CGE) and 1825 (BTH). Proctor (1956) described it as 'rather common', Hill (1967) as 'fairly common' and Whitehouse (1964) as 'abundant on tree-bases and stumps'. On excursions in the 1960s and 1970s *Brachytheciastrum velutinum* was often mentioned in the same breath as *Rhynchostegium confertum*, both being medium-sized pleurocarps which might be encountered. Its decline since then is apparent from the maps and is also evident at a national scale (Hill & Preston 2014). In Cambridgeshire it cannot be explained by previous taxonomic confusion with *R. confertum* – 35 of the 38 records of *B. velutinum* made between 1940 and 1961 and compiled by Whitehouse for his flora were based on fruiting material, and his numerous vouchers in CGE are correctly named. Its habitats in the mid 20th-century were similar to those in which it has been found recently, although there were rather more records from shaded ground than we have. Hill (1967) pointed out that, unlike *R. confertum*, *B. velutinum* 'is not a calcicole' and the reduction in $SO_2$ pollution might have played a part in its decline, though it is not a marked calcifuge and in mid Wales most of its sites are on calcareous rocks and masonry (Bates 2015).

Autoicous. Capsules very frequent (86% tetrads); young setae November, capsules swollen, green December–February, swollen, brown December–February, freshly dehisced January, February.

### Homalothecium sericeum

We have rather more records of this attractive and easily recognised pleurocarp on basic stonework, concrete and brickwork (54% of tetrad records) than as an epiphyte (46%). We have found it on 85% of our churchyard visits, growing on church and churchyard walls and monuments. It also occurs as an epilith elsewhere on walls, bridges and roof tiles, and it is frequent on Carboniferous limestone in rockeries in Cambridge Botanic Garden, TL45N, and elsewhere. It often grows in unshaded sites but sometimes extends into moderately shaded places (it is very drought-tolerant, and *Homalothecium sericeum* sens. *lat*. is common in the lowland Mediterranean region). Epiphytic plants are found in

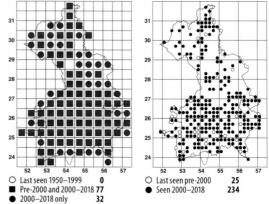

| | |
|---|---|
| ○ Last seen 1950–1999 | 0 |
| ■ Pre-2000 and 2000–2018 | 77 |
| ● 2000–2018 only | 32 |

| | |
|---|---|
| ○ Last seen pre-2000 | 25 |
| ● Seen 2000–2018 | 234 |

ancient and more recent woodland, plantations, scrub in disused brick pits and chalk pits and on chalk embankments, in orchards, parkland and gardens and by rivers, streams and tracks. The most frequent hosts are elder (29% of tetrad records), apple (14%), willow (14%) and ash (14%) but it also grows on a range of other native and introduced species (Appendix 3). Robin Stevenson recorded it on 149 (16%) of the 951 apple trees he surveyed in orchards, and three (2%) of the 173 pears; the discrepancy reveals its greater preference for base-rich bark. It appears to be rather a slow colonist and as an epiphyte it is often found on only a few trees in a site; characteristic hosts in ancient woods include old coppice stools and pollards on boundary banks. However its frequent presence on elders, where it is usually found on mature or over-mature individuals, shows that it must be a reasonably effective colonist. It is very rare on the ground, though we have seen it on chalky soil as well as on the bases and exposed roots of trees in beech woodland.

First record: Cambridge, 'On ye Wall of ye grove of Peterhouse exactly in yt [that] corner next Silks', TL45N, W. Vernon, *c*. 1696 (Vernon's annotated Ray 1696: 38, as *Muscus terrestris luteo-viridis, sericeus, repens*). J. Martyn (1729b: 15, as *Hypnum repens, trichoides, terrestre, luteo-virens, vulgare, majus, capitulis erectis*) knew it 'In muris atque ad arborum radices ubique' [Everywhere on walls and at the roots of trees] and T. Martyn (1763: 31, as *Hypnum sericeum*) published a record from Moor Barns Thicket, TL45E. There are fruiting specimens collected by Skrimshire at Wisbech, TF40NE, in 1795 (WBCH), where it was described as common, by Henslow at Coton, TL45E, in 1821 (CGE) and by Jenyns at Anglesey Abbey, TL56G, in 1825 (BTH). There is no evidence for any change in frequency since Proctor (1956), unconsciously echoing Martyn, described it as 'common on walls, stonework, roofs, and trunks and bases of trees'.

Dioicous. Capsules occasional (16% tetrads), found in well-established colonies on both stonework and living hosts but more frequent on the former. Young setae November–December; capsules swollen, green October–February; swollen, brown December–January; dehiscing February–March. Deciduous branchlets and shoot apices act as vegetative propagules (Fritz *et al*. 2010).

Early herbals (e.g. Gerarde 1597) include 'the mosse growing on the skull of a man' as a medical remedy. An example is preserved (as *Usnea Cranii Humani*) in the cabinet of *materia medica* assembled by the Cambridge physician William Heberden in the 1740s and now preserved in St John's College, Cambridge; its identity is *Homalothecium sericeum* (Belcher & Swale 1998).

### Homalothecium lutescens

*Homalothecium lutescens* is a habitat specialist. It grows in short turf in well-established chalk grassland, in lawns and on the verges and banks of roads, tracks and ditches, always over base-rich soils. It is also found on chalky waste ground, open soil in clay, chalk and gravel pits, on railway ballast and on chalky soil in beech woods. It may occur as a thin weft of stems in grassland or sometimes as dense masses with other pleurocarps in disused chalk pits, where it extends into shaded sites amongst scattered bushes or at the fringe of scrub. It lacks the ability of *Calliergonella, Pseudoscleropodium* or *Rhytidiadelphus squarrosus* to persist in denser turf, and many churchyard records are from soil or, more frequently, stone chippings on graves. It is very rare on concrete and stonework alongside its grassland sites. It was widespread on Magog Down, TL45W, by 2004, only 13 years after the site had been converted to grassland from arable land, and abundant in young woodland alongside the established beechwood on Wort's Causeway, TL45X, in 2004, 12 years after it was planted on arable land.

First record: Gog Magog Hills, TL45SE, Relhan (1786: 20, as *Hypnum lutescens*); vegetative specimens were collected here by Leonard Jenyns in 1825 (BTH) and it was still present at several sites on the Gogs in 2017. It was always more frequent in the county than more demanding chalk grassland pleurocarps *Abietinella*, *Ctenidium* and *Entodon*, and is clearly able to persist in the modern countryside. There is no evidence for any great

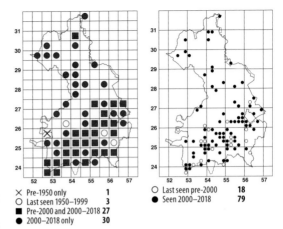

| | | |
|---|---|---|
| ✕ | Pre-1950 only | 1 |
| ○ | Last seen 1950–1999 | 3 |
| ■ | Pre-2000 and 2000–2018 | 27 |
| ● | 2000–2018 only | 30 |
| ○ | Last seen pre-2000 | 18 |
| ● | Seen 2000–2018 | 79 |

change in frequency in recent decades; some of the small chalk pits in which it grew have been lost but it has clearly colonised some newly available habitats. The many additional records in the north of the county presumably reflect our more intensive survey of Fenland, although Bosanquet (2010) suggests that the species has been introduced with limestone chippings into graveyards in Pembrokeshire.

Dioicous. Green and brown capsules seen in one place in East Pit, Cherry Hinton, TL45X, in December 2008, the only recent record (1% tetrads). Fruiting plants were collected near Madingley in February 1880 (CGE), and recorded at North Pit, Haslingfield, TL45A, in October 1904 and in Madingley Woods, TL35/45, in December 1904 (*Richards file*) but we know of no later 20th-century records. Studies of this species in Sweden have shown that vegetative and female shoots predominate, whereas full-sized male shoots, 'dwarf males' (small male plants living epiphytically on the females) and sporophytes are rare. The normal open, dry grassland habitat appears to be unfavourable for the establishment or growth of dwarf males, and sexual reproduction is more likely to occur in partially shaded grassland where moisture levels are higher (Rosengren & Cronberg 2014, Rosengren *et al.* 2014). The records of fruiting plants in the county are consistent with these conclusions. Like *H. sericeum*, it may spread vegetatively by means of deciduous branchlets and shoot apices (Fritz *et al.* 2010).

*Homalothecium lutescens* and *H. sericeum* are closely related (Huttunen *et al.* 2008). We have sometimes had difficulty separating them in churchyards where populations of *H. sericeum* on gravestones grow close to those of *H. lutescens* on grave chippings. Dwarf males of *H. sericeum* will grow to maturity from spores sown on to shoots of *H. lutescens* under experimental conditions, suggesting that hybridisation between the species is a possibility (Rosengren & Cronberg 2015). We have based our identifications on habit and have not tested the microscopic character (protruding teeth on the basal leaf margin) sometimes used to separate *H. sericeum* from *H. lutescens* (Hedenäs *et al.* 2014).

# HYPNACEAE

### *Campylophyllum calcareum*
Only found since 2000 on chalky soil under beech trees in the Beechwood Nature Reserve on the Gog Magog Hills, TL45X. It has been seen on the edge of a shallow chalk pit and on a trampled path in the mature woodland, and by 2017 it had also spread into the adjacent area planted in 1992 on former arable land.

First record: Chalky bank in beechwood by Babraham Corner, TL55A, P.W. Richards, 1940, NMW; refound here, sometimes with *Porella platyphylla*, until 1958. It was first found in the Gogs beechwood by E.F. Warburg in 1945 (OXF). It was also recorded between 1951 and 1965 under beeches near Wormwood Hill, TL45W, at Wandlebury fort, TL45W, in a chalk pit at Little Abington, TL55F and at Mutlow Hill on Fleam Dyke, TL55M; from the bases of trees in an old chalk pit on St Margaret's Mount near Hauxton, TL45K; from a stump on the Gog Magog Hills close to Babraham Road, TL45W; and from the base of an ash in Lime Kiln Close, TL45Y (last seen here in 1994). The species, although rather inconspicuous, is distinctive and several of these sites are represented by correctly identified vouchers in CGE. The chalk area south-west of Cambridge has not been searched as intensively in recent years as in the past, and it is possible that *C. calcareum* might be refound in some of these sites.

Autoicous. Capsules frequent (100% tetrads); young setae November, January–February, capsules just beginning to expand February, dehiscing June.

## Calliergonella cuspidata

This large and very distinctive, ground-living pleurocarp is found in all but the driest grasslands, including chalk grassland, lawns and roadside and trackside verges. With *Rhytidiadelphus squarrosus* it is the most frequent of the specialised grassland pleurocarps in churchyards; we have found it in 67% of the sites visited. It is most frequent in the more mesic grasslands, being very much more abundant on the north- than on the south-facing side of the Devil's Dyke, for example. Even more luxuriant, almost pure swards may occur in semi-aquatic habitats, lining the edges of lakes, ponds or fen ditches. Its other habitats include fen droves, herbaceous fenland communities, reed beds and wet fen carr, woodland rides, newly planted woodlands and moist ground in chalk, clay and gravel pits. It may extend onto rotting wood on the woodland floor. Although it is very characteristic of water's edge communities, it is absent from washland subject to prolonged annual flooding. There are a few records from stubble and set-aside fields, shaded stone ledges in churchyards and as an epiphyte in fen carr.

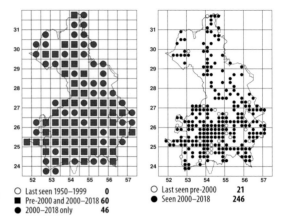

○ Last seen 1950–1999   **0**
■ Pre-2000 and 2000–2018   **60**
● 2000–2018 only   **46**

○ Last seen pre-2000   **21**
● Seen 2000–2018   **246**

First record: Hinton Moor, TL45NE, W. Vernon (Ray 1696: 39, as *Muscus ramosus palustris major, foliis membranaceis acutis*), the first British record. Martyn (1729a: 15) added 'the bogs near Gamlingay' to Vernon's locality. Henslow collected fruiting material near Cambridge, TL45, in 1821 and 1822 (BTH, CGE, as *Hypnum cuspidatum*) and at Gamlingay, TL25SW, in 1827 (CGE). R.E. Parker's view (dated 1953, *Whitehouse species file*) that the species occurs in dry calcareous turf and moist turf but not usually in intermediate conditions is not directly quoted by Proctor (1956) or Whitehouse (1964) but apparently informs their accounts. It does not accord with our experience.

Dioicous. Capsules rare (3% tetrads); they have only been seen recently in four wetland sites and in wet areas in Gamlingay Wood, TL25L, and Eltisley Wood, TL25U. It appears to fruit frequently at Wicken and this is probably the case in other wetlands. We have seen fruits only in March and April, as swollen green or brown capsules which on one occasion were starting to lose their calyptrae. Henslow also collected fruiting plants in May.

## Pylaisia polyantha

An apparently rare epiphyte, recorded only from apple trees in orchards. It is known from five orchards in the Wisbech area, TF40D, J, N, T, and further south from Ashley Farm Orchard, Rampton, TL46J, and Franklin's Old Orchard, Cottenham, TL46N. It grows on a range of varieties including Bramley's Seedling, Lord Derby and unidentified cultivar(s). Robin Stevenson, who has made almost all the records, has found it on just eight (1%) of the 951 apple trees he has examined systematically. We may have overlooked it on other hosts in rather unshaded habitats.

First record: On apple trees in old orchard north of Rummers Lane, Wisbech St Mary, TF41D, C.R. Stevenson, 2004, BBSUK. There has been a modest increase in the national records of this species in recent years (Hill & Preston 2014).

Autoicous. Capsules always present but it would be difficult to detect the species in their absence; immature and mature March, setae with unexpanded capsules May.

## Hypnum cupressiforme

This is a very frequent but not a ubiquitous species, found on a very wide range of stable, open or lightly shaded substrates. It is frequent on old brickwork, stonework, concrete, clay roofing tiles and stone chippings on graves, and sometimes found on shaded tarmac, slate tiles and even on flint. It is equally frequent on acidic as on basic substrates; it is often the only species on acidic sandstone gravestones (which are much less common here than in many other areas) and it is the dominant moss on sandstone rocks in Cambridge Botanic Garden, TL45N. It is uncommon on soil, found on sandy ground and on chalk soil in open calcareous grassland and in beech woods but rarely in more fertile sites. As an epiphyte it grows on trees and shrubs in both open sites and in hedges and woodland. Our data show little indication of any host preferences; we have recorded it most frequently on ash (14% of tetrad records), willow (13%), hawthorn (12%), elder (11%), apple (7%) and sycamore (5%), but there are records from over 30 other taxa, both native and introduced (Appendix 3). It is the most frequent bryophyte on orchard trees; var. *cupressiforme* was recorded on 731 (77%) of the 951 apples and 128 (74%) of the 173 pears surveyed by Robin Stevenson and the species is even more frequent as var. *resupinatum* was recorded separately. It is more frequent on the acid bark of oaks in woodland than other pleurocarps. It is also frequent on rotting

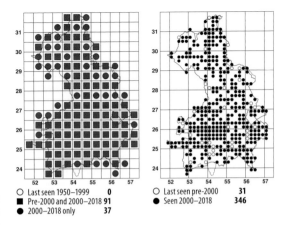

○ Last seen 1950–1999    **0**
■ Pre-2000 and 2000–2018 **91**
● 2000–2018 only    **37**

○ Last seen pre-2000    **31**
● Seen 2000–2018    **346**

logs and stumps, and it colonises worked wood such as roof shingles, old benches and farm trailers. Unlike *Amblystegium serpens* and *Brachythecium rutabulum*, it is rarely found on random human artefacts dumped in the countryside.

First record: T. Martyn, 1760–61 (*Martyn letters*) and Martyn (1763: 25). The oldest localised record is a specimen collected at Wisbech by W. Skrimshire in 1796 (WBCH). There is no evidence for any change in the frequency or habitat preferences of the species in the last century.

Dioicous. Capsules frequent (39% tetrads); young setae October–December; capsules swollen, green October–December; brown November–February; dehiscing December–March. By early March most capsules have dehisced.

This account includes all the varieties of this very variable species. Var. *cupressiforme* is the commonest taxon and is itself variable; it is not very unusual to see morphologically different patches growing side by side in the same habitat. Var. *lacunosum* has been recorded (sometimes as var. *tectorum*) in sandy and chalk grassland and on roofs but intermediates with var. *cupressiforme* are too frequent for it to be worth recognising. Var. *resupinatum* has been recorded inconsistently. Plants growing on vertical surfaces with long, sparingly branched stems and only weakly curved leaves, the stems turning up like a quiff at the ends, were usually included in this variety by Cambridgeshire recorders but patches of var. *cupressiforme* on horizontal sites (such as the tops of gravestones) can adopt this habit when they turn to grow vertically downwards. Plants with more richly branched stems and more or less straight leaves directed obliquely upwards are more convincingly distinct and indeed are treated as a species (*H. resupinatum*) by Hedenäs et al. (2014). For var. *heseleri*, see below.

### Hypnum cupressiforme var. heseleri

This morphologically distinctive moss is known only in the county as a single patch, measuring 18 × 12 cm, growing with *Brachythecium rutabulum* on the upper trunk of a Lord Derby apple tree (planted in 1965).

First record: W. Norman's Orchard, Begdale Road, Elm, TF40N, M.O. Hill, 2007, BBSUK (see Appendix 2). This was only the second British record of this plant, which appears to be a genetic mutation of *Hypnum cupressiforme* but might not initially be recognised as this species. It was first collected in the Netherlands in 1984 and has since been recorded in France, Germany and the Czech Republic. It was first found in Britain in 2005, when Robin Stevenson discovered a single patch, similar in size to that later seen in Cambridgeshire, in the Royal Orchards at Flitcham, W. Norfolk (Blockeel & Stevenson 2006).

Dioicous. Capsules not known in Britain.

## Hypnum andoi

In Cambridgeshire this is a species of wet woodland, including ancient woods on the Boulder Clay and secondary woodland on Woburn Sands or in the Fens. In recent years there are records from Gamlingay Heath Plantation, TL25F, East Quarter, Hayley Wood, TL25W, Eversden Wood, TL35L, Ten Wood, TL65S and Chippenham Fen, TL66P. It has been seen on the bark of ash and oak, on a fallen conifer and on decorticated oak logs.

First record: On sallow in carr near Barnes Mere, Wicken Fen, TL57K, M.O. Hill, 1997, BBSUK. In the following year it was found on the base of an ash and, with *Nowellia curvifolia*, on a decorticated oak log in the East Quarter, Hayley Wood. *Hypnum andoi* is an abundant epiphyte in western Britain,

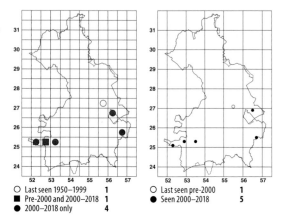

| | |
|---|---|
| ○ Last seen 1950–1999 | 1 |
| ■ Pre-2000 and 2000–2018 | 1 |
| ● 2000–2018 only | 4 |

| | |
|---|---|
| ○ Last seen pre-2000 | 1 |
| ● Seen 2000–2018 | 5 |

especially on oak, but until the publication of Smith's moss flora (1978a) it was much confused with *H. cupressiforme*. It is uncertain whether it has spread into Cambridgeshire in recent years or whether it was previously overlooked.

Dioicous. Fruits frequent (40% tetrads); capsules swollen, green November, recently dehisced February.

## Hypnum jutlandicum

*Hypnum jutlandicum* is another member of the *H. cupressiforme* aggregate which is very common in acidic habitats in western Britain and Ireland but rare in Cambridgeshire. It is perhaps most frequent on acidic ground, tree bases and rotting wood on the Woburn Sands in Gamlingay Heath Plantation, TL25F. It is rarer in similar habitats, especially rotting wood, in ancient boulder-clay woods, in carr at Wicken Fen, TL56P, 57K, and in woodland at Chippenham Fen, TL66J, P. The northern records are from clinker in disused railway sidings at March, TL49E, and, more surprisingly, from orchards near Wisbech, TF30X, 40E and 41A, where it is a rare epiphyte on pear trees but has not been recorded on the more basic bark of apple.

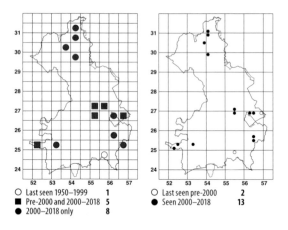

| | |
|---|---|
| ○ Last seen 1950–1999 | 1 |
| ■ Pre-2000 and 2000–2018 | 5 |
| ● 2000–2018 only | 8 |

| | |
|---|---|
| ○ Last seen pre-2000 | 2 |
| ● Seen 2000–2018 | 13 |

First record: Great Heath Plantation, Gamlingay, TL25F, P.W. Richards, 1930, NMW (as 'near var. *ericetorum*'), det. M.O.H.; still present in 2018. The next record, from Hildersham Furze Hills, TL54P, H.L.K. Whitehouse, 1952 (*Whitehouse species file*), has hitherto been regarded as the first record. It was recorded before 2000 in similar habitats to those of recent years. It was first found at Wicken Fen in 1979 and by 1989 it had become locally abundant in some areas of fen carr (Lock 1990), much of which has now been cleared.

Dioicous. Capsules not recorded.

## Ctenidium molluscum var. molluscum

The largest population is in calcareous grassland on the Devil's Dyke, where the species is concentrated in places which have escaped previous scrub encroachment and which support a rich assemblage of calcicolous bryophytes and vascular plants. It is luxuriant on the north-facing side of the disused railway cutting across the Dyke, and also the most frequent pleurocarp in the open grassland on the south-facing side in a few stretches in TL66A, B. Smaller populations are found on Fleam Dyke, TL55L, M, Great Wilbraham Common, TL55I, in a few chalk pits which have escaped land-fill and scrub encroachment, and on chalky ground in beech woods, notably in the Beechwood Nature Reserve on the Gog Magog Hills, TL45X. It still grows on the Carboniferous limestone rocks on which it was introduced to the Botanic Garden, TL45N, in 1955–57. *Ctenidium* also grows in mown calcareous fen vegetation at Wicken Fen, TL57K, and Chippenham Fen, TL66P. The population on a ride and in adjacent woodland at Gamlingay Wood, TL25G, where it has been known since 1912, is now anomalous in growing on clay in a less calcareous site.

First record: T. Martyn, 1760–61 (*Martyn letters*) and Martyn (1763: 25, as *Hypnum crista-castrensis*). Relhan (1785: 411) reported it from the Gog Magog Hills and from Chalk-pit Close, Cherry Hinton, TL45Y, two areas in which it still survives. The numerous sites at which we have failed to refind the plant include boulder-clay woods such as Hayley Wood, TL25W (last seen 1966), Hardwick Wood, TL35N (1965), and Langley Wood, TL64B (1946), chalk pits such as those at Harlton, TL35W (1973), and Coploe Hill, TL44W (1982), and other chalk grassland sites including the Roman Road, TL45X, TL55B (1979), and Quy Fen, TL56B (1984). It was probably never frequent in the boulder-clay woods, where there are single records from each site listed – 'in small quantity on clayey mire' at Hayley Wood, in a ditch by Hardwick Wood and on a ride at Langley Wood. However, P.W. Richards described it as common along the Roman Road on the Gogs in 1932 and E.W. Jones found it 'in extraordinary abundance and luxuriance – almost a dominant plant' in Harlton clunch pit in 1934. The northern locality is Bassenhally Pit, TL29Z, where it was last seen in 1987.

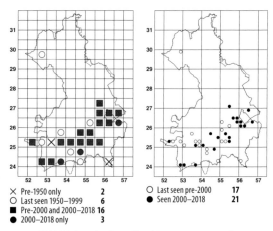

× Pre-1950 only 2
○ Last seen 1950–1999 6
■ Pre-2000 and 2000–2018 16
● 2000–2018 only 3

○ Last seen pre-2000 17
● Seen 2000–2018 21

Dioicous. Capsules not seen in the recent survey and rather rare nationally. As with *Homalothecium lutescens*, there are more early fruiting specimens than one would expect: Gog Magog Hills (J.S. Henslow, 1821, CGE), Cherry Hinton (Henslow, 1826, CGE, WARMS) and near Hardwick (G.D. Haviland and J.J. Lister, 1880, CGE, OXF). There are no later records of fruiting plants from the county. There are similarities between these two species, as both have normal-sized and dwarf male plants, but the reproduction of *C. molluscum* has not received detailed study. This is one of several pleurocarps which Swinscow (1957) knew only as vegetative plants in Hertfordshire but which had been collected in the county with sporophytes by W.H. Coleman in the 1840s.

## PTERIGYNANDRACEAE

### Pterigynandrum filiforme

Known on a single dessert apple tree in a small, sheltered orchard at Elm, where it grows with *Hypnum cupressiforme*, *Orthotrichum lyellii* and *Syntrichia montana*.

First record: Cranwell Lodge, High Street, Elm, TF40T, C.R. Stevenson, 2010, BBSUK. This is an unexpected addition to our flora, as there are only two other sites for this Boreal-montane species in southern England. Richard Fisk found it at Wordwell, West Suffolk, in 2005 (Fisk 2005) and at Brandon, 10 km north of this, in 2016 (Pescott & Preston 2016). It is otherwise an upland plant in Britain, although it has spread in the Netherlands in recent years.

Dioicous. Capsules not recorded and rare in Britain. The species reproduces by gemmae and, more rarely, by deciduous branchlets (Bergamini 2006) although we have not looked for these on the Cambridgeshire material.

## HYLOCOMIACEAE

### †Pleurozium schreberi

A common moss in acidic regions of Britain and Ireland, last recorded in Cambridgeshire in 1999.

First record: Hardwick Wood, TL35N, G.D. Haviland and J.J. Lister, 1880, CGE. It was refound at Hardwick Wood by M.O.H. in 1965, growing over thick litter in a small open place with abundant *Lathyrus sylvestris* and *Lophocolea bidentata*, *Eurhynchium striatum*, *Hylocomium splendens*, *Kindbergia praelonga* and *Thuidium tamariscinum*. Adamson (in Evans 1913) recorded it from the Woburn Sands area at Gamlingay and there are single records there from Great Heath Plantation, TL25F (1930) and a ride in White Wood, TL25SW (1955). It has also been found on a decaying blackthorn branch at Elsworth Wood, TL36A (1982) and in a conifer plantation on sandy soil at Chippenham, TL66NE (1965), where it grew mainly on a ride but also under the conifers. In some of these sites it may have been casual, but it became well-established, widespread and locally common as an invading calcifuge at Wicken Fen, TL56P, 57K, Q, where it was first found in 1966 and last seen in 1999.

Dioicous. Capsules not recorded and rare in lowland Britain. Vegetative reproduction is by deciduous shoot apices, branchlets and, more rarely, leaves (Fritz *et al.* 2010).

## *Rhytidiadelphus triquetrus*

The Cambridgeshire populations of this handsome species are usually very small. There are seven sites in boulder-clay woodland, almost all in ancient woodland, where it grows on the woodland floor with *Cirriphyllum piliferum, Eurhynchium striatum, Plagiomnium undulatum* and *Thuidium tamariscinum*. In some of these woods the plants have straggly stems and seem to lack vigour. The other populations grow in scrub (two sites) and grassland (five sites) on calcareous clay or chalk at the edges of parkland woods, in chalk or clay pits or on tracksides. These plants appear healthier; at Orwell Clunch Pit, TL35Q, the chalk grassland in which they grow is mown and the stems are unusually short but the plant appears able to withstand this treatment. The northernmost record is of a patch *c.* 10 cm wide which had colonised a clay slope in the Kings Dyke Nature Reserve, TL29N, a disused brick pit.

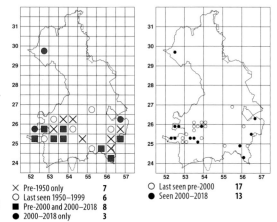

| | |
|---|---|
| ✕ Pre-1950 only | 7 |
| ○ Last seen 1950–1999 | 6 |
| ■ Pre-2000 and 2000–2018 | 8 |
| ● 2000–2018 only | 3 |

| | |
|---|---|
| ○ Last seen pre-2000 | 17 |
| ● Seen 2000–2018 | 13 |

First record: Madingley Wood, TL35/45, J. Martyn (1729b: 14, as *Hypnum repens, triangularibus, majoribus* and *pallidioribus foliis*); published by T. Martyn (1763: 25, 31, as *Hypnum triquetrum*). It was last seen in Madingley Wood in 1960 but it persists in scrub on Madingley Slip Road and along a grassy track by the woodland extension (Madingley 800 Wood) nearby, TL35Z. The maps suggest a species in long-term decline. It was apparently locally frequent in the early 20th century – Adamson (1912) listed it as locally abundant in Gamlingay Wood, TL25SW, and in a few weeks in early 1914 A.W. Graveson found it 'in considerable quantity in shady places' in Kingston Wood, TL35SW, 'in great abundance' at Whitepits Plantation, TL35U, and 'a good deal' by the Cambridge Road near Hildersham, TL54NW. Robert Ross recorded it as one of the most abundant species in hawthorn scrub on abandoned agricultural land in the 1930s (Tansley 1939). Proctor (1956) described it as 'a very common constituent of the ground flora in the drier parts of the boulder clay woods' and Whitehouse (1964) as 'locally abundant' in most of the woods. This clearly puzzled Hill (1967) who scarcely ever saw it in the woods in the mid 1960s. There are 25 sites with no recent record, of which 18 are boulder-clay woods. It was last recorded in 10 of these woods between 1930 and 1949, and eight between 1950 and 1969. Hill regarded it as rather light-demanding and intolerant of water-logging, and the most likely explanation for its decline is a reduction in woodland management leading to darker woods and the loss of grassland on rides and clearings. In Derbyshire Tom Blockeel (*in litt.*) finds that it is much more abundant and luxuriant in light hazel woodland than in more shaded sites, supporting this explanation. The species has declined elsewhere in southern England but the explanation for the decline observed by Bates (1993, 1995) in Berkshire and Oxfordshire, that it has been eliminated from the more acidic soils by $SO_2$ pollution, is unlikely to apply in calcareous Cambridgeshire.

Dioicous. Capsules not recorded recently, although Haviland and Lister's specimen collected at Hardwick Wood, TL35N, in February 1880 (CGE) is fruiting, and Graveson found a few capsules in Whitepits Plantation in 1914. They are rare nationally.

## *Rhytidiadelphus squarrosus*

This is very much a species of short grassland, and it is frequently abundant in lawns and churchyard turf (we recorded it in 65% of churchyards). It is also found on roadside verges and tracksides, disused railway lines, woodland rides, especially rides through patches of conifers and along the margins of the conifer stands, newly planted deciduous woods and in clay and gravel pits. We have sometimes found small quantities growing on churchyard monuments or on low brick walls alongside lawns, possibly arising from scraps thrown up by the lawn mower. Although it is sometimes found in churchyards and cemeteries over chalk soils, it is absent from long-established chalk grassland, including the Fleam and Devil's Dykes, although it grows near the latter in the mown turf of Newmarket Heath, TL66A, B.

First record: Newmarket, TL66, J. Hemsted, 1796, WBCH, as *Hypnum stellatum* (see Appendix 2). The next certain record is a specimen from Hardwick, TL35, collected by G.D. Haviland and J.J. Lister in 1880 (CGE). The many additional 5-km squares we have added since 2000 presumably reflect the improved recording of churchyards and villages. It may have been lost to agricultural improvement at some sites on acidic soils, such as the field with *Cytisus scoparius* at Gamlingay, TL25F, in which it was recorded in 1960.

Dioicous. H. N. Dixon collected a fruiting specimen from a roadside at Trumpington, TL45, in May 1883 (BM) but capsules have not been recorded since and are rare in lowland Britain. We have been advised to look for them on plants of *R. squarrosus* at the foot of banks or slopes, but most of our populations are on flat ground. Like some other pleurocarps which fruit sparingly, it may spread vegetatively by deciduous shoot apices and branchlets (Fritz *et al.* 2010).

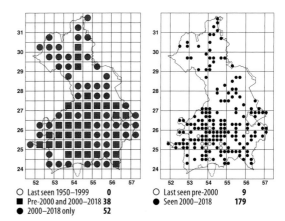

○ Last seen 1950–1999     **0**
■ Pre-2000 and 2000–2018  **38**
● 2000–2018 only         **52**

○ Last seen pre-2000      **9**
● Seen 2000–2018    **179**

## †*Rhytidiadelphus loreus*

Known only as one of the calcifuges which formerly colonised Wicken Fen.

First record: Verrall's Fen, Wicken Fen, TL57K, A.C. Leslie, 1974, BBSUK, CGE (see Appendix 2). A few small patches were seen in fen carr in scattered localities on the Fen until 1989 (CGE).

Dioicous. Capsules not seen.

## †*Loeskeobryum brevirostre*

This species is also known only as a former colonist at Wicken Fen.

First record: West of Barnes Mere, Wicken Fen, TL57K, A.C. Leslie, 1974, CGE. It was also found further north on Verrall's Fen in 1975 (CGE) and it was last seen in 1989 growing in small quantity under birches with *Dicranum scoparium* and *Thuidium tamariscinum* (Lock 1990). These are the only East Anglian records of a predominantly western species in Britain. In much of its British range the species occurs in rather base-rich localities (Blockeel *et al.* 2014), although the habitat at Wicken was identical to that of the calcifuge colonists.

Dioicous. Capsules not recorded and rare nationally.

## *Hylocomium splendens*

Currently known as only a single patch about 1 m across, found in Sixteen Acre Plantation, Newmarket, TL66R, by M.O.H. in 2016. It grew over a tussock in an area of species-rich chalk grassland, with *Brachypodium sylvaticum, Clinopodium vulgare, Myosotis arvensis, Thymus pulegioides* and *Veronica chamaedrys*.

First record: Bucket Hill Plantation, Hardwick, TL35P, P.S.B. Digby, 1941 (*Richards file*; see Appendix 2). There were two sites where the species was clearly established in the 20th century, Harlton clunch pit, TL35W (1943–62, CGE), where it grew in deep chalk turf, and Pampisford Hall Wood, TL54E (1948–78). There were also single records from Hardwick Wood, TL35N, where it grew on thick leaf litter in 1965 (see *Pleurozium schreberi*), Orwell

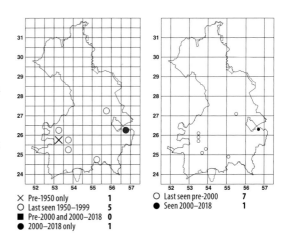

✕ Pre-1950 only         **1**
○ Last seen 1950–1999    **5**
■ Pre-2000 and 2000–2018  **0**
● 2000–2018 only         **1**

○ Last seen pre-2000      **7**
● Seen 2000–2018    **1**

Clunch Pit, TL35Q (1976), New Wood, Childerley, TL36K (1958, CGE) and Wicken Fen, TL57K (1979, CGE). This is a frequent species in base-poor habitats in the non-calcareous regions of Britain but it will also grow in calcareous sites, as in Sixteen Acre Plantation and presumably formerly at Harlton.

Dioicous. Capsules not recorded and very rare nationally.

## RHYTIDIACEAE

### †*Rhytidium rugosum*
First and only record: Grass heath, Isleham Plantation, TL67SE, P.W. Richards, 1930, NMW (as *Hylocomium rugosum* 'near Fordham') and *Richards file*. The specimen shows that the plants here were vigorous, but the species has never been seen in the county again. *R. rugosum* has a disjunct distribution in open, calcareous habitats in both upland and lowland sites in Britain and Ireland. The Cambridgeshire site is on the fringe of the Breckland, a stronghold of the species where there are still some large populations, although others have been lost (Beckett *et al.* 1999, Sanford & Fisk 2010).

Dioicous. Capsules are unknown in Britain.

## PLAGIOTHECIACEAE

*Plagiothecium undulatum* is a distinct species, but the taxonomy of the other Cambridgeshire taxa was not well understood until Greene (1957) published a revision of the British species. All the Cambridgeshire species are markedly calcifuge with the exception of *Plagiothecium nemorale*, which is only a mild calcifuge.

### *Plagiothecium denticulatum* var. *denticulatum*
The few recent records are from a rotting stump and (with *Calypogeia fissa*) a bank by a ride in Gamlingay Wood, TL25L; on wet ground in sallow carr (with *Polytrichastrum formosum*) at Wicken Fen, TL56P, 57Q; a rotting log (with *P. nemorale*) in the coniferised Little Widgham Wood, TL65S; and mossy tree bases in damp birch/alder woodland at Chippenham Fen, TL66P.

First record: Great Heath Plantation, Gamlingay, TL25F, E.W. Jones and P.W. Richards, 1934 (*Richards file*). The 20th-century records were from acidic ground, rotting wood and tree bases in ancient and recent woodland and in hedges. The ground-dwelling colonies included one on sandy soil and pine litter, with *Lophocolea heterophylla* and *P. curvifolium*, at Chippenham, TL66NE, and another on

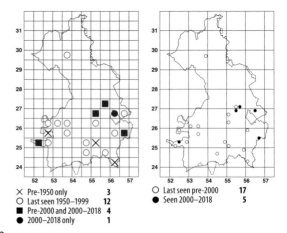

| | |
|---|---|
| × Pre-1950 only | 3 |
| ○ Last seen 1950–1999 | 12 |
| ■ Pre-2000 and 2000–2018 | 4 |
| ● 2000–2018 only | 1 |

| | |
|---|---|
| ○ Last seen pre-2000 | 17 |
| ● Seen 2000–2018 | 5 |

swampy ground in fen carr at Wicken. It was rather widespread at Wicken in the mid 1960s (Lock 1964). The decline in Cambridgeshire reflects a wider decline in the British lowlands since 1980 (Blockeel *et al.* 2014), presumably caused by the reduction in $SO_2$ pollution and thus the decreasing availability of acidic habitats.

Autoicous. Capsules frequent (60% tetrads); young setae April.

At least some plants from Chippenham Fen and Wicken Fen are referable to the variant previously recognised as *P. denticulatum* var. *undulatum* or *P. ruthei*, but now included in *P. denticulatum*.

### †*Plagiothecium laetum*
First and only record: On living bark at base of oak, Hardwick Wood, TL35N, M.O. Hill, 1991, BBSUK. This species is closely related to *Plagiothecium curvifolium* and is sometimes regarded as a variant of that species; it is poorly recorded nationally and may have been overlooked elsewhere in Cambridgeshire.

Autoicous. Capsules not recorded.

### *Plagiothecium curvifolium*
*Plagiothecium curvifolium* has a narrow habitat range; its crowded, glossy shoots grow on the bases of trees (including ash, birch, hawthorn, larch and oak), on rotting stumps and logs, especially the long-lasting stumps of oak, and rarely on decaying wood covered with a thin layer of sandy soil or on sandy soil itself. It has a strong preference for ancient woodland (Preston & Hill 2016) but is also found in some well-established plantations and in fen carr and fen woodland. It is rarely frequent, and we often find only one or two patches at a site. *Lophocolea heterophylla* and *Orthodontium lineare* are characteristic associates.

First record: Copse south of Madingley, TL35NE, M.C.F. Proctor, 1951, BBSUK. Only known here and from White Wood, Gamlingay, TL25SW, to Proctor (1956), when it was treated as a variety (var. *aptychus*) of *P.*

denticulatum, but several further sites were known to Whitehouse (1964). There are several woodland sites in the west of the county with 20th-century records which we have not refound, as well as Bassenhally Pit, TL29Z, and Gray's Moor Pits, TF40A, in the north. The Cambridgeshire records fit the national trend of an increase between 1970 and 1990 followed by a decline (Blockeel *et al.* 2014). Its preference for ancient woodland is a result of Cambridgeshire's restricted geology; in areas with acidic soils it is a frequent species in conifer plantations.

Autoicous. Capsules frequent (68% tetrads); young setae February, rarely April; swollen green capsules March–April; freshly dehisced capsules April. Gemmae sometimes abundant.

## Plagiothecium nemorale

*Plagiothecium nemorale* grows on coppice stools, on the base and lower trunks of trees, on adjacent clay soil and shaded woodland banks, and on rotting stumps and logs. It is most frequent on ash (54% of tetrad records) and oak (25%), with single records from alder, birch, elder, hazel and sycamore. Although normally found close to ground level, it sometimes ascends to heights of over 1 m on the trunks of oaks. About half its sites are ancient woodland; it also grows in other woodland including well-established plantations, fen carr and in disused clay and gravel pits. Although it certainly grows in acidic habitats (e.g. with *Mnium hornum* on a log of pH 5.1 at Fordham Abbey, TL66J), it extends into rather more circumneutral sites than the county's

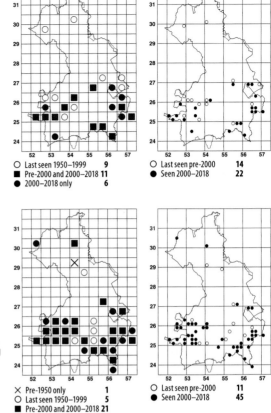

other *Plagiothecium* species and it is not infrequent in some of the boulder-clay woods.

First record: Hayley Wood, TL25W, E.F. Warburg and A.S. Watt, 1941, CGE, OXF, conf. S.W. Greene. Unlike the other *Plagiothecium* species, *P. nemorale* does not appear to be in decline in the county, presumably because it is less restricted to acidic sites.

Dioicous. Capsules occasional (36% tetrads). Gemmae frequent, sometimes forming masses like small pom-poms in the leaf axils.

Cambridgeshire is the only British vice-county from which the closely related *P. succulentum* has not been recorded (Hill *et al.* 2008). The younger leaves of our plants are sometimes a shining golden yellow, a character sometimes said to indicate *P. succulentum*, but on microscopic examination such specimens have always turned out to be *P. nemorale*.

## Plagiothecium undulatum

The most surprising colony of this distinctive calcifuge seen during the recent survey was at Little Crishall Plantation, TL44L, on the chalk, where two small patches were found on a decaying pine log. The other records are of a vigorous patch on damp ground under brambles in an open area of Little Widgham Wood, TL65S, from a rotten log in Basefield Wood, TL65N, and a large mass at the base of one alder, above a zone of *Mnium hornum*, in wet birch/alder wood at Chippenham Fen, TL66P.

First record: Old *Molinia caerulea* tussock in carr, Verrall's Fen, Wicken Fen, TL57, J.M. Lock, 1965, CGE. It became quite frequent on the sides of *Molinia*

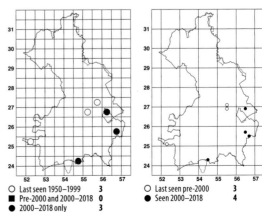

tussocks at Wicken, TL56P, 57K, in the 1970s but it had declined by 1990 (Lock 1990) and was last recorded in 1999. The only other 20th-century record was from Great Heath Plantation, Gamlingay, TL25F, where one patch was found in 1988.

Dioicous. Capsules not recorded.

### Pseudotaxiphyllum elegans

Most of the recent records are from sandy soil at Gamlingay, where it has been seen on the side of a burrow in White Wood, TL25B, on rootplates and banks at Great Heath Plantation, TL25F, and under conifers on a low bank by a ride in Gamlingay Wood, TL25L, and in an area cleared of conifers in the same wood. The only other record is from shaded soil in a leached zone at the base of a coppice stool at Out Wood, TL65M.

First record: Sandy bank, White Wood, Gamlingay, TL25A, H.L.K. Whitehouse, 1973, BBSUK, CGE. The colony by the ride at Gamlingay Wood was first found in 1989 and these were the only two sites known at the start of the recent survey.

Dioicous. Capsules not recorded and rather rare nationally. Vegetative propagation is by axillary branchlets which are always present and often frequent.

### Herzogiella seligeri

All the colonies of this species are on the rotting wood of conifers or broad-leaved trees (including birch and elm). We have recent records from five ancient woods and one more recent plantation on Boulder Clay; in each of these sites we found it on just one or two decaying stumps, logs or branches. It is slightly more widespread at Chippenham Fen, TL66P, where it grows on logs with *Cephalozia bicuspidata* and *Lepidozia reptans* in a long-established colony in Forty Acre Wood.

First record: At foot of a birch tree in a young plantation [south of Bulls Close] between Madingley and Girton, TL46A, P.W. Richards, 1946, BBSUK. Richards (1947a) considered that the plantation could scarcely be more than 30 years old, so the

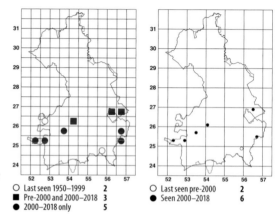

| | |
|---|---|
| ○ Last seen 1950–1999 | 2 |
| ■ Pre-2000 and 2000–2018 | 3 |
| ● 2000–2018 only | 5 |

| | |
|---|---|
| ○ Last seen pre-2000 | 2 |
| ● Seen 2000–2018 | 6 |

plant was clearly a recent colonist. There were no further records from this part of the county until it was found on two logs in Ladybush Close, TL46A, in 2013. It was discovered at Chippenham Fen in 1961 and refound there on several subsequent visits. The only other 20th-century records are from a hawthorn stump at Croxton, TL26K (1964) and the stump of a coppiced hazel in Balsham Wood, TL54Z (1966), where it grew with *Isothecium alopecuroides*.

Autoicous. Capsules always present (100% tetrads). Young setae November, February; capsules swollen, green March (but mixed with dehisced capsules); dehisced but some still full of spores November.

## ENTODONTACEAE

### †Entodon concinnus

An extinct calcicole, not seen in the county since 1973.

First record: Coploe Hill [as 'Corporal Hill'], Great Chesterford, TL44W, F.Y. Brocas, 1874, SWN (as *Isothecium insidiosum*). There were no further records from this site, but it was first collected on the Gog Magog Hills by H.N. Dixon in 1882 (BM). It was found 'sparingly in short turf' on the Roman Road on the Gogs, TL45X, by P.W. Richards in 1932, and it continued to be recorded there until 1971. The other well-known site was an old lawn at Wandlebury, also on the Gogs, TL45W, where it was found 'in undisturbed very short grass' between 1957, when C.C. Townsend described it as

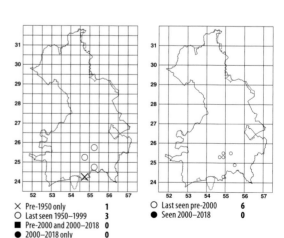

| | |
|---|---|
| ✕ Pre-1950 only | 1 |
| ○ Last seen 1950–1999 | 3 |
| ■ Pre-2000 and 2000–2018 | 0 |
| ● 2000–2018 only | 0 |

| | |
|---|---|
| ○ Last seen pre-2000 | 6 |
| ● Seen 2000–2018 | 0 |

'abundant' (E), and 1973. There are also records from the banks of the Fulbourn-Shelford road near the top of the hill, TL45R (1934), the lawn at Hildersham Hall, TL54P (1951, 1961) and chalk turf on Fleam Dyke, TL55H (1955). The formerly rich calcicole flora in the main area in which it grew has suffered particularly badly. The chalk grassland sites have lost many of their distinctive species to scrub encroachment, and the lawns are now too lush for the rarer species, presumably because of natural succession or horticultural improvement. It is not easy to say why *Entodon* is absent from the Devil's Dyke, although, unlike *Abietinella abietina* and *Thuidium assimile*, it does not extend eastwards into Breckland or to any other East Anglian sites.

Dioicous. Capsules unknown in Britain.

## PYLAISIADELPHACEAE

### *Platygyrium repens*

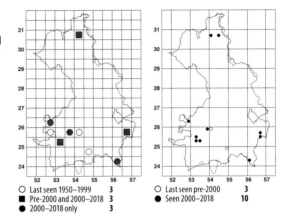

An epiphyte of orchards in the north of the county and of ancient woodland in the south. It is recorded in two orchards in the Wisbech area, TF40D, N, growing on a single apple tree in each. In the ancient woodlands it is found on ash, blackthorn, hazel, oak and willow; it sometimes persists for a while on fallen trunks but we have not seen it on decorticated logs or rotting wood. It is frequent within limited areas in some of our woods but we have found it on only a single tree in others.

First record: On trunks of fallen ash and willow trees in wet woodland, Whittlesford Mill, TL44Z, H.J.B. Birks, 1977, BBSUK, E. This is not ancient woodland, but three of the next four sites in which it was found between 1985 and 1992 were ancient woods. It was first found in an orchard, at Rummers Lane, TF40D, in 1999. *Platygyrium* was first collected in Britain near Oxford in 1945, although it was not recognised until 1962, and it has subsequently appeared to increase in range. Monks Wood in Huntingdonshire was the first locality in which it was seen away from the Oxford area, in 1968, and it is more frequent there than in any of its Cambridgeshire sites.

Dioicous. Capsules not recorded; vegetative reproduction is by axillary branchlets which are produced in quantity at the tips of the shoots.

## CRYPHAEACEAE

### *Cryphaea heteromalla*

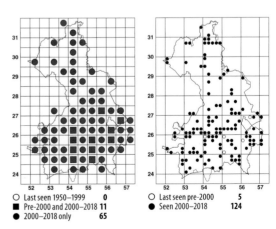

*Cryphaea* is an epiphyte, found on trees and shrubs in sheltered situations in a wide range of woodlands from ancient woods to recent plantations, in scrub, orchards and large gardens and on waterside trees. It is shade-tolerant, and is often found in woodland interiors. Most colonies are small, consisting of one patch or of thinly scattered patches; it is only really frequent in moist scrub such as fen carr or wet willow scrub in disused gravel pits. In orchards Robin Stevenson has found it on 33 (3%) of the 951 apple trees he has examined but none of the 173 pears. Elder (25% of tetrad records), willow (20%) and ash (13%) are the most frequent hosts, with apple (9%) in orchards; there are fewer records from hawthorn (5%), field maple (4%), sycamore (4%) and several other trees and shrubs (Appendix 3).

First record: Moor Barns Grove and Madingley Wood, TL45E, J. Martyn (1729b: 16, as *Sphagnum cauliferum*, and *ramosum, minus hirsutum, capitulis crebris, pilosis, per ramulorum longitudinem adnascentibus*); published by T. Martyn (1763: 24, as *Sphagnum arboreum*). Relhan (1820: 447, as *Neckera heteromalla*) added Eversden Wood, TL35L, White Wood, TL25SW, '&c.' and he gave Skrimshire an unlocalised specimen (WBCH).

Fruiting plants were collected by Henslow at Madingley in 1821 (CGE), Jenyns at Bottisham, TL56, in 1825 (BTH) and G.D. Haviland and J.J. Lister from an apple tree at Histon, TL46SW, in 1881 (CGE). It did not quite disappear from the county at the height of $SO_2$ pollution in the middle of the 20th century. It was recorded at six sites between 1942 and 1984, although sometimes as vegetative shoots and in small quantity, and it apparently persisted on elders in the small, sheltered chalk pit at Underwood Hall, TL65D. Four more sites were added between 1989 and 1996, and it has been found with increasing frequency from 2000 onwards.

Autoicous. Capsules frequent (64% tetrads). Occasional plants consist solely of pioneer stems appressed to the bark but most plants have erect stems and are fertile but the young capsules are obscured by the perichaetial leaves and our observations probably under-estimate their frequency. Capsules very young October, December, March; green, swollen November–April, June; dehisced March, September.

## LEUCODONTACEAE

### Leucodon sciuroides var. sciuroides

In seven tetrads there are recent records of *Leucodon* as an epilith; in the other six it grows as an epiphyte. The largest population is on bricks made from Gault Clay at the top of the outer garden wall in Wimpole Park, TL35F, where it extends for 30 metres; it does not grow on the older, inner wall of red bricks. It also grows in the Park on the Wimpole Stone, a glacial erratic, and Simon Damant found it on the stone roof of the stable block but that has now been covered with lead. The other epilithic populations are on an old brick wall at Graveley, TL26M, on the top of an exposed concrete wall in suburban Cambridge, TL45S, a limestone ledge of the church wall at Gamlingay, TL25L, and on a limestone monument and oolite gravestones

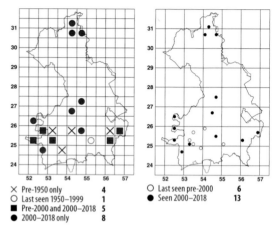

| | |
|---|---|
| ✕ Pre-1950 only | 4 |
| ○ Last seen 1950–1999 | 1 |
| ■ Pre-2000 and 2000–2018 | 5 |
| ● 2000–2018 only | 8 |

| | |
|---|---|
| ○ Last seen pre-2000 | 6 |
| ● Seen 2000–2018 | 13 |

in three more churchyards (listed below). As an epiphyte it grows on an ash at Tadlow Bridge, TL24Y, and on at least nine apple trees in six orchards in the five northerly tetrads on the map.

First record: T. Martyn, 1760–61 (*Martyn letters*, as *Hypnum sciuroides*); reported from Moor Barns Thicket, TL45E, by Martyn (1763: 31). It was accidentally collected by Larbalestier (1879) from a tree at Gamlingay, TL25SW, with the lichen *Hyperphyscia adglutinata*, but the next localised records by bryologists were not made until 1930–33, when it was recorded on ash trees at Caldecott, TL35N, and Babraham Park, TL55A, oak near Stetchworth, TL65NW, and an unidentified tree at Barrington, TL34Z. There is no evidence to suggest that it survived from this period into the late 20th century as an epiphyte, and the recent epiphytic plants are almost certainly recent colonists. However, *Leucodon* almost certainly persisted on monuments in Croxton churchyard, TL25P, from its discovery on a tombstone in 1934 until 1985, when it was rediscovered on a medieval monument (still present 2004). The other 20th-century records were from a wall top at Babraham, TL55A (1951–1964) and the extant sites at Wimpole Park (first found 1998) and Gamlingay, TL25L (1988), Weston Colville, TL65B (1988) and Kirtling, TL65Y (1991) churchyards.

Dioicous. Capsules not recorded and rare nationally. Small deciduous branchlets are frequent at the apex of the older branches.

### Antitrichia curtipendula

A healthy patch of *Antitrichia* some 10 cm across was found in 2006 on a Bramley apple tree (planted in 1976) in a commercial orchard. Its mundane associates were *Amblystegium serpens*, *Brachythecium rutabulum*, *Bryum capillare*, *Dicranoweisia cirrata*, *Grimmia pulvinata*, *Hypnum cupressiforme*, *Orthotrichum affine*, *O. diaphanum* and *Rhynchostegium confertum* (Hodgetts *et al.* 2006). The tree was cut down soon afterwards and an attempt by Robin Stevenson to transplant the *Antitrichia* on another tree was unsuccessful.

First record: White Engine Hall, Leverington Common, TF41F, N.G. Hodgetts, 2006, BBSUK. This was one of the most surprising records in the recent survey. Fossil evidence suggests that *Antitrichia* was abundant during the Late Glacial period (Dickson 1973); although it declined as a result of subsequent vegetation change it was still widespread, although probably rare, in south-east England in the 19th century (Hodgetts *et al.* 2006). It then declined dramatically, probably as a result of air pollution. It has been found at several sites in recent years, including an orchard near Elm in nearby West Norfolk, but only as single patches rather than self-sustaining populations. It has also increased in frequency in the Netherlands, where willow carr is its normal habitat.

Dioicous. Capsules not recorded.

# NECKERACEAE

### †*Neckera crispa*

Known only as an introduction on Carboniferous limestone in rock gardens; last seen in the county in 1973.

First record: Carboniferous limestone recently imported from Westmorland, Cambridge Botanic Garden, TL45N, H.L.K. Whitehouse, 1955 (*Whitehouse diary* 1: 59). *N. crispa* survived on this limestone for at least 18 years; it was last seen in the garden in 1973 (Preston & Whitehouse 1992b). It was also recorded by M.O.H. on shady limestone rocks in his garden in Chaucer Road, Cambridge, TL45N, in 1963 but died out some years later. These rocks had been imported in the inter-war years.

Dioicous. Capsules not recorded.

### *Neckera complanata*

*Neckera complanata* is an epiphyte, growing on the exposed roots and bases of trees and on coppice stools; it occasionally ascends to 1 m above ground level but very rarely exceeds this. It is a plant of 'ancient countryside', found inside ancient woods or on their boundary banks, in the older recent woods, along hedgerows and trackways and on the banks of streams and ditches (including parish boundary ditches). The most recent woods in which it grows are normally adjacent to older sites, such as a wooded chalk pit alongside Madingley Wood, TL45E, and another alongside an old track at Callow Bank, Soham, TL57V. Ash is the most frequent host (50% of tetrad records), followed by field maple (24%), elm (6%) and a few other species, both native

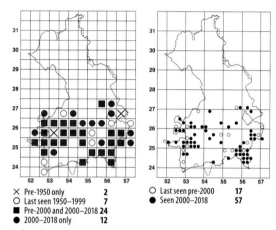

| | |
|---|---|
| ✕ Pre-1950 only | **2** |
| ○ Last seen 1950–1999 | **7** |
| ■ Pre-2000 and 2000–2018 | **24** |
| ● 2000–2018 only | **12** |

| | |
|---|---|
| ○ Last seen pre-2000 | **17** |
| ● Seen 2000–2018 | **57** |

and introduced (Appendix 3). Unusual occurrences include plants growing in dense masses on prostrate laburnum trunks in Crishall Grange Plantation, TL44L, and a single plant well above ground level on a birch in wet birch/alder wood at Chippenham Fen, TL66P. There are six non-epiphytic records, on the Wimpole Stone (a glacial erratic), TL35F, a concrete drainpipe by a stream at Childerley Hall, TL36K, Carboniferous limestone in Cambridge Botanic Garden, TL45N (on which it was introduced from Westmorland), an oolite gravestone (probably 18th century in date) in Milton churchyard, TL46W, streamside stonework at Swaffham Prior House, TL56R, and, the oddest record, on the decaying body of an ancient lorry in Borley Wood, TL54U.

First record: T. Martyn, 1760–61 (*Martyn letters*, as *Hypnum complanatum*) and Martyn (1763: 25). There are undated specimens in Skrimshire's herbarium (WBCH) collected by Hemsted in Newmarket, TL66, and by Relhan. The records collected for the 1964 flora are in general similar to ours. It was, however, recorded in chalk grassland on both Fleam Dyke ('in small quantity') and Devil's Dyke (one stem found in TL66SW in 1960, although it has often been found at the wooded end of the Dyke in TL65P). There are few sites from which it appears to have been lost, the most notable being Lime Kiln Close, TL45Y, where it was regularly recorded until 1970.

Dioicous. Capsules recorded recently on just one plant, in Hayley Wood, TL25W (2% tetrads), which had old capsules and capsules just starting to swell in November; there are three earlier records of fruiting plants. Vegetative reproduction is by flagelliform branches, which are frequent.

### *Homalia trichomanoides*

*Homalia*, like *Neckera complanata*, grows as an epiphyte on exposed tree roots, tree bases and coppice stools, and sometimes extends onto the adjacent soil. It is usually found on ash (91% of tetrad records) but there are single records from beech, elm, field maple, oak, sycamore and willow. It is more closely associated with ancient woodland than *Neckera* (Preston & Hill 2016), but it is also found in older recent woods and in one or two lanes and wooded chalk pits. It favours slightly moister and shadier places than

*Neckera*, often growing by streams or ditches within woodland; when the two species grow on the same tree, *Homalia* tends to grow below *Neckera* and in more shaded recesses. This niche also allows it to evade competition from the larger pleurocarps on the lower trunks of ash, such as *Isothecium alopecuroides* and *Thamnobryum alopecurum*. There is one record from the concrete of a weir below Decoy Pond, Arrington, TL35G.

First record: White Wood near Gamlingay, TL25SW, Relhan (1793: 10, as *Hypnum complanatum β*). Relhan (1820: 455, as *Hypnum trichomanoides*) adds Wood Ditton, TL65NE. There are early specimens of fruiting plants collected by Hemsted from Newmarket (WBCH), Henslow from Madingley in 1821 (CGE) and Jenyns at Bottisham, TL56, in 1824

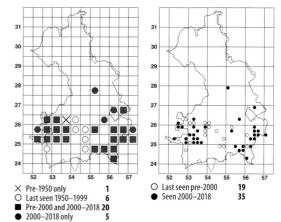

| | |
|---|---|
| × Pre-1950 only | 1 |
| ○ Last seen 1950–1999 | 6 |
| ■ Pre-2000 and 2000–2018 | 20 |
| ● 2000–2018 only | 5 |

| | |
|---|---|
| ○ Last seen pre-2000 | 19 |
| ● Seen 2000–2018 | 35 |

(BTH). Although most of the 20th-century records are from woodland, it was also recorded from a *Salix triandra* thicket near Lord's Bridge Station, TL35X, and from Carboniferous limestone in the Botanic Garden in Cambridge, TL45N, but only immediately after its introduction in 1955, and in a garden at Chaucer Road, TL45N, in 1965. The absence of any recent records from the Cambridge area, except in Madingley Wood, TL35Z, is noteworthy.

Autoicous. Capsules frequent (44% tetrads), young setae November; capsules swollen, green turning brown March; brown February, March; freshly dehisced February, March.

## Thamnobryum alopecurum

*Thamnobryum*, our most robust terrestrial pleurocarp, is mainly a plant of the woodland floor. It is found in all sorts of woodland and scrub including primary woodland, ancient or recent secondary woodland (including woods over ridge and furrow), plantations, in disused chalk, clay and gravel pits and in scrub on chalk earthworks. It extends (as rather small plants) onto the lowest parts of trees with base-rich bark, especially ash and field maple. It is often abundant in well-drained sites but, although frequent by running water, it is not very tolerant of prolonged flooding and in a few places which are particularly wet (and in at least one which is particularly acidic) it is confined to tree bases. It is much less frequent outside woods but

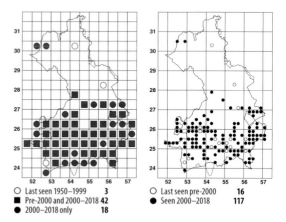

| | |
|---|---|
| ○ Last seen 1950–1999 | 3 |
| ■ Pre-2000 and 2000–2018 | 42 |
| ● 2000–2018 only | 18 |

| | |
|---|---|
| ○ Last seen pre-2000 | 16 |
| ● Seen 2000–2018 | 117 |

it is found along green lanes, by ditches, streams and rivers and in old gardens. We have found it in 11% of churchyards visited, where it grows on banks, in shaded turf or under trees. With the exception of Thorney Abbey, TF20X, all the churchyards lie within the general range of the species; most of the isolated northern records, unlike those of the ecologically similar *Plagiomnium undulatum*, are from scraps of woodland rather than churchyards. There are a few records from the base of brick walls, shaded concrete and stonework, and oolitic limestone and sandstone rocks in gardens.

First record: Madingley, TL35/45, W. Vernon, c. 1696 (Vernon's annotated Ray 1696: 32, as *Muscus dendroides sylvarum erectus, ramulis Kali aemulis, radice repente*). It was reported from Moor Barns Thicket, TL45E, by T. Martyn (1763: 31, as *Hypnum alopecurum*). There is a splendid herbarium sheet of fruiting plants collected by Henslow at Madingley in 1826 (CGE), and H.E. Lowe gathered fruiting plants by the side of Madingley Bath in 1837 (CGE, WARMS). There is no evidence for any marked change in frequency in the 20th century.

Dioicous. Capsules rare (7% tetrads), just swelling November; swollen, green December; brown February; just dehiscing February–April. Although *Thamnobryum* lacks specialised vegetative propagules, its ability to grow as loose balls when disturbed is well known. We have also seen badger setts where it has clearly been used for bedding and this may be another way in which it is dispersed over short distances.

## LEMBOPHYLLACEAE

### *Isothecium myosuroides* var. *myosuroides*

*Isothecium myosuroides* grows as an epiphyte in two rather different situations. In ancient woods, in the older recent woods and occasionally in parkland it grows at the base of trees or on old coppice stools. There are a few records from rotting logs and decaying oak stumps in such woodland, where its populations are presumably long-established. It is, however, much less frequent than *I. alopecuroides*, presumably because it is rather more calcifuge than that species. Alternatively, it can be found growing higher up the trunks of trees, often as single patches, particularly in orchards but also on waterside willows and in hawthorn scrub. In orchards Robin Stevenson has found it on 20 (2%) of the 951 apples he has surveyed and three (2%)

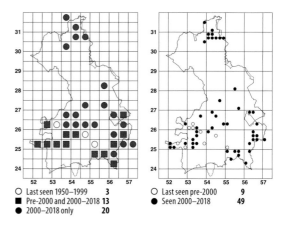

| | |
|---|---|
| ○ Last seen 1950–1999 | **3** |
| ■ Pre-2000 and 2000–2018 | **13** |
| ● 2000–2018 only | **20** |

| | |
|---|---|
| ○ Last seen pre-2000 | **9** |
| ● Seen 2000–2018 | **49** |

of the 173 pears – though rare, it is much more frequent than *I. alopecuroides* in such sites. These plants appear to be recent colonists, and they account for the scattered records in the centre of the county and the concentration south of Wisbech. There are a few records which cannot be neatly slotted into these categories, such as that from the canopy of a 150–160 year-old oak felled during coppicing at Hardwick Wood, TL35N, in 2007. When all records are aggregated, apple (29% of tetrad records) and ash (24%) are the most frequent hosts, followed by oak (13%), hawthorn (7%), willow (7%) and the species listed in Appendix 3.

First record: Oak and hazel roots, Cantley Park Wood near Great Abington, TL54NW, E.W. Jones, 1933 (*Richards file*). All the authors from Relhan (1785: 417) to Evans (1911) list *I. myosuroides* but none makes any mention of *I. alopecuroides* (see the latter for the history of confusion between the two species). Jones found both species in 1933–34, and Proctor (1956) and Whitehouse (1964) realised that *I. myosuroides* was the less frequent species in the county's woodlands.

Dioicous. Capsules rare (8% tetrads), swollen, green November; green, brown and freshly dehisced February.

### *Isothecium alopecuroides*

*Isothecium alopecuroides* grows on coppice stools and on the bases of mature trees. It occurs in primary woodland, secondary woodland (including sites over ridge and furrow) and a few plantations; about half of its sites are regarded as ancient woods (Preston & Hill 2016). Other sites include the wooded south end of the Devil's Dyke, TL65P, 66F, some drier areas of fen carr and woodland at Wicken Fen, TL56P, 57Q, and Chippenham Fen, TL66J, P, and a few wooded chalk pits and orchards. The records in the north of the county are from both woods and orchards. Ash is much the most frequent host (59% of tetrad records) followed by apple (8%), field maple (8%), willow (6%) and the species listed in Appendix 3. In orchards, Robin Stevenson found it on only four of the 951 apples he has surveyed, and

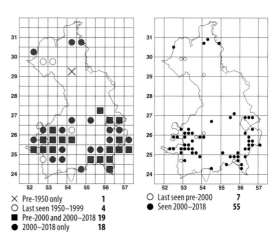

| | |
|---|---|
| ✕ Pre-1950 only | **1** |
| ○ Last seen 1950–1999 | **4** |
| ■ Pre-2000 and 2000–2018 | **19** |
| ● 2000–2018 only | **18** |

| | |
|---|---|
| ○ Last seen pre-2000 | **7** |
| ● Seen 2000–2018 | **55** |

on no more than a single tree in any one orchard, and on none of the 173 pears.

First record: J. Martyn (1729b: 15, as *Hypnum repens, triangularibus angustis foliis, ramulis subrotundis*); published by T. Martyn (1763: 25, as *Hypnum myosuroides β*). Relhan (1785: 417) confused this with *Isothecium myosuroides* (as *Hypnum myosuroides*) and J. Hemsted's specimen (WBCH), collected at Newmarket, TL66, in 1796, is also labelled *Hypnum myosuroides*. Henslow collected it at Madingley, TL35/45, in 1821 (CGE) and named it correctly (as *Hypnum curvatum*), although for some reason he did not mark it as a Cambridgeshire species in his checklists (Henslow 1829, 1835). The undergraduate A.W. Graveson was the next person to recognise the species in the county, when he found fruiting plants in Kingston Wood, TL35SW, in 1914, and noted in his diary that 'it does not appear to have been recorded from Cambridgeshire, but there does not seem much doubt of its identity'. However he kept the record to himself and the first record known to Proctor (1956) and Whitehouse (1964) was made by P.W. Richards in Over Wood, TL64J, in 1932 (NMW). There is little evidence for any change in its frequency since then although one of its few Fenland sites, Doddington Wood, TL49A, was grubbed up soon after it was recorded there in 1946.

Dioicous. Capsules occasional (31% tetrads), dehiscing February, March.

## ANOMODONTACEAE

### Anomodon viticulosus

*Anomodon* grows as an epiphyte on the exposed roots or bases of trees or on coppice stools in ancient woods, parkland, by streams, ditches and wooded moats and alongside old trackways. A good way to find it is to make a point of examining the oldest trees, as it is normally found on the base of very large coppice stools or old pollards. This means that several of its sites are on woodland boundary banks or ditches along parish boundaries, but it can also grow in woodland interiors. It is most frequent on ash (59% of tetrad records) and field maple (19%) and there are only single records from elder, elm, horse chestnut, lime, sycamore and willow (*Salix alba* or *S.* × *fragilis*). In many sites we have seen it on only a single tree. *Neckera complanata* is a characteristic associate; others include *Metzgeria*

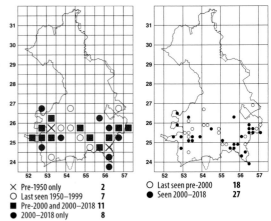

| | |
|---|---|
| ✕ Pre-1950 only | 2 |
| ○ Last seen 1950–1999 | 7 |
| ■ Pre-2000 and 2000–2018 | 11 |
| ● 2000–2018 only | 8 |

| | |
|---|---|
| ○ Last seen pre-2000 | 18 |
| ● Seen 2000–2018 | 27 |

*furcata, Porella platyphylla, Homalia trichomanoides, Homalothecium sericeum, Isothecium alopecuroides* and *Thamnobryum alopecurum*. There are also records from the concrete of a bridge at Lord's Bridge, TL35W, and of a single clump on chalky ground by a population on ash trees at the wooded end of the Devil's Dyke, TL65P. It survives on the Carboniferous limestone on which it was introduced to Cambridge Botanic Garden, TL45N, in 1957.

First record: J. Martyn (1729b: 15, as *Hypnum repens trichoides, arboreum, majus, capitulis* and *surculis erectis, minus ramosis*; published by T. Martyn 1763: 25, as *Hypnum viticulosum*). Hemsted collected it at Newmarket, TL66, in 1796 (WBCH, as *Neckera viticulosa*), and F.Y. Brocas found it 'on willows near and under water by the farm between Hildersham and Linton very fine and large', TL54 (SWN). The map suggests a long-term decline. It was recorded on the ground in the beechwood on Wort's Causeway, TL45X, on many occasions from 1949 onwards and Proctor (1956) describes it as 'very locally a conspicuous constituent of the ground flora' but it was only present in 'small quantity' in 1965 (Hill 1967) and last seen there in 1971. So many of the current plants grow on old trees, and the species appears to have so little colonising ability, that it is difficult to imagine anything other than a continuing slow decline. One or two of our records are of colonies on recently dead trees which have probably been lost by now, although on a stream bank at Papworth St Agnes, TL26S, in 2007 the very large elm on which it had grown was dead but suckering and the plant survived on its exposed roots and silty stems. One stronghold for the species is Wimpole Park and the nearby Eversden Wood, TL35F, K, L.

Dioicous. Capsules not recorded recently. The specimen from Hemsted illustrated in *English Botany* (Smith 1795) is fruiting and, although unlocalised, it may well have come from the Newmarket area. There is a fine fruiting specimen in Henslow's herbarium, supposedly collected at Madingley in 1824 (CGE), but it is labelled *Daltonia heteromalla* (i.e. *Cryphaea heteromalla*) and perhaps the label has become misplaced.

# Summary

Cambridgeshire (vice-county 29) is a lowland county with subdued topography; it has a maximum altitude of 128 m and almost half its area is below 5 m. It lies in an area of eastern England characterised by low rainfall, warm summers and moderately (and increasingly) warm winters. Woodland cover has been low for many centuries, and most of the county's land is now devoted to intensive arable farming. Population density is low, but increasing.

The first bryophyte records from the county were published in 1660. For the next 300 years fieldwork was concentrated around the university town of Cambridge. William Vernon made notable early records in the 1690s and both John Martyn and Thomas Martyn added species in the 18th century. There were more substantial contributions in the late 18th and early 19th centuries by Richard Relhan and in the 1820s and 1830s by John Stevens Henslow and his associates. After a lull in the Victorian period, and a brief revival before the First World War, systematic recording was started by the undergraduate Paul Richards in 1927 and has continued to the present day. The only attempts to survey the entire county, as opposed to sites of particular interest, were made by Harold Whitehouse (with the help of Philip Bourne) in the early 1960s and by us and our colleagues between 2000 and 2018.

There are 341 species recorded from the county, comprising one extinct hornwort, 53 liverworts (of which 15 have not been seen in the 2000–18 survey) and 287 mosses (41 not seen recently). Since 2000 species have been added to the county flora at an average rate of 1.4 species per annum. An analysis of the habitat preferences of the county's species shows that the most widespread groups are plants with very broad habitat preferences, or those which grow in arable or ruderal sites or are found in the built environment. Epiphytes are slightly less frequent and there are numerous but rarer species of chalkland habitats, acidic substrates, woodlands, fens and aquatic or waterside habitats. Outside Britain our species generally have wide geographical ranges in the Boreo-temperate, Temperate and Southern-temperate zones. There are very few Boreal and very few Oceanic species.

Although only the most conspicuous bryophytes were recorded in the 17th and 18th centuries, there are sufficient records to show that parliamentary enclosure followed by agricultural improvement was as destructive to bryophytes as it is known to have been to the vascular plant flora. Both groups show a peak of extinctions in the first half of the 19th century. The drainage of the calcareous fens ('moors') near Cambridge and of the acidic bogs at Gamlingay eliminated many bryophyte species.

In assessing changes in the bryophyte flora since 1930, we have had to take into account marked changes in the popularity of different bryophyte habitats. Woodland and chalkland habitats have been recorded throughout the period. We have recently visited as wide a range of sites as possible whereas formerly a few well-known places were visited repeatedly. Arable fields were popular in the early 1960s and the early 2000s. It is only since the 1980s that churchyards have been surveyed, except for one or two favourites near Cambridge. An analysis of the records, taking these changes into account, shows that the chalkland species have declined as there are now fewer active quarries than there were, and many small chalk pits have been filled in or become overgrown. Epiphytes have increased greatly since the 1980s in response to decreasing $SO_2$ pollution, whereas some calcifuges have declined. The area of orchards in the county has decreased massively since 1950 but, paradoxically, their interest has increased as growers no longer attempt to eliminate epiphytic bryophytes and lichens from the tree bark. Most woodland bryophyte species have remained relatively stable.

In addition to these medium- and long-term trends, the recent records are sufficiently detailed to reveal a flux of short-term colonists in the 20th and early 21st centuries. The dynamic nature of the flora is particularly apparent for the calcifuge species, as their habitats are so restricted, and for the newly colonising epiphytes, but commoner bryophyte species also have casual populations though they are less easy to detect. The dynamic nature of the flora is one explanation for the continuing discovery of species in the county after over 350 years of bryophyte recording, and one reason to conclude that the exploration of the bryophyte flora will continue to be of interest to bryologists in the years to come.

# Excluded species

## Hornworts

**Anthoceros agrestis** was listed by Crompton & Whitehouse (1983). They interpreted Henslow's *A. punctatus* as that species, but it must be treated as *A. punctatus sens. lat.* for the reasons explained in the text.

## Liverworts

**Chiloscyphus polyanthos** records are believed to be errors, based on misidentifications of *C. pallescens* (see Appendix 2).

**Jungermannia sphaerocephala** was recorded by Skrimshire from 'Wisbeach, on the Brinks of Ponds' (Relhan 1802: 438–439, 1820: 467); its identity is unknown.

**Nardia scalaris** was recorded from a wet slope in a rough meadow, with *Pseudephemerum nitidum*, at Mill Hill, Gamlingay, TL233513, by S.D. Atkins *et al.*, 1977, on a bryological excursion led by H.L.K. Whitehouse. However, it was never submitted as a new vice-county record and must therefore be regarded as unconfirmed. By 1983 the site had been drained and ploughed.

**Reboulia hemisphaerica** was reported by Relhan from wet places on Sawston Moor, Hinton Moor and Fulbourn Moor (1788: 18, as *Marchantia hemisphaerica*; 1802: 442). It is not a plant of permanently wet places and the records may have been based on *Preissia quadrata* or some other thallose liverwort, but there are no vouchers.

**Saccogyna viticulosa** is a western liverwort and Relhan's record from Chevely Park Lane (1802: 438, as *Jungermannia viticulosa*) must be an error. The species was confused with *Chiloscyphus* spp. by early bryologists but Relhan's report was from the branches of young trees, so he must have made some other error.

**Scapania aspera** was collected by H.L.K. Whitehouse (CGE, det. D.G. Long as a 'very poor stunted form') from Carboniferous limestone rocks soon after they were imported to Cambridge University Botanic Garden from Westmorland in 1957, but it did not persist (Preston & Whitehouse 1992b).

**Solenostoma gracillimum** was recorded from Cherry Hinton by Relhan (1820: 468, as *Jungermannia gracillima*) but it is a calcifuge and his record presumably refers to *Leiocolea turbinata*, as noted in the account of that species.

## Mosses

**Anomobryum julaceum** is a northern and western species. Relhan's unlocalised record (1820: 450, as *Bryum julaceum*) must have been an error, presumably for *Bryum argenteum* with which it was sometimes confused (Braithwaite 1887–1905).

**Campylopus brevipilus** was recorded as one of the calcifuge colonists of Wicken Fen in the 1970s, initially from the Godwin Plots by S.M. Walters and H.L.K. Whitehouse in 1974, and from just one of these plots (2C) in A.C. Leslie's detailed survey later that year, and finally in fen carr south of Cross Dyke by H.J.B. Birks in 1975. It was published in the normal way as a new vice-county record (Crundwell 1976) but we can find no voucher in BBSUK, CGE, E or NMW, and therefore regard the records as doubtful.

**Dicranella rufescens** was Whitehouse's (1964: 288) initial identification of *D. staphylina*. He later realised that it was a different, and hitherto unknown, species.

**Dicranum majus** is known only from Relhan's record (1820: 439) from Eversden Wood, which was accepted by Proctor (1956) and Whitehouse (1964). It is a frequent and conspicuous species of acidic woods in northern and western Britain and it has been recorded since 1950 in such woods in Bedfordshire, Norfolk and Suffolk. The Cambridgeshire record may therefore be correct, especially as other calcifuges such as *Calypogeia fissa*, *Fissidens bryoides* and *Polytrichastrum formosum* have been found there subsequently. However, in the absence of a voucher we suspect a misidentification.

**Philonotis calcarea** was recorded for vc 29 in Duncan's *Census catalogue* (1926) on the basis of information supplied by W. Watson, but the source of the record has never been discovered and we assume that it is erroneous.

**Sciuro-hypnum plumosum** is a plant of swiftly flowing streams in northern and western Britain; Relhan's records (1820: 459, as *Hypnum plumosum*) from Eversden Wood and Madingley Wood must have been errors.

**Sphagnum contortum** was reported in *Transactions of the British Bryological Society* 1: 118 (1948) on the basis of material collected by C.E. Moss at Gamlingay in 1910 and determined by A. Thompson. By the time of Proctor's account (1956) it was thought to be *S. inundatum* (see below). The specimen in NMW has recently been redetermined by M.O.H. as *S. denticulatum*.

**Sphagnum cuspidatum** was reported by Relhan (1820: 433) from Gamlingay Bogs but his record has to be discounted as his concept was broad and would have included plants now recognised as other species, including *S. fallax*. Proctor (1956) and Whitehouse (1964) misinterpret as *S. cuspidatum* a record by P.W. Richards at Heath Wood, Gamlingay (1930) which is indeed *S. fallax* (see Preston & Hill 2007).

**Sphagnum inundatum** was reported from Cambridgeshire by Proctor (1956) on the basis of a specimen collected at Gamlingay by C.E. Moss in 1910; Whitehouse (1964) also cited this as the only record. The specimen known to Richards and presumably Proctor was supposedly in CGE (*Richards file*, where the specimen appears as *S. contortum*) but the only specimen we have located which matches this description is in NMW (as *S. contortum*) and it has been redetermined as *S. denticulatum* by M.O.H.

**Tortella flavovirens** was the name applied to *T. inclinata* from the Devil's Dyke by Rhodes (1911); the identification was corrected by Proctor (1956).

**Tortula cuneifolia** cannot be the plant reported by Relhan as *Bryum murale* β (1785: 403, 1802: 423) and later as *Tortula cuneifolia* (1820: 444), as the true *T. cuneifolia* is a rare and predominantly coastal plant.

**Trichostomum tenuirostre** was reported from the Cambridge Botanic Garden by Whitehouse (1974) but was later reidentified as *Didymodon umbrosus* when that species was recognised as a member of the British flora (Crundwell & Whitehouse 1978).

**Warnstorfia fluitans** was reported from several sites in the 19th and early 20th centuries. Proctor (1956) plausibly suggests that the records may refer to *Drepanocladus aduncus* or other species. Specimens named, or tentatively named, '*Hypnum fluitans*' are *Drepanocladus aduncus* (R. Relhan, WBCH, cf. Proctor 1956; Parson Drove, 1828, M.J. Berkeley, CGE) and *Leptodictyum riparium* (Wisbech, 1797, W. Skrimshire, WBCH).

# Notes on first records

We have reviewed the first records of Cambridgeshire bryophytes while preparing this flora. We have chosen to discuss some of the decisions we have made in this Appendix rather than as digressions in the main text.

## Liverworts

***Cephaloziella divaricata*** E.W. Jones thought that plants he had collected at Great Heath Plantation, Gamlingay, TL25F, in 1934 (CGE) were probably this species but he could not be certain because of the 'miserable' condition of the material. Whitehouse (1964) also thought that a sterile and thus indeterminable *Cephaloziella* which he found on raw humus at the Beechwood, Gog Magog Hills, TL45X, in 1955 was possibly this.

***Chiloscyphus pallescens*** Richards' 1939 record of *C. polyanthos* from Little Widgham Wood (*Richards file*) is the first localised record of a *Chiloscyphus* in the county; the source of an earlier and unlocalised record of *C. polyanthos* (Wilson 1930) is unknown. There are no confirmed records of *C. polyanthos*, and we have followed Whitehouse (1964) in assuming that all Cambridgeshire records relate to *C. pallescens*. In 2001 plants from Chippenham which appeared to conform vegetatively to *C. polyanthos* using Paton's (1999) criteria were submitted to T.H. Blackstock who was able to demonstrate that they were *C. pallescens* by excavating aged perianths below the recent vegetative growth.

***Fossombronia pusilla*** Although Relhan's (1786) record of *Jungermannia pusilla* from 'Gamlingay Heath, near the Town' is traditionally ascribed to this species, it could have been *F. wondraczekii*. Although vegetative *Fossombronia* plants (unidentifiable to species) were found in Gamlingay Wood in 1945, the presence of *F. pusilla* in the county was not confirmed until H.L.K. Whitehouse found fruiting material there in 1957 and 1960 (*Whitehouse file*).

***Frullania tamarisci*** Relhan's (1785) record 'On the Ground, and Trunks of Trees' was rejected by Proctor (1956) and W. Skrimshire's comments on his *Frullania* specimens (WBCH) certainly show that he had problems distinguishing *F. dilatata* from *F. tamarisci*, although the differences are clear to modern bryologists.

***Lunularia cruciata*** Skrimshire's specimen of *Lunularia cruciata*, collected in 1795 (WBCH, as *Marchantia cruciata*) and cited as the first record by Proctor (1956) and Whitehouse (1964) is actually *Pellia* cf. *endiviifolia*. The actual specimen comes from Walsoken Marsh (vc 28) although Skrimshire added that the plant was frequent by the sides of ditches about Wisbech. Relhan's record from Sawston Moor (1802: 442) is also doubtful as there was much confusion between *Lunularia* and other thallose liverworts in the early 19th century. Hooker (1833) does not have an entry for *Lunularia*, and describes its lunate gemmae cups under *Marchantia hemisphaerica*.

***Marchantia polymorpha*** **subsp.** ***ruderalis*** Ray's record (1660: 86) of 'Lichen … *Liverwort, or common ground Liverwort. In humidis umbrosis* [In moist shady places]' was not identified to species by Oswald & Preston (2011) and it was perhaps based on more than one thallose liverwort, almost certainly including *M. polymorpha*. Our work for this bryophyte flora has thrown doubt on the suggestion that it might also have included *Lunularia cruciata*. '*Hepatica stellata* … *Star headed Liverwort. On the north side of Peterhouse chappel abundantly, observed by M*ʳ *Dent*', reported three years later (Ray 1663), must have been the female plant of *Marchantia polymorpha*. '*Hepatica umbellata* … *Small ground Liverwort with round heads. On the moors.*', also listed by Ray (1663), was probably the male plant, unless it was a misidentification of *Preissia quadrata*. Ray (1690: 20) later recorded it, as *Lichen petraeus umbellatus*, from Teversham Moor.

***Pellia epiphylla*** In the absence of a voucher we cannot rule out the possibility that Relhan's (1793) plant from Gamlingay Bogs was *P. neesiana* rather than *P. epiphylla*, but the recent records of *P. epiphylla* from Great Heath Plantation, Gamlingay, TL25F, suggest that it was this species.

***Ptilidium pulcherrimum*** Proctor's date for the first record, 1939, is an error (Whitehouse 1958).

***Riccia cavernosa*** Skrimshire's specimen 'Gathered by the side of some silt-pits, in a field opposite the Black-Boy-Low, Walsoken 1796' (WBCH) has hitherto been regarded as the first record but it was almost certainly collected in West Norfolk. (We are grateful to Charles Nelson for advice on this point.)

**Riccia glauca** Relhan (1786: 21) recorded *Riccia glauca* from the corn fields 'on the right, and left hand side of the Road to Histon, near the first Pond', TL46SW. This might have been either *R. glauca* or *R. sorocarpa*, which were not distinguished at that time. Interestingly, *Lythrum hyssopifolia* also grew in this area, 'In the Ditches on the Right Hand Side of the Road to Histon, near the first Pond' (Relhan 1802: 182). Relhan (1802: 443) also recorded *R. glauca* from Barnwell gravel pit, TL45U. The specimen named *Riccia glauca* by Skrimshire (WBCH) and identified as *R. sorocarpa* by Crompton & Nelson (2000) is *R. cavernosa*.

**Sphaerocarpos michelii** We give Relhan's record of *Sphaerocarpus terrestris* as the first record, although *S. texanus* was not separated from *S. michelii* in Relhan's day and there is no voucher.

### Mosses

**Abietinella abietina** was listed, as *Hypnum abietinus* [*sic*], by Thomas Martyn amongst the species he had seen in the winter of 1760–61 (*Martyn letters*). However, it is the only bryophyte in the list which he did not include subsequently in *Plantae Cantabrigienses* (Martyn 1763) so it seems best to disregard the record.

**Acaulon muticum** The record from Skrimshire's herbarium (WBCH) cited by Proctor (1956) and Whitehouse (1964) appears to be based on his specimen of *Phascum cuspidatum*.

**Aulacomnium androgynum** Henslow (1829, 1835) recorded *A. androgynum* (as *Bryum androgynum*) from Cambridgeshire but in error for *A. palustre*, which he did not list. The error is demonstrated by the note '*Bryum androgynum*' against *Bryum palustre* (i.e. *Aulacomnium palustre*) in his annotated copy of Relhan (1820: 449). Rhodes (1911) detected the error and knew of no reliable record of *A. androgynum* from the county.

**Barbula convoluta** *Muscus minimus pallidus, foliis angustissimis acutis, corniculatis tenuissimis* was recorded from Gamlingay by Vernon in his annotated copy of Ray (1696: 30). This species is usually identified as *Barbula convoluta* but Vernon's plant might have been one of any number of small acrocarpous mosses.

**Brachytheciastrum velutinum** Proctor (1956) and Whitehouse (1964) give T. Martyn (1763: 25, as *Hypnum velutinum*) as the first county record but we have discounted this as the superficially similar *Rhynchostegium confertum* was not described until 1801. Relhan (1785: 416, 1802: 437, 1820: 458) did not recognise *R. confertum*, even in his later editions, so his records are doubtful for the same reason.

**Brachythecium rutabulum** Ray (1660: 101) listed *Muscus terrestris vulgaris* Dod. Lob. Ger. as a Cambridgeshire plant, and this was identified as *Hypnum rutabulum* by T. Martyn (1763: 25) following the synonymy of Dillenius (1741: 295–297) and Linnaeus (1753: 1124). Proctor (1956) tentatively follows Martyn, and Whitehouse (1964) does so unequivocally. However, it is clear that Ray's Cambridgeshire plant cannot be equated to a single modern species (Oswald & Preston 2011).

**Bryum algovicum** The 1829 specimen from Shelford Common was not identified as this species until 2017. Specimens in E collected in 1957 by C.C. Townsend and determined by E.V. Watson from sandy soil and damp sand at Red Lodge Gravel Pits are ascribed to Cambridgeshire but were not published as a new vice-county record at the time or reported to Harold Whitehouse. The locality as usually understood is just over the border in West Suffolk, vc 26, so we think that Townsend's material was only doubtfully collected in Cambridgeshire. The species has been recorded in this area, TL66Z, from both sides of the county boundary since 2000.

**Bryum archangelicum** Recorded from districts 4 (Lower Greensand of Gamlingay) and 6 (blown sand over chalk, as at Chippenham and Kennett) by R.S. Adamson in Evans (1913). In the absence of vouchers, it seems best to treat these records as doubtful.

**Bryum intermedium** Recorded by R.S. Adamson in Evans (1913), from district 2 (the Oxford, Ampthill, Kimmeridge and Gault Clays). As with *B. archangelicum*, we prefer to treat the record as dubious in the absence of a voucher.

**Bryum violaceum** The first record is given by Whitehouse (1964) as P.J. Bourne and H.L.K. Whitehouse 1960, but these are separate collections. Bourne's specimen was collected on 8 November 1960 and Whitehouse's, from an arable field at Cherry Hinton, TL45X, on 20 November 1960 (CGE).

**Campylopus introflexus** Crompton & Whitehouse (1983) attribute the first record to J.M. Lock and J.H. Dickson, 1965, but the contemporary published records (*Transactions of the British Bryological Society* 5: 193, 1966; Whitehouse 1966b) attribute it to Lock alone.

**Dicranella schreberiana** Whitehouse (1964) attributes the first record jointly to B. Reeve and himself, dating both records as 1959, but in his manuscript records he dates Reeve's record as ?9/10.1959 and his own (from The Cringles, Fulbourn) as 13.12.1959.

**Dicranella staphylina** Whitehouse (1964) attributes the first record of 'Dicranella rufescens' to P.J. Bourne and H.L.K. Whitehouse, 1960, but these are in fact separate records. In his manuscript records Whitehouse dates Bourne's record as 8.11.1960 and his own (from Papworth St Agnes, TL263650) as 21.12.1960 (see also Whitehouse 1969). Whitehouse (1969) published the Papworth record in the list of vice-county records accompanying his description of the species.

**Didymodon fallax** The specimen of Dicranella varia with D. fallax admixed (WARMS) which is cited in the text as the first record of this species is labelled by Lowe as collected at Hinton in March 1827. He (unusually) omits his name as collector but he is nevertheless given as the collector on the 20th-century packet. However, Lowe was not admitted to Trinity College until 1832 and he clearly obtained his specimen from Henslow. There is a mounted sheet of Dicranum varium collected by Henslow at Hinton on 13 March 1827 (CGE), and further loose material labelled as duplicate in a packet from which Lowe presumably took his specimen.

**Didymodon sinuosus** Richards' specimen from Grantchester (NMW) is dated April 1927, before he took up residence in Cambridge, but he recorded the date as 1929 in Richards file and that date is almost certainly correct. Richards also collected Schistidium crassipilum at Grantchester church in April 1929.

**Didymodon vinealis** Proctor (1956) cited a Skrimshire specimen from walls at Wisbech, 1797 (WBCH), as the first record, and Whitehouse (1964) followed this, but we can find no such specimen in the collection.

**Drepanocladus aduncus** Early records are too unreliable to be cited as first records in the absence of specimens. Relhan's Hypnum aduncum (1785: 412) could be correctly identified but an unlocalised Relhan specimen (WBCH) of H. aduncum is Scorpidium cossonii, and Henslow's Hypnum aduncum specimens (CGE) are Scorpidium revolvens. Relhan's Hypnum fluitans from a small pond in a pasture opposite Great Founders Closes, Cambridge (1786: 20) might have been D. aduncus, rather than D. fluitans, as an unlocalised Relhan specimen of H. fluitans (WBCH) is D. aduncus.

**Fissidens bryoides** var. **bryoides** This was recorded by W. Vernon in his annotated Ray (1696), by T. Martyn (1763) and by several subsequent bryologists but it was not until the early 1940s that Cambridgeshire bryologists reliably distinguished F. bryoides, F. incurvus and F. viridulus. Early specimens collected as Dicranum bryoides by Henslow (1821, CGE) and Garnons (1825, SWN) and as Fissidens bryoides by Haviland and Lister (1881, CGE) are F. incurvus.

**Fissidens viridulus** The first record accepted by Proctor (1956), Comberton etc., E.W. Jones and P.W. Richards, 1932–34, is supported by two specimens in NMW collected in February 1934, one gathered by Jones from a ditch at the side of a field between Comberton and Toft and the other by Richards from a ditch at Comberton, perhaps the same site. Both are F. incurvus. Whitehouse rather surprisingly regarded Henslow's (1829) Dicranum bryoides var. viridulum as the first record, even though he knew of no specimen to support it.

**Funaria hygrometrica** Ray's record of Adianthum aureum minus (1660: 4) was attributed to this species by Cambridge authors from J. Martyn (1727a) onwards, but only with reservations by Proctor (1956). Ray listed so few mosses that it is much more likely that this entry covered numerous small, acrocarpous species (Oswald & Preston 2011).

**Hygroamblystegium varium** P.W. Richards' record from pollard willow trunks by Ely road, halfway from Cambridge, TL46, with Brachytheciastrum velutinum (CGE) was collected earlier than the two 1929 records cited in the text but has been redetermined by M.O.H. as Amblystegium serpens.

**Hylocomium splendens** Proctor (1956) and Whitehouse (1964) treated T. Martyn's record of Hypnum parietinum as the first county record of this species. However, Linnaeus confused Thuidium tamariscinum and Hylocomium splendens and 'this led to similar misunderstanding among some of his immediate successors' (Braithwaite 1887–1905 vol. 3: 140). Thomas Martyn was one of those affected; he treated Ray's Muscus filicinus as Hypnum parietinum (Hylocomium splendens) in the main list (1763: 25) but included Ray's records as H. proliferum (Thuidium tamariscinum) in the site lists ('Herbationes', pp. 39, 41). Relhan's records (1785: 411) of Hylocomium splendens from Madingley, Kingston and Eversden Woods, all sites listed by Martyn, are doubtful for the same reason. Adamson's record (in Evans 1913) from the Blown sand division on the eastern fringe of the county is very plausible but we have not accepted it in the absence of either a specimen or a localised record.

**Hypnum cupressiforme var. heseleri** The Cambridgeshire plant grew on a Lord Derby apple tree (Preston & Hill 2007), not a Bramley as was reported in the national literature (Rothero 2008, Blockeel *et al.* 2014).

**Leucobryum glaucum** William Vernon recorded *Leucobryum glaucum sens. lat.* (as *Muscus trichoides montanus albidus fragilis*) from Gamlingay in his annotated copy of Ray (1696: 339). The record is an intriguing one and might well be correct, but there are no later records from Gamlingay or from nearby sites in neighbouring Bedfordshire (Boon & Outen 2011). We have therefore decided that we cannot accept Vernon's record.

**Orthotrichum affine** The poor specimen from Newmarket collected in 1796 (WBCH, as *O. striatum*), mentioned by Proctor (1956) as probably *O. affine*, has emergent capsules and is neither *O. affine* nor *O. striatum*. The capsules are overgrown by fungus so we cannot identify the plant with certainty but it might be *O. anomalum*. One of C.E. Broome's specimens lent from BTH in 1978 and never returned was listed as *O. affine*, collected at Cambridge in March 1835. If it is ever relocated and proves to be correctly identified, it would be the earliest localised record.

**Orthotrichum cupulatum** We have not accepted Relhan's record (1820: 446, as *O. nudum*) as the habitat, willows by the R. Cam near Fen Ditton, is an unlikely one for this species in East Anglia, although it does grow by streams and rivers in upland areas. Proctor (1956) and Whitehouse (1964) cite Henslow (1829) as the first record but he might well have listed it on the basis of Relhan's record. R.S. Adamson's record (in Evans 1913) is unlocalised and also best disregarded in the absence of a voucher.

**Palustriella commutata** We have disregarded R.S. Adamson's unlocalised record from the Fenland area (Evans 1913), which could have been *P. commutata* or *P. falcata*.

**Plagiomnium affine** In view of the history of over-recording, the earliest herbarium specimen is given as the first confirmed record. The first published record was Adamson's unlocalised report (in Evans 1913) from Boulder Clay and from sandy soil on the eastern fringe of the county. The latter plants may well have been correctly identified, and the species was later recorded from the Breckland fringe by E.W. Jones (undated) and R.E. Parker (1952).

**Plagiomnium cuspidatum** As with *Rhizomnium punctatum*, Proctor (1956) doubted Relhan's (1785) record for reasons which appear to us to be valid, but Whitehouse accepted it. Adamson (in Evans 1913) reported its presence on blown sand at the eastern edge of the county and on alluvial or peaty soils, but we are unwilling to accept these unlocalised records without voucher specimens.

**Pleuridium acuminatum** Relhan's record (1786, 1802) of *Phascum subulatum* from 'Dry Banks' was taken by Proctor (1956) as the first county record of *Pleuridium acuminatum*. However, this species was not distinguished from *P. subulatum* by British bryologists until Wilson's *Bryologia Britannica* (1855) so Relhan's record cannot be attributed to either of the Cambridgeshire species.

**Polytrichastrum longisetum** The voucher supporting the 'first certain record' listed by Whitehouse (1964), from Great Heath Wood, Gamlingay, 1934, is actually *P. formosum* (Preston & Hill 2006).

**Pterygoneurum lamellatum** L.J. Sedgwick recorded *Phascum cuspidatum* growing abundantly with *Pterygoneurum lamellatum* and *Tortula lanceola* on the earth banks of the north face of the South Pit, Haslingfield Hill, in 1905 (*Richards file*). Curiously there is no corresponding record of the *Pterygoneurum* in the Richards file and we know of no specimen of either it or *Phascum cuspidatum*. In the absence of a specimen we have not accepted this record because of the possibility of confusion with *P. ovatum*.

**Rhizomnium punctatum** In his annotated copy of Ray (1696: 35), William Vernon noted *Muscus Polytrichoides foliis latis subrotundis* from Madingley. The name refers to *Rhizomnium punctatum* but there were no further records from this well-visited locality until the 20th-century records of small plants in Madingley Wood, so it is possible that Vernon saw *Plagiomnium rostratum*, which was recorded from Madingley in the 19th century. *R. punctatum* was also reported by Relhan (1802: 420, as *Mnium punctatum*) from 'Sandy Places. Gog Magog Hills.' The extent to which the habitats in Relhan's flora refer to the Cambridgeshire sites of the species is not clear, but *R. punctatum* is not a species of sandy places and the Gogs is an unlikely locality. Henslow (1829, 1835) listed the species for Cambridgeshire but there is no evidence that this was based on anything other than Relhan's record. Proctor (1956) shared our suspicions of Relhan's record but Whitehouse (1964) rather surprisingly accepted it as the first county record though it is queried as an error on his data sheet.

**Rhytidiadelphus loreus** Relhan's records from the border of Hinton Moor (1785: 413) and from Shelford Moor (1820: 461) are very implausible. Proctor (1956) suggests that they may be misidentifications of *Rhytidiadelphus squarrosus* (see below).

**Rhytidiadelphus squarrosus** As Proctor pointed out, the habitat provided by Relhan for this species (1785: 413, as *Hypnum squarrosum*), 'Moist Meadows, and watery Places', suggests that his record is an error for *Campylium protensum* or *C. stellatum*. He goes on to suggest that Relhan's *R. loreus* (as *Hypnum loreum*) 'Heaths, and dry Pastures. On the border of Hinton Moor' could have been *R. squarrosus*. This may be so, but is too uncertain to provide the basis of the first record. Hemsted's specimen provides a first record, but Henslow's records from Cambridgeshire (1829, 1835) might have been based on Relhan's report, and there are no surviving specimens from the early 19th century.

**Schistidium crassipilum** As Proctor (1956) suggests, Relhan's (1785) record of *Grimmia apocarpa* 'On Trees' is probably *Orthotrichum diaphanum* and is certainly very unlikely to be this species.

**Sciuro-hypnum populeum** The first record was attributed to J. Harding and P.D. Brown by Whitehouse (1961, 1964) but his original datasheet clearly states 'J. Harding det. P.D. Brown' and the specimens (BBSUK, CGE), the record published in *Transactions of the British Bryological Society* 4: 172 (1961) and a later account (Richards & Whitehouse 1988) give Harding as the sole recorder.

**Sphagnum palustre** The early records of T. Martyn (1763) and Relhan (1785, 1802) cannot be accepted in the absence of specimens, as this name was then applied much more broadly than it is now.

**Syntrichia ruralis var. ruraliformis** The first record cited by Proctor (1956) and Whitehouse (1964) is from Kentford Heath, 1955, but the locality is in West Suffolk.

**Syntrichia ruralis var. ruralis** This was reported by T. Martyn (1763: 24, as *Bryum rurale*) and Relhan (1785: 403) but these early bryologists included *S. laevipila* and *S. montana* in their concept of *S. ruralis*, as Relhan's habitats ('On thatched Houses, Walls, and Trees') perhaps indicate. Skrimshire's specimen of *Tortula ruralis* (WBCH) is *S. laevipila*.

**Tetraphis pellucida** An early record 'On the bank of the ditch that parts Coe-fen and Peterhouse, in January; Mr. [R.] Davies' (J. Martyn 1729b: 17, as *Mnion minus, non ramosum angustioribus & pellucidis foliis*) seems very unlikely to refer to this species. It was the basis of the inclusion of the species in all the later floras, and often attributed to Relhan (1785: 398) by later authors, until it was questioned by Proctor (1956).

**Tortula modica** An undated specimen collected by W. Skrimshire at Walsoken Marsh, Wisbech (WBCH, as *Gymnostomum pyriforme*) is much earlier than the cited first records but probably comes from vc 28.

**Tortula truncata** W. Vernon also recorded *Muscus trichoides minimus, capitulis creberrimis, parvis, ruffis, brevibus, in pediculis brevissimis* Vernon from 'Chesterton Wall' in his annotated copy of Ray's *Synopsis* (1696: 33). Unlocalised specimens of this taxon in the Sloane Herbarium (e.g. 302 f. 36) are *Tortula truncata* (but see *Weissia controversa* below). J. Martyn's record of *Bryum exiguum, erectis parvis, subrotundis, creberrimis, capitulis rufis, foliolis serpylli angustis, pellucidis* (1729b: 14) from the walls of Anglesey Abbey cannot be identified with certainty. T. Martyn's record (1763: 24, as *Bryum truncatulum*) was queried by Proctor (1956) and Whitehouse (1964) on the grounds that it might have referred to *Microbryum davallianum*.

**Trichodon cylindricus** Whitehouse (1964) attributes the first record to both P.F. Lumley and P.J. Bourne. Lumley's material was collected in September 1960 whereas Bourne's specimen, collected with *Ephemerum minutissimum, Riccia glauca* and *R. sorocarpa* from a stubble field on Oxford Clay near Papworth St Agnes, TL26S, was not collected until November 1960 (CGE). Bourne also collected *T. cylindricus* from a stubble field near Thorney, TF20Q, in November 1960 (BBSUK, CGE).

**Weissia controversa var. controversa** An undated and unnamed specimen 'growing in a bank att Chesterton' in Robert Uvedale's herbarium (Herb. Sloane 302 f. 23, n. 11) was almost certainly collected by Vernon and may be *W. controversa* but the capsules are too immature for determination. Vernon certainly bryologised at Chesterton (see *Tortula truncata* in this Appendix).

**Zygodon viridissimus var. viridissimus** *Z. viridissimus* was reported from Cambridgeshire by Ingham (1907) but no localised records were known to Rhodes (1911), so the record presumably did not come from him or from Sedgwick, the two most active bryologists in the county at that time. In the absence of any detail, it seems best to discount this record.

# Hosts of epiphytes

## Names of hosts

The scientific names of the hosts listed by English name in the text are as follows:

Alder – *Alnus glutinosa*
Apple (including cultivars such as Bramley's
    Seedling and Discovery) – *Malus pumila*
Ash – *Fraxinus excelsior*
Beech – *Fagus sylvatica*
Birch – *Betula*
Blackthorn – *Prunus spinosa*
Box – *Buxus sempervirens*
Buddleia – *Buddleja davidii*
Cedar of Lebanon – *Cedrus libani*
Cherry – *Prunus*
Cherry plum – *Prunus cerasifera*
Douglas fir – *Pseudotsuga menziesii*
Elder – *Sambucus nigra*
Elm – *Ulmus*
False acacia – *Robinia pseudoacacia*
Field maple – *Acer campestre*
Ginkgo – *Ginkgo biloba*
Hawthorn – *Crataegus*
Hazel – *Corylus avellana*
Horse chestnut – *Aesculus hippocastanum*
Laburnum – *Laburnum anagyroides*
Larch – *Larix*
Lilac – *Syringa vulgaris*
Lime – *Tilia*
Norway maple – *Acer platanoides*
Oak – *Quercus*
Ornamental crab apple – *Malus*
Pear (including cultivars such as Conference) – *Pyrus
    communis*
Plum – *Prunus domestica*
Poplar – *Populus*
Rose – *Rosa*
Sallow – *Salix* (shrubby species, usually *S. cinerea*)
Sweet chestnut – *Castanea sativa*
Sycamore – *Acer pseudoplatanus*
Traveller's Joy – *Clematis vitalba*
Walnut – *Juglans*
White Willow – *Salix alba*
Willow – *Salix*
Yew – *Taxus baccata*.

## List of minor hosts

*Liverworts*

**Frullania dilatata:** *Acer cappadocicum, A. platanoides, A. pseudoplatanus, Aesculus hippocastanum, A. × neglecta, Alnus cordata, A. glutinosa, Betula, Buddleja davidii, Catalpa bignonioides, Carpinus betulus, Clematis vitalba, Corylus avellana, Cotinus coggygria, Euonymus, Fagus sylvatica, Juglans microcarpa, Mahonia × media, Malus pumila, Populus* (including *P. alba, P. × canescens, P. nigra* 'Italica' and *P. tremula*), *Prunus* species and cultivars (including *P. cerasifera*), *Pyrus communis, Sambucus nigra, Sorbus, Syringa vulgaris, Tilia, Ulmus, Viburnum lantana.*

**Lophocolea heterophylla:** *Acer campestre, A. pseudoplatanus, Buxus sempervirens, Fagus sylvatica, Malus pumila, Platanus, Populus, Pyrus communis, Sambucus nigra, Ulmus,* unidentified conifer.

**Metzgeria furcata:** *Acer cappadocicum, A. negundo, A. platanoides, Aesculus hippocastanum, Alnus glutinosa, Betula, Buxus sempervirens, Castanea sativa, Cercis siliquastrum, Clematis vitalba, Cornus mas, Corylus avellana, Euonymus europaeus, E. japonicus, Fagus, Garrya elliptica, Hedera helix, Juglans microcarpa, Koelreuteria paniculata, Larix, Malus pumila, Picea abies, Platanus, Populus, Pseudotsuga menziesii, Pyrus communis, Rhamnus cathartica, Quercus, Syringa vulgaris, Tilia, Ulmus, Viburnum opulus.*

**Metzgeria violacea:** *Acer negundo, A. platanoides, Betula, Buxus sempervirens, Clematis vitalba, Cornus sanguinea, Corylus avellana, Euonymus europaeus, Hedera helix, Malus pumila, Populus, Quercus, Rhamnus cathartica.*

**Radula complanata:** *Acer platanoides, Alnus glutinosa, Betula, Buddleja davidii, Corylus avellana, Euonymus europaeus, Frangula alnus, Malus pumila, Populus* (including *P. tremula* and cultivated poplars), ornamental *Prunus* cultivars, *Pyrus communis, Quercus, Rhamnus cathartica, Rosa, Sambucus nigra, Tilia, Ulmus, Viburnum opulus.*

*Mosses*

**Amblystegium serpens var. serpens:** *Acer campestre, Aesculus hippocastanum, Buddleja davidii, Clematis vitalba, Corylus, Cotinus coggygria, Euonymus, Fagus sylvatica, Frangula alnus, Juglans regia, Laburnum, Ligustrum, Mahonia, Populus, Prunus domestica, Prunus* (flowering cherry), *Pyrus communis, Quercus, Rhamnus cathartica, Rosa, Taxus baccata, Tilia, Ulmus, Viburnum opulus.*

**Aulacomnium androgynum:** *Aesculus hippocastanum, Alnus glutinosa, Betula, Fagus sylvatica, Malus pumila, Sambucus nigra, Ulmus.*

**Brachythecium rutabulum:** *Acer campestre, Aesculus hippocastanum, Buddleja davidii, Buxus sempervirens, Corylus avellana, Crataegus, Euonymus, Fagus sylvatica, Juglans regia, Laburnum anagyroides, Magnolia, Populus domestica, Pyrus communis, Quercus, Robinia pseudoacacia, Sorbus anglica, Ulmus.*

**Bryum capillare:** *Acer campestre, A. pseudoplatanus, Alnus cordata, Betula, Buxus, Corylus avellana, Fagus sylvatica, Ginkgo biloba, Koelreuteria paniculata, Laburnum, Mahonia × media, Metasequoia glyptostroboides, Pinus, Populus, Prunus domestica, P. spinosa, Quercus, Rosa, Syringa vulgaris, Tilia, Ulmus, Wisteria.*

**Bryum moravicum:** *Acer pseudoplatanus, Alnus glutinosa, Fagus sylvatica, Laburnum, Pinus, Prunus domestica, P. spinosa, Pyrus communis, Quercus, Rhamnus cathartica, Ulmus.*

**Ceratodon purpureus** *Aesculus hippocastanum, Betula, Crataegus, Fagus sylvatica, Magnolia, Populus, Prunus.*

**Cryphaea heteromalla:** *Acer platanoides* and other ornamental species, *Aesculus hippocastanum, Corylus avellana, Euonymus, Frangula alnus, Hedera, Koelreuteria paniculata, Laburnum, Ligustrum, Mahonia × media, Populus alba, Prunus* (including *P. spinosa*), *Pyrus communis, Quercus, Ulmus.*

**Dicranoweisia cirrata:** *Acer pseudoplatanus, Aesculus hippocastanum, Alnus glutinosa, Buddleja davidii, Cedrus deodara, Cotinus coggygria, Fagus sylvatica, Ginkgo biloba, Metasequoia glyptostroboides, Populus, Rhus potaninii, Sorbus anglica, Syringa vulgaris, Taxus baccata, Tilia, Ulmus.*

**Grimmia pulvinata:** *Acer campestre, A. pseudoplatanus, Aesculus hippocastanum, Araucaria araucana, Betula, Cedrus libani, Cotinus coggygria,*

*Fagus sylvatica, Ficus carica, Ginkgo biloba, Laburnum, Prunus* (cherry), *Quercus, Tilia, Ulmus.*

**Homalothecium sericeum:** *Acer campestre, A. pseudoplatanus, Aesculus hippocastanum, Crataegus, Fagus sylvatica, Laburnum, Mahonia × media, Morus, Platanus, Populus, Pyrus communis, Quercus, Syringa vulgaris, Tilia, Ulmus, Wisteria.*

**Hypnum cupressiforme:** *Acer campestre, Aesculus hippocastanum, Alnus cordata, A. glutinosa, Betula, Buddleja davidii, Buxus sempervirens, Carpinus betulus, Castanea sativa, Cercis siliquastrum, Cornus mas, Corylus avellana, Fagus sylvatica, Fraxinus ornus, Ginkgo biloba, Hedera, Laburnum, Ligustrum, Metasequoia glyptostroboides, Morus, Platanus, Populus, Prunus* (including *P. domestica, P. spinosa* and flowering cherry), *Pyrus communis, Quercus* (including *Q. ilex*), *Rhamnus cathartica, Rosa, Sorbus, Syringa vulgaris, Taxus baccata, Tilia, Ulmus, Viburnum opulus, Wisteria.*

**Isothecium alopecuroides:** *Acer pseudoplatanus, Corylus avellana, Crataegus, Fagus sylvatica, Laburnum, Quercus, Ulmus.*

**Isothecium myosuroides var. myosuroides:** *Acer campestre, Alnus glutinosa, Betula, Carpinus betulus, Castanea sativa, Corylus avellana, Pyrus communis, Salix.*

**Kindbergia praelonga** (all hosts): *Acer campestre, A. pseudoplatanus, Alnus glutinosa, Buddleja davidii, Cornus sanguinea, Corylus avellana, Cotinus coggygria, Crataegus, Fagus sylvatica, Fraxinus excelsior, Malus pumila, Populus, Prunus domestica, P. spinosa, Pyrus communis, Quercus, Salix, Sambucus nigra, Syringa vulgaris, Ulmus.*

**Leskea polycarpa:** *Acer campestre, A. pseudoplatanus, Aesculus hippocastanum, Alnus glutinosa, Fagus sylvatica, Pyrus communis, Ulmus, Viburnum opulus.*

**Neckera complanata:** *Acer pseudoplatanus, Betula, Crataegus, Fagus sylvatica, Laburnum, Prunus spinosa, Sambucus nigra, Taxus baccata.*

**Orthotrichum affine:** *Acer platanoides, Aesculus hippocastanum, Alnus cordata, Betula, Buddleja davidii, Carpinus betulus, Cercis siliquastrum, Clematis vitalba, Cornus sanguinea, Corylus avellana, Cotinus coggygria, Euonymus europaeus, Fagus sylvatica, Ficus carica, Frangula alnus, Fraxinus ornus, Ginkgo biloba, Juglans microcarpa, J. regia, Koelreuteria paniculata, Laburnum, Ligustrum vulgare, Magnolia, Prunus domestica, P. spinosa, Rhamnus cathartica,*

Sorbus, Syringa vulgaris, Taxus baccata, Tilia, Viburnum opulus.

**Orthotrichum diaphanum:** Acer campestre, A. platanoides, Aesculus hippocastanum, Alnus cordata, A. glutinosa, Araucaria araucana, Betula, Buddleja davidii, Buxus sempervirens, Clematis vitalba, Cornus sanguinea, Cotinus coggygria, Euonymus, Fagus sylvatica, Ficus carica, Ginkgo biloba, Jasminum officinale, Juglans regia, Laburnum, Ligustrum, Magnolia, Metasequoia glyptostroboides, Morus, Populus, Prunus domestica, Prunus spinosa, Pyrus communis, P. salicifolia, Quercus, Rhamnus cathartica, Sorbus, Syringa vulgaris, Taxus baccata, Tilia, Ulmus, Viburnum opulus, Wisteria.

**Orthotrichum lyellii:** Acer pseudoplatanus, Acer (cultivated sp.), Aesculus hippocastanum, Cotinus coggygria, Corylus avellana, Fagus sylvatica, Fraxinus (cultivated sp.), Ginkgo biloba, Larix, Populus, Prunus domestica, Prunus sp. (cherry), Sambucus nigra, Syringa vulgaris, Ulmus.

**Orthotrichum pulchellum:** Acer pseudoplatanus, Betula, Corylus avellana, Crataegus, Frangula alnus, Prunus spinosa, Pyrus communis, Quercus, Sambucus nigra.

**Rhynchostegium confertum:** Acer campestre, A. pseudoplatanus, Betula, Buddleja davidii, Buxus sempervirens, Catalpa, Corylus avellana, Fagus sylvatica, Laburnum, Platanus, Populus, Prunus domestica, Prunus spinosa, Prunus (including flowering cherry), Pyrus communis, Quercus, Rhamnus cathartica, Rosa, Sorbus, Syringa vulgaris, Taxus baccata, Tilia, Ulmus.

**Syntrichia laevipila:** Acer campestre, A. platanoides, A. pseudoplatanus, Aesculus hippocastanum, Fagus sylvatica, Juglans microcarpa, J. regia, Morus, Prunus, Pyrus communis, Quercus, Tilia, Ulmus.

**Syntrichia latifolia:** Acer campestre, A. pseudoplatanus, Aesculus hippocastanum, Cotinus coggygria, Fagus sylvatica, Juglans microcarpa,

Malus, Platanus, Populus, Prunus spinosa, Tilia, Ulmus.

**Syntrichia montana:** Acer (including A. platanoides and A. pseudoplatanus), Aesculus hippocastanum, Buddleja davidii, Cedrus libani, Cercis siliquastrum, Crataegus, Fagus sylvatica, Populus, Quercus, Rosa (the old bases of garden rose bushes), Tilia, Ulmus.

**Syntrichia ruralis var. ruralis:** Acer pseudoplatanus, Crataegus, Fagus sylvatica, Ficus carica, Fraxinus excelsior, Juglans regia, Laburnum, Pinus, Populus, Prunus (including P. spinosa), Salix, Ulmus, Wisteria.

**Syntrichia virescens:** Acer campestre, A. pseudoplatanus, Aesculus hippocastanum, Buddleja davidii, Cercis siliquastrum, Crataegus, Fagus sylvatica, Ficus carica, Ginkgo biloba, Juglans regia, Metasequoia glyptostroboides, Platanus, Populus, Prunus (including P. spinosa), Rhamnus cathartica, Syringa vulgaris, Tilia.

**Tortula muralis:** Acer pseudoplatanus, Aesculus hippocastanum, Betula, Fagus sylvatica, Fraxinus excelsior, Pinus, Populus.

**Ulota bruchii:** Acer pseudoplatanus, Aesculus hippocastanum, A. × neglecta, Alnus glutinosa, Carpinus betulus, Corylus avellana, Fraxinus ornus, Ginkgo biloba, Populus, Prunus domestica, P. spinosa, Rhamnus cathartica, Sambucus nigra, Syringa vulgaris.

**Ulota phyllantha:** Acer campestre, A. pseudoplatanus, Corylus avellana, Populus, Prunus domestica, P. spinosa, Rosa, Syringa vulgaris, Ulmus.

**Zygodon viridissimus var. viridissimus:** Acer campestre, A. pseudoplatanus, Aesculus hippocastanum, Clematis vitalba, Corylus avellana, Fagus sylvatica, Ginkgo biloba, Jasminum, Ligustrum, Metasequoia glyptostroboides, Populus, Prunus spinosa, Pyrus communis, Rhamnus cathartica, Rosa, Syringa vulgaris, Tilia, Ulmus, Viburnum opulus.

# List of recorders

All those who are known to have collected or recorded bryophytes in the county before 1950 are listed below. For later dates, recorders are included if they are credited with at least 10 records in the database or have made at least one new vice-county record. Recorders who sent specimens in response to Harold Whitehouse's appeal for material from under-recorded 10-km squares in 1959–60 are marked with an obelus (†); we know nothing about them other than their names. The list for 2000–18 also includes those who attended the bryophyte excursions frequently while they lived in or near Cambridgeshire and thus assisted in recording for the recent flora in this way.

**1660–1820**
Davies, J.
Davies, R.
Dent, P.
Dickson, J.
Hemsted, J.
Holme, J.
Jackson, R.
Martyn, J.
Martyn, T.
Ray, J.
Relhan, R.
Skrimshire, W.
Tozer, J.S.
Vernon, W.

**1821–1900**
Baber, H.
Babington, C.C.
Berkeley, M.J.
Brocas, F.Y.
Broome, C.E.
Brown, I.
Bunbury, C.J.F.
Coleman, W.H.
Dixon, H.N.
Garnons, W.L.P.
Haviland, G.D.
Henslow, J.S.
Hillhouse, W.
Jenyns (later Blomefield), L.
Larbalestier, C. du B.
Leefe, J.E.
Lister, J.J.
Lowe, H.E.
Shrubbs, A.S.

**1901–1914**
Adamson, R.S.
Compton, R.H.
Graveson, A.W.
Hough, E.M.

Moss, C.E.
Rhodes, P.G.M.
Sedgwick, L.J.
Shrubbs, A.S.
Sturdy, A.C.
Waddell, C.H.
West, W.

**1927–1949**
Allison, J.
Armitage, E.
Bagenal, T.
Balkwill, S.
Banwell, A.D.
Bingley, F.J.
Buxton, P.A.
Carpenter, J.
Catcheside, D.G.
Chamberlain, P.J.
Chapman, V.J.
Conolly, A.P.
Coombe, D.E.
Corner, E.J.H.
Crawford, G.I.
Digby, P.S.B.
Fincham, J.R.S.
George, E.A.
Gilbert Carter, H.
Gilson, H.C.
Godwin, H.
Harris, T.M.
Hill, R.
Hodgson, P.C.
Jones, E.W.
Lewin, R.A.
Lupton, F.G.
McMuir, R.G.
Perring, F.H.
Petch, C.P.
Priestley, P.M.
Proctor, M.C.F.
Radcliffe, J.D.

Richards, P.W.
Rishbeth, J.
Shepherd, C.S.
Simmonds, N.W.
Sporne, K.R.
Stearn, W.T.
Tutin, T.G.
Walters, S.M.
Warburg, E.F.
Watt, A.S.
White, F.
Whitehouse, H.L.K.

**1950–1999**
Adam, P.
Akeroyd, J.R.
Anderson, M.C.
Bell, F.
Birks, H.H.
Birks, H.J.B.
Bloom, G.
Bourne, P.J.
Brown, L.F.
Chamberlain, D.F.
Chater, A.O.
Coombe, D.E.
†Cox, J.
Crompton, G.
Damant, S.
Dickson, J.H.
Duckett, J.G.
Evans, I.M.
Faulkner, J.C.
Finch, R.A.
Frost, L.C.
Gardiner, J.C.
George, E.A.
†Graves, A.
Halliday, G.
Harding, J.L.
Hill, M.O.
Hodgetts, N.G.

Jackson, P.E.
†Jackson, W.
Jardine, N.
Jones, E.W.
Laflin, T.
Leslie, A.C.
Little, E.R.B.
Lock, J.M.
Long, D.G.
Luck, K.E.
†Lumley, P.F.
Martin, M.H.
McFarlane, M.G.
McVean, D.N.
Milnes-Smith, M.D.
Mountford, J.O.
Newton, A.E.
Outen, A.R.
Parker, R.E.
Perring, F.H.
Peterken, J.H.G.
Pigott, C.D.
Poore, M.E.D.
Porley, R.D.
Preston, C.D.
Proctor, M.C.F.
Rackham, O.
†Readshaw, C.
†Reeve, B.
Richards, P.W.
Rook, P.
Seilly, D.J.
Sell, P.D.
Smith, M.E.
Stevens, F.

Stevenson, C.R.
Townsend, C.C.
†Wallis, O.E.
Walters, S.M.
Warburg, E.F.
Waters, S.J.P.
Whitehouse, H.L.K.

**2000–2018**
Arbon, A.
Barden, D.J.
Beckmann, B.C.
Buckton, S.J.
Burton, M.
Burton, M.A.S.
Carter, R.H.
Charman, T.G.
Cheffings, C.M.
Cooke, E.L.
Crompton, G.
Damant, S.
Denyer, J.L.
Dobson, D.
Ellis, R.W.
Evans, L.
Finch, R.A.
Fisk, R.J.
Ghullam, M.P.
Glenister, O.T.
Graham, J.J.
Harding, M.
Harley, V.
Hartley, S.
Heywood, E.
Hill, M.O.

Hodgetts, N.G.
Hooper, E.
Howarth, A.
Jamie, G.A.
Jardine, N.
Jukes, A.R.
Leonard, P.G.
Meek, W.R.
Michna, P.
Millar, N.P.
Moss, G.
Mott, J.J.
Mountford, J.O.
Pinches, C.E.
Porley, R.D.
Pounsett, H.
Preston, C.D.
Rackham, O.
Reynolds, P.J.
Saunders, A.
Saunders, L.
Scott, D.J.
Seilly, D.J.
Sell, P.D.
Shanklin, J.D.
Smith, K.
Spence, L.
Stevenson, C.R.
Stroh, P.A.
Tipper, C.T.W.
Turner, C.
Walker, K.J.
Wildman, D.

# Herbarium abbreviations

BBSUK British Bryological Society (held with NMW at Cardiff)
BIRM Birmingham Museum
BM Natural History Museum, London
BTH Bath Royal Literary and Scientific Institution
CGE Department of Plant Sciences, University of Cambridge
E Royal Botanic Garden, Edinburgh
HTN North Hertfordshire Natural History Museum Service
LINN Linnean Society, London
LSR Leicestershire Museums
NMW National Museum of Wales, Cardiff
OXF Department of Plant Sciences, University of Oxford
SWN Saffron Walden Museum
WARMS Warwickshire Museum
WBCH Wisbech and Fenland Museum

# Acknowledgements

Our debt to all those who have investigated the bryophytes of Cambridgeshire since 1660 must be obvious from the text. Here we thank those who have helped us since we started the recent survey in 2000, but we should first mention the earlier contributions of Harold Whitehouse, who kept meticulous records of the county's bryophytes for the 50 years preceding our survey, and Angela Newton, who matched his accuracy when digitising these records in 1985 to create the database on which we have built.

Much of the recording for this flora has been a communal effort undertaken on the fortnightly winter bryophyte excursions by many naturalists, listed in Appendix 4. Cambridgeshire has a mobile population and many of those listed made valuable contributions for several years before moving to other areas. We must make particular mention of Jonathan Graham, Nick Jardine and Robin Stevenson for their frequent attendance throughout the period of the recent survey. In addition Jonathan Graham has contributed records from several site surveys and Robin Stevenson has made available the details of his remarkable research into the bryophytes of orchard trees. Jonathan and Robin have also recorded more than their fair share of species-poor Fenland tetrads. We must also mention Jonathan Shanklin whose recording of liverworts has been so assiduous that we have had to modify our analytical methods to cope with it.

Bryological recording is sustained in Britain by the structures, publications and meetings of the British Bryological Society and we are fortunate that throughout our bryological lives it has maintained a welcoming atmosphere in which we have been able to develop our interests amongst friends. Our records are held in the BBS database at the Biological Records Centre, Centre for Ecology and Hydrology, Wallingford. We owe a great debt to Steph Rorke, the database manager at BRC, for much help including the production of several rounds of distribution maps. Oli Pescott has also helped in numerous ways, and we also thank Björn Beckmann for assistance and David and Helen Roy for generous hospitality during C.D.P.'s visits to Wallingford after his retirement in 2015.

In preparing the introductory chapters we have often referred to Gigi Crompton's website on the county's vascular plants, *Cambridgeshire Flora Records since 1538*. We could not have hunted down historic herbarium specimens without the warm welcome and expert help given to us by Christine Bartram and latterly Lauren Gardiner on many visits to CGE, and similarly by Katherine Slade (BBSUK,

NMW), Mark Carine, Fred Rumsey and Mark Spencer (BM), Rob Randall and Matt Williams (BTH), Pete Hollingsworth and David Long (E), Serena Marner (OXF), Sarah Kenyon (SWN), Laura McCoy (WARMS) and Robert Bell and Charles Nelson (WBCH). Charles Nelson also advised us about the whereabouts of some of Skrimshire's collecting sites near Wisbech. Geoffrey Hall kindly sent us photographs of the Cambridgeshire specimens at LSR. We thank the staff of Cambridge University Library (especially the Manuscripts Reading Room and the Rare Books Room) and the British Library for facilitating access to these collections. Thanks also to Christine Alexander (Department of Plant Sciences, Cambridge), Lynda Brooks and Isabelle Charmantier (Linnean Society of London), Monica Frisch (Cambridge Natural History Society), Andrea Hart (Natural History Museum), Trevor James and Bob Press (North Hertfordshire Natural History Museum Service) and Patricia McGuire (King's College, Cambridge) for help with books and archives in their care and to Rupert Baker (Royal Society) for identifying J.J. Lister's obituarist. Tom Blockeel kindly copied documents he holds as the BBS Recorder for Mosses.

Katie Sarll and Tim Sparks kindly provided weather data from Cambridge University Botanic Garden and Oli Pescott and Steph Rorke generated the national climate maps. We are grateful to Ursula Revill for information on her father, Philip Bourne, and for providing the photograph of her parents, and to the Archivists of Corpus Christi College (Lucy Hughes) and Girton College (Hannah Westall), the Biographical Assistant at St John's College (Paul Everest) and the Librarians of Christ's College (John Wagstaff) and Murray Edwards College (Kirstie Preest) for information on various alumni and alumnae. Rupert Baker (Royal Society) and Sam Tonks (Bryanston School) also answered similar queries and John Faulkner, Paul Hackney, Hilary Kirkpatrick, Caroline Pannell and Jo Whatmough helped with what proved to be a remarkably difficult attempt to establish the years of Reg Parker's birth and death, a question finally answered by Tim Parker, Reg's son.

We thank Ruth Angrave (Natural England), John and Hilary Birks, Jeff Duckett, Richard Fisk, Jonathan Graham, Peter Leonard, Martin Lester (National Trust), Robin Stevenson and Pete Stroh for their photographs, Mike Taylor (Natural England) for looking out photos of Chippenham Fen, Robert Bell and the Lilian Ream Exhibition Gallery Trust for permission to reproduce Lilian Ream's orchard photos, Jakki Racey (Wisbech Library) for advice about these and Jane Cooper for her mother's picture of the 1950 Botany School excursion. For permission to reproduce images of other items we thank the British Library Board, the Master and Fellows of Corpus Christi College, Cambridge, the Syndics of Cambridge University Library and the Linnean Society of London. The Richard Relhan watercolours held by the University Library are the property of the Cambridge Antiquarian Society and are reproduced with their kind permission. The distribution maps were plotted using the DMAP program written by Dr A.J. Morton.

Several people have read and commented on draft sections of the flora, including Simon Damant (Wimpole Hall), Steve Hartley (all habitat chapters), Jonathan Shanklin (liverworts), Robin Stevenson (orchards) and Richard West (geology). Tom Blockeel and Oli Pescott very kindly read though the entire text. All provided valuable comments, and we are very grateful to them for their time and expertise. We also thank Jeff Duckett for his generous Foreword.

## Manuscript sources

**BBS ledger.** Ledger and associated papers held by the British Bryological Society Recorder for Mosses. The ledger was started by J.B. Duncan in 1923 and it documents additions to the periodically published census catalogues.

**CNHS minutes.** Minute books of the Cambridge Natural History Society. References to the creation of the card index for vascular plants by D.H. Valentine, assisted by J.L. Crosby, appear in the minutes of several meetings of the Botanical Section in 1937 and early 1938 (e.g. pp. 80, 95, 104) and the expenses are listed in the Treasurer's report for 1937–38.

**Coleman Calendar** and **Coleman Localities.** W.H. Coleman's notebooks *Floral calendar, Cambridge, 1835* and *Localities of plants observed by W.H. Coleman, in 1833–34–35*, both held with C.C. Babington's Flora of Cambridgeshire papers in the Department of Plant Sciences, University of Cambridge.

**Graveson diary.** A.W. Graveson's natural history diary for 1914. We have consulted the copy at the North Hertfordshire Natural History Museum Service at Hitchin; the original is held at Dorset County Museum, Dorchester.

**Lecture list.** Notebook entitled *Names of men who attended the Botanical Lectures 1828–*, classmark O.XIV.261, University Archives, Cambridge University Library. The names of women are included from 1874 onwards. The record continued until 1891.

**Martyn letters.** Letters between Thomas Martyn and Richard Pulteney, held at Linnean Society, London. Some are printed by Gorham (1830), with omissions which are sometimes but not always indicated in his text.

**Rackham notebooks.** Notebooks of Oliver Rackham. Rackham left several hundred field notebooks to Corpus Christi College, Cambridge when he died in 2015. They are held in the College archives and are gradually being digitised and made available in the Digital Library on the Cambridge University Library website. They contain numerous references to bryophytes in the county. These are likely to provide further details of species at known sites rather than new localities, but we have not yet been able to work through them systematically.

**Richards file.** Loose-leaf file of Cambridgeshire bryophyte records arranged alphabetically by species, with mosses preceding liverworts. Paul Richards started it in 1928 or 1929 (the latter is the more probable date) and he passed it on to M.C.F. Proctor when he left for Bangor in 1949 (see Chapter 3). It was maintained until February 1951. Currently held by C.D. Preston.

**Royal Literary Fund archive.** This is held by the British Library; the Relhan file is Loan 96 RLF 1/71.

**Smith letters.** Correspondence of James Edward Smith, held by the Linnean Society and available in the excellent Online Collections on the Society's website.

**Sowerby drawings.** Original drawings and proof plates of bryophytes drawn by James Sowerby for J.E. Smith's *English botany*, held in the cryptogamic herbarium of the Natural History Museum, London. Some of the specimens drawn are stored with the drawings and are cited as 'BM (*Sowerby drawings*)', others held in the main bryophyte herbarium are simply cited as BM.

**Whitehouse diaries.** H.L.K. Whitehouse's *East Anglian Bryophytes* diaries, six volumes from May 1950 to October 1968 (see Chapter 3). Currently held by C.D. Preston.

**Whitehouse site files.** H.L.K. Whitehouse's Cambridgeshire bryophyte files, including those covering sites visited on excursions and records collected for the 1964 flora. Currently held by C.D. Preston.

**Whitehouse species file.** Box-file of foolscap sheets with species' records, arranged alphabetically but with liverworts preceding mosses. Whitehouse started this as a replacement to *Richards file* in 1950 or 1951 (see Chapter 3) and continued to add records until December 1961 when he used it as the basis for his bryophyte flora (Whitehouse 1964). Held in the Department of Plant Sciences, University of Cambridge.

## Published sources, annotated books and unpublished reports

Details of the annotated copies of books cited in the text are given after the main entry for the book in the bibliography below. Relhan (1820) should, for example, be consulted for details of Babington's, Henslow's and Jenyns' annotated copies of that work.

**Adam, P. & Akeroyd, J.R. 1978.** The Cambridgeshire saltmarsh. *Nature in Cambridgeshire* 21: 26–30.

**Adams, K.J. & Preston, C.D. 1992.** Evidence for the effects of atmospheric pollution on bryophytes from national and local recording, in P.T. Harding, ed., *Biological recording of changes in British wildlife*, pp. 31–43. HMSO, London.

**Adamson, R.S. 1912.** An ecological study of a Cambridgeshire woodland. *Journal of the Linnean Society, Botany* 40: 339–387.

**Allan, M. 1967.** *The Hookers of Kew 1785–1911*. Michael Joseph, London.

**Allen, D.E. 1967.** John Martyn's Botanical Society: a biographical analysis of the membership. *Proceedings of the Botanical Society of the British Isles* 6: 305–324.

**Allen, D.E. 1986.** *The botanists*. St Paul's Bibliographies, Winchester.

**Allen, D.E. 1999.** C.C. Babington, Cambridge botany and the taxonomy of British flowering plants. *Nature in Cambridgeshire* 41: 2–11.

**Allen, D.E. 2004a.** Martyn, John (1699–1768), in Matthew & Harrison (2004), vol. 37, pp. 38–39.

**Allen, D.E. 2004b.** Gibson, George Stacey (1818–1883), in Matthew & Harrison (2004), vol. 22, pp. 77–78.

**Anderson, M.C. 1958.** The distribution of parish pits in the county of Cambridge (excluding the Isle of Ely). *Nature in Cambridgeshire* 1: 30–32.

**Anon. 1887.** Christopher Edmund Broome. *Proceedings of the Linnean Society of London* 1886–1887: 34–35.

**Anon. 1963.** National Trust Wicken Fen Local Committee. Extracts from the Report for 1961–62. *Nature in Cambridgeshire* 6: 10–13.

**Anon. 1973.** National Trust. Extracts from the Report of the Wicken Fen Local Committee. *Nature in Cambridgeshire* 16: 6–7.

**Anon. 2008.** Peter James Chamberlain. *Annual Report of King's College, Cambridge* 2008: 100–102.

**Anon. 2018.** In memoriam. Peter S.B. Digby. *The Linnean* 34: 29.

**Arts, T. 1986.** The occurrence of moniliform tubers in *Pohlia melanodon* (Brid.) J. Shaw, the differences between juvenile plants of related species and their distribution in Belgium and the Grand-Duchy of Luxembourg. *Bulletin de la Société royale de botanique de Belgique* 119: 114–120.

**Atherton, I., Bosanquet, S. & Lawley, M. 2010.** *Mosses and liverworts of Britain and Ireland: a field guide*. British Bryological Society.

**B[abington], A.M., ed. 1897.** *Memorials journal and botanical correspondence of Charles Cardale Babington*. Macmillan & Bowes, Cambridge.

**Babington, C.C. 1860.** *Flora of Cambridgeshire*. John van Voorst, London. An interleaved copy annotated by Babington is in the library of the Department of Plant Sciences, Sainsbury Laboratory, as is H.N. Dixon's annotated copy.

**Baker, M. 2018.** Devils Dyke, Cambridgeshire: its wildlife, history and restoration. *Nature in Cambridgeshire* 60: 3–13.

**Barlow, N., ed. 1958.** *The autobiography of Charles Darwin 1809–1882*. Collins, London.

**Barratt, D.R., Mountford, J.O., Walker, K.J., Warman, E.A. & Sparks, T.H. 1999.** The effects of field elevation on the establishment of 'plug' plants introduced onto former arable land at Baker's Fen, Wicken Fen NNR. *Nature in Cambridgeshire* 41: 58–64.

**Bates, J.W. 1993.** Regional calcicoly in the moss *Rhytidiadelphus triquetrus*: survival and chemistry of transplants at a formerly $SO_2$-polluted site with acid soil. *Annals of Botany* 72: 449–455.

**Bates, J.W. 1995.** A bryophyte flora of Berkshire. *Journal of Bryology* 18: 503–620.

**Bates, J.W. 2015.** *The mosses and liverworts of Mid-west Wales*. Privately published, Ascot.

**Bates, J.W. & Preston, C.D. 2011.** Can the effects of climate change on British bryophytes be distinguished from those resulting from other environmental changes?, in Z. Tuba, N.G. Slack & L.R. Stark, eds, *Bryophyte ecology and climate change*, pp. 371–407. Cambridge University Press, Cambridge.

**Beckett, G., Bull, A. & Stevenson, R. 1999.** *A flora of Norfolk*. Privately published.

**Belcher, H. & Swale, E. 1998.** Moss that grows on skulls: a curious old remedy run to earth in Cambridge. *Nature in Cambridgeshire* 40: 74–75.

**Belcher, H. & Swale, E. 2005/06.** E.A. George, M.A., 1920–2005. *FBA News* 32: 3.

**Bendall, A.S. 1992.** *Maps, land and society: a history, with a carto-bibliography of Cambridgeshire estate maps, c. 1600–1836*. Cambridge University Press, Cambridge.

**Benson-Evans, K. & Brough, M.C. 1966.** The maturation cycles of some mosses from Fforest Ganol, Glamorgan. *Report and Transactions of the Cardiff Naturalists' Society* 92: 4–23.

**Bergamini, A. 2006.** Caducous branchlets in *Pterigynandrum filiforme* (Bryopsida: Pterigynandraceae). *Journal of Bryology* 28: 149–151.

**Birks, H.J.B. 1974.** Distribution maps of bryophytes in Britain and Ireland. *Tortula vahliana* (Schultz) Wils. *Journal of Bryology* 8: 125.

**Birks, H.J.B. & Birks, H.H. 2015.** Derek Ratcliffe – botanist and plant ecologist, in D.B.A. Thompson, H.H. Birks & H.J.B. Birks, eds, *Nature's conscience: the life and legacy of Derek Ratcliffe*, pp. 39–89. Langford Press, Kings Lynn.

**Birks, H.J.B. & Birks, H.H. 2018.** Michael Proctor (1929–2017). *BSBI News* 138: 66–70.

**Blackstock, T.H., Bosanquet, S.D.S., Long, D.G. & Preston, C.D. 2005.** *Conocephalum* in Britain and Ireland: a BBS mini-survey. *Field Bryology* 87: 11–14.

**Blockeel, T.L. 1991.** The *Racomitrium heterostichum* group in the British Isles. *Bulletin of the British Bryological Society* 58: 29–35.

**Blockeel, T.L. 2017.** The *Ulota crispa* group in Britain and Ireland, with notes on other species of the genus. *Field Bryology* 117: 8–19.

**Blockeel, T.L. & Fisk, R.J. 2018.** *Orthotrichum patens* Bruch & Brid. (Bryophyta, Orthotrichaceae) in Suffolk and Derbyshire, another epiphytic moss new to Britain. *Journal of Bryology* 40: 56–61.

**Blockeel, T.L. & Stevenson, C.R. 2006.** *Hypnum cupressiforme* Hedw. var. *heseleri* (Ando & Higuchi) M.O. Hill (Bryopsida, Hypnales) in Norfolk, new to the British Isles. *Journal of Bryology* 28: 190–193.

**Blockeel, T.L., Bosanquet, S.D.S., Hill, M.O. & Preston, C.D., eds 2014.** *Atlas of British and Irish bryophytes.* 2 vols. Pisces Publications, Newbury.

**Blomefield, L. 1887.** Address to the members of the Bath Field Club, in reference to the death of C.E. Broome, Esq., FLS. *Proceedings of the Bath Natural History and Antiquarian Field Club* 6: 144–153. Reprinted by Wallace (2005), pp. 240–246.

**Boon, C.R. 1998.** British and Irish floristic elements applied to the Bedfordshire flora. *Bedfordshire Naturalist* 52: 78–91.

**Boon, C.R. & Outen, A.R. 2011.** *Flora of Bedfordshire.* Bedfordshire Natural History Society.

**Bosanquet, S.D.S. 2010.** *The mosses and liverworts of Pembrokeshire.* Privately published.

**Bosanquet, S.D.S. 2012.** Vagrant epiphytic mosses in England and Wales. *Field Bryology* 107: 3–17.

**Bosanquet, S.D.S. 2015.** *Orthotrichum rogeri* Brid. in England, new to Britain. *Journal of Bryology* 37: 329–331.

**Bosanquet, S.[D.S.] 2016.** Wildlife reports. Bryophytes. *British Wildlife* 27: 367–368.

**Bosanquet, S.D.S. & Preston, C.D. 2005.** *Weissia squarrosa* in Britain: a re-evaluation of its identification and ecology in the light of recent records. *Field Bryology* 86: 2–13.

**Bosanquet, S.D.S. & Preston, C.D. 2010.** BBS Summer Meeting: Co. Cork and Co. Kerry, 27 June–11 July 2009. *Field Bryology* 100: 47–63.

**Bosanquet, S.D.S., Graham, J.J. & Motley, G.S. 2005.** *The mosses and liverworts of Carmarthenshire.* Privately published.

**Boulger, G.S., revised by Sherbo, A. 2004a.** Martyn, Thomas (1735–1825), in Matthew & Harrison (2004), vol. 37, pp. 40–41.

**Boulger, G.S., revised by McConnell, A. 2004b.** Relhan, Richard (1754–1823), in Matthew & Harrison (2004), vol. 46, pp. 454–455.

**Boulger, G.S. & Britten, J. 1918.** Joseph Andrews and his herbarium. I. Introductory. *Journal of Botany* 56: 257–261.

**Bourne, P.J. 1960.** A layman looks at bryophytes. *Nature in Cambridgeshire* 3: 25–26.

**Bower, F.O. 1938.** *Sixty years of botany in Britain (1875–1935).* Macmillan & Co., London.

**Bradley, S. & Pevsner, N. 2014.** *The buildings of England: Cambridgeshire.* Yale University Press, New Haven & London.

**Braithwaite, R. 1887–1905.** *The British moss-flora.* 3 vols. L. Reeve & Co., London.

**Brocas, F.Y. 1887.** *A commemorative poem of Britannia's Jubilee.* Privately published, London.

**Bunbury, F.J., ed. [1894]** *Life, letters and journals of Sir Charles J.F. Bunbury, Bart.* Vol. I. Privately published.

**Bunting, M.J., Briggs, D. & Block, M. 1995.** The Cambridge British Flora (1914–1920). *Watsonia* 20: 195–204.

**Burton, M. & Preston, C.D. 2013–2018.** Bryophyte records. *Nature in Cambridgeshire* 55: 137–139 (2013); 56: 79–81 (2014); 57: 139–141 (2015); 58: 98–99 (2016); 59: 79–82 (2017); 60: 69–71 (2018).

**Cambient 1958.** Cambridgeshire and Isle of Ely Naturalists' Trust Ltd. First Annual Report, 1957. *Nature in Cambridgeshire* 1: 4–10.

**Cambient 1959.** Cambridgeshire and Isle of Ely Naturalists' Trust Ltd. Second Annual Report, 1958. *Nature in Cambridgeshire* 2: 4–7.

**Cambient 1960.** Cambridgeshire and Isle of Ely Naturalists' Trust Limited. Third Annual Report, 1959. *Nature in Cambridgeshire* 3: 3–8.

**Cambridgeshire and Isle of Ely County Council Planning Department 1965.** *Survey report 1965. Nature reserves and Sites of Scientific Interest.* Cambridgeshire and Isle of Ely County Council, Cambridge.

**Cambridgeshire and Peterborough Biodiversity Partnership 2008.** *Local Habitat Action Plan for Cambridgeshire and Peterborough. Traditional orchards.* Cambridgeshire and Peterborough Biodiversity Partnership.

**Cambridgeshire County Planning Department 1956.** *Survey reports. The common lands of Cambridgeshire.* Cambridge.

**Cano, M.J., Werner, O. & Guerra, J. 2005.** A morphometric and molecular study in *Tortula subulata* complex (Pottiaceae, Bryophyta). *Botanical Journal of the Linnean Society* 149: 333–350.

**Capparós, R., Lara, F., Draper, I., Mazimpaka, V. & Garilleti, R. 2016.** Integrative taxonomy sheds light on an old problem: the *Ulota crispa* complex (Orthotrichaceae, Musci). *Botanical Journal of the Linnean Society* 180: 427–451.

**Carey, P.D. 1999.** Changes in the distribution and abundance of *Himantoglossum hircinum* (L.) Sprengel (Orchidaceae) over the last 100 years. *Watsonia* 22: 353–364.

**Carroll, L., Sparks, T. & Upson, T. 2008.** 100 years of Cambridge meteorological records. *Nature in Cambridgeshire* 50: 10–17.

**Carter, P. 2004.** Jackson, Richard (1704/5–1782), in Matthew & Harrison (2004), vol. 29, p. 517.

**Catcheside, D.G. 1983.** Reminiscences of some members of the British Bryological Society. *Bulletin of the British Bryological Society* 42: 19–21.

**Charman, T.G. & Preston, C.D. 2011–2012.** Bryophyte records. *Nature in Cambridgeshire* 53: 90–91 (2011); 54: 78–80 (2012).

**Chopra, R.N. & Rawat, M.S. 1977.** Studies on the initiation of sexual phase in the moss *Leptobryum pyriforme. Beiträge zur Biologie der Pflanzen* 53: 353–357.

**Clapham, A.R. 1978.** Thomas Gaskell Tutin, in H.E. Street, ed., *Essays in plant taxonomy*, pp. ix–xiv. Academic Press, London.

**Clifton-Taylor, A. 2014.** Building materials, in Bradley & Pevsner (2014), pp. 362–364.

**Clokie, H.N. 1964.** *An account of the herbaria of the Department of Botany in the University of Oxford.* Oxford University Press, London.

**Codd, L.E. 1980.** Robert Harold Compton (1886–1979). *Bothalia* 13: 244–245.

**Colston, A. & Friday, L. 1999.** Wicken Fen – 100 years either side of the Millennium. *Nature in Cambridgeshire* 41: 46–58.

**Coombe, D.E. 1987.** Spiked speedwell, soil stripes and polygons, and the vanishing chalk heaths of Cambridgeshire. *Nature in Cambridgeshire* 29: 26–37.

**Coombe, D.E. 1988.** More on soil stripes, polygons and fairy rings. *Nature in Cambridgeshire* 30: 13–15.

**Coombe, D.E., Mills, T.J.N. & Upchurch, P. 1990.** The history of Madingley brickpits: contrasts in succession. *Nature in Cambridgeshire* 32: 3–14.

**Corley, M.F.V. & Hill, M.O. 1981.** *Distribution of bryophytes in the British Isles: a census catalogue of their occurrence in vice-counties.* British Bryological Society, Cardiff.

**Crompton, G. 1959.** The Peat Holes of Triplow. *Nature in Cambridgeshire* 2: 24–34.

**Crompton, G. 1972.** History and flora of Thriplow Meadows. *Nature in Cambridgeshire* 15: 25–33.

**Crompton, G. 1994.** William Skrimshire 1766–1829 " ...happily devoted to natural science and most skilled in his surgeon's art....". *Annual Report of The Wisbech Society* 55: 17–20.

**Crompton, G. 1997.** Botanizing in Cambridgeshire in the 1820s. *Nature in Cambridgeshire* 39: 59–73.

**Crompton, G. 2001.** *Catalogue of Cambridgeshire flora records since 1538. Part 1.* Unpublished report; for an updated version, see http://www.cambridgeshireflora.com.

**Crompton, G. & Nelson, E.C. 2000.** The herbarium of William Skrimshire (1766–1829) of Wisbech. *Watsonia* 23: 23–38.

**Crompton, G. & Whitehouse, H.L.K. 1983.** *Annotated check list of the flora of Cambridgeshire.* Privately published, Cambridge.

**Crundwell, A.C. 1962.** *Bryum sauteri* and *B. klinggraeffii* in Britain. *Transactions of the British Bryological Society* 4: 334.

**Crundwell, A.C. 1976.** New vice-county records and amendments to the census catalogues. Musci. *Bulletin of the British Bryological Society* 28: 21–33.

**Crundwell, A.C. & Nyholm, E. 1963.** Two new European species of *Bryum. Botaniska Notiser* 116: 94–98.

**Crundwell, A.C. & Nyholm, E. 1964.** The European species of the *Bryum erythrocarpum* complex. *Transactions of the British Bryological Society* 4: 597–637.

**Crundwell, A.C. & Nyholm, E. 1972.** A revision of *Weissia*, subgenus *Astomum* I. The European species. *Journal of Bryology* 7: 7–19.

**Crundwell, A.C. & Whitehouse, H.L.K. 1978.** *Trichostomopsis umbrosa* (C. Müll.) Robins. in England. *Journal of Bryology* 10: 5–8.

**Damant, S. 2005.** Saproxylic hoverflies at Wimpole estate. *Nature in Cambridgeshire* 47: 3–8.

**Dandy, J.E. 1969.** *Watsonian vice-counties of Great Britain.* Ray Society, London.

**Darby, H.C., ed. 1938.** *A scientific survey of the Cambridge district.* British Association for the Advancement of Science, London.

**Darby, H.C. 1940.** *The draining of the fens.* Cambridge University Press, Cambridge.

**Dickson, J. 1790.** *Plantarum cryptogamicarum Britanniae. Fasciculus secundus.* London.

**Dickson, J.H. 1962.** Autumn meeting, 1961. *Transactions of the British Bryological Society* 4: 384–386.

**Dickson, J.H. 1973.** *Bryophytes of the Pleistocene.* Cambridge University Press, Cambridge.

**Dillenius, J.J. 1741.** *Historia muscorum.* Oxford.

**Dixon, H.N. 1884.** New localities for rare mosses. *Journal of Botany* 22: 149.

**Dixon, H.N. 1924.** *The student's handbook of British mosses,* ed. 3. V.V. Sumfield, Eastbourne.

**Dore, A.J., Vieno, M., Tang, Y.S., Dragosits, U., Dosio, A., Weston, K.J. & Sutton, M.A. 2007.**

Modelling the atmospheric transport and deposition of sulphur and nitrogen over the United Kingdom and assessment of the influence of SO$_2$ emissions from international shipping. *Atmospheric environment* 41: 2355–2367.

**Duckett, J.G. 2018.** Harold Whitehouse (1917–2000): his life and legacy. *Field Bryology* 120: 20–29.

**Duckett, J.G. & Ligrone, R. 1994.** Studies of protonemal morphogenesis in mosses III. The perennial gemmiferous protonema of *Rhizomnium punctatum* (Hedw.) Kop. *Journal of Bryology* 18: 13–26.

**Duckett, J.G. & Matcham, H.W. 1995.** Studies of protonemal morphogenesis in mosses VII. The perennial rhizoids and gemmiferous protonema of *Dicranella heteromalla* (Hedw.) Schimp. *Journal of Bryology* 18: 407–424.

**Duckett, J.G. & Pressel, S. 2017.** The colorful phenology of five common terricolous mosses in London, England. *Bryophyte Diversity and Evolution* 39: 44–56.

**Duncan, J.B. 1926.** *A census catalogue of British mosses*, ed. 2. British Bryological Society, Berwick-upon-Tweed.

**East of England Apples and Orchards Project 2005.** *The condition of orchards in Cambridgeshire November 2005. Cambridgeshire and Peterborough Phase 1 Orchard Survey*. Report for the Cambridgeshire and Peterborough Biodiversity Partnership.

**England, J. & Jeger, M. 2005.** The effect of nozzle size, water pressure and nozzle height on dispersal of *Marchantia polymorpha* gemmae, using an overhead sprinkler system. *Proceedings of the 13th EWRS Symposium, Bari, Italy, 19–23 June 2005*, unpaginated.

**Evans, A.H. 1911.** A short flora of Cambridgeshire, chiefly from an ecological standpoint, with a history of its chief botanists. *Proceedings of the Cambridge Philosophical Society* 16: 197–284.

**Evans, A.H. 1913.** Notes on additions to the Flora of Cambridgeshire. *Proceedings of the Cambridge Philosophical Society* 17: 229–235.

**Everitt, A. 2007.** Bryologists invade the village. *Swaffham Crier* 31(4): 9.

**Farmer, A.M., Bates, J.W. & Bell, J.N.B. 1992.** Ecophysiological effects of acid rain on bryophytes and lichens, in J.W. Bates & A.M. Farmer, eds, *Bryophytes and lichens in a changing climate*, pp. 284–313. Clarendon Press, Oxford.

**Faulkner, J.C. 1963.** Hildersham Wood. A botanical survey. *Nature in Cambridgeshire* 6: 26–31.

**Fausey, J.C. 2003.** Controlling liverwort and moss now and in the future. *HortTechnology* 13: 35–38.

**Fincham, J.R.S. & John, B. 1995.** David Guthrie Catcheside 31 May 1907 – 1 June 1994. *Biographical Memoirs of Fellows of the Royal Society* 41: 118–134.

**Fisk, R. 2005.** *Pterigynandrum filiforme*: an addition to the 'montane' bryoflora of Suffolk. *Field Bryology* 86: 13–14.

**Forbes, C.L. 1965.** Geology and ground-water, in Steers (1965), pp. 1–17.

**Frahm, J.-P. & Ahmed, J. 2004.** *Barbula sardoa* (Schimp.) J.-P. Frahm, a new name for *Barbula convoluta* Hedw. var. *commutata* (Jur.) Husn. *Journal of Bryology* 26: 29–35.

**Friday, L.E., ed. 1997.** *Wicken Fen: the making of a wetland nature reserve*. Harley Books, Colchester.

**Friday, L.E. & Chatfield, M.P. 1997.** The next 100 years, in Friday (1997), pp. 277–282.

**Friday, L.E. & Harley, B.H., eds 2000.** *Checklist of the flora and fauna of Wicken Fen*. Harley Books, Colchester.

**Friday, L.E., Grubb, P.J. & Coombe, D.E. 1999.** The Godwin Plots at Wicken Fen: a 55-year record of the effects of mowing on fen vegetation. *Nature in Cambridgeshire* 41: 32–46.

**Friday, L.E., Moore, N.W. & Ballard, S.M. 1997.** Ecology, research and education at Wicken Fen, in Friday (1997), pp. 255–276.

**Friday, L.E., Walters, S.M. & Lock, J.M. 1997.** Carr and woodland, in Friday (1997), pp. 82–97.

**Fritz, S., Lieske, K. & Frey, W. 2010.** Vegetative (asexual) reproduction by propagules in six dioicous pleurocarpous mosses (*Abietinella abietina, Homalothecium lutescens, H. sericeum, Pleurozium schreberi, Pseudoscleropodium purum, Rhytidiadelphus squarrosus*). A morphological study. *Nova Hedwigia, Beiheft* 138: 325–333.

**Fuge, R. & Andrews, M.J. 1988.** Fluorine in the UK environment. *Environmental geochemistry and health* 10: 96–104.

**Furness, S.B. & Grime, J.P. 1982.** Growth rate and temperature responses in bryophytes I. An investigation of *Brachythecium rutabulum*. *Journal of Ecology* 70: 513–523.

**Gage, A.T. & Stearn, W.T. 1988.** *A bicentenary history of the Linnean Society of London*. Academic Press, London.

**Gardiner, J.S., ed., 1925–32.** *The natural history of Wicken Fen, Parts II–VI*. Bowes & Bowes, Cambridge.

**Gardiner, J.S. & Tansley, A.G., eds, 1923.** *The natural history of Wicken Fen, Part I*. Bowes & Bowes, Cambridge.

**George, E.A. 1963.** The diatoms of Wicken Fen and Hayley Wood. *Nature in Cambridgeshire* 6: 39–42.

**Gerarde, J. 1597.** *The herball, or generall historie of plantes*. London.

Gibbs, J.N. & Howell, R.S. 1972. *Dutch Elm Disease survey 1971.* Forest Record no. 82. Her Majesty's Stationery Office, London.

Gibbs, J.N. & Howell, R.S. 1974. *Dutch Elm Disease survey 1972–73.* Forest Record no. 100. Her Majesty's Stationery Office, London.

Gilbert, O.L. 1968. Bryophytes as indicators of air pollution in the Tyne valley. *New Phytologist* 67: 15–30.

Gilbert, O.L. 1970. Further studies on the effect of sulphur dioxide on lichens and bryophytes. *New Phytologist* 69: 605–627.

Gilbert, O.L. 1971. Urban bryophyte communities in north-east England. *Transactions of the British Bryological Society* 6: 306–316.

Gilmour, J.[S.L.] & Walters, [S.]M. 1954. *Wild flowers.* Collins, London.

Godwin, H. 1978. *Fenland: its ancient past and uncertain future.* Cambridge University Press, Cambridge.

Goode, J.A., Stead, A.D., Ligrone, R. & Duckett, J.G. 1994. Studies of protonemal morphogenesis in mosses IV. *Aloina* (Pottiales). *Journal of Bryology* 18: 27–41.

Gorham, G.C. 1830. *Memoirs of John Martyn, F.R.S., and of Thomas Martyn, B.D., F.R.S., F.L.S., Professors of Botany in the University of Cambridge.* Hatchard & Son, London.

Graham, J.[J.] 2009a. *Bryophyte survey of Cherry Hinton East Pit. Final report.* Unpublished report to Bedfordshire and Cambridgeshire Wildlife Trust.

Graham, J.[J.] 2009b. *Cherry Hinton East Pit – transplantation of locally uncommon bryophytes.* Unpublished report to Bedfordshire and Cambridgeshire Wildlife Trust.

Graham, J.[J.] 2011. *Bryophyte and lichen survey of Cambridge University Botanic Garden. Final report.* Unpublished report.

Graham, J.[J.] 2012. *A resurvey of the bryophytes of Cherry Hinton East Pit following positive management works. Final report.* Unpublished report to Bedfordshire and Cambridgeshire Wildlife Trust.

Graham, J.[J.] 2013. *Bryophyte and lichen survey of Graysmoor Pit, Cambridgeshire.* Unpublished report to Bedfordshire, Cambridgeshire and Northamptonshire Wildlife Trust.

Greene, S.W. 1957. The British species of the *Plagiothecium denticulatum-P. silvaticum* group. *Transactions of the British Bryological Society* 3: 181–190.

Grubb, P.J. & Key, B.A. 1975. Clearance of scrub and re-establishment of chalk grassland on the Devil's Dyke. *Nature in Cambridgeshire* 18: 18–22.

Gunther, R.W.T. 1928. *Further correspondence of John Ray.* Ray Society, London.

Haslam, J. 1984. The development and topography of Saxon Cambridge. *Proceedings of the Cambridge Antiquarian Society* 72: 13–29.

Hawkins, T.D. 1990. *The drainage of Wilbraham, Fulbourn and Teversham Fens: a study in landscape history.* Privately published, Cambridge.

Hedenäs, L. 2003. The European species of the *Calliergon-Scorpidium-Drepanocladus* complex, including some related or similar species. *Meylania* 28: 1–116.

Hedenäs, L., Reisborg, C. & Hallingbäck, T. 2014. *Nationalnyckeln till Sveriges flora och fauna. Bladmossor: Skirmossor–baronmossor.* ArtDatabanken, SLU, Uppsala.

Henrey, B. 1975. *British botanical and horticultural literature before 1800.* 3 vols. Oxford University Press, Oxford.

Henslow, J.S. 1829. *A catalogue of British plants.* Cambridge.

Henslow, J.S. 1830. *Plants gathered in five herborizing excursions in Cambridgeshire, during April and May, 1830.* Printed circular. A copy is held in Cambridge Central Library, classmark Cambridge Miscellanies C.01.

Henslow, J.S. 1835. *A catalogue of British plants,* ed. 2. Cambridge.

Hesse, M. 2007. The East Fields of Cambridge. *Proceedings of the Cambridge Antiquarian Society* 96: 143–160.

Hey, R.W. & Perrin, R.M.S. 1960. *The geology and soils of Cambridgeshire.* Cambridge Natural History Society, Cambridge.

H[ickson], S.J. 1928. Obituary notices of Fellows deceased. Joseph Jackson Lister — 1857–1927. *Proceedings of the Royal Society of London* 102: i–v.

Hill, M.O. 1967. *Manuscript Bryophyte Flora of Cambridgeshire.* Later titled *M.O. Hill's notes on Cambridgeshire Bryophytes ... with a letter to H.L.K. Whitehouse.* Loose-leaf file in the Department of Plant Sciences, University of Cambridge.

Hill, M.O. 1984. *Racomitrium elongatum* Frisvoll in Britain and Ireland. *Bulletin of the British Bryological Society* 43: 21–25.

Hill, M.O. 1988. A bryophyte flora of North Wales. *Journal of Bryology* 15: 377–491.

Hill, M.[O.] 2000. Harold Whitehouse (1917–2000). *Nature in Cambridgeshire* 42: 73–75.

Hill, M.O. 2006. Rare and interesting bryophytes in Britain and Ireland. *Field Bryology* 89: 43–45.

Hill, M.O. 2012. Local frequency as a key to interpreting species occurrence data when recording effort is not known. *Methods in Ecology and Evolution* 3: 195–205.

Hill, M.[O]. 2016. A natural history of Cambridge. *Nature in Cambridgeshire* 58: 108–110.

**Hill, M.O. & Preston, C.D. 1998.** The geographical relationships of British and Irish bryophytes. *Journal of Bryology* 20: 127–226.

**Hill, M.O. & Preston, C.D. 2014.** Changes in distribution and abundance, 1960–2013, in Blockeel *et al.* (2014), vol. 1, pp. 34–49.

**Hill, M.O. & Preston, C.D. 2015.** Disappearance of boreal plants in southern Britain: habitat loss or climate change? *Biological Journal of the Linnean Society* 115: 598–610.

**Hill, M.O., Blackstock, T.H., Long, D.G. & Rothero, G.P. 2008.** *A checklist and census catalogue of British and Irish bryophytes: updated 2008.* British Bryological Society, Middlewich.

**Hill, M.O., Harrower, C.A. & Preston, C.D. 2013.** Spherical k-means clustering is good for interpreting multivariate species occurrence data. *Methods in Ecology and Evolution* 4: 542–551.

**Hill, M.O., Preston, C.D., Bosanquet, S.D.S. & Roy, D.B. 2007.** *BRYOATT: attributes of British and Irish mosses, liverworts and hornworts.* Centre for Ecology and Hydrology, Huntingdon.

**Hill, M.O., Preston, C.D. & Smith, A.J.E., eds 1991–1994.** *Atlas of the bryophytes of Britain and Ireland. Volume 1, Liverworts (Hepaticae and Anthocerotae)*, 1991; *Volume 2, Mosses (except Diplolepideae)*, 1992; *Volume 3, Mosses (Diplolepideae)*, 1994. Harley Books, Colchester.

**Hodge, C.A.H. & Seale, R.S. 1966.** *The soils of the district around Cambridge.* Memoirs of the Soil Survey of Great Britain. Agricultural Research Council, Harpenden.

**Hodgetts, N.G., Preston, C.D. & Stevenson, C.R. 2006.** *Antitrichia curtipendula* in a Cambridgeshire orchard. *Field Bryology* 89: 8–10.

**Holyoak, D.T. 2003.** A taxonomic review of some British coastal species of the *Bryum bicolor* complex, with a description of *Bryum dyffrynense* sp. nov. *Journal of Bryology* 25: 107–113.

**Holyoak, D.T. & Pedersen, N. 2007.** Conflicting molecular and morphological evidence of evolution within the Bryaceae (Bryopsida) and its implications for generic taxonomy. *Journal of Bryology* 29: 111–124.

**Hooker, W.J. 1833.** *The English Flora of Sir James Edward Smith. Class XXIV. Cryptogamia.* Longman, Rees, Orme, Brown, Green, and Longman, London.

**Horridge, G. [undated]** *The growth and development of a family firm: Chivers of Histon 1873–1939.* [Received by Cambridge University Library in 1988.]

**Hughes, J.G. 1969.** Factors conditioning development of sexual and apogamous races of *Phascum cuspidatum* Hedw. *New Phytologist* 68: 883–900.

**Hugonnot, V., Celle, J. & Vergne, T. 2012.** *Ephemerum cohaerens*, an exquisite survivor of functional alluvial habitats. *Field Bryology* 108: 20–27.

**Huttunen, S., Hedenäs, L., Ignatov, M.S., Devos, N. and Vanderpoorten, A. 2008.** Origin and evolution of the northern hemisphere disjunction in the moss genus *Homalothecium* (Brachytheciaceae). *American Journal of Botany* 95: 720–730.

**Ingham, W., ed. 1907.** *A census catalogue of British mosses.* Moss Exchange Club, York.

**Ingram, D. & Robertson, N. 1999.** *Plant disease.* HarperCollinsPublishers, London.

**James, T.J. 2009.** *Flora of Hertfordshire.* Hertfordshire Natural History Society, Welwyn Garden City.

**Jenkins, S. 2003.** *England's thousand best houses.* Allen Lane, London.

**Jermyn, S.T. 1974.** *Flora of Essex.* Essex Naturalists' Trust, Colchester.

**J[ones], D.A. 1935.** Philip Grafton Mole Rhodes (1885–1934). *Report of the British Bryological Society* 3: 246–247.

**Jones, E.W. 1953.** A bryophyte flora of Berkshire and Oxfordshire II. Musci. *Transactions of the British Bryological Society* 2: 220–277.

**Jones, E.W. 1965.** A flora of Cambridgeshire. [Review]. *Transactions of the British Bryological Society* 4: 833–834.

**Jones, E.W. 1973.** Frederick Archibald Sowter 1899–1972. *Journal of Bryology* 7: 465–468.

**Jones, E.W. 1983.** Reminiscences of some members of the British Bryological Society. *Bulletin of the British Bryological Society* 42: 23–27.

**Jones, E.W. 1991.** What am I – botanist, forester, physiologist, ecologist or taxonomist? *Bulletin of the British Bryological Society* 57: 12.

**Kassas, M. (as El-Kassas, M.A.F.) 1950.** *Studies in the ecology of Chippenham Fen.* PhD thesis, Cambridge University.

**Kassas, M. 1951.** Studies in the ecology of Chippenham Fen II. Recent history of the Fen, from evidence of historical records, vegetational analysis and tree-ring analysis. *Journal of Ecology* 39: 19–32.

**Kassas, M. 1952.** Studies in the ecology of Chippenham Fen IV. Tree and bush colonization in South Chippenham Fen. *Journal of Ecology* 40: 62–73.

**Kennett, T. 2016.** *The Lord Treasurer of Botany: Sir James Edward Smith and the Linnaean collections.* Linnean Society of London, London.

**Kerr, C. 1975.** Ecology teaching in Gamlingay Cinques. *Nature in Cambridgeshire* 18: 35–40.

**Kirk, G.J.D., Bellamy, P.H. & Lark, R.M. 2010.** Changes in soil pH across England and Wales in response to decreased acid deposition. *Global Change Biology* 16: 3111–3119.

Koepp, R. 2002. *Clusters of creativity*. John Wiley & Sons, Chichester.

Kohn, D., Murrell, G., Parker, J. & Whitehorn, M. 2005. What Henslow taught Darwin. *Nature* 436: 643–645.

Koponen, T. 1968. The moss genus *Plagiomnium* Kop. sect. *Rosulata* (Kindb.) Kop. in northwestern Europe. *Annales botanici fennici* 5: 213–224.

Koponen, T. 1971. A monograph of *Plagiomnium* sect. *Rosulata* (Mniaceae). *Annales botanici fennici* 8: 305–367.

Koponen, T. 1980. A synopsis of Mniaceae (Bryophyta). IV. Taxa in Europe, Macaronesia, NW Africa and the Near East. *Annales botanici fennici* 17: 125–162.

Kučera, J. 1999. A taxonomic study of the *Didymodon rigidulus* group (Bryopsida, Pottiaceae) in Europe. Doctoral thesis, University of South Bohemia, České Budějovice.

Larbalestier, C. du B. 1879. *Physcia adglutinata*, in *Lichen-herbarium* Fascicle II, no. 49. West, Newman & Co., London. [Consulted in CGE].

Lea, V. 2011. Conservation of the Chalkhill Blue and other butterflies on the Devil's Dyke. *Nature in Cambridgeshire* 53: 24–27.

Leslie, A.C. 1974. *The calcifuge bryophytes on Wicken Fen*. Unpublished report; there are copies in the library of the Department of Plant Sciences, University of Cambridge, and in *Whitehouse site files*.

Leslie, A.C. 1979. Gamlingay revisited. *Nature in Cambridgeshire* 22: 42–47.

Leslie, A.C. 2011. An annotated check list of the flora of the Devil's Ditch, Cambridgeshire. *Nature in Cambridgeshire* 53: 3–24.

Leslie, A.C. 2015. Annotated checklist of the flora of Chippenham Fen. *Nature in Cambridgeshire* 57: 3–43.

Linnaeus, C. 1753. *Species plantarum*. 2 vols. Stockholm.

Lock, J.M. 1964. Some recent bryophyte records from Wicken Fen. *Nature in Cambridgeshire* 7: 34–38.

Lock, J.M. 1968. *List of the bryophytes of Wicken Fen*. Guides to Wicken Fen no. 5. Wicken Fen Local Committee, National Trust.

Lock, J.M. 1990. Calcifuge bryophytes at Wicken Fen. *Journal of Bryology* 16: 89–96.

Lock, J.M. & Bennett, T.J. 1993. New water bodies at Wicken Fen. *Nature in Cambridgeshire* 35: 25–28.

Lock, J.M., Friday, L.E. & Bennett, T.J. 1997. The management of the fen, in Friday (1997), pp. 213–254.

Lockwood, R. 2003. Professor Norman Simmonds. *Experimental agriculture* 39: 1–3.

Long, D.G. 1988. *Pogonatum urnigerum* with caducous leaves in Scotland. *Journal of Bryology* 15: 495–496.

Lowell, J. 2009. Epiphyte colonization in v.-c. 59. *Field Bryology* 99: 24–29.

Lush, M., Robertson, H.J., Alexander, K.N.A., Giavarini, V., Hewins, E., Mellings, J., Stevenson, C.R., Storey, M. & Whitehead, P.F. 2009. *Biodiversity studies of six traditional orchards in England*. Research Report no. 025. Natural England, Sheffield.

Maddock, A., ed. 2008. *UK Biodiversity Action Plan Priority Habitat Descriptions. Traditional orchards*. Joint Nature Conservation Committee.

Malim, T. 1997. New evidence on the Cambridgeshire Dykes and Worsted Street Roman Road. *Proceedings of the Cambridge Antiquarian Society* 85: 27–122.

Marsh, T.J. 2004. The UK drought of 2003: a hydrological review. *Weather* 59: 224–230.

Marsh, T.J, Cole, G. & Wilby, R. 2007. Major droughts in England and Wales, 1800–2006. *Weather* 62: 87–93.

Martin, H. 1956. Modern fungicides and insecticides, in T. Wallace & R.G.W. Bush, eds, *Modern commercial fruit growing*, pp. 79–100. Country Life, London.

Martin, M.H. 1963. *Nowellia curvifolia* (Dicks.) Mitt. in Hayley Wood. *Nature in Cambridgeshire* 6: 42–43.

Martin, P. 2007. *Grimmia tergestina*: frequent and fruiting on limestone roof tiles in the Cotswolds. *Field Bryology* 93: 14–15.

Martyn, J. 1726. *A course of botany*. London. (This leaflet and the *Proposals* printed by Martyn in 1727 and 1728 are rare survivals; we have consulted them in the British Library, classmark 443.d.27).

Martyn, J. 1727a. *Methodus plantarum circa Cantabrigiam nascentium*. London. Privately distributed by the author (see Preston in press). Cambridge University Library holds interleaved copies annotated by John Martyn (classmark CCD.47.414, bound with his copy of Ray's *Catalogus*), and Thomas Martyn (CCE.47.49). A copy annotated by Richard Jackson is in the Wren Library, Trinity College, Cambridge (Adv.e.1.7).

Martyn, J. 1727b. *Proposals for a course of botany in the University of Cambridge*. London.

Martyn, J. 1728. *Proposals for a course of botany at London*. London.

Martyn, J. 1728[–1737]. *Historia plantarum rariorum*. London.

Martyn, J. 1729a. *The first lecture of a course of botany*. London.

Martyn, J. 1729b. *Methodus plantarum circa Cantabrigiam nascentium*, ed. 2. The first 24 pages of an unfinished second edition, privately distributed by the author (see Preston in press). A copy annotated by Thomas Martyn is in Cambridge University Library, classmark CCE.47.49. Jackson's annotated copy of Martyn (1727a) also incorporates these pages.

**Martyn, J. 1732.** *Tournefort's History of plants growing about Paris ... Translated into English, with many additions, and accommodated to the plants growing in Great-Britain.* 2 vols. London.

**Martyn, J. 1770.** *Dissertations and critical remarks upon the Aeneids of Virgil ... To the whole is prefixed, some account of the author and his writings.* London.

**Martyn, T. 1763.** *Plantae Cantabrigienses: or, a catalogue of the plants which grow wild in the county of Cambridge, disposed according to the system of Linnaeus.* London.

**Martyn, T. 1770.** The Preface, in J. Martyn (1770), pp. i–xxxii. This biographical memoir of John Martyn was republished with minor additions by Gorham (1830).

**Matejko, M., Dore, A.J., Hall, J., Dore, C.J., Blaś, M., Kryza, M., Smith, R. & Fowler, D. 2009.** The influence of long term trends in pollutant emissions on deposition of sulphur and nitrogen and exceedance of critical loads in the United Kingdom. *Environmental science & policy* 12: 882–896.

**Matthew, H.C.G. & Harrison, B., eds 2004.** *Oxford Dictionary of National Biography.* 61 vols. Oxford University Press, Oxford.

**McMillan, J.A. 1938.** The agriculture of Cambridgeshire (B) General survey, in Darby (1938), pp. 138–148.

**Melbourne, R.W.L. 1940.** *The Land of Britain,* ed. by L. Dudley Stamp. *Part 71 Isle of Ely.* Geographical Publications, London.

**Miles, C.J., Odu, E.A. & Longton, R.E. 1989.** Phenological studies on British mosses. *Journal of Bryology* 15: 607–621.

**Morgan, N.G. & Marsh, R.W. 1956.** Pests and diseases and their control, in T. Wallace & R.G.W. Bush, eds, *Modern commercial fruit growing,* pp. 203–221. Country Life, London.

**Morton, D., Rowland, C., Wood, C., Meek, L., Marston, C., Smith, G., Wadsworth, R. & Simpson, I.C. 2011.** *Final Report for LCM2007 – the new UK land cover map.* Countryside Survey Technical Report No. 11/07. Centre for Ecology and Hydrology, Lancaster.

**Murray, G. 1887.** Christopher Edmund Broome. *Journal of Botany* 25: 148–150.

**Newton, A.E. 1985.** *Bryophyte site register for Cambridgeshire.* Unpublished report to the Nature Conservancy Council.

**Newton, A.E. 1986.** Bryophyte sites in Cambridgeshire. *Nature in Cambridgeshire* 28: 23–28.

**O'Shea, B.J. & Buck, W.R. 2001.** Bryophytes of Uganda. 5. *Bryocrumia* L.E. Anderson (Hypnaceae), a monotypic moss genus new to Africa. *Tropical Bryology* 20: 103–107.

**Oswald, P.[H.] 1991.** The Revd John Hemsted (1747?–1824). *Nature in Cambridgeshire* 33: 26–29.

**Oswald, P.H. & Preston, C.D., eds 2011.** *John Ray's Cambridge Catalogue (1660).* Ray Society, London.

**Parker, J.[S.] 2006.** The development of the Cambridge University Botanic Garden. *Curtis's Botanical Magazine* 23: 4–19.

**Parker, J.S. 2014.** The science of John Stevens Henslow, in *Selected papers, 1821–38 [by] John Stevens Henslow,* pp. v–xiv. Cambridge University Press, Cambridge.

**Parker, R.E. 1973.** *Introductory statistics for biology.* Edward Arnold, London. A second edition was published in 1979.

**Paton, J.A. 1990.** *Riccia subbifurca* Warnst. ex Crozals in the British Isles. *Journal of Bryology* 16: 5–8.

**Paton, J.A. 1999.** *The liverwort flora of the British Isles.* Harley Books, Colchester.

**Paton, J.A. & Birks, H.J.B. 1968.** *Lophozia perssonii* Buch & S. Arnell – new to Britain. *Transactions of the British Bryological Society* 5: 439–442.

**People's Trust for Endangered Species [undated]** *Traditional orchards: a guide to wildlife and management.* People's Trust for Endangered Species, London.

**Perrin, R.M.S. & Hodge, C.A.H. 1965.** Soils, in Steers (1965), pp. 68–84.

**Perring, F.H. 1961.** Field meetings, 1959. September 5th and 6th, 1959. Wisbech. *Proceedings of the Botanical Society of the British Isles* 4: 206–208.

**Perring, F.H., Sell, P.D. & Walters, S.M. 1964.** *A flora of Cambridgeshire.* Cambridge University Press, Cambridge.

**Pescott, O.L. & Preston, C.D. 2014.** Some environmental factors influencing the distribution of bryophytes in Britain and Ireland, in Blockeel *et al.* (2014), vol. 1, pp. 26–33.

**Pescott, O.L. & Preston, C.D. 2016.** Rare and interesting 15. *Field Bryology* 115: 36–41.

**Pescott, O.L., Simkin, J.M., August, T.A., Randle, Z., Dore, A.J. & Botham, M.S. 2015.** Air pollution and its effects on lichens, bryophytes, and lichen-feeding Lepidoptera: review and evidence from biological records. *Biological Journal of the Linnean Society* 115: 611–635.

**Petiver, J. 1699.** *Musei Petiveriani centuria quarta & quinta.* London.

Petiver, J. 1702. *Gazophylacii naturae & artis decas prima*. London.

Pettit, G.H.N. 1941. *The Land of Britain*, ed. by L. Dudley Stamp. *Part 74 Cambridgeshire (excluding the Isle of Ely)*. Geographical Publications, London.

Pilkington, S. 2010. Large, new population of *Lophozia perssonii* discovered on Salisbury Plain Defence Training Estate. *Field Bryology* 101: 2–4.

Porley, R. & Hodgetts, N. 2005. *Mosses and liverworts*. Collins, London.

Porley, R.D., Preston, C.D. & Hill, M.O. 2004. *Grimmia trichophylla* and related mosses in Cambridgeshire. *Nature in Cambridgeshire* 46: 72–76.

Preece, R.C. & Sparks, T.H., eds 2012. *Fauna Cantabrigiensis. The vertebrate and molluscan fauna of Cambridgeshire by the Rev. Leonard Jenyns (1800–1893): transcript and commentaries*. Ray Society, London.

Pressel, S., Matcham, H.W. & Duckett, J.G. 2005. Studies of protonemal morphogenesis in mosses. X. Ephemeraceae revisited; new dimensions underground. *Journal of Bryology* 27: 311–318.

Pressel, S., Matcham, H.W. & Duckett, J.G. 2007. Studies of protonemal morphogenesis in mosses. XI. *Bryum* and allied genera: a plethora of propagules. *Journal of Bryology* 29: 241–258.

Preston, C.D. 1989. The ephemeral pools of south Cambridgeshire. *Nature in Cambridgeshire* 31: 2–11.

Preston, C.D. 1991. History of bryophyte recording in the British Isles, in Hill *et al.* (1991), pp. 13–20.

Preston, C.D. 2000. Engulfed by suburbia or destroyed by the plough: the ecology of extinction in Middlesex and Cambridgeshire. *Watsonia* 23: 59–81.

Preston, C.D. 2001. Harold Leslie Keer Whitehouse M.A., Sc.D. (1917–2000). *Journal of Bryology* 23: 155–160.

Preston, C. D. 2006. Additions to the bryophyte flora of Cambridgeshire (v.c. 29) in the last 50 years. *Nature in Cambridgeshire* 48: 73–80.

Preston, C.D. 2012. Three annotated copies of Babington's *Flora of Cambridgeshire*. *Nature in Cambridgeshire* 54: 27–33.

Preston, C.D. 2013. Reconstructing the history of Cambridgeshire's wild plants: the importance of annotated floras. *Bulletin of the Friends of Cambridge University Library* 33–34: 10–15.

Preston, C.D. 2018. Where was the Hill of Health, and what plants grew there? *Nature in Cambridgeshire* 60: 53–60.

Preston, C.D. in press. The "abortive edition" of John Martyn's *Methodus plantarum circa Cantabrigiam nascentium* (c. 1729). *Archives of natural history*.

Preston, C.D. & Hill, M.O. 2000a–2010. Bryophyte records. *Nature in Cambridgeshire* 42: 94–95 (2000a); 43: 55–58 (2001); 44: 55–57 (2002); 45: 76–79 (2003); 46: 90–93 (2004); 47: 92–95 (2005); 48: 96–98 (2006); 49: 96–99 (2007); 50: 124–128 (2008); 51: 92–95 (2009); 52: 72–73 (2010).

Preston, C.D. & Hill, M.O. 2000b. A new survey of the bryophytes of Cambridgeshire (v.c. 29). *Nature in Cambridgeshire* 42: 96.

Preston, C.D. & Hill, M.O. 2016. Does Cambridgeshire have ancient woodland bryophytes? *Nature in Cambridgeshire* 58: 3–15.

Preston, C.[D.] & Walker, K.J. 2005. Bryophytes of Monks Wood, in C. Gardiner & T. Sparks, eds, *Ten years of change: woodland research at Monks Wood NNR, 1993–2003*, pp. 146–156. English Nature Research Report no. 613. English Nature, Peterborough.

Preston, C.D. & Whitehouse, H.L.K. 1985. *Trichostomopsis umbrosa* in semi-natural chalk habitats. *Journal of Bryology* 13: 471–474.

Preston, C.D. & Whitehouse, H.L.K. 1986a–1999. Bryophyte records. *Nature in Cambridgeshire* 28: 60–62 (1986a); 29: 77–78 (1987); 30: 61–63 (1988); 31: 65–66 (1989); 32: 80–83 (1990); 33: 67–69 (1991); 34: 73–74 (1992a); 35: 85–86 (1993); 36: 94 (1994); 37: 51–52 (1995); 38: 78–79 (1996); 39: 87 (1997); 40: 85–87 (1998); 41: 102–103 (1999).

Preston, C.D. & Whitehouse, H.L.K. 1986b. The habitat of *Lythrum hyssopifolia* L. in Cambridgeshire, its only surviving English locality. *Biological Conservation* 35: 41–62.

Preston, C.D. & Whitehouse, H.L.K. 1992b. Bryophytes on imported limestone in Cambridge University Botanic Garden, 1955–1991. *Nature in Cambridgeshire* 34: 45–49.

Preston, C.D., Hill, M.O., Pilkington, S. & Pywell, R.J. 2009. The effect of disturbance on the bryophyte flora of Salisbury Plain, western Europe's largest chalk grassland. *Journal of Bryology* 31: 255–266.

Preston, C.D., Hill, M.O., Porley, R.D. & Bosanquet, S.D.S. 2010. Survey of the bryophytes of arable land in Britain and Ireland 1: a classification of arable field assemblages. *Journal of Bryology* 32: 61–79.

Price, J.H. 2004. Berkeley, Miles Joseph (1803–1889), in Matthew & Harrison (2004), vol. 5, pp. 387–388.

Proctor, M.C.F. 1956. A bryophyte flora of Cambridgeshire. *Transactions of the British Bryological Society* 3: 1–49.

Proctor, M.C.F. 1984. A checklist of the flora of Cambridgeshire. [Review.] *Journal of Bryology* 13: 295–296.

Purcell, D. 1967. *Cambridge stone*. Faber & Faber, London.

Rackham, O. 1975. *Hayley Wood: its history and ecology*. Cambridgeshire and Isle of Ely Naturalists' Trust, Cambridge.

Rackham, O. 1986. *The history of the countryside*. J.M. Dent & Sons, London.

Rackham, O. 1987. The making of Old Court. I – The original building. *Letter of the Corpus Association* 66: 33–48.

Rackham, O. 1990. *Trees and woodland in the British landscape*, ed. 2. J.M. Dent & Sons, London.

Rackham, O. 1992. Gamlingay Wood. *Nature in Cambridgeshire* 34: 3–15.

Rackham, O. 1999. The woods 30 years on: where have the Primroses gone? *Nature in Cambridgeshire* 41: 73–87.

Rackham, O. 2003. *Ancient woodland: its history, vegetation and uses in England*, ed. 2. Castlepoint Press, Dalbeattie.

Rackham, O. & Coombe, D.E. 1996. Madingley Wood. *Nature in Cambridgeshire* 38: 27–54.

Ramsbottom, J. 1931. Charles Edward Moss (1872–1930). *Journal of Botany* 69: 20–23.

Raven J.[E.] & Walters, [S.]M. 1956. *Mountain flowers*. Collins, London.

[Ray, J.] 1660. *Catalogus plantarum circa Cantabrigiam nascentium*. Cambridge. John Martyn's interleaved and annotated copy is in Cambridge University Library, classmark CCD.47.414, bound together with his copy of his own *Methodus* (1727).

[Ray, J.] 1663. *Appendix ad Catalogum plantarum circa Cantabrigiam nascentium: continens addenda et emendanda*. Cambridge.

Ray, J. 1670. *Catalogus plantarum Angliae, et insularum adjacentium*. London.

Ray, J. 1690. *Synopsis methodica stirpium Britannicarum*. London.

Ray, J. 1696. *Synopsis methodica stirpium Britannicarum*, ed. 2. London. William Vernon's annotated copy is in the British Library, classmark 969.f.20.

Ray, J. 1724. *Synopsis methodica stirpium Britannicarum*, ed. 3. London.

Relhan, R. 1785. *Flora Cantabrigiensis*. Cambridge.

Relhan, R. 1786. *Florae Cantabrigiensi supplementum*. Cambridge.

Relhan, R. 1788. *Florae Cantabrigiensi supplementum alterum*. Cambridge.

Relhan, R. 1793. *Florae Cantabrigiensi supplementum tertium*. Cambridge.

Relhan, R. 1802. *Flora Cantabrigiensis*, ed. 2. Cambridge. Leonard Jenyns' annotated copy is in Cambridge University Library, classmark CCC.47.346.

Relhan, R. 1820. *Flora Cantabrigiensis*, ed. 3. Cambridge. There are copies in Cambridge University Library annotated by C.C. Babington (classmark CCC.47.354–355) and J.S. Henslow (CCC.47.356–357). Leonard Jenyns' annotated copy is in the Bath Royal Literary and Philosophical Institution.

Reynolds, P. 2003. Kingston Wood. *Nature in Cambridgeshire* 45: 2–29.

Rhodes, P.G.M. 1910. Notes on mosses, hepaticae and lichens from the Channel Islands. *Report and Transactions of the Guernsey Society of Natural Science and Local Research* 1909: 88–91.

Rhodes, P.G.M. 1911. Bryophyta, in Evans (1911), pp. 252–258.

Richards, P.W.M. 1923. A preliminary moss-flora of Glamorgan. *Transactions of the Cardiff Naturalists' Society* 53: 44–53.

Richards, P.W. 1932. The Bryophyta of Wicken Fen, in Gardiner (1925–32), Part VI, pp. 539–43.

Richards, P.W. 1947a. Localities and status of *Plagiothecium Seligeri* (Brid.) Lindb. (*P. silesiacum* (Selig.) B. & S.). *Transactions of the British Bryological Society* 1: 23–24.

Richards, P.W. 1947b. *Ptil[i]dium pulcherrimum* (Web.) Hampe in Cambridgeshire. *Transactions of the British Bryological Society* 1: 25.

Richards, P.W. 1967. Edmund Fredric Warburg 1908–1966. *Transactions of the British Bryological Society* 5: 375–377.

Richards, P. W. 1983. The revival of the B.B.S. after World War II. *Bulletin of the British Bryological Society* 42: 18.

Richards, P.[W.] 1993. Eustace Wilkinson Jones (1909–1992). *Journal of Bryology* 17: 689–692.

Richards, P.[W.] 1995. David Catcheside (1907–1994). *Journal of Bryology* 18: 833–835.

Richards, P.W. & Whitehouse, H.L.K. 1988. Fifty years of the Cambridge Bryological Excursions. *Nature in Cambridgeshire* 30: 41–49.

Riley, M. 2006. The club at Temple Coffee House revisited. *Archives of natural history* 33: 90–100.

Rishbeth, J. 1948. The flora of Cambridge walls. *Journal of Ecology* 36: 136–148.

Robertson, H., Marshall, D., Slingsby, E. & Newman, G., eds 2012. *Economic, biodiversity, resource protection and social values of orchards: a study of six orchards by the Herefordshire Orchards Community Evaluation Project*. Commissioned report NECR 090. Natural England.

Robertson, R. 1986. George Edward Briggs 25 June 1893 – 7 February 1985. *Biographical Memoirs of Fellows of the Royal Society* 32: 35–64.

Robinson, D.P. 1987. *Cambridgeshire inventory of ancient woodlands*. Unpublished report. East Midlands Region and Chief Scientist's Directorate, Nature Conservancy Council, Peterborough.

Robinson, R.A. & Sutherland, W.J. 2002. Post-war changes in arable farming and biodiversity in Great Britain. *Journal of Applied Ecology* 39: 157–176.

Rodwell, J.S., ed. 2000. *British plant communities. Volume 5: Maritime communities and vegetation of open habitats*. Cambridge University Press, Cambridge.

Rosengren, F. & Cronberg, N. 2014. The adaptive background of nannandry: dwarf male distribution and fertilization in the moss *Homalothecium lutescens*. *Biological Journal of the Linnean Society* 113: 74–84.

Rosengren, F. & Cronberg, N. 2015. Selective spore germination on shoots of *Homalothecium lutescens*, a moss with dwarf males. *Biology Letters* 11: 20150427. http://dx.doi.org/10.1098/rsbl.2015.0427.

Rosengren, F., Cronberg, N., Reitalu, T. & Prentice, H.C. 2014. Sexual reproduction in the phyllodioicous bryophyte *Homalothecium lutescens* (Hedw.) H.Rob. in relation to habitat age, growth conditions and genetic variation. *Journal of Bryology* 36: 200–208.

Rosman-Hartog, N. & Touw, A. 1987. On the taxonomic status of *Ulota bruchii* Hornsch. ex Brid., *U. crispa* (Hedw.) Brid. and *U. crispula* Bruch ex Brid. *Lindbergia* 13: 159–164.

RoTAP 2012. *Review of Transboundary Air Pollution (RoTAP): Acidification, eutrophication, ground level ozone and heavy metals in the UK*. Centre for Ecology and Hydrology, Wallingford.

Rotherham, I.D., ed. 2008. *Orchards and groves: their history, ecology, culture and archaeology*. Landscape Archaeology and Ecology 7. Wildtrack Publishing, Sheffield.

Rothero, G.P. 2008. New vice-county records. Musci. *Field Bryology* 95: 52–67.

Rowell, T.A. 1997. The history of the Fen, in Friday (1997), pp. 187–212.

Royal Commission on Historical Monuments 1968. *An inventory of historical monuments in the county of Cambridge. Volume 1. West Cambridgeshire*. Her Majesty's Stationery Office, London.

Salmon, M.A. 2000. *The Aurelian legacy: British butterflies and their collectors*. Harley Books, Colchester.

Sanders, T.W. 1919. *Fruit and its cultivation*, ed. 2. W.H. & L. Collingridge, London.

Sanford, M. & Fisk, R. 2010. *A flora of Suffolk*. Privately published, Ipswich.

S[axton], W.T. 1926. Leonard John Sedgwick. *Proceedings of the Linnean Society of London* 1925–26: 98–99.

Seale, R.S. & Hodge, C.A.H. 1976. *Soils of the Cambridge and Ely district*. Soil Survey Special Survey no. 10. Rothamsted Experimental Station, Harpenden.

Sell, P.[D.] 1989. The changing face of nature in Bassingbourn (1930s–1980s). *Nature in Cambridgeshire* 31: 12–18.

Seppelt, R.D. & Laursen, G.A. 1999. *Riccia cavernosa* Hoffm. emend Raddi, new to the Arctic and the bryoflora of Alaska. *Hikobia* 13: 71–76.

Seward, A.C. 1922. Botany. Report of the Professor. *Cambridge University Reporter* 22 December 1922: 431–432.

Sheail, J. 1976. *Nature in trust: the history of nature conservation in Britain*. Blackie & Son, Glasgow & London.

Sinden, N. 1989. Orchards and places, in *Orchards: a guide to local conservation*, pp. 5–11. Common Ground, London.

Smith, A.J.E. 1978a. *The moss flora of Britain and Ireland*. Cambridge University Press, Cambridge.

Smith, A.J.E., ed. 1978b. *Provisional atlas of the bryophytes of the British Isles*. Biological Records Centre, Huntingdon.

Smith, A.J.E. 2004. *The moss flora of Britain and Ireland*, ed. 2. Cambridge University Press, Cambridge.

Smith, A.J.E. & Whitehouse, H.L.K. 1978. An account of the British species of the *Bryum bicolor* complex including *B. dunense* sp. nov. *Journal of Bryology* 10: 29–47.

[Smith, J.E.] 1794. *Bryum calcareum*. English Botany 3: t. 191. London.

Smith, J.E. 1795. *Hypnum viticulosum*. English Botany 4: t. 265. London.

Smith, J.E. 1796a. *Phascum curvicollum*. English Botany 5: t. 330. London.

Smith, J.E. 1796b. *Bryum carneum*. English Botany 5: t. 360. London.

Smith, J.E. 1798. *Phascum serratum*. English Botany 7: t. 460. London.

Smith, J.E. 1801. *Phascum curvicollum*. English Botany 13: t. 905. London.

Smith, J.E. 1802. *Hypnum scorpioides*. English Botany 15: t. 1039. London.

Smith, K. & Harding, M. 2001. *Wetland plant communities of Chippenham Fen NNR, Cambridgeshire*. English Nature Suffolk Team, Bury St Edmunds.

Söderström, L. & Jonsson, B.G. 1989. Spatial pattern and dispersal in the leafy hepatic *Ptilidium pulcherrimum*. *Journal of Bryology* 15: 793–802.

Sparks, B.W. & West, R.G. 1965. The relief and drift deposits, in Steers (1965), pp. 18–40.

Stanley, P.E., Argent, G.C.G. & Whitehouse, H.L.K. 1998. A botanical biography of Professor Paul Richards C.B.E. *Journal of Bryology* 20: 323–370.

**S[tapf], O. 1907.** G.D. Haviland. *Bulletin of miscellaneous information, Royal Botanic Gardens, Kew* 1907: 197–198.

**Stearns, R.P. 1952.** James Petiver: Promoter of natural science, c.1663–1718. *Proceedings of the American Antiquarian Society* n.s. 62: 243–365.

**Steers, J.A., ed. 1965.** *The Cambridge region 1965.* Cambridge Local Executive Committee, British Association for the Advancement of Science, London.

**Stern, R.C. 2010.** *Atlas of the bryophytes of South Hampshire.* Pisces Publications, Newbury.

**Stevenson, C.R. 2003.** Moss and other grave matters. *Transactions of the Norfolk and Norwich Naturalists' Society* 36: 1–29.

**Stevenson, C.R. 2006.** Rummers Lane: a moss-rich Cambridgeshire orchard. *Nature in Cambridgeshire* 48: 33–43.

**Stevenson, [C.]R. & Rowntree, J.[K.] 2009.** Bryophytes in East Anglian orchards. *Field Bryology* 99: 10–18.

**Stevenson, C.R., Davies, C. & Rowntree, J.K. 2017.** Biodiversity in agricultural landscapes: the effect of apple cultivar on epiphyte diversity. *Ecology and evolution* 7: 1250–1258.

**Stoate, C. 1996.** The changing face of lowland farming and wildlife. Part 2: 1945–1995. *British Wildlife* 7: 162–172.

**Stroh, P.A. & Croft, J.M. 2015.** Emerging from slumber – Fen Violet (*Viola persicifolia*) at Wicken Fen National Nature Reserve, Cambridgeshire. *Nature in Cambridgeshire* 57: 91–97.

**Swale, E. & Belcher, H. 1993.** The search for Moor Barns Bath. *Nature in Cambridgeshire* 35: 17–25.

**Swinscow, T.D.V. 1959.** A bryophyte flora of Hertfordshire. *Transactions of the British Bryological Society* 3: 509–557.

**Syed, H. 1973.** A taxonomic study of *Bryum capillare* Hedw. and related species. *Journal of Bryology* 7: 265–326.

**Tansley, A.G., ed. 1911.** *Types of British vegetation.* Cambridge University Press, Cambridge.

**T[ansley], A.G. 1916.** Albert Stanley Marsh. *New Phytologist* 15: 81–85.

**T[ansley], A.G. 1931.** Charles Edward Moss. *Journal of Ecology* 19: 209–214.

**Tansley, A.G. 1939.** *The British islands and their vegetation.* Cambridge University Press, Cambridge.

**Taylor, A. 1999.** *Cambridge: the hidden history.* Tempus Publishing, Stroud.

**Taylor, A.G. 1981.** *Late Devensian ground-ice hollows in Southern Cambridgeshire.* PhD thesis, Cambridgeshire College of Arts and Technology [now Anglia Ruskin University].

**Taylor, C. 1973.** *The Cambridgeshire landscape.* Hodder & Stoughton, London.

**Thirsk, J. 1997.** *Alternative agriculture.* Oxford University Press, Oxford.

**Tipper, C.T.W. 2007.** *Hennediella heimii* growing by salted roads in Hertfordshire. *Field Bryology* 91: 15–16.

**Tomkins, S. 1998.** The Kingfisher's Bridge Wetland Creation Project: a report from the project's inception to autumn 1996. *Nature in Cambridgeshire* 40: 37–52.

**Trist, P.J.O. 1988.** Hildersham Furze Hills. *Nature in Cambridgeshire* 30: 4–12.

**Turner, D., ed. 1835.** *Extracts from the literary and scientific correspondence of Richard Richardson, M.D., F.R.S., of Bierley, Yorkshire.* Privately published, Yarmouth.

**Turner, M. 1980.** *English parliamentary enclosure.* W. Dawson & Sons, Folkestone.

**Vancouver, C. 1794.** *General view of the agriculture in the county of Cambridge.* London.

**Walker, K.J. & Preston, C.D. 2006.** Ecological predictors of extinction risk in the flora of lowland England, UK. *Biodiversity and Conservation* 15: 1913–1942.

**Wallace, E.C. 1963.** Distribution maps of bryophytes in Britain. *Ptilidium pulcherrimum* (Weber) Hampe. *Transactions of the British Bryological Society* 4: 513.

**Wallace, I., ed. 2005.** *Leonard Jenyns: Darwin's lifelong friend.* Bath Royal Literary and Scientific Institution, Bath.

**Walters, S.M. 1981.** *The shaping of Cambridge botany.* Cambridge University Press, Cambridge.

**Walters, S.M. & Stow, E.A. 2001.** *Darwin's mentor: John Stevens Henslow 1796–1861.* Cambridge University Press, Cambridge.

**Warburg, E.F. & Crundwell, A.C. 1959.** *Tortula virescens* (De Not.) De Not. new to the British Isles. *Transactions of the British Bryological Society* 3: 568–570.

**Warburton, C. 1902.** *Orchard and bush-fruit pests and how to combat them.* John Murray, London.

**Wareham, A.F. & Wright, A.P.M., eds 2002.** *A history of the county of Cambridge and the Isle of Ely. Volume X. North-eastern Cambridgeshire.* Oxford University Press, Oxford.

**Watt, A.S. 1938.** The climate of Cambridgeshire, in Darby (1938), pp. 31–43.

**Webb, R.H. & Coleman, W.H. 1849.** *Flora Hertfordiensis.* William Pamplin, London.

**Wedge, C. & Robertson, H. 2010.** *Traditional orchards: orchards and wildlife,* ed. 2. Technical Information Note TIN020. Natural England.

**West, R.G. 2017.** Patterned ground and superficial deposits at Hare Park, Swaffham Bulbeck, Cambridgeshire, England. *Proceedings of the Yorkshire Geological Society* 61: 197–216.

West, R.G. & Gibbard, P.L. 2017. The Observatory Gravels and the Travellers' Rest Pit, Cambridge, England. *Proceedings of the Yorkshire Geological Society* 61: 313–322.

West, W. 1898. Notes on Cambridgeshire plants. *Journal of Botany* 36: 246–259, 491–492.

Whitehouse, H.L.K. 1958. Additions to the bryophyte flora of Cambridgeshire. *Nature in Cambridgeshire* 1: 25–27.

Whitehouse, H.L.K. 1959. *Riccia* in Cambridgeshire. *Nature in Cambridgeshire* 2: 37.

Whitehouse, H.L.K. 1960. Bryophytes added to the county list during 1959. *Nature in Cambridgeshire* 3: 27.

Whitehouse, H.L.K. 1961. Bryophytes added to the county list during 1960. *Nature in Cambridgeshire* 4: 43–44.

Whitehouse, H.L.K. 1962. Bryophytes added to the county list during 1961. *Nature in Cambridgeshire* 5: 38–39.

Whitehouse, H.L.K. 1964. Bryophyta, in Perring *et al.* (1964), pp. 281–328.

Whitehouse, H.L.K. 1965. P.J. Bourne, an obituary. *Nature in Cambridgeshire* 8: 58.

Whitehouse, H.L.K. 1966a. The occurrence of tubers in European mosses. *Transactions of the British Bryological Society* 5: 103–116.

Whitehouse, H.L.K. 1966b. Cambridgeshire bryophyte records since publication of "A Flora of Cambridgeshire". *Nature in Cambridgeshire* 9: 51–53.

Whitehouse, H.L.K. 1969. *Dicranella staphylina*, a new European species. *Transactions of the British Bryological Society* 5: 757–765.

Whitehouse, H.L.K. 1974. Recent bryophyte records for Cambridgeshire. *Nature in Cambridgeshire* 17: 20–24.

Whitehouse, H.L.K. 1985. Bryophyte records. *Nature in Cambridgeshire* 27: 7–8.

Whitehouse, H.[L.K.] 1996. Professor Paul W. Richards CBE (1908–1995). *Nature in Cambridgeshire* 38: 69–70.

Whitehouse, H.L.K. & Newton, M.E. 1988. *Tortula brevis* sp. nov. and *T. stanfordensis* Steere: morphology, cytology and geographical distribution. *Journal of Bryology* 15: 83–99.

Whitelaw, M. & Burton, M.A.S. 2015. Diversity and distribution of epiphytic bryophytes on Bramley's Seedling trees in East of England apple orchards. *Global ecology and conservation* 4: 380–387.

Wigginton, M.J. 1995. *Mosses and liverworts of North Lancashire*. Centre for North–west Regional Studies, Lancaster University, Lancaster.

Wilczek, R. & Demaret, F. 1976. Les espèces belges du "complexe *Bryum bicolor*" (Musci). *Bulletin du Jardin botanique national de Belgique* 46: 511–541.

Williamson, R. 1961. John Martyn and the Grub-street Journal, with particular reference to his attacks on Richard Bentley, Richard Bradley and William Cheselden. *Medical History* 5: 361–374.

Willis, R. & Clark, J.W. 1886. *The architectural history of the University of Cambridge and of the colleges of Cambridge and Eton*. 4 vols. Cambridge University Press, Cambridge.

Wilson, A. 1930. *A census catalogue of British hepatics*, ed. 3. British Bryological Society, Berwick-upon-Tweed.

Wilson, W. 1855. *Bryologia Britannica*. Longman, Brown, Green & Longmans, London.

Wittering, S. 2013. *Ecology and enclosure: the effect of enclosure on society, farming and the environment in South Cambridgeshire, 1798–1850*. Windgather Press, Oxford.

Woodland Trust 2017. The big picture of woods and trees in UK. www.woodlandtrust.org.uk, accessed 14 December 2017.

Woods, R.K.S. 1995. John Rishbeth 10 July 1918 – 1 June 1991. *Biographical Memoirs of Fellows of the Royal Society* 41: 360–376.

Worsley, P., Gurney, S.D. & Collins, P.E.F. 1995. Late Holocene 'mineral palsas' and associated vegetation patterns: a case study from Lac Hendry, northern Québec, Canada and significance for European Pleistocene thermokarst. *Quaternary science reviews* 14: 179–192.

Worssam, B.C. & Taylor, J.H. 1969. *Geology of the country around Cambridge*. Her Majesty's Stationery Office, London.

Wright, C. & Ward, J.F. 1929. *A survey of the soils and fruit of the Wisbech area*. His Majesty's Stationery Office, London.

Yapp, R.H. 1908. Sketches of vegetation at home and abroad. IV. – Wicken Fen. *New Phytologist* 7: 61–81.

Young, A. 1805. Minutes concerning parliamentary inclosures in the county of Cambridge. *Annals of agriculture and other useful arts* 43: 42–59.

# Index

The main entry for each species is indexed in **bold numerals**; references to the species in the introductory chapters and entries in the appendices are listed in roman type, but incidental references in the accounts of other species are not indexed. Synonyms are given in *italics* and include only the names used by Proctor (1956) and those subsequently applied to the plant in the county, including those employed by Atherton *et al.* (2010). They are followed by the accepted name of the plant to which they were applied in Cambridgeshire and just one page reference, to the main entry for the species. We have used the abbreviation 'auct.' sparingly to indicate some of the potentially confusing cases in which the synonym formerly used in the county was misapplied.

Loeskeobryum brevirostre 97, 103, 140, **281**
Lophocolea bidentata 27, 77, 78, 84, 87, 130, 134, 135, **161**
    *cuspidata* = L. bidentata **161**
    heterophylla 39, 70, 72, 77, 78, 80, 84, 86, 87, 92, 122, 134, **161**, 299
Lophozia excisa 68, 126, 139, 140, 144, **166**
    perssonii 50, 108, 109, 143, **166**
    ventricosa 29, 96, 104, 138, **166**
Lunularia cruciata 34, 40, 70, 126, **147**, 294
Marchantia *alpestris* auct. = M. polymorpha subsp. ruderalis **148**
    polymorpha 22, 70, 118, 126
    polymorpha subsp. polymorpha **148**
    polymorpha subsp. ruderalis **148**, 294
Metzgeria consanguinea 68, 131, **155**
    *fruticulosa* = M. violacea **155**
    furcata 39, 78, 84, 92, 94, 131, 132, 134, **155**, 299
    *temperata* = M. consanguinea **155**
    violacea 46, 84, 92, 131, 134, 135, **155**, 299
Microbryum curvicollum 29, 108, 109, 115, **215**
    davallianum var. davallianum 33, 34, 41, 45, 48, 70, 115, 117, 118, **214**
    floerkeanum 36, 70, 117, **215**
    rectum 30, 108–110, 115, 130, **214**
Mnium *affine* = Plagiomnium affine **247**
    *cuspidatum* = Plagiomnium cuspidatum **246**
    hornum 35, 68, 77, 78, 86, 87, 97, 98, 103, 105, 123, 124, **245**
    *longirostrum* = Plagiomnium rostratum **249**
    *punctatum* = Rhizomnium punctatum **246**
    *rugicum* = Plagiomnium ellipticum **248**
    *seligeri* = Plagiomnium elatum **247**
    *undulatum* = Plagiomnium undulatum **248**
Nardia scalaris **292**
Neckera complanata 27, 70, 77, 81, 82, 122, 124, 134, 135, **287**, 300
    crispa 108, 110, 124, 140, 142, **287**
    pumila 36
Nowellia curvifolia 49, 77, 85, 99, 100, 163, **164**
*Octodiceras fontanum* = Fissidens fontanus **184**
Odontoschisma sphagni 29, 96, 104, 138, 163, **165**
*Omalia trichomanoides* = Homalia trichomanoides **287**
Orthodontium lineare 44, 77, 86, 103, 105, 122, 142, **250**
Orthotrichum acuminatum 138
    affine 68, 78, 80, 84, 85, 92, 94, 100, 114, 131, 132, 134, 222, **225**, 297, 300
    anomalum 34, 73, 74, 124, 126, 128, 129, 222, **226**
    *anomalum* var. *saxatile* = O. anomalum **226**
    cupulatum 46, 70, 124, 126, 130, **227**, 297
    diaphanum 34, 65, 78, 80, 85, 92, 94, 127–129, 134, 222, **228**, 301
    lyellii 36, 80, 84, 91, 92, 94, 100, 131, 134, 222, **224**, 301
    obtusifolium 68, 92, 93, 131, 141, 144, **226**
    patens 138
    pulchellum 70, 80, 84, 92, 131–134, **229**, 301
    pumilum 68, 131, 141, **228**
    rogeri 138

    scanicum 138
    speciosum 78, 92, 131, 144, **225**
    stramineum 80, 92, 103, 131, **227**
    striatum 32, 84, 92, 131, **224**
    tenellum 92, 103, 131, **228**
Oxyrrhynchium hians 34, 65, 78, 85, 90, 92, 117, 127–129, **267**
    pumilum 77, **267**
    speciosum 102, 137, **268**
    *swartzii* = O. hians **267**
Palustriella commutata 40, 97, 98, 100, 102, 140, **252**, 297
    falcata 36, 68, 97, 98, 102, 140, **253**
Pellia endiviifolia 22, 77, **154**
    epiphylla 96, 103, 106, **153**, 294
    *fabbroniana* = P. endiviifolia **154**
    neesiana 77, **154**
Phascum *curvicollum* = Microbryum curvicollum **215**
    cuspidatum 26, 53, 65, 68, 70, 117, 118, 129, **213**
    cuspidatum var. bivalens **214**
    *cuspidatum* var. *curvisetum* = var. cuspidatum **214**
    cuspidatum var. cuspidatum **214**
    *cuspidatum* var. *maximum* = var. schreberianum **214**
    cuspidatum var. papillosum **214**
    cuspidatum var. piliferum 53, **214**
    cuspidatum var. schreberianum **214**
    *floerkeanum* = Microbryum floerkeanum **215**
Philonotis calcarea **292**
    fontana 23, 96, 98, 104, 138, 139, **232**
*Physcomitrella patens* = Aphanorrhegma patens **176**
Physcomitrium pyriforme 98, 100, 136, 137, **175**
Plagiochila asplenioides 23, 24, 39, 42, 72, 77, 78, 80, 81, 83, 84, 86, **163**
    *asplenioides* var. *major* = P. asplenioides **163**
    porelloides 69, 126, **163**
Plagiomnium affine 68, 100, 124, 127, **247**, 297
    cuspidatum 40, 45, 69, 92, 120, 127, **246**, 297
    elatum 39, 97, 102, **247**
    ellipticum 97, 100, 143, **248**
    rostratum 77, 78, **249**
    undulatum 30, 77, 78, 87, 129, **248**
Plagiothecium curvifolium 77, 82, 84, 102, 105, 140, **282**
    *denticulatum* var. *aptychus* = P. curvifolium **282**
    denticulatum var. denticulatum 96, 97, 102, **282**
    laetum 68, 77, 140, **282**
    nemorale 43, 70, 76–78, 82, 86, 87, 102, 122, 134, 282, **283**
    *ruthei* = P. denticulatum var. denticulatum **282**
    *seligeri* = Herzogiella seligeri **284**
    *sylvaticum* = P. nemorale **283**
    undulatum 96, 100, 103, 106, 282, **283**
Plasteurhynchium striatulum 68, 108, 110, 141, **262**
Platygyrium repens 77, 91, 92, 142, **285**
Platyhypnidium riparioides 26, 137, **263**
Pleuridium acuminatum 69, 77, 124, 139, **185**, 297
    subulatum 77, 139, 141, **185**
Pleurozium schreberi 36, 96, 103, 106, 140, **279**
Pogonatum aloides 96, 104, 139, **171**
    nanum 23, 96, 104, 139, **171**